Date Due

DIAGRAM OF A PRODUCTION SYSTEM

HAVING AS CORE ELEMENTS; DESIGN OF PRODUCT, DESIGN OF PROCESS, AND FLOW OF MATERIAL

STANDARDS OF OUTPUT

PRODUCTION CONTROL INCLUDING: PLANNING, RATE-AND-LOT SIZE DECISIONS, LOADING, SCHEDULING, RE-LEASING, REPORTING, AND EXPEDITING

PROCESS STEP NO. 3

FINISHED GOODS INVENTORY

DISTRIBUTION INVENTORY

ATERIAL

FACILITIES MAINTENANCE

LABOR ISTRATION SELECTION, PERVISION, RATION,

MARKETING

LABOR RELATIONS

Basic Problems,
Concepts,
and Techniques

ARCH R. DOOLEY, *Professor of Business Administration*

WILLIAM K. HOLSTEIN, *Assistant Professor of Business Administration*

JAMES L. McKENNEY, *Associate Professor of Business Administration*

RICHARD S. ROSENBLOOM, *Associate Professor of Business Administration*

C. WICKHAM SKINNER, *Professor of Business Administration*

PHILIP H. THURSTON, *Professor of Business Administration*

Harvard University Graduate School of Business Administration

CASEBOOKS IN PRODUCTION MANAGEMENT

Basic Problems,

Concepts,

and Techniques

Revised Edition

A WILEY/HAMILTON PUBLICATION

JOHN WILEY & SONS, INC.

SANTA BARBARA ● NEW YORK ● LONDON ● SYDNEY ● TORONTO

To Franklin Erton Folts

Preface

The distinctive characteristic of the production manager's job is his responsibility for the performance, over time, of a complex man-machine system functioning in an organizational context with cost as a significant criterion of success. This book is an aid for training decision makers through practice in confronting realistic situations of such a nature. It is intended for use in a first course in production management, to provide either a basic foundation for those students planning further study or careers in the field or a broader background of preparation for those whose careers will be built in other domains.

These cases describe particular operating situations as they were faced by real managers in business. The skillful manager brings to bear on such problems, consciously or intuitively, a diverse background of knowledge about the technologies and techniques of his field, some basic disciplines in the quantitative and behavioral sciences, and an understanding of the specific situational context. This book contains materials designed to provide the necessary background in topics specifically relevant to production problems. We have assumed that the student has had some preparation in more basic disciplines, some experience in prior problem-solving courses, and a general understanding of the common environment of the business manager.

The focus of this book is on offering a cumulative set of experiences in decision making. An important, continuing problem for a decision maker is one of defining his problem. Another key administrative skill, often overlooked in preparation of teaching materials, is the ability to devise effective means for implementing problem solutions. These cases present an arena for the application and refinement of skills in problem definition and analysis and in the synthesis and implementation of solutions. Substantive material, in notes, in read-

ings, and in the cases themselves, serves an auxiliary purpose in providing the necessary background for wise consideration of the case problems.

The management decisions called for by the cases in this book are principally at the operating level. In the context of numerous case situations, however, the discerning student will observe repeatedly the relationship between policy guidelines and operating decisions, and he will see evidence of the numerous ways in which the nature of specific operating problems may demonstrate the need for revisions in, additions to, or clarifications of, existing policies.

The case materials do not attempt to present single-dimensioned abstractions of reality. Instead, as in the world of production management, the problems dealt with are commonly characterized by a mix of technological, economic, and human considerations. In numerous instances, analysis will indicate that these elements are in conflict. Realistic portrayal of the multidimensioned complexities of production problems is an effective pedagogic device for developing insight into the true character of production management. A distinctive aspect of production management is the continuing responsibility not only for detecting and evaluating the technological, economic, and human considerations in a specific situation, but also for dealing with the complex amalgam created when all three converge and commingle.

In most case situations the student must base his analysis not on perfect information, but rather on an array of facts and judgments, not all of which are necessarily consistent with the others, and some of which may represent only indirect evidence relative to the problem at issue. Furthermore, as in the practice of production management, it may often be impossible to obtain information that would reduce or eliminate uncertainties inherent in the problem.

In these respects, the cases are accurate portrayals of reality. The world of production management is seldom a world of perfect information. Nor can it be. Time pressures, cost considerations, the multiple activities involved in the production process and the complex interrelations existing among those activities, and the sheer unavailability of certain types of information repeatedly create situations in which managers have no alternative but to employ judgment to buttress imperfect knowledge. Except for rare instances, the case studies employed in the series provide the student with no less information than that used by the company personnel in dealing with the problem described. Frequently, information in the case is available in more precise and documented form than that utilized by company personnel.

We believe that an authentic portrayal of the degree and quality

of the information available in specific production situations provides valuable opportunities for the student to gain further insights into the applicability of techniques of formal analysis which presuppose the availability of certain types of data, to assess the contributions such techniques can render, and to recognize the steps and costs that may be required before they can be employed in a specific situation.

The study of case problems also helps to create an environment in which the student will discern the purposefulness of the knowledge that he is required to master. In the aggregate, the materials in this volume provide an extensive inventory of information regarding practices, concepts, and techniques that are unique to the functions of production management. They also provide various insights into the characteristics of the manufacturing processes employed in a number of industries. In the main, such knowledge is conveyed as part of the information relating to specific case situations. Wherever it has seemed pedagogically useful to do so, however, such material has been incorporated into reference notes or readings.

But whatever the form in which it is presented, the flow of information in this volume is ordered in such a way that, with reflection on the previous experiences to which the volume has exposed him, the student will be able to perceive the purposefulness of new knowledge as it is made available to him and to discern how its mastery and judicious use will increase his effectiveness in dealing with production management problems. The materials in this volume are arranged so that they also provide repeated opportunities for the student to test and strengthen his command of knowledge previously acquired by utilizing it in ensuing case situations.

Parts 1 through 3 of this volume present a progression of situations, starting with analysis of the single unit (machine or workstation) and proceeding through analysis of flow problems to management of the total operating situation. Each Part includes reference material, specifically prepared or reprinted from the literature, to help build the necessary technical background for subsequent cases. Parts 4 and 5 deal first with basic approaches and subsequently with analytical frameworks for planning and controlling operations and the related inventories. Part 6 provides a brief, and intentionally incomplete, introduction to problems of wage administration for courses where some treatment of the subject is desired. As is true of every subject included here, more comprehensive coverage of that topic may be obtained through use of supplementary readings and cases. The final Part contains two long cases of comprehensive review and integration of topics previously approached separately.

This book is part of a case series composed of material employed in Production courses in the MBA Program of the Harvard Graduate School of Business Administration. This revised edition of the volume *Basic Problems, Concepts and Techniques* retains the objective of the first edition—that of providing the material for an introductory course—but it has been strengthened in two respects. The concept of a "production system" has gained in importance and the cases and readings here have been augmented to strengthen the opportunity for a "systems" approach. Furthermore, we have given greater emphasis to problems in the control of production and to basic concepts and techniques—primarily quantitative—which aid in their resolution. In all, the new material in this book comprises two reference notes, two readings, eight cases, and three exercises in the form of abbreviated cases. The changes, we feel, will make possible a stronger, more comprehensive first course in production.

THE AUTHORS

Soldiers Field
October 1967

Acknowledgments

Any volume that relies primarily on case studies of authentic business situations owes a major debt of gratitude to those companies and individuals whose cooperation has made such materials available. The authors of this series acknowledge this indebtedness without reservation. Our deep appreciation to the numerous production management personnel who have given so generously of their time and advice to assure that the cases in this series present accurate, realistic accounts of production problems they encountered is heightened by our awareness of the continuing challenges and time pressures which characterize the day-to-day business responsibilities of these individuals.

The authors wish to acknowledge with gratitude the support and encouragement of Harvard Business School Dean George P. Baker and Associate Dean George F. F. Lombard which have made possible this revised edition. It is impossible, in a literal sense, for us to acknowledge individually all the contributions that others have made to this volume. These teaching materials have been developed over the years within the Production course at the Harvard Business School. As a consequence, nearly two dozen present and former members of the faculty or staff of the school have contributed in a significant way to the creation of the cases and notes. The six whose names appear on the title page are responsible for this particular structuring of the materials, for authorship of all the reference notes, and for a majority of the cases. Substantial contributions to the case materials have also been made by Professors Franklin E. Folts and Powell Niland and by Mr. William Howard Hart. For other contributions to the cases we are grateful to R. D. Cies, H. B. Eyring, F. R. Garrity, P. Jacobson, P. Lawrence, R. E. McGarrah, C. P. McLaughlin, J. Neff, D. R. Riehl, M. V. Sears, H. F. Stewart, W. H. Warrick, and H. E. Wrapp. The sources of numerous illustrations and the several sections of text for which others hold copyrights are cited with particular material. Our work in preparing the manuscript for this volume was aided considerably by the secretarial efforts of Mrs. Phyllis Furst.

Contents

Basic Problems,

Concepts,

and Techniques

INTRODUCTION

Absolute Level Company

In March 1963, Thomas Mancuso, vice president of the Absolute Level Company, was considering the establishment of an assembly line that would use conveyors to transfer work from one station to the next in the company's assembly department. In his opinion, use of an assembly line would reduce the confusion now typical of the department's operation and would lower assembly costs significantly. Since the Absolute Level Company was losing money despite a high volume of sales, cost reduction was an important problem facing the company's management.

Thomas discussed the idea with his father, Albert Mancuso, president of the company. The senior Mancuso expressed interest but pointed out that he knew very little about assembly-line operation. He suggested that his son look further into the idea and prepare a written report embodying the latter's analysis and recommendations. Thomas Mancuso also had mentioned the possibility of an assembly line based on conveyors to Ralph Baker, foreman of that department. Mr. Baker's response had been noncommittal, leaving Thomas with the feeling that Mr. Baker was not very much impressed by the idea.

History of the Company

Albert Mancuso had founded the Absolute Level Company in 1930. The company is located in Bellefont, Connecticut, a rural community of 1,500 people. Starting with seven employees, the company had grown rapidly during World War II and in 1963 employed 60 production workers. The level business is highly cyclical, broadly following the trend of construction activity. In normal times, competition is severe.

Thomas Mancuso had been around the shop from the time he was a small boy; by the time he was 18 he could operate practically any

3

machine in the plant. After acquiring an undergraduate engineering degree, he continued his education in the graduate business school of a large eastern university. Following his graduation in June 1962, he assumed a full-time job in his father's business.

The Product Line

The Absolute Level Company makes a full line of levels, of which it produces some 85 different models. Only about half of these, however, are sold in any volume, and about 12 models account for over half the total sales. The 12 models are manufactured for stock, but all others are made against orders on hand. Exhibit 1 shows two of the company's largest sellers, an aluminum level made in four lengths and a metal-bound level made in seven lengths. The 24-inch aluminum level and the 48-inch metal-bound level have been the two most important items in Absolute's line. In the week ending March 9, 1963, 1,695 of the aluminum levels were assembled, along with 383 metal-bound levels; these figures compared with a total of 2,700 units of all types but one assembled during the week. Also assembled were 1,608 "line" levels—single vials mounted in hexagonal aluminum casings three inches long—whose aluminum bodies had a hook at either end to permit suspending each level on a string. These levels were used mainly in determining grades and in laying foundations, brick walls, and tile pipes. The line levels sold for $.25 to $.33 each.

The Assembly Department

The assembly department is located on the second floor of the main building of Absolute's plant. The ground floor houses the company's offices and other departments, including the woodworking shop and paint spray booth. The space on the second floor not used by the assembly department is given over to the inspection and shipping departments and to the finished-goods storeroom.

Some 30 girls were employed in March 1963 in the company's assembly department, along with two boys to move material, and the foreman, Robert Baker. The girls were paid $1.40 per hour for a 40-hour week; in early 1963 the plant worked an additional four hours about every other Saturday morning, for which all employees received time-and-a-half pay. A majority of the girls in the assembly department had relatively short service records, but a few key employees had worked for the Absolute Level Company for five to ten years. These old-time employees were assigned to operations which they had performed in the same way, at the same bench or workplace,

EXHIBIT 1 ABSOLUTE LEVEL COMPANY

TYPICAL LEVELS

Carpenter's Level. Model Al-24, 24-inch aluminum level (same design comes in four lengths, 18 to 30 inches)

Mason's Level. Model 700-48, 48-inch mahogany brass-bound level (same design comes in seven lengths, 18 to 48 inches)

OTHER LEVELS

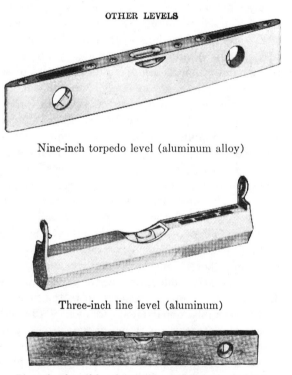

Nine-inch torpedo level (aluminum alloy)

Three-inch line level (aluminum)

Pine plumb and level (12-, 18-, and 24-inch models)

for many years. Thomas Mancuso realized that it might be difficult to change the old-timers' way of doing things.

Mr. Baker was also assistant plant superintendent and was responsible for preparing a weekly production schedule, not only for the assembly department but also for each of the other departments—foundry, metalworking, woodworking, and wood binding. The company had not compiled any time standards; Mr. Baker's estimates were made on the basis of experience.

Actual production of completed levels usually varies substantially from planned production. Sometimes the cause lies in failure to have raw materials on hand in the amounts required. During one week early in 1963 the supply of aluminum ingots became dangerously low, and the foundry's planned production of one type of level was revised in the middle of the week to change to the production of a different kind of level which used considerably smaller amounts of aluminum. In the fall of 1962, the company unexpectedly received orders for a large quantity of metal-bound, mahogany levels. One day the woodworking-shop foreman notified Thomas Mancuso that only two weeks' supply of mahogany remained on hand; since the time required to purchase and kiln-dry mahogany was a month and a half, the company fell a month behind in its deliveries of these levels.

In the case of supplies—for example, vials, cover glasses, and cardboard boxes—the company places a standing order, such as 20,000 units per month. There is no central storeroom and no procurement planning. Supplies used in the assembly department are kept alongside the bench of the person using them, and he or she advises the foreman, Mr. Baker, who in turn notifies Thomas Mancuso when the supply of the item is exhausted or dangerously low and more should be ordered. The only mechanism to change the standing order with the supplier is the worker's or foreman's visual control and the latter's oral report to Thomas Mancuso, perhaps at the regular weekly foremen's meeting held for an hour at the end of each work week.

In the opinion of Albert Mancuso, an equally important reason for failure to achieve planned production was the lack of better organization in the flow of levels from one operation to the next. Operators, especially in the assembly department, frequently ran out of work; it was not uncommon for an operator, or sometimes a foreman, to walk to the preceding operation—even though that operation might be in a different department—and return to his workplace with an armful of levels. Because of its lack of working capital, the management tried to minimize the inventories preceding and subsequent to each operation. This factor was the cause of running wood levels,

the most expensive to produce, through the assembly department in lots of 10 and 20, and carrying them upstairs and downstairs by hand, rather than using a hand truck and the elevator.

Steps in Assembling Aluminum Levels

The assembly processes for wood and for aluminum levels are similar, though each has minor variations. Wood levels and aluminum levels, however, are assembled by different groups of operators at different workplaces. The assembly of aluminum levels will be used to illustrate the assembly process.

Aluminum "bodies" are cast in the company's foundry and machined in the machining department. After machining, the level bodies are taken first to the inspection department, which is on the second floor of the same building which houses the assembly department. There a girl prints the company's name in red in raised letters on the web of each level. The process is similar to using a stamp pad to ink the raised characters on a rubber stamp. This girl, who is an inspector, uses this job as a fill-in to her regular duties. Levels are next subjected to a primary inspection, to cull out those on which further work would be a waste of time. This operation was added when Thomas Mancuso found that levels with obvious, nonrepairable defects, such as a casting flaw, had nevertheless passed through all assembly operations—only to be discarded upon final inspection.

The levels then are moved to bench 1 (Exhibit 4) where a girl applies a sealer to the holes in which the vials are to be mounted. This is done because previous sand blasting has conditioned the metal surfaces so that plaster applied directly will not dry properly. The shellac dries in five to ten minutes and the same girl then puts in small bits of plastiline. This first girl carries several units at a time over to the adjoining bench, no. 2, to supply the next operator; or sometimes operator no. 2 comes over and picks up several levels, exchanging a few pleasantries with operator no. 1. Operator no. 2 has both a vertical and a horizontal test bar which she uses to support the level in position while leveling the bubble in each vial. After "presetting" several levels, she helps operator no. 3 move the levels to the latter's bench; sometimes one of the boys working in the department moves a large lot for the girls. Operator no. 3 sets the vial in place with plaster. Operator no. 4, using her vertical and horizontal test bars at her work place, then tests the bubbles in the vials again, and makes any minor adjustments required. After this operation, the levels can undergo no further operations for three to four hours, the time required for the plaster to harden solidly.

The levels have to be moved with reasonable care at all times, but require particular care in handling during the foregoing operation to avoid moving the vials from "true" position.

After the plaster has set, operator no. 5 bores out the vial casing to make a smooth, even seat for the cover glasses and closures. This operation is done on a special machine tool, called a "carbo-lathe." The "carbo-lathe" is a noisy machine, and has been placed in its present location because of this characteristic and because it needs sturdy underpinning.

After boring, the level goes to operator no. 6, who cleans out dust from the vial casing with compressed air, and checks each piece visually for obvious defects. Operator no. 7 adds a paper masking ring printed with the company's name and address, a cover glass, and a metal closing ring, in that order, and seals the closing ring using a special forming (peening) tool attached to a drill press. These pieces are added to each side of each vial assembly, making a total of six closure assemblies per level.

One of the boys in the department transports the levels, usually in hand-truck loads, to the spray room on the first floor, using the elevator. Here the top, bottom, and ends are painted red. The spray booth, under the supervision of the woodworking-department foreman, is also used to lacquer (two coats) the entire surface of all wooden levels produced.

After three or four hours' drying, the levels' excess paint is removed by passing each level through a belt sanding machine located in the metalworking shop. Although only the tops of levels are painted, this operation is required because they are laid pressing against one another, and capillary action draws some of the paint down between adjacent levels onto the sides.

With excess paint removed from their sides, the levels are transported again on a hand truck to the inspection room on the second floor of the main building, where the inspector checks each level, using vertical and horizontal test bars and indicator gauges. About 10 per cent of the aluminum levels are usually rejected. Most of these are salvaged by reworking; the rest are melted down as scrap.

Levels passing inspection are transported to the packing room on the second floor of the main building for packaging in individual boxes; 24 levels are then packed in a shipping carton. When business is good, most aluminum levels are shipped immediately after packing; otherwise, they are placed in the finished-goods stockroom.

Exhibit 2 is a flow chart of the assembly operations on a cast aluminum-alloy level, and Exhibit 3 shows the assembly operations

EXHIBIT 2 ABSOLUTE LEVEL COMPANY

Assembly of Aluminum Levels

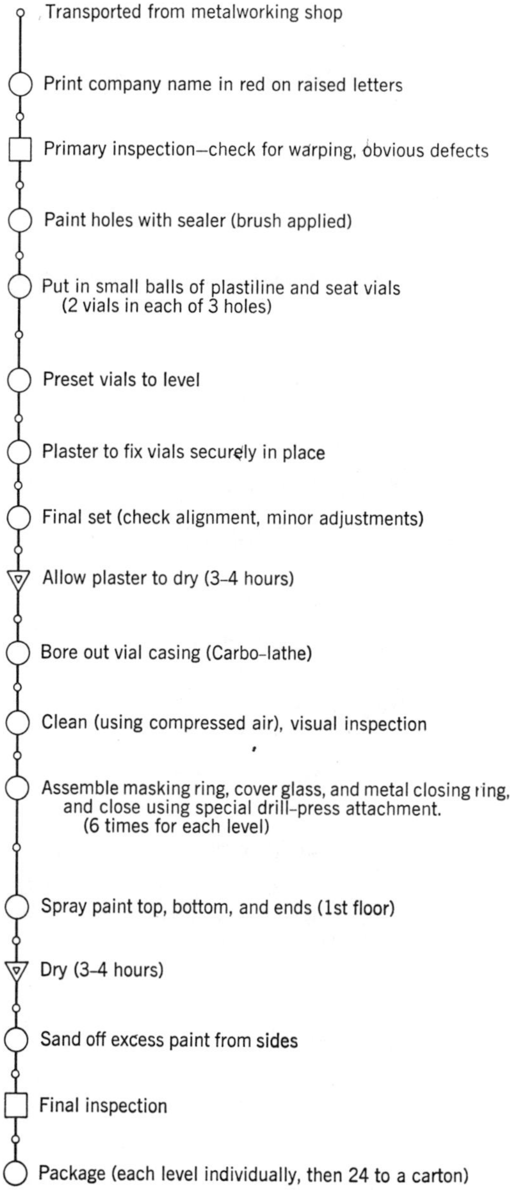

Transported from metalworking shop

Print company name in red on raised letters

Primary inspection—check for warping, obvious defects

Paint holes with sealer (brush applied)

Put in small balls of plastiline and seat vials
(2 vials in each of 3 holes)

Preset vials to level

Plaster to fix vials securely in place

Final set (check alignment, minor adjustments)

Allow plaster to dry (3–4 hours)

Bore out vial casing (Carbo–lathe)

Clean (using compressed air), visual inspection

Assemble masking ring, cover glass, and metal closing ring,
and close using special drill–press attachment.
(6 times for each level)

Spray paint top, bottom, and ends (1st floor)

Dry (3–4 hours)

Sand off excess paint from sides

Final inspection

Package (each level individually, then 24 to a carton)

EXHIBIT 3   ABSOLUTE LEVEL COMPANY

Assembly of 48-inch Wood Level

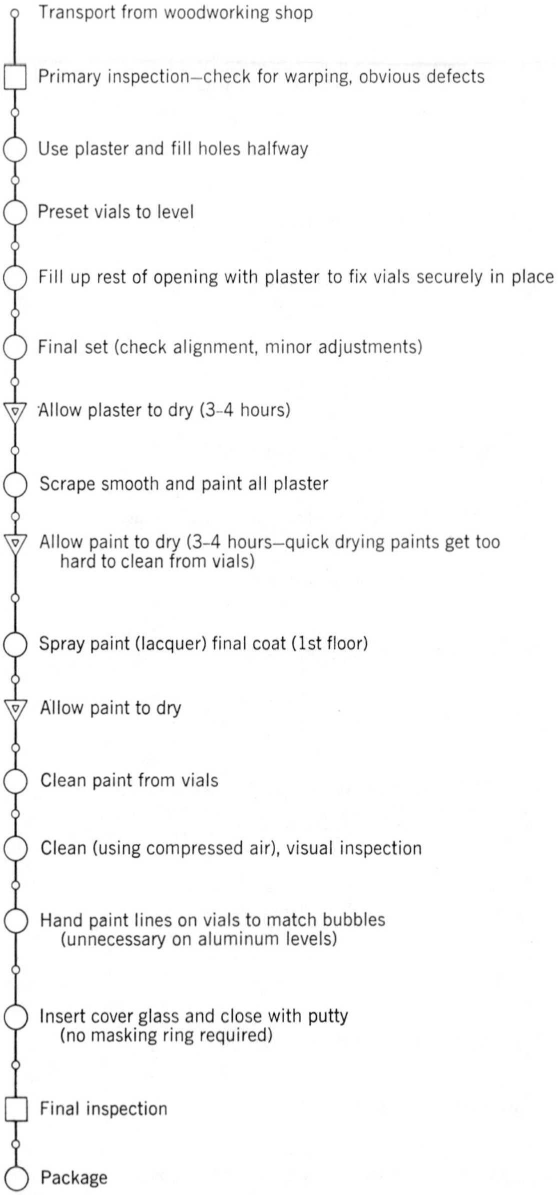

○ Transport from woodworking shop

□ Primary inspection—check for warping, obvious defects

○ Use plaster and fill holes halfway

○ Preset vials to level

○ Fill up rest of opening with plaster to fix vials securely in place

○ Final set (check alignment, minor adjustments)

▽ Allow plaster to dry (3–4 hours)

○ Scrape smooth and paint all plaster

▽ Allow paint to dry (3–4 hours—quick drying paints get too hard to clean from vials)

○ Spray paint (lacquer) final coat (1st floor)

▽ Allow paint to dry

○ Clean paint from vials

○ Clean (using compressed air), visual inspection

○ Hand paint lines on vials to match bubbles (unnecessary on aluminum levels)

○ Insert cover glass and close with putty (no masking ring required)

□ Final inspection

○ Package

on a 48-inch, metal-bound, wood level. The actual flows of these two models through the assembly department are diagrammed on Exhibits 4 and 5. Exhibit 6 is a plan of the department.

Problems in the Assembly Operations

Except in slack times, the assembly department is a center of great activity and often confusion. Bodies produced by other departments are frequently not forwarded to the assembly department in adequate quantity to keep some operators from running out of work. When this happens one of the boys working in the department will run downstairs to the metalworking department, or the woodworking shop, as the case might be, and return with an armload of bodies. Perhaps once or twice a year the assembly department runs short of supplies, such as vials or cover glasses, and assembly will have to be suspended.

Thomas Mancuso was aware that a substantial amount of working capital was tied up in rejected levels which had entered but never left the assembly department. He had noted several hundred rejected levels at various places throughout the department, some of which probably could be salvaged by reworking them. When an operator found a defective piece, the partially completed level usually was piled underneath her bench, or stacked in a nearby corner, after which she proceeded to work on the next level.

As a first step to improve the situation, Thomas Mancuso was considering the introduction of a conveyor-based assembly line for assembling aluminum levels. The 24-inch model was one of the few items which Thomas Mancuso and his father decided to manufacture for stock. Exhibit 7 shows weekly production of all four sizes of aluminum levels from October 1962 through February 1963. Thomas Mancuso knew the company was unable to undertake large expenditures at this time, despite the fact that orders had been heavy since December. Exhibit 8 shows a recent company balance sheet. He believed, however, that the company could afford to make the expenditures involved in buying any conveyor or conveyors needed, in making changes in wiring, and in moving equipment and benches as required. He believed the changes might be made over a weekend while the plant was shut down.

The test bars in the assembly room were large, vertical, steel I-beams, difficult to move and re-erect, but shifting them could be accomplished. Thomas also felt that the benches not used in the assembly of aluminum levels might be moved almost anywhere within the confines of the space presently available to the assembly department. He believed that it would be difficult to obtain any additional

EXHIBIT 4 ABSOLUTE LEVEL COMPANY

SECOND FLOOR, MAIN PLANT BUILDING

Layout of Assembly Department and Flow of Aluminum Levels
through Assembly

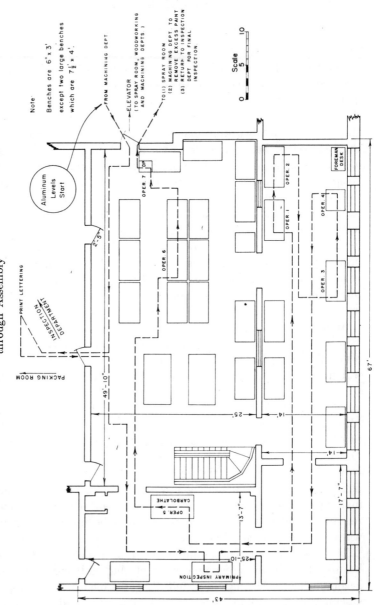

EXHIBIT 5 ABSOLUTE LEVEL COMPANY

SECOND FLOOR, MAIN PLANT BUILDING

Layout of Assembly Department and Flow of Wood Levels through Assembly

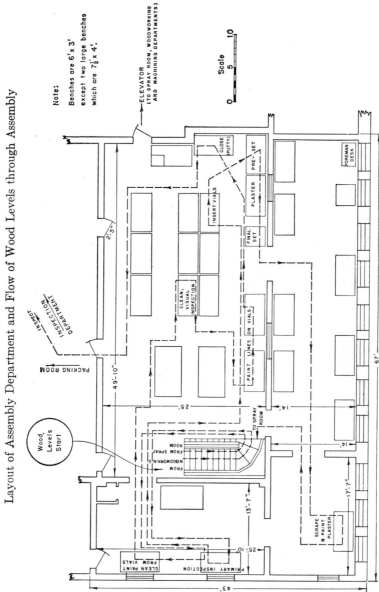

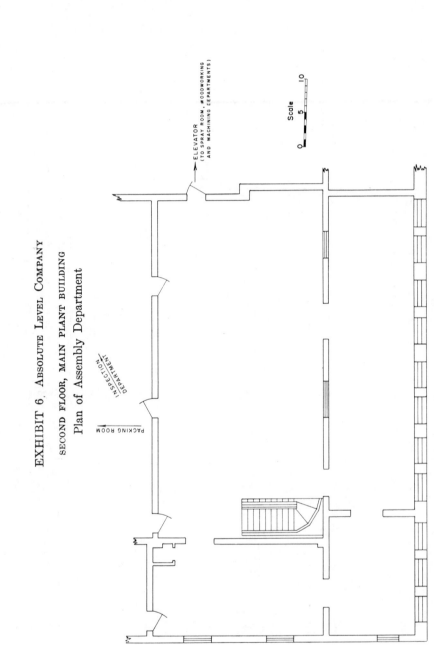

EXHIBIT 6. ABSOLUTE LEVEL COMPANY

SECOND FLOOR, MAIN PLANT BUILDING

Plan of Assembly Department

EXHIBIT 7 ABSOLUTE LEVEL COMPANY

WEEKLY PRODUCTION OF ALUMINUM LEVELS, BY SIZE
October 1962—February 1963

	Al 18″	Al 24″	Al 28″	Al 30″	Total
October	6	533	48	12	599
	6	868	107	53	1,034
	0	793	315	4	1,112
	227	735	238	76	1,276
	80	620	292	24˙	1,016
November	76	633	25	50	784
	84	859	81	10	1,034
	49	706	68	108	931
	226	606	7	97	936
December	129	360	180	112	781
	8	745	366	60	1,179
	16	630	358	104	1,108
	N.A.	N.A.	N.A.	N.A.	N.A.
January	N.A.	N.A.	N.A.	N.A.	N.A.
	0	733	23	4	760
	78	854	82	5	1,019
	84	857	17	28	986
	31	821	2	53	907
February	178	845	0	0	1,023
	4	840	109	3	956
	158	892	3	0	1,053
	15	1,104	17	0	1,136

N.A. = Not Available.

EXHIBIT 8   ABSOLUTE LEVEL COMPANY

BALANCE SHEET, NOVEMBER 30, 1962
(figures in thousands of dollars)

Cash in Bank	$ 0.8	Accounts Payable	$ 44.9
Accounts Receivable	40.9	Notes Payable—Bank	37.0
Inventory	95.3	Accruals	9.8
Total Current Assets	137.0	Total Current Liabs.	91.7
Land	3.0		
Buildings	90.1	Mortgage Payable	91.2
Machinery & Equipment	188.2		
	281.3		
Less Reserve for Deprec.	119.7		
Net Fixed Assets	161.6		
Other Assets (Misc.			
Receivables, prepaid		Common Stock	83.0
expenses)	6.9	Surplus	39.6
Total Assets	$305.5	Total	$305.5

space at the present time and did not plan to ask for any unless he were convinced the proposed assembly line would not be otherwise feasible. If he asked for more space, he knew he would have to advance strong arguments in favor of his plan.

Possible Design Change

In planning any changes in the assembly of aluminum levels, Thomas Mancuso realized he would have to give due weight to the possibility that a preassembled vial insert might displace the present method of hand-fitted inserts. Present thinking called for a plastic cylinder, into which the vials would be cemented. This plastic insert would be made to close tolerances, with a bevel on one side (Exhibit 9). The assembly would be designed for a force fit using an arbor press; a thin coat of adhesive would be brushed on the vial insert a few minutes before the arbor press operation. After the insert had been pressed into place, the vials would be adjusted to place the air bubbles between the prepainted lines on the vials; the cement used would permit adjustments of the vial for a period of 45 minutes following application. The inside diameters of the vial supports on the insert would be made 0.006 inch larger than the outside diameter of the glass vials themselves, thus permitting final adjustment of the vials—within the 45-minute cement drying time—of 0.003. If greater adjustment were required, the whole assembly would have to be pressed out and

EXHIBIT 9 ABSOLUTE LEVEL COMPANY

PROPOSED PLASTIC INSERT

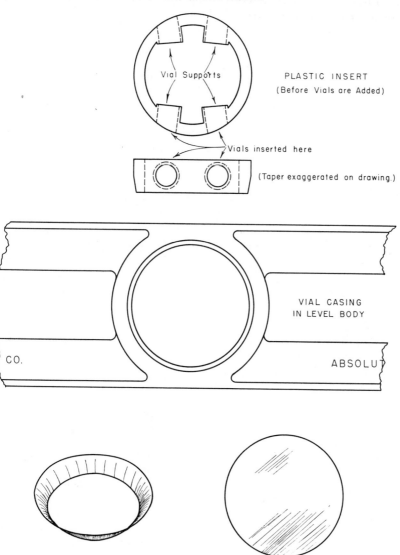

Vial Supports

PLASTIC INSERT
(Before Vials are Added)

Vials inserted here

(Taper exaggerated on drawing.)

VIAL CASING
IN LEVEL BODY

CO.

ABSOLU

ALUMINUM CLOSURE

COVER GLASS

a new insert used. The vial casings would then be closed, using a metal ring, as performed currently. This possible design change was still in the experimental stage, and Thomas Mancuso believed that if it were eventually adopted, it would not affect operations for six months or more. Manufacture of the dies alone, he knew, would consume three to four months.

The Concept of a Production System[1]

The manager of a production operation deals with the design of products, rates of flow of materials, level of training of workers, machine capacities, and a host of other factors. But he does not deal with each of these separately. The redesign of a product can call for additional training in the work force, and the level of training influences the rate of flow of material. These and more complicated interrelationships suggest that productive operations may usefully be thought of as production systems. The word "system" has been used to describe integrated bodies, both mechanical and human, in a number of different settings and is appropriate here.

The aim of this article is to present one concept of a production system that should be useful in considering a wide variety of productive operations. However, a disclaimer must be added. Although this article will identify the factors which appear over and over again in varying degrees and in different combinations in all productive systems and it will describe the common core elements, it will go only a short distance in building a general concept of production. Much will remain undone. The all-important steps of identifying the factors of greatest importance in a particular situation and determining how these factors interrelate must be taken by the manager concerned, case by case. It is doubtful whether the relative importance and specific pattern of interrelationships of the factors of production ever can be structured in a universal, rigorous model. That is, no theorist can present a general how-to-do-it blueprint to replace the analytical thinking of operating managers.

---

[1] Adapted from "The Concept of a Production System" by Philip H. Thurston, *Harvard Business Review*, Nov.–Dec. 1963, with permission.

Core and Outer Elements

Basic to any productive operation is a process for changing materials. The materials may be thought of as flowing through the one or more steps of the process. Whether they actually flow as do petroleum products in a refinery or move intermittently as do parts in a machine shop does not matter; in both instances management is concerned with the efficient movement or flow of the materials through the process steps.

For this to take place, however, there is a prior requirement of design—design of both the product to be made and the process for making it. Thus within any productive operation there are three basic elements:

Product design
Process design
Material flow

Influencing these core elements are a number of other factors, and the next step is to identify the many factors present in a production system. Rather than simply listing them, it is useful to picture them around a process and flow of material. This is intended to emphasize that the many activities of production exist primarily to facilitate the efficient movement of material through a well-designed process. The accompanying chart presents such a grouping of factors of production around the core elements. The selection for this diagram of three process steps and a single path for material flow is arbitrary, intended simply to convey the basic idea.

Interrelationships

The manager faced with a production problem has the initial tasks of identifying the relevant factors and assessing their interrelationships. In a somewhat curious fashion, all relevant factors are bound to attract attention sooner or later; if the manager initially fails to recognize them, they will, because of the highly integrated nature of production, create sore points. This can be illustrated by brief examples:

If the material specifications for a plastic toy are changed (design change) and if provision is not made for a longer "cure time" required by the new material (process change), the reject rate will climb (quality).

If a manufacturer of electrical controls increases the ratio of special products to standard products but does not plan further, he may

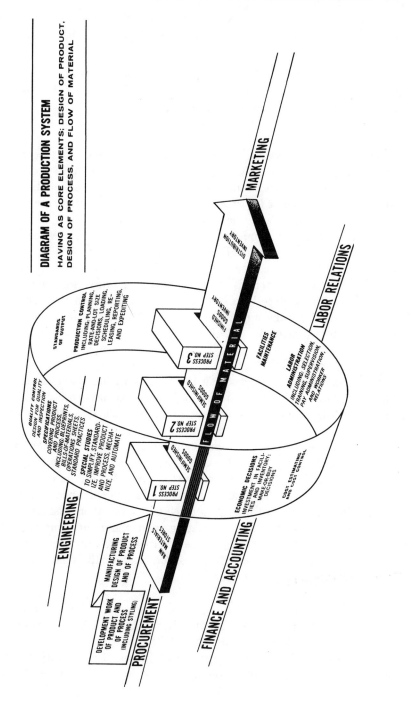

DIAGRAM OF A PRODUCTION SYSTEM

HAVING AS CORE ELEMENTS; DESIGN OF PRODUCT, DESIGN OF PROCESS, AND FLOW OF MATERIAL

not wait long before he is faced with an overload in the design section, confusion in production control, and a reduction in the number of units manufactured.

The moral is clear. The competent manager is the one who integrates the factors shown on the chart to good advantage for the design, process, and material flow of his product.

Adaptive Features

Because systems consist of parts designed to work together, intercommunication is essential. Production systems require forecasts, production plans, performance reporting, expediting, and quality and cost control. All these information flows constitute a broad, secondary network facilitating the primary flows of materials.

The pattern of communications may be seen, in part, as a feedback system. But it is not enough that the information subsystem enable the manager to take corrective action within the production system. If the production system is to continue to be vital over time, communications must place before the manager information that will permit him also to take advantage of new opportunities to meet the competitive environment.

Relation to Other Systems

The chart, besides emphasizing the factors within the area of production, shows at the periphery relationships with other business areas. In theoretical terms, a system may interact with other external systems.

A misreading of the diagram might suggest that production is the most important, the central part of a business operation. On the contrary, the chart focuses on production only for the immediate objective of a better understanding of that functional area. Actually, production systems are highly interrelated with other business functions, such as finance and marketing, and the relative importance of each to any single business operation depends on the nature of the industry and the competitive position of the individual company; they often will change over time.

Conclusion

The heart of this article is the chart. It presents the core and the scope of production and suggests the integrated nature of the factors shown. Other writers have dealt in useful ways with production systems for particular industries, or with segments of production

systems, and some have presented models in which parts are related mathematically. The attempt here has been more general—to present an over-all concept of production, one that should be valuable in thinking about production as a whole and in developing a background understanding for the analysis of specific production problems.

The objective has not been to convince the reader to accept in detail a particular structure for production systems. It is hoped, however, that this article may have had some success in influencing the reader to view the management of a production operation as the management of a system of interrelated parts. The reader may make changes within the general concept which will suit his own way of looking at systems. Surely, when it comes to specific production situations, he will have the task of relating the relevant factors to deal with problems and opportunities.

PART 1. PRODUCT AND

PROCESS TECHNOLOGIES

Laboratory Equipment Corporation of America

In the spring of 1956, Harold Quillian, vice president of Laboratory Equipment Corporation of America, considered hiring a part-time draftsman to prepare shop drawings of the numerous parts involved in the manufacture of the approximately 100 items in the company's product line. Use of such drawings would represent a change in the practices which the organization had followed for more than a half-century. Mr. Quillian was therefore anxious that such a move be made only if it would result in significant advantages to the company.

The Laboratory Equipment Corporation is located in Mason, Connecticut, near a large metropolitan center. Although small in size, the company has enjoyed a reputation as one of the world's outstanding manufacturers of laboratory equipment for teaching and research in the field of physiology. The firm's principal customers have been secondary schools, universities, medical colleges, hospitals, and research laboratories, both in the United States and abroad.

Origins

The company was established as a single proprietorship in 1904 by a doctor who was well known as a teacher and researcher in physiology. At the time of its founding, physiological laboratory equipment was produced almost exclusively by German manufacturers and available in the United States only at considerable cost. As a result, medical schools and universities were restricted in their ability to offer physiological laboratory courses that would demand large quantities of equipment for student use. Research in the field similarly was hampered by the high cost of equipment. In an effort to overcome this situation, the doctor established a small manufacturing organization and began to produce, at reasonable cost, equipment for use in his own teaching and research activities. Word of this spread quickly

among professional circles, and the organization soon was besieged with requests to manufacture similar equipment for sale to schools and laboratories. As a result, the doctor, although retaining his faculty affiliation, formed a small company to produce such items.

The company's sales volume grew steadily over the years, and more than doubled during the period following the Second World War. This reflected the large increases in college enrollments and in the volume of research activity throughout the world at that time. Foreign orders particularly increased during this period, due in large measure to financial grants by private foundations to support medical research and education in underdeveloped regions of the world.

Sales and Products

The year 1955 brought the largest sales volume in company history, and indications were that 1956 would equal or exceed this level of activity. The current volume approached the limits of company capacity with existing facilities and manpower. If this rate of growth continued, it would soon be necessary for the company to consider such courses as physical expansion, multishift operation, or a large increase in the use of subcontractors.

Changes in the current product line of approximately 100 items were infrequent, and the majority of items had been manufactured in their present form for many years. Items rarely were dropped from the line, even when their typical annual sales volume had fallen to modest levels.

Retention of slow-moving items reflected both the company's desire to render service to the profession and the characteristics of the demand for certain of its products. Rugged, long-lasting designs had been developed for many types of basic laboratory equipment. Most schools needing such equipment had purchased sufficient quantities to meet normal student requirements for a long period of time. Thus, even though thousands of such items might still be in active use throughout the world, new orders coming into the company for these products were small during any given year. Inevitably, however, a few orders would be received to replace units that had become lost or damaged beyond repair. In the interest of classroom uniformity, purchasers usually desired that the replacements be exact duplicates of the items purchased in prior years. To satisfy these needs, Laboratory Equipment Corporation carried such items in the product line, even though their total annual sales were modest.

Similar conditions existed with regard to replacement parts. It was company policy to offer repair service on all items it sold, without any

time limit. Since a small but steady volume of service orders was received constantly, it was necessary for the company to continue to produce and stock replacement parts for products for which the volume of new sales was almost negligible.

From time to time new items were added to the company's line when new inventions were perfected or new research techniques were adopted in the field of physiology. In the past the development of such new products had been infrequent and at most had involved only a few items during any single year. New developments were taking place in the field of physiology, however, particularly in research techniques. Mr. Quillian believed that opportunities for new products, especially those involving electronic applications, were considerable, and that the company probably would accelerate the launching of new items in the future. Recently the firm's capacity had been absorbed almost entirely in the production of the established product line, making it necessary to subcontract the manufacture of new products. Mr. Quillian believed that it would be necessary to continue this practice for the immediate future, since most new items supplemented rather than replaced existing products.

The regularly manufactured items varied as to size and complexity. Some were relatively simple and posed few manufacturing problems. An example would be stainless steel probing instruments used for dissections. Other products, such as "recorders," which were used to record and measure slight variations in pressure or in nerve impulses, were complicated pieces of equipment consisting of numerous parts and requiring a high order of manufacturing skill.

The Shop

The company's shop area is equipped with the basic machine tools commonly employed in metalworking operations. The company also maintains its own plating department and a large assembly area. All production activities are under the supervision of the production manager, E. F. Bush. In the machine shop, Mr. Bush has the assistance of a working foreman.

None of the firm's fifteen production employees is specialized but all are capable of performing a number of different types of manufacturing operations. When parts are machined in small lots it is not uncommon for a single operator to perform a number of different process steps requiring the set-up and operation of several types of machine tools.

In none of its manufacturing activities had the company ever employed shop drawings. Instead, an alternative system had been

developed over the years to preserve and to convey information about each of the numerous manufactured parts.

Immediately adjacent to the shop area, a series of shelves had been constructed to a height of approximately ten feet along a wall (Exhibit 1). The shelves were eight inches apart, and each of them contained a row of small wooden boxes, approximately 5 x 6 x 15 inches in size. Each box held all of the tools and fixtures required to manufacture one particular part, together with actual samples of that part as it appeared at each of the successive stages of its manufacture. Originally these items had been prepared through the combined efforts of a designer and various shop personnel when the item was first added to the product line. The designer would describe what was required and the shop personnel would make experimental models until a satisfactory prototype of the part was obtained. If special tools or fixtures were required, these were developed experimentally at the time, with the assistance of a tool-and-die maker. The completed items would then be placed in the box for future use.

EXHIBIT 1 LABORATORY EQUIPMENT CORPORATION OF AMERICA

THE SHELF AREA

EXHIBIT 2   LABORATORY EQUIPMENT CORPORATION OF AMERICA

BOX AND ITS CONTENTS IMMEDIATELY AFTER REMOVAL FROM SHELF

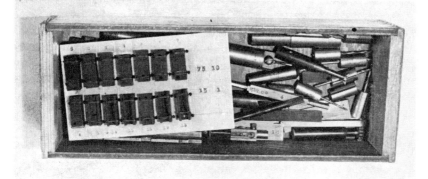

EXHIBIT 3   LABORATORY EQUIPMENT CORPORATION OF AMERICA

CONTENTS THEMSELVES

Exhibit 2 shows one of the boxes and its contents immediately following the box's removal from the shelf.   Exhibit 3 shows the contents
removed from the box.

Use of the Boxes

Each box bore a label identifying its contents.   Other than the
practice of placing less frequently used boxes on the upper shelves, the

location of the boxes did not follow any regular pattern. From experience and repeated use, however, the machine-shop foreman knew the location of each of the boxes and could usually locate any particular one of them in a matter of seconds.

An example of the use of the boxes may be illustrated by reference to a part whose manufacture required several machining operations on a casting purchased from an outside foundry. The required operations consisted, in sequence, of (1) a turning and facing operation on an engine lathe, (2) the milling of two slots on a milling machine, and (3) the drilling of two small holes on a drill press. The box for that part contains each of the following:

1. a sample of the casting as originally received from the foundry;
2. the facing and turning tools required for the lathe operations;
3. a sample of a casting after completion of the lathe operations;
4. the milling cutters required to mill the two slots;
5. a sample of a casting after completion of the lathe operations and the milling operation;
6. the drills needed for the holes;
7. a sample of a casting after completion of all the machining operations, including the two drilled holes;
8. any jigs or fixtures needed for any of the manufacturing steps.

When a lot of this particular part was scheduled into production, the machine-shop foreman would go to the shelf area and would locate and pull down the box containing the objects previously mentioned. In some of the boxes, the various samples were mounted on cards, in proper sequential order. In other boxes, the contents were mixed together in a wholly random fashion. In the latter event it would be necessary for the foreman, drawing upon his personal knowledge and experience, to sort out and arrange the items to show, step by step, the various manufacturing stages (Exhibit 4).

By use of the box's contents, the foreman could provide an operator with actual samples of the part at each process stage, and with the tools and fixtures to be used in its production. These samples could be picked up and examined by the operator. Any dimensions in doubt could be confirmed by actual measurements.

After the operator had completed all of the manufacturing operations on an item, it was his responsibility to replace the contents of the box and to return it to the foreman. The foreman would, in turn, replace the box on the shelf, making a mental note of its position so that he would be able to relocate it in the future.

Since most of the machine-shop operators were "old-timers" with

EXHIBIT 4   LABORATORY EQUIPMENT CORPORATION OF AMERICA

BOX CONTENTS AFTER BEING ARRANGED INTO SEQUENCE BY FOREMAN

many years of company service, there were many occasions in which it was not necessary to refer to the boxes unless they contained special tools or fixtures that were not otherwise available in the shop. Instead, the operator would know from memory what operations were required, and could use the shop's supply of general-purpose tools.

Mr. Quillian's Problem

Although no accurate records had been kept on the subject, Mr. Quillian estimated that 40 or 50 per cent of the boxes saw regular use one or more times each year. Another 15 or 20 per cent probably were used no more than once every two years. The remainder, he believed, contained inactive items which were scheduled into production very infrequently. As a result, these boxes were probably used once every three or four years, at most.

Mr. Quillian, who had been with the company since 1953, knew that this particular method of preserving information about manufactured parts differed from that used by most manufacturers. Firms doing subcontracting work for the company often asked for blueprints. In such cases it was necessary for the company's designer to prepare rough sketches showing shape, dimensions, etc. These, plus verbal instructions from the designer, usually had enabled the subcontractor to proceed satisfactorily. Mr. Quillian knew, however, that in at least some instances subcontractors had seen fit to prepare a conventional blueprint of the item for use in their own shops.

On balance it seemed that the company's system apparently had worked reasonably well for more than 50 years. Mr. Quillian was therefore undecided as to whether there would be any real advantages in moving to the more conventional use of shop drawings. He had discussed the matter with both the shop superintendent and the

machine-shop foreman.   Neither of them had indicated any strong reaction either in favor of or in opposition to the idea.

While considering the matter, Mr. Quillian had conducted exploratory conversations with an experienced draftsman who would be available for part-time work in the near future.   The man's qualifications were such that Mr. Quillian was sure that he could prepare accurate drawings from the items contained in each of the boxes.   For such work the draftsman would receive $2 per hour and could be available for approximately ten hours per week.   Suitable space could be arranged easily for the draftsman in the company offices, and Mr. Quillian did not feel that any close supervision of his activities would be necessary.

Since there were approximately 350 boxes on the shelves, Mr. Quillian felt that this was a reasonable estimate of the number of drawings that would have to be prepared if it were decided to make a complete conversion to their use.   The wide variations in the complexity of parts made it difficult, however, to estimate the total hours of a draftsman's services required for such an undertaking.   In discussing the matter, the draftsman said that he believed that it would require about two hours to prepare a drawing of a "simple" part, such as the double clamp (Exhibit 5).   This would include careful lettering

EXHIBIT 5   LABORATORY EQUIPMENT CORPORATION OF AMERICA

DOUBLE CLAMP

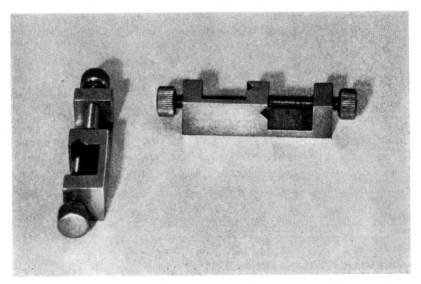

of all written material, exact measurement of all drawings to scale, accurate spacing of the various views on the page, and other steps required to produce a "finished drawing." If Mr. Quillian would be satisfied with "rough drawings," requiring less care in preparation but showing the same information, the draftsman estimated that the time could be cut by perhaps a third. Parts more complicated than the double clamp would, of course, require proportionately more time for either rough or finished drawings. Like Mr. Quillian, the draftsman found it difficult to estimate the total workload required to prepare drawings for all of the parts in the entire product line.

Mr. Quillian knew that most of the present operators had used shop drawings before joining the company, either while employed by other firms or while students in trade schools. Since the majority of these men had been with Laboratory Equipment Corporation for at least ten years, however, Mr. Quillian found it difficult to estimate how much of this skill had been forgotten through disuse and whether refresher training would be necessary. Three of the men had joined the company as apprentices, and had had no other form of training or experience. For such men, the introduction of shop drawings definitely would require a certain amount of preliminary instruction.

Reference Note on Product Specification

Substantial separations, both geographic and temporal, between the design, production, and consumption of products are one characteristic of the organization of modern industry. It was not always so. A sixteenth-century artisan concerned himself with all three, conceiving the design and frequently executing the sale of the products of his workshop. His goods, furthermore, were produced and sold as unique items. The bargain was struck after the prospective purchaser had directly examined the article he would receive. The contemporary American family, in contrast, will buy as complex an article as a washing machine or an automobile without having seen the particular unit that will be delivered. This sale is made on the basis of examination of a representative unit and some descriptive literature; it assumes that the item ultimately delivered will be entirely equivalent to the demonstration model, except for variations specified by the purchaser. In the case of the automobile those variations will generally be such that the car is "custom made" to the buyer's order. Nevertheless, the final product will be the same whether it is assembled in California or New Jersey, even though its design was probably prepared in Michigan and its parts produced in more than a dozen states.

There are two important links in the chain of communication that joins designers, producer, and consumer. One of those links is concerned with the specification of product *performance*. This tells what a product can do; it is a description of the product in an active sense, prepared from the point of view of the consumer, defining what he may expect of what he buys. The second link is concerned with the specification of product *design*. This tells what a product is, the shape, dimensions, and composition of its materials; it is a description of the product in a passive sense, prepared from the point of view of the

producer, defining a combination of properties which are necessary and sufficient to yield the desired product performance. The common means of product design specification in metalworking industries is the engineering drawing.[1]

Engineering Drawings

The function of the engineering drawing is the communication of information. It is an example of a specialized written language. Like several other languages which are useful in handling problems of business administration (for example, accounting or statistics), the use of engineering drawings is not limited to particular industries, or to this nation. The need to use the information offered, furthermore, extends in practice from general manager to machine operator and stockroom clerk. It is important to realize, however, that one need not study extensively and be able to prepare these drawings in order to use them effectively. On the contrary, the ability to obtain useful information from drawings and to interpret them for others can be quickly acquired.

Appendix A contains a series of explanations and exercises which can be used to develop your ability to obtain information from engineering drawings in a way that will be useful in the handling of administrative problems in industrial organizations. In addition, it will provide a concise reference to employ as an aid to the interpretation of drawings as they are encountered in the other materials in this book.

The Role of Design Specifications in Production

The design specification plays a central role in any process; it will be an important determinant of both the cost of achieving the desired outcome and even the probability that a satisfactory product will result. It is obvious that actions geared to a vague or ambiguous specification may well fail to produce any useful result. The grandfather of all "shaggy dog" stories came into being as a result of just such a specifications problem. The story did, indeed, concern a shaggy dog who became separated from his owner during a trip to Europe. On returning, the owner placed an ad in the newspaper of the particular European city: "LOST: ONE SHAGGY DOG, spot on left ear, black coat, Labrador breed, answers to the name of Rover." Several weeks later the owner, home again in New York, answered his

---

[1] This also may be called the shop drawing or blueprint. We will use all three terms synonymously.

doorbell and there met a man who said, "I've found your dog, and, since I was coming to New York anyway, I brought him along." The owner looked at the dog and then shook his head sadly. "That's not my dog," he said. "Why not?" said the European. "He is a black Labrador, has a spot on his left ear, is shaggy, and answers to the name of Rover." "True," said the American, "but my dog was not so shaggy."

Incomplete specifications often stir up industrial problems as well. But specifications problems do not arise only from inadequate specifications in the hands of overly meticulous customers; excessive detail, conservatism, or "overspecification" can also cause difficulty. Production on a new drive motor for an aircraft autopilot was held up for months over the inability of the production organization to meet the specification that the clutch slip at a torque "not less than 80 inch-pounds plus or minus 1 inch-pound." The manufacturing engineers were unable to control the force of a spring-loaded detent (a holding device in which a metal ball or prong slips into a groove and holds until forced out by increasing pressure) within the limits specified. Time-consuming metallurgical changes were made in the spring and in the grooved piece, but the desired consistency eluded all efforts. Finally the design engineers agreed to loosen the tolerance to make the product producible. They did so only after lengthy discussion and with the utmost reluctance, because, as they stated, "The aircraft has not yet been flown, and the flight pressures on the clutch have been calculated but not tested. If the clutch slips at too low a torque the autopilot will not function; too high and the ailerons could be torn off." Unusually tight limits imposed on the factory because of basic design uncertainty resulted in expensive problems and delays. The engineers had played it safe, but at a high price in terms of cost and delivery.

The appropriateness of any specification or system of specifications must be judged in terms of its communications effectiveness within a given production system. Ordinarily, a production system includes vendors for purchased parts, a production-control department (for scheduling materials and parts), a purchasing department, manufacturing engineers, foremen, workers, and inspectors. A language is required and wise decisions must be made concerning the particular specifications communicated in this language if misunderstandings are to be avoided and the product is to be made satisfactory to customers without excessive cost.

Choice of a language to be used for this sort of communication is only the first of several management decisions involved. Once the

language or form of communication is selected, each product, assembly, subassembly, part, operation, and material needs to have its specifications established in terms of that language or some other communications medium.

For example, consider a pair of shoes. How does the buyer for a large chain of stores specify what shoes are acceptable? What language does he use? Will inches (for the measurement of length and width) be sufficient? What about weight, color, smoothness, softness, durability, or stretch? How does the buyer know that he is getting what he wants? How does the shoe-factory manager design and control his entire process so that his shoes are satisfactory, yet not too "good" or too expensive?

Finished product specifications must be translated into specifications for parts and materials in order that material buyers, tool designers, gauge designers, machine operators, inspectors, stockmen, and assemblers can understand and perform their jobs. At each stage in the process there are specification decisions to be made which may affect quality, cost, lead times, equipment, worker skill, and materials-handling techniques.

Essentially, these decisions often are:

1. the explicitness or clarity with which a specification is stated;
2. the tightness of the specification;
3. the number of variables or points in the process which should be under specification control;
4. the degree of redundancy of the specifications used.

Some examples may help to define these choices:

EXPLICITNESS—CLARITY—PRECISION OF SPECIFICATIONS. Even with a "good" language or communications medium a production management must be careful that its specifications are explicit to the proper degree to avoid ambiguity. This is not as easy as it might at first appear. Take this drawing. What does it tell the reader?

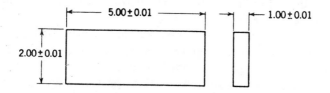

It seems to suggest a 2 x 5 x 1 block held to tolerances of ±.01. But what about these tolerances—can the error all be on one (or

two) sides? Can one side be "perfectly" flat (impossible, of course) and the other side have little hills and valleys of up to ±.01 in height? How straight must the edges be? Are the corners at 90°? Would 89° suffice? What about the smoothness of the surfaces? There is nothing said about that quality. Where should the parts be measured—is the 2 at the left end, right end, middle, or everywhere? Is the "grain" of the material important?

We have grown to accept certain conventions which do not always carry the necessary precision. If certain measurements are left undefined the part can meet specs and still not work or fit. Yet, if these dimensions or specs are spelled out unnecessarily, extra care or time in manufacture is required.

Is this a technical problem? To some extent it is. But frequently these problems occur not because of a lack of technical know-how but because of a failure to recognize that the communications are being carried on informally rather than by clear decision and explicit specification. For instance, a construction foreman complained that the millwork he received required too much hand fitting (filing, planing, forcing, etc.). The millwork shop claimed it had made no changes and its millwork had always been acceptable in the past. The solution followed the realization that certain dimensions were not spelled out on the prints. Analysis of cost alternatives suggested that it was less expensive to hand fit than to provide tooling and equipment necessary to supply parts not needing hand fitting.

TIGHTNESS OF THE SPECIFICATION. By and large those responsible for the satisfactory performance of a product will tend to be more rigid in its specification than those charged with making it. The manager must be aware of this silent struggle and recognize that while issues appear to be settled they may not necessarily have been settled ideally. The degree of tightness may have been settled by personality, fiat, or lack of recognition of the implicit decision in accepting a blueprint, model, or standard for production. The dominating individual or department may not have the total company view in mind. Production managers must feel free, even obligated, to question the specifications received.

It would be a mistake to assume that overly tight tolerances represent a conspiracy of engineers, salesmen, and inspectors to make life difficult for the grease-covered production man. More often it is a simple lack of understanding on the part of the engineer of the actual production process and its capabilities. Some companies have been able to introduce their manufacturing-engineering personnel into

the design process from the start in the effort to influence product design for better producibility. Successful manufacturing-engineering departments view their jobs as consisting in part of educating and informing designers of the realities of the world of manufacturing. A production manager frequently may find that this problem of "tightness" of specifications is a fertile ground for achieving proper quality at lower net cost.

VARIABLES OR PROCESS POINTS TO BE UNDER SPECIFICATION CONTROL. This decision concerns both the points to be specified and the points to be inspected. The process of making a shirt illustrates this decision area. Parts usually are cut out using patterns. Should all these parts be inspected? Should the pattern be measured once? Should it be checked occasionally? Should a sampling be made of the parts on a daily basis? All parts? How would the parts be measured? Should the production manager check for loose threads due to a dull knife or cutter? Should this be left up to the worker? Indeed, what does the worker need to know? These questions all get answered, implicitly by abdication or habit, or explicitly by order, on specification or process sheet.

In a bookbinding shop of five employees a skilled worker decides on the amount of "rounding" which should be given to the outer (board) end of a book. There seems to be no formal specification as to what is "good" or "right" or "best." But in a 200-man shop, with 30 "rounders," should there be some specification on this operation? How does the production manager decide? What does the worker need to know?

Electronics assembly requires soldering wires to terminals. What is a "good" solder joint? Should each joint be described somehow and checked? The electrical connection may be good, but will the joint stand up under continued vibration?

In many of these situations the manager must combine the technology of the operation with marketing and human demands. Sometimes through careful training, close supervision, or selection of adequate worker experience, the meeting of implicit product specifications may be assured without the cost of explicitly specifying certain requirements and insuring that these demands are met.

The fact that there are no rules and that each decision must be made on the basis of a careful appraisal of many factors makes it clear that this is an area for production-management consideration. Each step of the entire process may be examined with the questions: What results are necessary? Must they be specified? If so, how?

If not, what is our assurance of their accomplishment? By what means?

THE DEGREE OF REDUNDANCY OR OVERLAP OF THE SPECIFICATIONS USED. Why have *any* redundant specifications? Essentially the answer is that some overlaps may help to insure a proper quality level. Redundancy is a form of insurance and is one aspect of a "fail-safe" system. For example, why state that a ball bearing must turn with a certain maximum friction level when the tolerances and surfaces of each part all have been set at levels so that the friction level should never exceed the maximum? The final product performance is specified as well as that of the parts because of the possibility of a poor part slipping through, or the chance of random variables difficult to predict, or both, which might make a sticky bearing with apparently satisfactory parts. The manufacturer must determine the benefits of these overlapping specifications and what they cost. Might it be cheaper to inspect all parts 100 per cent than to make elaborate checks on later assemblies?

Redundant specifications set up to avoid confusion or ambiguity may sometimes create the opposite effect. Blueprints frequently may contain examples of dimensions which when added together over a length of a part actually can exceed the over-all length shown for the part, if actual individual measurements are on the high side of their respective tolerances. Such a blueprint may be an intentional redundancy, because all dimensions are critical, but it is easy to see how this also can cause confusion and rejects.

There are many decisions that must be made in bringing a product into being. They should be made in awareness of the fact that freedom of choice exists.

Reference Note on the Metalworking Process

Notable achievements in the allied fields of industrial management and industrial technology have been a mark of twentieth-century American life. The effects of this country's success in the development of large-scale, modern industry have been pervasive. They have shaped our society and culture as well as our economic structure and material wealth. One consequence of our technical capabilities has been the creation of entire industries to produce products or provide services otherwise impossible to achieve. The extent to which this is true is illustrated by the ease with which anyone could provide a list of examples. To mention only a few, we might point to the mass communication and mass transportation industries and the widespread use of automata to perform repetitive tasks in the home and in industry. Another consequence has been the creation of plentiful and cheap supplies of things which, though simple and ancient, were even recently very dear. For example, before the American Revolution, nails "were so expensive that settlers migrating to a new area commonly burned their cabins and raked the nails out of the ashes so they could use the nails again. As late as 1810, 25 per cent of the nation's iron output was in the form of nail rods from which the purchaser hammered out individual nails in his spare time. This manufacturing method made nails so dear that they were used for bartering in village stores."[1]

The evolution of modern production technique can be traced to ancient times, when man first began to devise ways of employing machinery to do his labor. From the thirteenth century onward, there are scattered examples of the production of goods in central work-

---

[1] Robert Malcolm Keir (editor), *Industries of America: Manufacturing,* New York: The Ronald Press Company, 1928.

shops—prototypical factories—instead of the home. It wasn't until the end of the eighteenth century, however, that the locus of manufacture moved decisively out of the home and into the factory. At the same time, the idea of specialization and division of labor excited interest. Adam Smith's *The Wealth of Nations*, published in 1776, discusses the advantages of division of labor and describes a pin-making enterprise which increased production by a multiple of 4,000 through task specialization. Just before 1800, two great innovations provided the necessary technical means for the development of modern production technology: James Watt perfected the steam engine and Henry Maudslay built the first machine tool of all-metal construction.

Possible applications of the steam engine spurred a circular demand for better engines, for machines utilizing the new power source, and for more advanced production tools. A measure of the capability of contemporary tools can be gained from the fact that Watt praised the workmanship that produced an 18-inch cylinder that was only three-eighths of an inch out-of-round. In many engines the space between piston and cylinder wall had to be stuffed with paper, cork, putty, or even old hats to maintain steam pressure.

The rugged, all-metal construction of Maudslay's lathe (and of subsequent metalworking tools) made possible both greater precision and use of stronger materials in manufacture. Precision was also enhanced by his use of a slide rest for support and control of the cutting tool, which previously had been held in the hand, like a chisel. Nevertheless, this lathe like its predecessors was powered by a man turning a crank on a large wheel.

Another pressure for more productive and more precise metalworking tools came from the desire to produce products from interchangeable parts. The manufacture of interchangeable parts was attempted as early as 1717 in France without commercial success. Early in the nineteenth century in the United States, Eli Whitney manufactured rifles from interchangeable parts, but he was nine years late completing a two-year contract. His workmen used hand files to finish the parts to final dimensions, a process which was time-consuming and inexact despite the use of jigs to hold the part and guide the file. The use of interchangeable parts probably did not yield any appreciable savings in manufacture at that time.[2]

The need for precise and productive tools to fabricate standardized parts in large quantities and to achieve the economies of mass pro-

---

[2] Robert S. Woodbury, "The Legend of Eli Whitney and Interchangeable Parts," *Technology and Culture*, 1, p. 235 (1960).

duction was exploited both in this country and in Britain during the first half of the nineteenth century.   By 1850 engineer-entrepreneurs in one country or the other had developed early forms of most of the general-purpose machine tools now in use.   The first milling machines were built and used around 1820 by Eli Whitney and Robert Johnson, both of Connecticut.   With these tools, accurately shaped parts could be mounted easily in one efficient, special-purpose machine and then as easily mounted in a second for a different operation.   Thus the economies inherent in special-purpose machines and in the elimination of hand filing in many assembly operations could be realized.

As machine tools developed greater output capabilities and evolved into special-purpose, precise, and reliable machines toward the end of the century, and as steel-making processes yielded much greater volumes of better, cheaper raw material, the emphasis in manufacturing shifted to making the machine and its operator more efficient. The efforts of Frederick Taylor and others working from 1890 to 1920 were directed toward adapting machines so that they could be operated more effectively by men and toward defining men's jobs so that they could make machines produce more efficiently.

The early part of the twentieth century also saw the emergence of concepts aimed at linking the separate men and machines into more efficient overall systems.   The Ford Motor Company's moving assembly line was one of the earliest such integrating devices.   Prior to 1913, the chassis for Ford cars were assembled by a crew of workmen.   In 1913 this was changed to a moving assembly line in which the chassis was mounted on rails and propelled by an endless chain. The workmen were stationed along the line and each performed only a few operations.   This single change decreased labor time from more than 12 to less than 1½ man-hours per chassis.

The recent innovations in manufacturing management and technology are too complex and too numerous to be fully illuminated in a work of this scope.   Among the more notable developments we might mention are the continuing physical integration of once separate processes and the use of electronics to perform coordinating and control functions.   The integrative trend started by the assembly conveyor has been extended into fabricating processes.   Now single computers coordinate operations in entire plants and even those in supplier plants.   Numerical control of processes and machine tools is also finding increasing application in the factory.   A brief description of some of these current developments appears at the end of this note.

FIGURE 1. The body drop operation on the Ford Motor Company's moving body-and-chassis assembly line. This line decreased assembly labor time by 88 per cent between 1913 and 1914. (Courtesy Ford Motor Company.)

THE METALWORKING PROCESSES

Metalworking today is big business. The combined metalworking industries annually sell more than 140 billion dollars of products ranging from ships to watches. In 1960, suppliers shipped approximately 70 million tons of steel, 12 million tons of iron, 2 million tons of aluminum, and 2 million tons of copper to more than 80,000 metalworking plants. A census of 1960 indicated that there were 27,000 metalworking plants employing 20 or more people. These plants employed a total of 8 million people and owned or leased approximately 3 million machine tools.

The processes used in converting metallic ores into finished products can be divided into five stages: production of raw material, primary fabrication, secondary fabrication, assembly, and finishing operations. To produce raw material for operations in subsequent stages, ore is refined and formed into ingots and standard shapes such as sheet, bar, and tube. In primary fabricating processes, some of this material

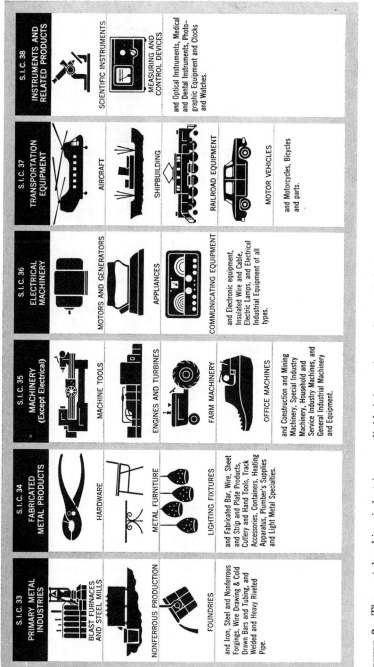

FIGURE 2. The metalworking industries are divided into nine major statistical groups which serve a variety of markets. Not shown are the ordnance, furniture, and miscellaneous manufacturing industries.

TABLE A   METAL SHIPMENTS AND PRICES

The 1960 volumes and approximate prices of four major metals and their alloys shipped by fabricators, foundries, and mills in the United States.

Shipped Form of Metal	Steel		Iron		Aluminum		Copper	
	Volume	Price	Volume	Price	Volume	Price	Volume	Price
Mill Products								
Ingots								
Blooms								
Slabs	1,756	4.0	n.a.	n.a.	425	26	n.a.	32
Billets etc.								
Sheets and								
Strip	29,001*	6.3	—	—	{693	{51	323	62
Plate	6,708	5.3	—	—			—	—
Bars	10,515	6.7	—	—	46	57	320†	62
Tube and								
Pipe	7,050	10.0	—	—	30	n.a.	292	65
Structural								
Shapes	4,836	5.5	—	—	n.a.	n.a.	—	—
Other	11,283	n.a.	—	—	735	n.a.	778	n.a.
Subtotal	71,149	7.5	n.a.	n.a.	1,929	n.a.	1,713	n.a.
Castings	1,072‡	n.a.	6,868§	n.a.	375	n.a.	381	n.a.
Forgings	1,268	n.a.	—	—	25	n.a.	50	n.a.

Volume is in thousands of tons.   Price is in cents per pound.

* Not included are 5,465,000 tons of tin plate.

† Nonelectrical wire is included.

‡ Not included are 320,000 tons for intracompany use.

§ Not included are 5,545,000 tons for intracompany use.

Sources:
  American Iron and Steel Institute.
  U. S. Bureau of the Census and Business and Defense Service Administration.
  "Metal Working Facts and Figures," *Steel*, Cleveland: The Penton Publishing Company, March 27, 1961.
  "106th Annual Issue," *Iron Age*, Philadelphia: Chilton Company, January 5, 1961.

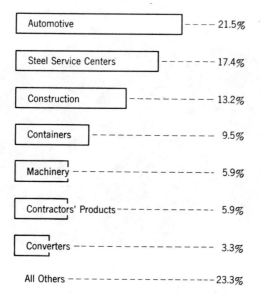

FIGURE 3. The distribution of finished steel by market in 1962. Service centers refer to warehouses and distributors. (Courtesy *Steel, Metalworking Facts and Figures,* © 1963, Penton Publishing Company, Cleveland.)

is roughly formed into the shape of particular parts by molds or dies produced according to the design of the finished part. Material from both of these stages can be more exactly shaped to a final form in the metal-cutting processes used in secondary fabrication. Completed parts are then assembled into products and, in the last stage, are submitted to finishing processes such as testing, reworking, and packaging. In addition to the processes in these five stages, there are others which can occur at any time in a product's stage of development—for example, heat treating, cleaning, and painting. This outline of the metalworking processes is illustrated by the flow diagram in Figure 4.

RAW MATERIAL

To produce the raw material used in the primary and secondary fabricating stages, ore is reduced to metal and is formed into a variety of standard shapes. The production of standard shapes facilitates both economical production of raw material and lower material-handling and machining costs in subsequent stages of fabrication.

FIGURE 5. Typical shapes of raw material fabricated by steel mills. (Courtesy United States Steel Corporation.)

Steel Making

The most important of the processes for refining and shaping metals are found in the steel industry, which produces about 80% of the metal used in this country. Iron ore is dug from mines and shipped to mills where it is loaded into blast furnaces together with a charge of coke. Molten iron is tapped from these furnaces and is either cast into "pigs" of a weight convenient for shipping or sent on for further intracompany processing in a liquid state.

Pig iron contains about 4 per cent carbon and a variety of impurities. It solidifies into a relatively weak and brittle metal. Steel is an alloy of carbon and iron containing less than 1.7 per cent of the former element. It is a stronger and more ductile material. Steel is produced from pig iron in electric, Bessemer, or open-hearth furnaces where the carbon and impurities are burned out and then controlled amounts of carbon and other alloying elements are added.

The amounts of carbon and other alloys added to the iron impart a wide variety of properties. Steels with a low carbon content are easily machined and formed in subsequent manufacturing processes. Higher-carbon steels, on the other hand, can be made more than five times as strong as low-carbon steels and are often more expensive to machine. Bright, corrosion-resistant stainless steel is made by alloying chromium and nickel with steel.

FIGURE 6. Blast furnace No. 1 at U.S. Steel's Fairless Works near Morrisville, Pennsylvania. (Courtesy United States Steel Corporation.)

Rolling Processes

In 1960, rolling processes converted more than 65 million tons of steel, aluminum, and brass ingots into plate, sheet, strip, bar, tube, and structural shapes.

Most steel-rolling operations, accounting for 90 per cent of all metal rolled, are performed at the steel works, frequently before the newly refined steel has had a chance to cool. After the steel is refined in the furnaces, some of which hold as much as 500 tons of molten

FIGURE 7. Red-hot ingots are stripped from their molds at the Fairless Works of United States Steel Corporation. The 150-ton stripper crane is shown removing a mold from the red-hot steel. Following this operation, the ingots, which have cooled on the outside, are placed in soaking pits to be brought up to a uniform temperature for rolling. (Courtesy United States Steel Corporation.)

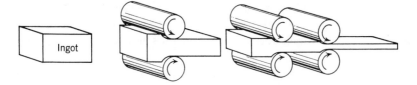

FIGURE 8. Steel ingots pass through a number of rolling stands as they are reduced to final shapes in the rolling process.

metal, it is poured into ingot molds and allowed to solidify into rectangular ingots weighing as much as 35 tons. Overhead cranes carry the solid, red-hot ingots to a rolling stand (called a blooming mill) at the beginning of the rolling process. In this machine, the ingot is forced between two rolls and squeezed into a longer, thinner shape. Next the still-glowing ingot passes through other rolling stands, which

FIGURE 9. Red-hot steel, passing through this six-stand 80-inch hot-strip mill, exits from the stand in the foreground at a speed of 2,300 feet per minute. (Courtesy United States Steel Corporation.)

reduce it to plate, sheet, or other shapes. During the hot rolling operations, large quantities of water are sprayed on the steel to remove the scale which forms on the metal's hot surface and to cool the rollers in the stands.

After cooling to room temperature, some of the hot rolled sheet and strip may be rolled again in order to reduce it to thicknesses below 0.050 inch, to increase the material's strength and hardness, or to improve its surface finish.

Rolled products are available in a wide range of standard alloys and with standard tolerances in sizes which range from less than 0.040 inch to more than 12 inches thick. Special tolerances are obtained from special mill runs or from selected warehouse stocks. For example, nominal 0.062-inch sheet steel has a standard tolerance of ±0.005 inch; selected stocks can be obtained with a ±0.003-inch tolerance at additional cost.

Approximately 770 thousand tons of aluminum and 950 thousand tons of copper are rolled annually in a similar process. These materials' lesser strengths and lower melting points allow more severe reduction in a single roll pass, and permit hot rolling at lower temperatures.

Inspection of Raw Material

Primary metal producers inspect their products to insure that they lie within the metallurgical range and the dimensional limits sought by their customers. The metallurgical properties of material are determined in laboratories which may be equipped with several hundred thousand dollars of apparatus and manned by full-time staffs. Careful quality control serves to prevent unsuitable raw material from being processed and to insure that final products meet specifications.

Dimensions of the products are checked both during processing and afterwards. In-process measuring (on rolling mills) can be done with electronic devices which are capable of measuring moving metal at temperatures up to 2,200°F in order to determine the effects of roll wear, roll speed variation, and metal temperature variation as they occur. Measuring systems, which can cost more than $40,000, may be linked to master controls so that corrective action can be taken automatically. After processing, material is commonly checked at company and warehouse shipping and receiving stations with a variety of hand measuring tools costing less than $100.

The investment required for building a fully integrated mill capable of producing 500,000 tons of rolled steel per year would amount to more than 200 million dollars.

PRIMARY FABRICATION

In the primary fabricating processes such as sand casting, die casting, forging, and stamping, either ingots or metal in standard shapes are formed into particular parts by preformed dies (or molds). In sand and die casting processes, molten metal flows into molds of the part's shape. In forging and stamping, hot (but not molten) or cold metal is forced to "flow" under great pressures created by the dies.

Sand Casting

Sand casting is used primarily to shape iron and steel into rough, complex shapes of almost any size. The shape and size of the casting is determined by a pattern and the mold inserts used by the mold maker.

FIGURE 10. Molten metal will be poured into the large sand molds these men are making on the foundry floor. In the foreground is a large, mobile sand slinger which carries its own sand supply that is conveyed to the unit's ramming head via a series of buckets and belts. The sand is rammed into the flask at a high constant velocity, assuring a mold of uniform density. (Courtesy Beardsley & Piper Division, Pettibone Mulliken Corporation.)

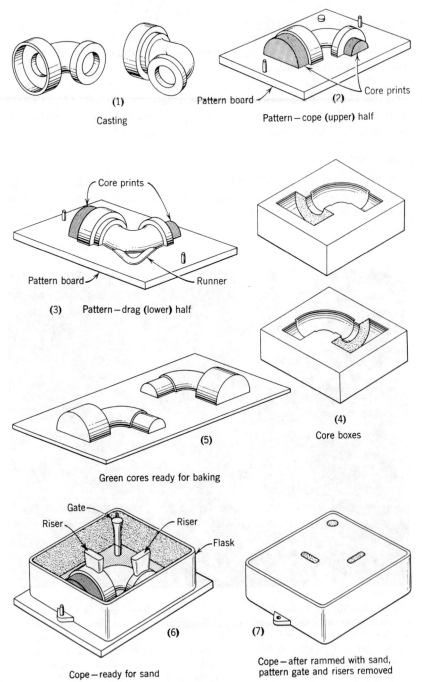

(1)

Casting

Pattern board

(2)

Core prints

Pattern – cope (upper) half

Core prints

Pattern board

Runner

(3)   Pattern – drag (lower) half

(4)

Core boxes

(5)

Green cores ready for baking

Gate

Riser

Riser

Flask

(6)

Cope – ready for sand

(7)

Cope – after rammed with sand,
pattern gate and risers removed

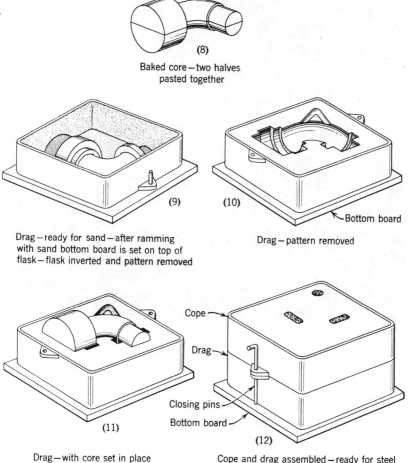

(8)

Baked core—two halves
pasted together

(9)

(10)

Bottom board

Drag—ready for sand—after ramming
with sand bottom board is set on top of
flask—flask inverted and pattern removed

Drag—pattern removed

Cope

Drag

Closing pins

Bottom board

(11)

(12)

Drag—with core set in place

Cope and drag assembled—ready for steel

(13)

Casting as removed from sand.

Risers and gate removed,
casting chipped and ground
where necessary, annealed,
inspected, and ready for
shipment.

FIGURE 11. In making a sand casting, wooden patterns are placed in flasks, and sand is packed around them. The patterns are removed, and the flasks are assembled. Molten metal is poured into the void and allowed to harden. The casting is then cleaned of sand and excess metal. (Courtesy Adirondack Steel Casting Company, Inc.)

FIGURE 12. Molten aluminum being poured into a sand mold at Alcoa's Cleveland, Ohio, works. (Courtesy Aluminum Company of America.)

Sand castings are made in foundries which are commonly isolated from other processes. Iron is melted in a cupola or furnace, poured into an insulated bucket, and carried to the mold on the foundry floor. The metal is poured into the mold and allowed to harden into the desired shape. Then the sand is broken away from the hardened casting, and the casting's surface is cleaned.

Sand molds, from which the process derives its name, are usually made using a pattern, special "green" (moist) sand, and a flask (a metal box). To make the mold, a pattern in the shape of the desired part is placed inside the flask and sand is packed around it. When tamped to the proper density, the moist sand becomes a firm mass which retains the pattern's shape. After tamping, the pattern is removed and the mold may be baked. If holes or special cavities are desired in the casting, cores or inserts are placed in the void. Then the mold is closed and filled with molten metal. The hardened casting is cleaned and undesired protrusions are removed.

Both the capital costs of sand-molding equipment and the operational costs of the process vary a great deal depending on the size and degree of mechanization of the foundry. A large melting furnace, a large pouring ladle, a crane, an inventory of flasks, and equipment for a pattern shop and for reclaiming sand can cost hundreds of thousands of dollars. Machines like squeezers or sand slingers, which pack the sand around the pattern mechanically, cost from several hundred to many thousand dollars.

This adaptable process can be the most economical way of producing a single piece or more than 10,000 pieces. Production rates range up to 1,000 small pieces per hour. Small patterns generally take only a few days to make and cost less than $100, while very large patterns may require several months and cost more than $100,000. Since the same sand, flasks, and core-making machinery are used in

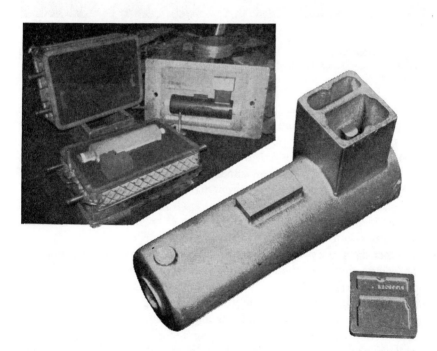

FIGURE 13. The iron casting requires cores (inserts) to form the hollow center and openings in its rectangular projection. At the left is the sand mold in its flask ready for closing. The drag (bottom half of the mold) has lighter color sand cores in place. At the right is the mold's pattern. (Courtesy Reading Gray Iron Casting, Inc.)

FIGURE 14. Large cast and machined screws are shown in the foreground. They have been machined on the lathe in the background. (Courtesy Aetna-Standard Division, Blaw-Knox Company.)

making many different products, there are no appreciable costs in shifting production from one product to another if no new patterns are required.

Small sand castings weigh a few ounces; large ones weigh as much as 250 tons. Tolerances on dimensions are commonly held within ±0.06 inch per inch, except in repetitive production, when the tolerances can be reduced to ±0.03 inch per inch.[3] Most castings are machined to smooth their rough surfaces or to impart more accurate dimensions before assembly with other parts.

Dimensions vary as a result of pattern wear, sand's flaking into the mold void, the metal's being poured at varying temperatures, and the sand's being packed to slightly different densities. Voids and cracks in the casting may result from gases released by the molten metal, from loose sand's being entrapped in the metal as it is poured, from the metal's hardening before it fills all the mold's cavities, and from uneven cooling of the poured metal. In practice, reject rates range from almost zero to higher than 30 per cent.

---

[3] A tolerance of ±0.06 inch per inch indicates that actual dimensions will vary from those desired by as much as 0.06 inch per inch of the original dimension. For example, a six-inch dimension may vary by as much as ±0.36 inch.

In 1960, 12,413,000 tons of iron and 1,392,000 tons of steel castings were poured by foundries. About half this volume was for use within the same factory; the remainder was for sale. Of the nonferrous metals, 65,000 tons of aluminum and 333,000 tons of copper were sand cast.

Other Casting Processes

Shell and investment molding processes are often used to increase dimensional accuracy to within ±0.008 inch per inch and to improve surface finish to the order of 125 microinches.[4] In effect, these substitute other materials for sand in the sand molding process. They have higher pattern and piece costs and ordinarily will not produce castings weighing more than 200 pounds.

Die Casting

In die casting, molten metal is poured into metal molds which can produce parts with complex shapes and accurate dimensions that require very little subsequent machining.

In operation, molten metal is forced under pressure (up to 100,000 pounds per square inch) into a metal mold (or die) and allowed to solidify. The mold is opened, the part ejected, and the mold closed in preparation for another cycle. Intricate parts can be formed by using molds having several sections and cores that withdraw in different directions.

The cost of a die-casting machine which will produce 150 ten-pound aluminum castings per hour is approximately $30,000. In most cases, dies can be made in several weeks at a cost between $200 and $5,000. Initial insertion of dies and a preliminary run to establish stable conditions can take several hours. Once in operation, a die-casting machine is commonly attended by one operator. This process is ordinarily most economical for production quantities of several thousand parts.

Die-cast dimensions can be held within ±0.003 inch and surface finishes on the order of 80 microinches are obtainable. Thin, fragile flash which forms along the mold's joints is usually removed in a flash-shaving (stamping) operation. Subsequent machining operations may be used to drill holes within ±0.001 inch and to tap (thread) holes. The weight of zinc and aluminum castings seldom exceeds 35 to 70 pounds, respectively. In 1960, 307,000 tons of zinc, 181,000

---

[4] Surface finish of 125 microinches indicates that projections or depressions on a flat surface do not exceed an average of 125 millionths of an inch.

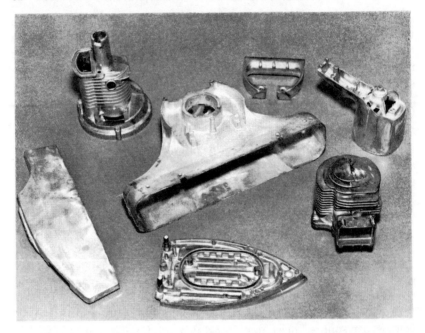

FIGURE 15. Some examples of aluminum alloy die castings: power drill body, industrial vacuum cleaner head, power tool handle, electric iron soleplate, power tool cylinder head, and a business machine housing. (Courtesy Aluminum Company of America.)

FIGURE 16. Aluminum, magnesium, or brass parts can be cast at a rate of 150 per hour in this die-casting machine. (Courtesy Cast-Master, HPM Division, Koehring Company.)

FIGURE 17. When a company switched from a sand-casting and machining process to a die-casting process, the cost of this housing decreased 54 per cent. (Courtesy American Die Casting Institute, Inc.)

FIGURE 18. The cost of the complex die used to make the housing in Fig. 17 was recovered after 1,800 pieces had been produced. (Courtesy American Die Casting Institute, Inc.)

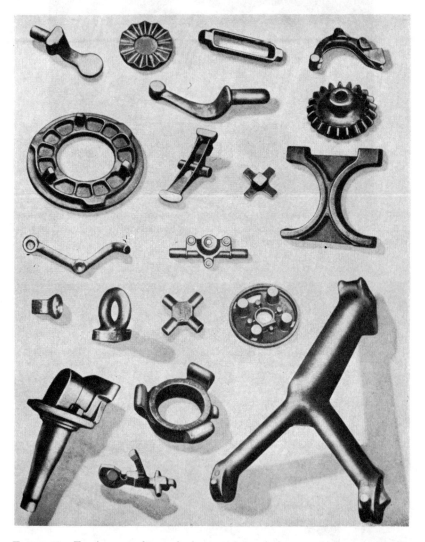

FIGURE 19. Forgings can be made in a variety of shapes, which are generally less complex than die-cast shapes. (Courtesy Drop Forging Association.)

tons of aluminum, and 7,000 tons of copper were die cast. Little of the latter is cast because molds wear rapidly when subjected to the 1,600°F melting temperature of copper. (Zinc and aluminum alloys melt at approximately 800°F and 1,200°F, respectively.)

Forging

In the forging and stamping operations, metal is forced to flow into desired shapes by enormous pressures exerted by dies. Generally, these two processes form less complex shapes than casting processes because a die's sections must be heavier in order to withstand the forming pressures and simpler to permit die withdrawal.

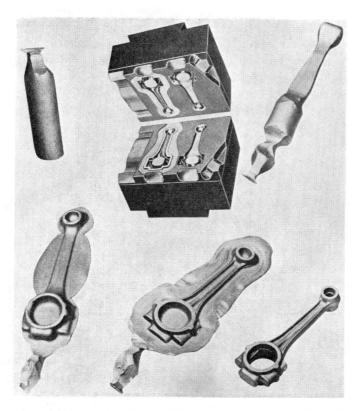

FIGURE 20. In these forging dies, a 1½-inch steel bar is formed progressively into a connecting rod. Between hammer blows, the work is moved from the right-hand portion of the die to the left-hand portion, to the middle right cavity, and to the left cavity, which imparts the final shape. The excess metal which escapes into the gutter around the finishing impression is removed in a subsequent operation. (Courtesy Drop Forging Association.)

Many forging shops are separated physically from other metal-working machinery because they require auxiliary heating furnaces and because the metal is worked in a red-hot state. The hot metal creates smoke and scale, and vibrations are set up by the pounding action of machines, all of which make isolation desirable.

A forging hammer (machine) consists of a frame which supports a table holding one die and a ram which carries a mating die. Together these form a cavity in the shape of the desired product. Heated metal is placed between the dies and the ram drives them together, creating the pressures which cause the metal to flow into the cavity's shape. Often several different die impressions are required to form a piece progressively into its final shape.

Hammers vary widely in size, productivity, and price. A small pneumatic hammer, capable of producing 140 ten-pound parts per hour, sells for approximately $25,000. Larger hammers which will work pieces weighing 50 tons cost up to $600,000. More automatic

FIGURE 21. An Impacter cuts off, heats, forges, and delivers stock with a minimum of noise and vibration. The unit shown is capable of forging at a rate of approximately 1,900 pounds of steel per hour with the attendance of only a single operator. The complete system (less dies) is priced at about $150,000. (Courtesy Chambersburg Engineering Company.)

FIGURE 22.   Scale is forming on the red-hot casting in this large hydraulic forging press.   A comparison of this large but simple machine with the Impacter is indicative of the variety of hydraulic forging presses in operation.   (Courtesy Mesta Machine Company.)

machines, selling for as much as $150,000, will produce more than 1,400 ten-pound pieces per hour.

In 1960, approximately 1.3 million tons of steel and 25 thousand tons of aluminum were forged.

One operator commonly loads and unloads material and operates a hammer.   Changing small dies and setting stops which govern the ram's travel usually take less than half an hour.   The design and

matching of dies takes about two weeks. Dies commonly cost between $100 and $1,000. Lot sizes exceeding 10,000 pieces are usually the most economical, and production rates on the order of 120 to 600 pieces per hour are most common.

Forged products commonly weigh from less than an ounce to hundreds of tons and are stronger than parts formed in any other process. This increased strength results from the rapid pounding of the hot metal, which enhances its metallurgical properties. Dimensions can be held within ±0.010 to ±0.030 inch. Surface finishes are rougher than die-cast surfaces because the heated metal tends to react with air during the process. Flash which collects along the parting lines of the dies is usually removed in subsequent operations.

Stamping

Stamping operations are ordinarily used to produce holes, complex contours, and complex outlines in sheet and tube material at very high production rates.

FIGURE 23. Three operators are manually feeding parts to these small punch presses. (Courtesy Clearing Machine Corporation, Division of U.S. Industries, Inc.)

FIGURE 24. Previously formed cups are being enlarged progressively on two dies in this large press. (Courtesy Clearing Machine Corporation, Division of U.S. Industries, Inc.)

Since the material is stamped at room temperature, the process does not create smoke or scale. In spite of noise and vibration created by a press's impacting ram, small machines are usually located in the same building with fabricating operations to reduce the material handling costs. Large presses, which can form products like automobile hoods, tops, and fenders in a single blow, are often isolated because they create much more noise and vibration.

A stamping press consists of a frame and a table which supports both a die (block) and a reciprocating ram, which carries a punch (the mating die). Material is fed between the two dies, and the ram descends, driving the upper die and the material against the die block. The shape of the cuts and the form imparted to the material are determined by the contours machined into the punch and die block. One hole, several holes, irregularly shaped holes, or irregular outlines and contours are easily and rapidly made in this process.

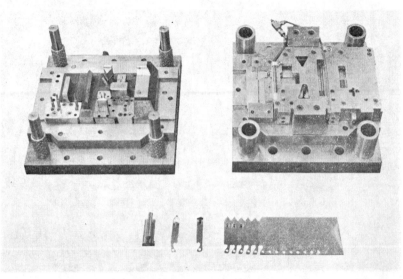

FIGURE 25. This progressive die performs 15 operations and completes one can opener in each stroke of the press. (Courtesy Verson Allsteel Press Company.)

A press which will exert a force of 200 tons and is capable of shearing approximately three square inches of steel costs $20,000. Larger presses, like those used in automobile hood and fender stamping, can cost more than $250,000 and must be installed on specially reinforced floors.

Unit operating costs are small, since usually only one man is required to feed, run, and remove material from a press which can stamp several thousand small parts per hour. Dies commonly are made in several weeks and must be used for a few days before they will produce satisfactorily. Dies that have been broken in can be placed in a press and material set up in less than half an hour. Carbide dies are the most expensive type of stamping tools and are seldom used for production quantities of less than a million pieces. For lesser quantities, dies made of different materials and combinations of standard tooling are available. Large carbide dies may cost more than $100,000. The cost for short-run tooling ranges from $400 to $2,000. The lot size required to justify short runs is commonly more than 10,000 pieces.

Ordinarily, material thicker than 0.375 inch is not stamped, although heated steel 3.5 inches thick has been. Parts as large as automobile

hoods, requiring excellent finishes and tolerances of ±0.001 inch, can be punched or formed.

Since there are no volume statistics available, the relative importance of this form of fabrication can only be inferred from machine-tool inventory figures. In 1958, presses accounted for about 10 per cent of the 2.8 million machine tools used in the 27,000 manufacturing plants which employ more than 20 people.

Inspection of Products Formed in the Primary Fabricating Processes

Products made by these processes generally are checked only for dimensional accuracy, except for sand castings, which also are inspected for voids and cracks. Chemical analysis and control is not required because these functions usually are performed by suppliers of raw material. Dimensions can be checked within ±0.001 inch, one at a time, using a variety of hand measuring tools costing less than $100. More elaborate, special-purpose inspection tools can check as many as 20 dimensions on a complex part at one time. If these gages are to be used to check precise die-cast parts within accuracies of ±0.001 inch, they might cost more than $2,000. If used to check

FIGURE 26. A Resotron 1000 is making a radiograph of a casting in a specially designed room. (Courtesy X-Ray Department, General Electric Company.)

rougher forgings to accuracies of ±0.01 inch, they would cost less than half as much.

If the incidence of voids and cracks in a single sand casting is high, weighing and visual inspection will detect many of the bad castings. When more reliable inspection is desired, the castings may be examined radiographically or electronically. The possibility of voids and cracks being produced in other processes is less because the metal is formed under high pressures (which close voids), and in temperature-controlled dies that reduce the chances of cracking.

SECONDARY FABRICATION

Raw material (standard shapes) as well as parts shaped by sand-casting, die-casting, forging, or stamping operations are often processed subsequently in metal-removing machine tools to produce more accurate final shapes and smoother surface finishes. The variety of metal-removing machine tools is great. Some are large enough to encompass 100-ton castings, and others will work on parts the size of watch gears. Some cut only straight, flat surfaces; others, only curved surfaces. Some can machine hundreds of parts per hour; a small number may complete only one part a week.

In these operations, small chips of metal are removed from the work by rigidly mounted single-point, multiple-point, and abrasive cutting tools which remove metal in a manner similar to the way ordinary chisels, files, and sandpaper remove chips of wood. In woodworking, the single-point chisel peels off relatively large chips as it moves across a workpiece; the multiple-point file shears a greater number of smaller chips in a stroke; and sandpaper tears off a much larger number of microscopic chips.

Because their cutting tools remove material in small increments (chips), machine tools share a number of common attributes which are different from those found in primary fabricating machines. First, a machine tool must move its cutting tool's edge into many positions with respect to the workpiece so that the tool will remove chips continuously and produce a useful cutting action. To facilitate this multipositioning of the cutting edge, machine tools establish a *basic motion* between the work and the tool. Some machines hold the tool at rest and move the work; others move the tool and hold the work at rest. The nature of this movement (the cutting action) may be circular, as in the lathe and milling machine, or it may be linear, as in the planer. The speed of this movement, the speed of the cutting edge moving through the workpiece, is called the cutting speed.

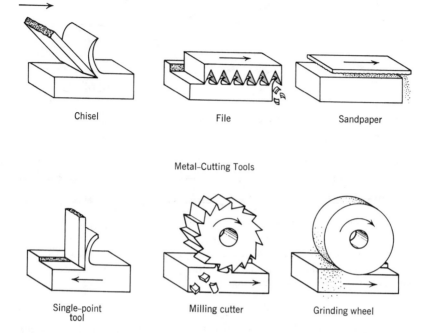

Wood-Cutting Tools

Chisel   File   Sandpaper

Metal-Cutting Tools

Single-point tool   Milling cutter   Grinding wheel

FIGURE 27. Wood- and metal-cutting tools remove material in a similar manner, although the latter must be made of harder material and mounted in heavier machines.

While the cutting action is sufficient to remove chips from the work, it will not generate a surface by itself. In order to produce a surface, the location of the cutting action on the workpiece must be continually changed. This is accomplished either by repositioning the tool (feeding the tool into the work), or by repositioning the work (feeding the work into the tool). The rate at which the cutting action is repositioned on the work is commonly called the feed rate, or simply feed. Feed is governed by accurate controls. Most machine tools are equipped with automatic feed to adjust the controls evenly and continuously.

The machine tool's frame is commonly large and heavy. It performs a multiplicity of functions. The frame provides a means of securing a cutting tool and a workpiece and establishes the basic relative motion between the two. A motor in the frame supplies the power for maintaining this movement. The frame supports the controls which govern the feed of tool (or work). It also provides

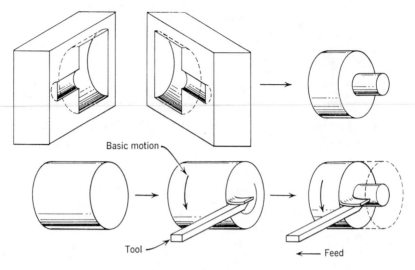

FIGURE 28. Primary fabricating processes use a preformed die or mold to impart a shape to raw material. Secondary fabricating processes slowly generate the desired shape by continuously removing small chips.

the strength required to maintain the location of the tool's edge accurately with respect to the work, in spite of the great forces created in stripping off metal chips.

Typically the cutting tools are small and easily mounted in and removed from a tool holder located on the frame. Both single- and multiple-point tools are in common use. Generally a wide assortment of multiple-point tools must be carried by a shop to facilitate machining various surfaces. The variety of single-point tools required is much smaller because these tools' points are easily reshaped to cut different surfaces. Single-point tools cost less and are cheaper to sharpen, whereas the other type commonly removes material faster and leaves smoother finishes. Multiple-point tools such as milling cutters are commonly made of solid, high-speed steel. Some types of milling cutters, however, are available with replaceable cutting edges made of various materials. The latter kind is called an "inserted-blade" or "inserted-tooth" cutter.

The frequency of tool resharpening depends on at least five factors: the tool's material, the work's material, the cutting speed, the feed rate, and the depth of cut. Cutting speed is the speed of the basic motion between the tool's cutting edge and the workpiece's surface. Feed is the rate at which the location of the cutting action on the

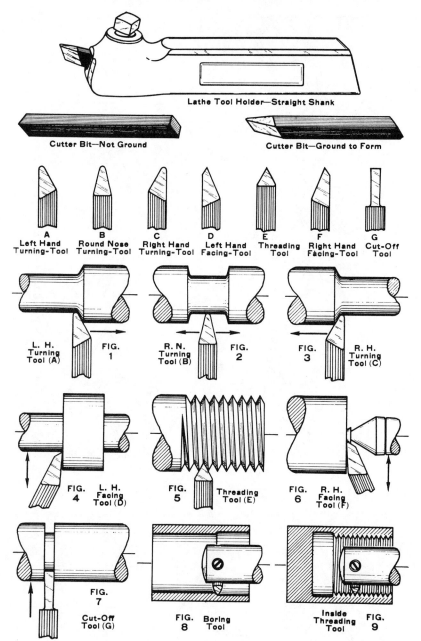

FIGURE 29.   Single-point lathe tools require a variety of tip shapes to turn circular, cylindrical, and thread surfaces on rotating workpieces.   (Courtesy South Bend Lathe, Inc.)

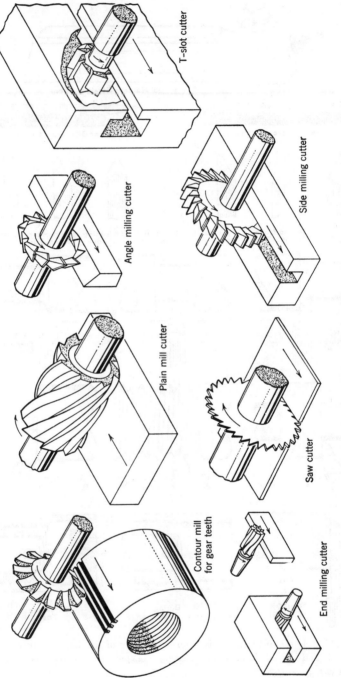

FIGURE 30.   A number of milling cutters are required to generate different surfaces.

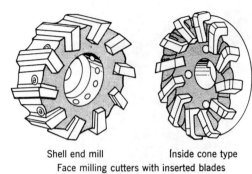

Shell end mill   İnside cone type
Face milling cutters with inserted blades

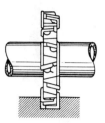

Inserted blade
Staggered–tooth
side mills

FIGURE 30 (*Continued*)

workpiece is changed.   Depth of cut is the distance the tool's point penetrates into the work.

Too great a cutting speed, feed, or depth will wear the tool rapidly and necessitate excessive tool replacement.   On the other hand, if either the speed or feed is too slow or if the depth of cut is needlessly shallow, material removal will take an unnecessarily long time.   There are tables which indicate the most economic selection of tool material, cutting speed, feed, and depth in limited applications.   However, because widely applicable tables would have to consider more than 15 variables, general tables usually only describe what is commonly accepted as satisfactory and base their selection on the surface finish required and on an assumed tool life.

The characteristics of the tool holder, of work-holding devices, and of the means of tool control are important not only because they partially determine the metal-removal rate of a machine tool but also because they determine how long the machine must be out of operation when it is switched from one product to another.   The time required for mounting tools in the holder, for mounting and adjusting a work-holding device, and for locating the cutting tool, is a major determinant of the time required to set up the machine for a different product.

The tool holder secures the tool rigidly to a machine's frame so that the tool's edge will not vibrate when cutting the work.   In some machines the mount is designed to move during cutting operations so that the tool's tip will generate the required surface on the workpiece.   Generally, the mount is also designed to facilitate rapid tool changing.

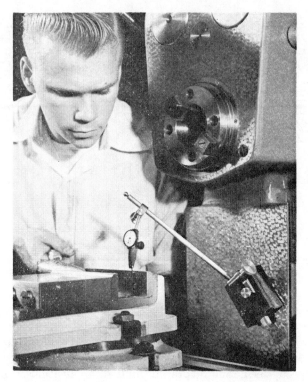

FIGURE 31. An operator is locating a vise in preparation for mounting parts in a milling machine. The dial indicator in the foreground shows the position of the vise within ±0.001 inch. (Courtesy Brown and Sharpe Manufacturing Company.)

Many devices are provided for mounting differently shaped parts on a table or on a shaft in a machine. These devices secure the workpiece rigidly and allow quick changing of parts. For machining small parts in small lots, a vise or another "universal" device is often attached to the table or the machine's shaft. In producing hundreds of parts, however, specially made fixtures are often used to reduce mounting time.

Controlling the relationship between the workpiece and the tool's cutting edge to generate the desired surface is accomplished by locating the workpiece and the tool's cutting point(s) with respect to the machine's frame. The workpiece is oriented to the frame when it is securely mounted in the machine. Similarly, the tool's cutting point is oriented when the tool is mounted in its holder. The relative movement of the workpiece and the tool (which determines the shape of

the cut) is controlled by moving either the tool holder or the work-piece mount. Manually, this movement commonly is controlled by hand wheels calibrated in thousandths of an inch. On more automatic machines, it is controlled by mechanical stops that govern the tool's or work's movement. Often, in producing a large number of parts, the tool's position is fixed and parts are mounted in a fixture which has been properly oriented and secured. Stops are set to control relative movement of the part and tool, and automatic feed is used to produce the movement. Thus, the operator's task is reduced to changing workpieces and occasionally replacing cutting tools.

We will describe a few common machine tools in terms of their usual application and their functional and physical characteristics. We will consider the planer, vertical boring mill, engine lathe, turret lathe, drill press, milling machine, grinding machine, and planer mill-ing machine. It should be noted that these machines are commonly located in the same shop, and a given part will often be processed on

FIGURE 32. A dial indicator which measures within ±0.001 inch is being used to locate a workpiece with respect to a tool-holding chuck (above the workpiece). (Courtesy Brown and Sharpe Manufacturing Company.)

several of these machines before it is ready for assembly. This physical integration is feasible because these machines usually are small and produce relatively little noise, vibration, or other adverse environmental effects.

Driven-Work Machines

Machine tools are divided into two major groups. The first group achieves a basic cutting motion by imparting movement to the workpiece; the other drives the cutting tool and holds the work relatively fixed. The planer, vertical boring machine, engine lathe, and turret lathe are machines of the first type. They produce straight or circular surfaces on parts of varied size.

PLANER. The planer generates long, smooth, straight surfaces on large parts at high material-removal rates by driving the workpiece past rigidly secured cutting tools. A planer consists of a large reciprocating table on which workpieces, or fixtures designed to hold

FIGURE 33. An operator is planing a flat surface on a casting. (Courtesy Joe Lawrence Morris, *Modern Manufacturing Processes*, © 1955, Prentice-Hall, Inc., Englewood Cliffs, N. J., and Rockford Machine Tool Company.)

FIGURE 34. A close-up of the cutting action shown in the preceding illustration.

workpieces, can be mounted and securely fastened. The table is usually at least several feet wide and 16 or more feet long. On each side of the table there is a massive, vertical column which supports a heavy cross rail extending in a horizontal plane over the surface of the table. A tool head, capable of holding a single-point cutting tool, is mounted on each of the vertical columns. In addition, the cross rail itself mounts two "rail heads," each of which also can hold a single-point cutting tool. In total, then, four cutting tools can be held simultaneously by the planer. All four can be positioned independently, and if the size of the workpiece and the specifications of the cuts permit, all four can be used simultaneously to cut metal.

When the various cutting tools have been mounted in their holders and brought into proper position relative to the workpiece to be machined, the table can be made to reciprocate horizontally under the rail. On the cutting stroke the workpiece moves into contact with various cutting tools held in the tool holders on the columns and on the cross rail. As the workpiece passes underneath it, each tool cuts a narrow strip of metal from the entire length of the workpiece surface.

A standard planer with a 12-foot stroke which will accept a workpiece up to six feet by six feet in cross section costs up to $60,000.

Setting up the stops which control the length of the planer table's

FIGURE 35. A vertical boring mill with two tool heads. (Courtesy Giddings and Lewis Machine Tool Company.)

stroke and the initial positioning of the tool takes approximately half an hour. Mounting a large workpiece (weighing several tons) can require even more time. Single-point cutting tools of the size commonly used in a planer cost less than $50, but must be resharpened after about an hour of machining.

The rate of material removal depends on the surface finish desired. Ordinarily, in machining a workpiece, "rough cuts" which remove material rapidly are followed by a "finish cut" which leaves a smoother and more accurate surface. In rough cuts, maximum feed and depth of cut (up to one inch) make the tool's point distort minutely during the cutting stroke so that it leaves a rough surface.

Consequently, these cuts are usually followed by a faster, finishing cut in which the feed and depth of cut may be reduced to a few thousandths of an inch.   In roughing cuts, high-speed steel tools will remove up to 60 cubic inches; carbide-tipped tools can remove up to 1,000 cubic inches of material per minute.   In finishing cuts, both these tools remove less than 10 cubic inches per minute.

Large planers will accept workpieces more than 60 feet long and can hold dimensions within ±0.001 inch.   Their principal advantage is that large castings weighing several tons can be mounted easily and relatively quickly on the reciprocating table.   In 1958, there were approximately 12,000 planers in the United States.

VERTICAL BORING MILL.   The vertical boring mill generates cylindrical and circular surfaces on large parts at high material-removal rates.   The boring mill's frame supports a single-point tool above a horizontal table on which the workpiece is secured.   Except for the motion of the work-holding table, this machine is similar to the planer.   Because the table rotates rather than reciprocates, circular cuts are made in the work by the cutting tool.

In the cutting process, the tool is slowly fed into the rotating work so that it shears a ribbon of material (the chip) off the piece.   The direction in which the tool is fed determines whether a flat circular

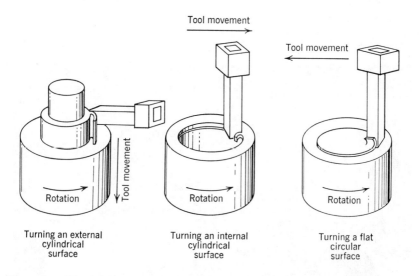

FIGURE 36.   The initial orientation of the tool and the direction of its feed into the rotating work determine the type of surface that will be generated in a vertical boring mill.

or a cylindrical surface will be produced. The type of surface and its dimensions are controlled by the operator, who keeps the tool's tip at a desired distance from the work's axis of rotation and from the top of the rotating table.

A boring machine capable of accepting a workpiece 12 feet in diameter and of working within a tolerance of ±0.001 inch costs approximately $100,000.

Mounting and positioning the tool and selecting the tool's feed and the rotating speed of the workpiece commonly take less than half an hour. Securing a workpiece can take more than an hour if no fixture is used to help locate it or if the part weighs several tons. Material-removal rates are similar to those in planing. There were fewer than 20,000 vertical boring mills in use in 1958.

ENGINE AND TOOLROOM LATHES. Engine and toolroom lathes machine circular and internal and external cylindrical surfaces, as well as threads, on parts of all sizes. In a lathe, the workpiece is held on a rotating shaft in the headstock at one end of the machine's frame by a face plate or a fixture (collet or chuck) designed to accept common shapes, and is rotated about a horizontal axis. Longer work is supported along the frame by using the tailstock or steady rests. A single-point cutting tool is held alongside or at the end of the rotating work in a tool post which is mounted on the machine's frame. (If the tailstock is not being used to support the workpiece, drill bits or other tools can be held in it.) The tip of the cutting tool mounted

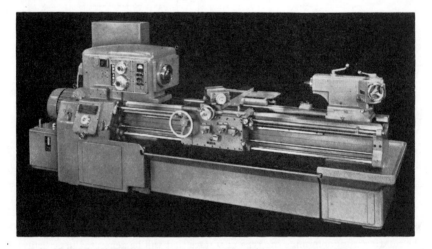

FIGURE 37. A toolroom lathe. (Courtesy Monarch Machine Tool Company.)

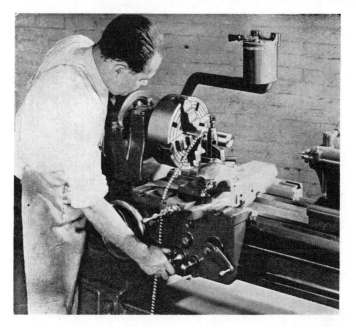

FIGURE 38. A workpiece is mounted in a four-jaw chuck secured to a rotating shaft in the lathe's headstock. A circular surface is being turned by a single-point tool mounted in the tool post. The motion of the tool's point (controlled by hand wheels) and of the work is similar to that depicted in Fig. 36. (Courtesy South Bend Lathe, Inc.)

in the tool post can be fed freely in three dimensions—up or down, into or out of the work, and toward or away from the headstock—by turning hand wheels.

As in the case of the vertical boring mill, the location and type of surface generated is determined by the direction in which the tool is fed into the rotating work. The hand wheels which control this movement are graduated so that the tool's movement can be measured within ±0.001 inch without stopping the lathe. As a result, nonproductive time that would otherwise be used for making tedious measurements with hand instruments during machining operations is kept small. The tool's movement can be geared to the rotation of the headstock (and thus of the workpiece) to permit thread cutting. This gearing also can be used to feed the tool automatically into the work. This not only frees the operator from manual adjustment of the tool's position, but also reduces tool wear and frequency of tool replacement by eliminating uneven feeding.

FIGURE 39. A thin shaft is being machined in a lathe. It is secured to a face plate at one end and supported at the other by a tailstock. A follower rest holds the work against the cutting tool. (Courtesy South Bend Lathe, Inc.)

FIGURE 40. An operator is finish turning a workpiece mounted on a face plate and supported by a tailstock. (Courtesy Sheldon Machine Company, Inc.)

Figure 41. In this rough-turning operation, a thick chip is being sheared off a steel rod. The single-point tool is mounted in a holder which is held in a tool post in the foreground. (Courtesy Sheldon Machine Company, Inc.)

High-speed steel cutting tools will remove up to 20 cubic inches of mild steel per minute, cost less than $3, and can be resharpened in a few minutes. Carbide-tipped tools cost about twice as much and will remove material three times as fast. Both tool types usually cut smooth surfaces in mild steel for more than an hour before they deteriorate sufficiently to require resharpening.

If several types of surfaces are to be machined on one part, a different cutting tool must be mounted for each type. Individual tools are shaped to turn either cylindrical surfaces, shoulders, grooves, or threads, as is shown in Figure 29. Even when several identical pieces are to be machined in an engine lathe, one piece is usually completely machined before the second is mounted in the lathe. Changing tools between different surface cuts, which takes approximately one minute, is usually faster than the alternative procedure of removing and remounting workpieces. A skilled machinist is commonly

FIGURE 42. In this thread-cutting operation, a tool with a specially shaped point is machining the work. The movement of the tool post has been geared to the work's rotation so that the tool's tip advances the width of one thread as the work goes through one revolution. (Courtesy Sheldon Machine Company, Inc.)

required to change and resharpen tools and to set up the lathe initially. The latter operation often takes half an hour.

Common engine lathes costing as much as $7,000 will machine pieces up to 14 inches in diameter and 30 inches long. Larger lathes costing as much as $100,000 will machine shafts up to six feet in diameter and 40 feet long. Both sizes will turn surfaces within ±0.001 inch of the desired dimension. In 1958, there were approximately 123,000 engine lathes in operation.

TURRET LATHE. When a large number of identical pieces requiring a series of lathe operations is desired, the job is commonly done more rapidly on a turret lathe.

The turret lathe is similar to the engine lathe except for multiple tool-holding devices situated in place of the tool post and the tailstock. These facilitate very rapid tool changing and make it possible to machine several surfaces simultaneously. Ordinarily, the workpiece is held in a collet, a special type of cylindrical vise, which fits into the headstock and can be coupled with a linkage that feeds, locates, and secures bar and rod material in a few seconds. The cross slide, alongside the work, usually supports a quick-indexing, square turret on which four single-point tools are mounted. By indexing (rotating) this square turret, an operator can bring any one of the four tools into cutting position in a few seconds without stop-

FIGURE 43. A turret lathe. (Courtesy Warner and Swasey Company.)

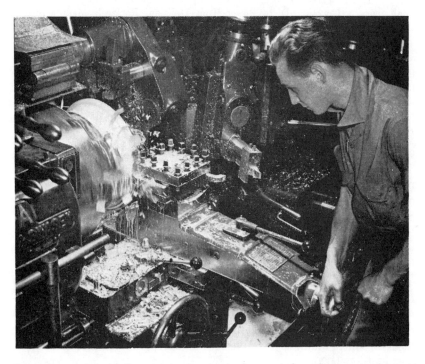

FIGURE 44. A turret-lathe operator is using tools mounted on the hexagonal turret and the cross-slide turret to make simultaneous cuts on a workpiece. (Courtesy Warner and Swasey Company.)

FIGURE 45. An operator is using a multiple-spindle drill and fixtures to drill some small parts. (Courtesy Delta Power Tool Division, Rockwell Manufacturing Company.)

ping the lathe. Another turret, located where the tailstock appears on an engine lathe, is used to hold more single-point tools, drill bits, reamers, and the like. This turret, which is hexagonal in shape, also indexes, so that each tool can be positioned for cutting in seconds. Often, tools both in the cross-slide turret and in the turret at the end of the lathe are fed into the work to turn different cuts simultaneously. The path a tool travels when making its cut is often controlled by mechanical steps which free the operator from having to read dials or make measurements when turning the work. Thus, the turret-lathe operator's task can be reduced to operating the material-feeding linkage, indexing the cutting tools into position, and engaging a semiautomatic feed which moves the tools along their predetermined paths.

The price of a turret lathe which feeds bar material up to 2.5 inches in diameter is more than $10,000. If the bar-feed mechanism is not used, parts up to 14 inches in diameter can be mounted in a chuck or on a face plate, as in an engine lathe. A turret lathe which quick-feeds six-inch diameter bar stock and accepts lengths up to seven feet costs $90,000.

A skilled and experienced worker is usually required for mounting tools, setting stops, and selecting semiautomatic feeds for different cuts. Mounting more than four tools and setting up simultaneous cutting operations commonly take more than an hour, although this

time depends on the worker and the previous set-up. Tool costs and material-removal rates are similar to those of the engine lathe. For larger quantities, however, the turret lathe's operating costs can be much lower because this machine reduces operator-skill requirements and drastically reduces tool-changing time. Since tool position, feed, and work speed are mechanically controlled, a semiskilled operator can produce several hundred small parts per hour.

Commonly, turret-lathe parts do not exceed 2.5 inches in diameter and six inches in length. Smooth surfaces and dimensional accuracy within ±0.0001 inch are possible, although within ±0.001 inch is more common. There were 73,000 turret lathes in use in 1958.

Driven-Tool Machines

Drilling, milling, and grinding machines, unlike the machines previously described, rotate their cutting tools in order to produce the

FIGURE 46. An operator is using a rotary fixture to mount small parts in a drill press. (Courtesy Delta Power Tool Division, Rockwell Manufacturing Company.)

FIGURE 47. The operator using this large radial drill inserts the different tools for different operations. A console in the foreground selects the proper speed and feed. (Courtesy The Carlton Machine Tool Company.)

motion required to remove chips from workpieces. Generally these machines will produce more complex surfaces than the previous group of machines. The multipoint or abrasive rotating tools commonly remove material faster, leave finer finishes, are higher priced, and cost more to resharpen than single-point tools.

DRILL PRESS. Drill presses employ rotating bits (a form of multiple-point tool) for cutting holes and threads rapidly in work of all sizes and shapes. A drill press consists of a frame which supports a drill chuck at one end and a work-mounting table on the other. Drills, taps for cutting threads, boring tools, and reamers (used to cut more accurate hole diameters) can be mounted in the drill chuck, which rotates during cutting operations.

The workpiece is ordinarily rigidly secured to the worktable below the cutting tool by clamps or by a special fixture. (A fixture is any special-purpose device that locates and holds a part in a particular place. It usually facilitates rapid mounting and removal of the part.) The diameter of the hole is determined by the diameter of the cutting

tool selected. In tapping, the thread characteristics are determined by the tap selected. The depth of the hole or thread is determined by how far the tool is fed into the work, and is commonly controlled by a hand wheel and a stop on the press. The most accurate location of a hole can be obtained by using jigs. Jigs are special-purpose devices that fit on the workpiece and guide the tool to the proper position on the work.

Set-up time generally is less than 15 minutes, since the operator need only insert the desired drill and position a holding device on the worktable. The cost of a drill bit depends on its size. Small drill bits cost less than a dollar, whereas a 3.5-inch bit costs about $350. Jig and fixture costs depend on the accuracy and complexity required, and commonly range between $50 and $500. A semiskilled worker using a high-speed drill can remove approximately four cubic inches

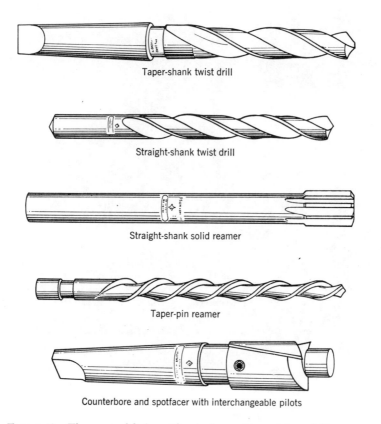

Taper-shank twist drill

Straight-shank twist drill

Straight-shank solid reamer

Taper-pin reamer

Counterbore and spotfacer with interchangeable pilots

FIGURE 48. These round hole-cutting tools can be used in a drill press.

of mild steel per minute and can drill several hundred holes in an hour.

Drill bits are available in sizes ranging from 0.014 to 3.5 inches in diameter. Very small drill bits will machine within ±0.001 inch of their nominal diameter; large ones are accurate only within ±0.012 inch. To locate holes within ±0.003 inch, fixtures are often used. Location within ±0.001 inch is possible using jigs.

A common, single-spindle drill press which will accept drills up to half an inch in diameter costs $150. In 1958 there were approximately 358,000 drill presses in use.

MULTIPLE-SPINDLE HEAD. Multiple-spindle heads, which facilitate drilling many different holes in a workpiece simultaneously, can be attached to standard drill presses. As many as 25 chucks, each

FIGURE 49. An operator is using a four-spindle multiple head to drill four holes simultaneously. (Courtesy Delta Power Tool Division, Rockwell Manufacturing Company.)

FIGURE 50. A horizontal milling machine. (Courtesy The Cincinnati Milling Machine Company.)

holding a drill, can be housed in a multiple head. The holes' locations are determined by the location of the chucks in the head. Jigs can be used to achieve more accurate locations.

A multiple-spindle head with six chucks commonly costs more than $300, takes less than half an hour to set up, and offers large potential savings over single-spindle drilling in many applications.

HORIZONTAL MILLING MACHINE. Milling machines use multiple-point rotating cutters of various shapes to machine curved, flat, and complex surfaces. In horizontal milling machines, the frame supports both a horizontal, rotating shaft (arbor), which holds and drives the multitooth milling cutters, and a moveable table on which the work is mounted. Milling cutters are available in many standard sizes and shapes and can also be custom-made to generate unusual shapes.

In operation, the work is secured on a table underneath the cutter and is fed into the rotating cutter by a vertical, horizontal, or crosswise

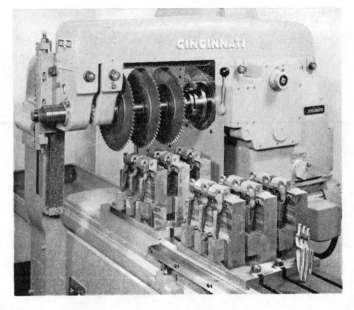

FIGURE 51. Three cutters ganged on an arbor have cut slots in six workpieces mounted in two fixtures on this milling machine's table. (Courtesy The Cincinnati Milling Machine Company.)

FIGURE 52. An operator is gang milling the ways of a grinding machine in a horizontal milling machine. (Courtesy Norton Company.)

table movement. Movement of the workpiece into the cutter can be controlled within ±0.001 inch by hand wheels or by stops. Automatic feed can be used to free the operator from continual attention and to maintain maximum feed speeds. When a wide, flat surface or more than one flat surface is desired, several cutters can be "ganged" on the arbor to machine all the surfaces in a single pass.

Milling machines which will accept workpieces weighing as much as 200 pounds with a table size of 12 x 56 inches cost approximately $12,000.

Setting up these machines usually takes less than an hour, depending on the number of cutters being mounted and the means used to secure the workpiece. A milling cutter costs as much as $50 and commonly requires expensive resharpening after an hour of operation, although this depends on the operator's selection of speed, feed, and depth of cut as well as on the material itself and the desired finish and accuracy.

Cutters are capable of removing more than 26 cubic inches of mild steel per minute. However, this rate cannot be maintained on jobs

FIGURE 53. A close-up of a gang-milling operation shows the profile of different cutters mounted on the arbor, the profile generated during the cutting pass, and some of the chips produced. (Courtesy Norton Company.)

requiring cutter change to complete the machining, since it commonly takes a quarter of an hour to change cutters. When no cutter change is required and the work is mounted in a fixture and is machined in a single pass, rates on the order of 300 small parts per hour can be achieved by a semiskilled workman.

Large milling machines will accept work more than five feet long and will machine to an accuracy of ±0.001 inch even when taking heavy cuts. In 1958, there were more than 60,000 horizontal milling machines in use.

PLANER MILLING MACHINE. The planer milling machine generates long, straight surfaces on very large parts. This milling machine, which looks like a planer, is typical of a group that incorporates features of two different machine tools. Its frame and reciprocating table and the location of the cutting tools are similar to those of the planer. It differs, however, in that multiple-point milling cutters are substituted for the planer's single-point tools. As with the planer, the work is mounted on the machine's reciprocating table and is fed into the cutters as the table passes below the cutting tools. Figure 54 shows four "gang-mounted" workpieces on the machine's table. The two on the right are both being machined on each pass. When the operator completes these, he will machine the two parts on the left.

In view of their ability to machine a far larger surface area per cutter per pass, planer millers can accomplish the removal of a given quantity of metal much more rapidly than planers. The initial and subsequent maintenance costs of milling cutters are, however, much greater than the initial cost of the single-point tools used on planers. The initial purchase price of a planer miller is also substantially higher than that of a planer capable of handling workpieces of comparable size.

Setting up the cutting tools commonly takes less than half an hour. Mounting large workpieces on the table can require more time. Cutting tools, similar to those used in milling machines, generally cost more than $50 and must be resharpened after an hour of machining. Cutters are capable of removing more than 400 cubic inches of mild steel per minute. Large machines will accept work more than 12 feet long and will generate smooth surfaces and dimensions within ±0.001 inch even when taking heavy cuts.

Planer-type milling machines capable of machining work weighing several tons cost from $40,000 to more than $100,000. There were approximately 3,500 of these machines operating in 1958.

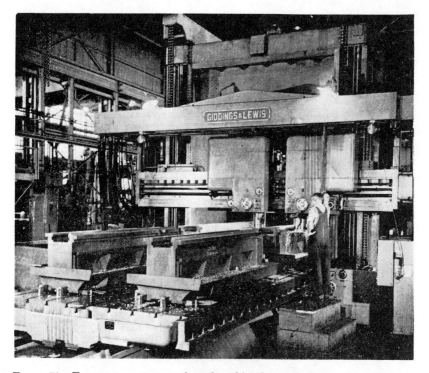

Figure 54. Four parts are mounted on the table of a planer-type milling machine. Each of the two vertical heads will transmit more than 100 horsepower to a cutting tool. Milling these parts replaced planing and grinding operations which previously had been used to achieve the required smoothness and accuracy. (Courtesy Giddings and Lewis Machine Tool Company.)

PRECISION GRINDING MACHINES. Precision grinding machines are used to generate smoother and more accurate surfaces than can be made by other metal-removal processes. The grinder is similar in construction to other machine tools, except that a cylindrical grinding wheel replaces a single- or multiple-point cutting tool. Most grinding machines can produce curved, flat, or complex surfaces. Accurate cuts can be made even in hardened steel because the sharp edges of very hard material in the grinding wheel remove metal in microscopic chips.

CYLINDRICAL- AND HORIZONTAL-GRINDING MACHINES. The cylindrical grinder, so called because it finishes cylindrical surfaces, is similar to the engine lathe in construction. Work is mounted in a rotating headstock and may be supported by a tailstock at the end of the frame.

The grinding wheel is mounted alongside the work. It cuts by either "plunging" into or traversing the work.

The horizontal-surface grinder finishes plane and complex surfaces. As in the horizontal-milling machine, the workpiece is secured to a table underneath the grinding wheel and is fed into the rotating wheel by a horizontal movement. Because the grinding wheel exerts lighter forces on the work than other cutting tools, parts are often held in place by a magnetic chuck which simply magnetizes the table top and holds the work firmly.

In both of these machines, the relative movement of the grinding wheel into the workpiece is commonly controlled by automatic feed and stops. The operator usually loads and unloads parts. For faster operation, a wheel's cutting face can be trued (formed) in a wide variety of shapes, or several wheels can be mounted simultaneously to grind complex or several surfaces at the same time.

FIGURE 55. A cylindrical grinding machine. (Courtesy Norton Company.)

Large, external, cylindrical-grinding machines commonly cost more than $10,000; the price of surface grinders ranges up from $3,000.

Setting up a machine usually takes less than half an hour, although truing a grinding wheel to finish several surfaces simultaneously can take more than an hour by itself. Frequent minor truing to keep the wheel's profile accurate may require a total of ten minutes during each shift. Grinding wheels vary widely in price depending on their size, composition, and construction and commonly cost between $2 and $100 each.

Grinding wheels on precision machines usually remove less than one cubic inch of material per minute. Rates as high as 50 cubic inches of cast iron per minute have been found practical, however, in some flat-grinding operations. An operator making light cuts (removing little material) on a surface grinder can produce about 300 small parts per hour by using a mounting fixture.

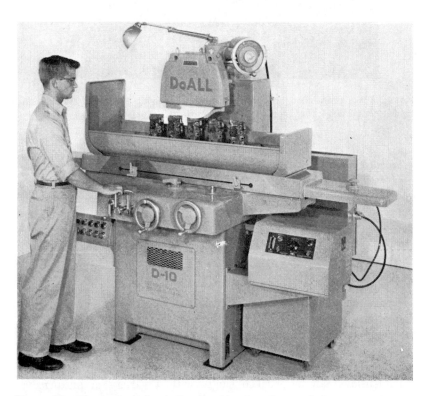

FIGURE 56. The horizontal grinding machine has five workpieces ganged on a magnetic chuck (table). (Courtesy The DoAll Company.)

FIGURE 57. A precision thread-grinding machine is using a specially trued grinding wheel to finish threads on a screw. (Courtesy Norton Company.)

Large cylindrical-grinding and surface-grinding machines will accept work more than ten feet long, will work within ±0.0001 inch of the desired dimensions, and will leave smooth finishes on the order of ten microinches or less. In 1958, there were 41,000 external, cylindrical-grinding and 59,000 surface-grinding machines in use.

Inspection

Inspection of machined parts is ordinarily performed to ensure that dimensions fall within the specified tolerances and that surface finishes are of proper smoothness. Often only samples from a production run are inspected to determine whether an operating machine is still producing parts within specifications.

Dimensions can be checked singly with a variety of inexpensive manual tools which read within ±0.001 inch of the actual dimension. More accurate measurements can be made using more expensive equipment. Special gauges designed for particular parts are commonly used

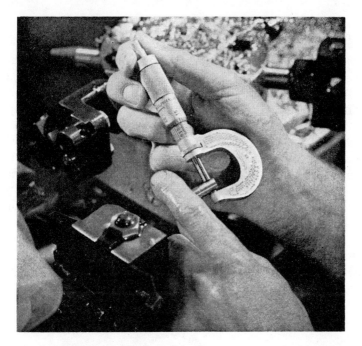

FIGURE 58. A micrometer is being used to measure a newly machined part. The vernier scale permits readings to 0.0001 inch. (Courtesy Brown and Sharpe Manufacturing Company.)

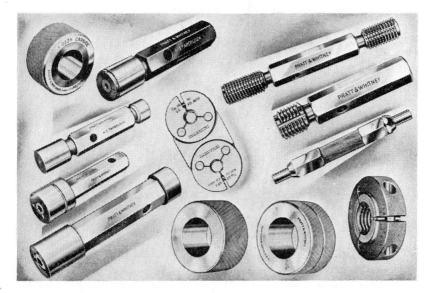

FIGURE 59. These "go, no-go" plug and ring gages are used to check threads and the diameters of cylindrical surfaces. (Courtesy Pratt and Whitney Company, Inc., West Hartford, Connecticut.)

where a great deal of dimensional checking is required. Generally, an operator can make two to ten measurements a minute using these tools.

Surface-smoothness inspection is difficult to perform with precision. Sometimes the operator will feel the part and then feel samples of known surface roughness in order to determine if the part is rougher than the sample. When greater precision is required, measurements accurate within a few millionths of an inch can be obtained using optical flats. These are discs of glass or quartz ground to almost perfect smoothness on one side. The flat is placed smooth side down on the surface to be inspected and observed under monochromatic light. Straight, evenly spaced, dark bands will be seen if the workpiece surface is perfectly flat. If unevenness or curvature is present, the bands will be distorted or irregular. More elaborate

FIGURE 60. A contour projector designed to project magnified images of a part onto a screen for precision measurements and inspection. The projector is equipped with 0.0001 inch measuring micrometers for gaging horizontal and vertical dimensions, a dial type of protractor readable to one minute of arc for angular measurements, and a vernier reading to five minutes of arc for measurements of helix rotation. (Courtesy Ex-Cell-O Corporation.)

FIGURE 61. A Profilometer (R) is measuring the roughness of a piston ring's groove electronically. (Courtesy Micrometrical Mfg. Company.)

electronic machines can inspect sections of a surface and measure the average roughness within less than a millionth of an inch.

ASSEMBLY PROCESS

Fabricating processes are used to form component parts which must be assembled into finished products. Assembly processes join parts fabricated in metalworking machines as well as those produced in other operations, such as glass making and plastic molding. Assembly unites an almost limitless variety of parts. They are made from different materials, in a host of shapes and sizes, and to widely different degrees of precision. Detailed discussion of assembly techniques and technology is beyond the scope of this work. Consequently, only a few typical examples of assembly processes are described in general terms.

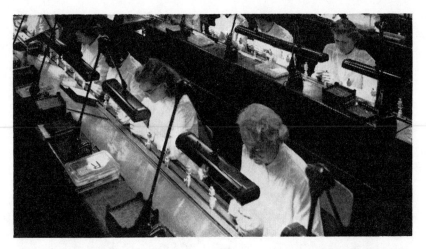

FIGURE 62. Assembly of mounts for electron tubes using a conveyorized line. (Courtesy Raytheon Company.)

FIGURE 63. The front sections of large diesel engines are assembled on chassis at the station in the foreground. Men stand on the moving conveyor and use tools which are suspended on cables over the working area. A section ready for assembly is hanging from a hoist in the foreground. (Courtesy Jervis B. Webb Company.)

Assembly operations begin with the collection of component parts and end with the completion of a finished product. In products composed of more than a few parts, components are commonly first joined into subassemblies to facilitate economical operation. The number of parts and subassemblies used in a particular product varies widely. For example, the telephone, automobile, and ballistic missile contain 200, 30,000, and several hundred thousand parts, respectively.

The operations of orienting and joining different parts are commonly performed manually, rather than by machines, because these tasks usually require complex motions and changing movement patterns. To reduce the complexity of and possible variations in movement patterns, assembly operations are often subdivided so that an operator can develop a high degree of proficiency in assembling a few parts. Thus, products requiring a large number of parts are often produced by a number of operators who work sequentially on each unit. Subdividing assembly functions into a number of more simple, progressive operations may also permit the use of special purpose machines.

FIGURE 64. This conveyorized line is used for assembly of guided missiles. (Courtesy Jervis B. Webb Company.)

FIGURE 65. This is the assembly department of a plant producing vacuum tubes for radio and television set manufacturers. (Courtesy Raytheon Company.)

Orienting

The assembly process is performed in two steps: orienting parts and joining them. In orienting small parts, the assembler is usually aided by fixtures which help him grasp the parts and which guide and hold the parts in the desired orientation. Generally, these fixtures cost less than $100 and may reduce orienting labor by more than 50 per cent.

Joining

After the parts have been oriented, they can be joined in processes which utilize special parts for joining or in those which require no additional parts. Joining with screws and nuts is typical of those processes which require additional parts; spot welding exemplifies those using no additional parts.

Screws and nuts are generally used where appearance, strength, or subsequent disassembly are required. These fasteners can cost several cents apiece and require both orienting and screwing in place. Time for the latter operation can be reduced to less than a second if power screw drivers or wrenches are used. Small machines that automatically release when the fastener is secure may cost from $50 to $4,000.

Spot welding rapidly forms a permanent bond between metal parts and requires no additional material or parts. The parts to be joined are pressed together at a number of points by electrodes and an electric current is passed through them. The current melts the metal at the parts' joint and forms small spot welds. Because the current is applied for only a fraction of a second, the spots melt and harden in less than a second. Multiple-electrode machines capable of welding 250 spots per minute commonly cost about $25,000. Operating time is small because heating and cooling is rapid and because spot welds usually are clean and require no subsequent finishing. Spot welding is seldom used to join parts more than one-quarter of an inch thick although pieces two inches thick have been welded on standard equipment. There were approximately 65,000 of these machines operating in 1958.

FINISHING PROCESSES

Following assembly, products are generally tested, repaired if necessary, and then packaged before being shipped to the customer. These finishing operations are performed to ensure that the product will be satisfactory upon reaching the customer.

Testing

Because metal parts commonly are inspected for defects in their surfaces and for faulty dimensions during or following fabricating processes, usually only functional testing is required after assembly. Ordinarily, this testing is performed in a separate area where special equipment is grouped together. In cases where a large percentage of the products must be checked, testing may be physically integrated with assembly operations.

The various kinds of test equipment share few common attributes, because products' functions are very diverse. Generally, testing machines are similar to machine tools in that capital and operating costs increase rapidly as finer precision is attained. Also, lower operating

FIGURE 66. This woman is performing finishing operations on germanium diodes. (Courtesy Raytheon Company.)

costs are usually accompanied by higher machine prices as well as by restriction in the variety of the jobs the machine will perform.

Repairing

Ordinarily, repair operations are segregated from other manufacturing processes because locating the problem, disassembly, repair or substitution of a part, and reassembly require both a variety of equipment and a flexible working schedule. The equipment used in repair and assembly operations is similar to the tools already described, except that it usually is better adapted to performing a wider variety of operations and is less efficient in volume production.

Packaging

Packaging is designed to protect products from damaging external influences such as moisture and rough handling. These operations are often located close to assembly functions so that products can be packed and moved out of the manufacturing area quickly.

Protection from corrosion is commonly accomplished by coating parts with grease, oil, solvents, or liquid plastics, using a dipping, spraying, or brushing process. Assemblies can be treated individually or in groups (using racks or baskets) to increase production rates.

Dipping tanks, spraying equipment, and brushes, plus necessary baskets or racks, seldom cost more than a few thousand dollars in total. Production rates usually are limited only by the speed with which material can be moved through the treating areas.

Metal parts are commonly wrapped in corrosion resistant paper, plastic films, or metal foils which will protect parts that otherwise are untreated. These coverings can be sealed at rates of 60 to 100 feet per minute in simple heat-sealing or gluing machines. Larger, more elaborate machines open, load, seal, and label cardboard cartons two feet in each dimension at rates up to 3,000 per hour, and often cost more than $5,000.

SERVICE PROCESSES

Service processes are used to change the internal or surface properties of a part or assembly rather than to modify its physical configuration as fabricating and assembly processes do. Generally, processes such as heat treating, cleaning, and painting can occur at any stage or between several stages of a product's manufacture.

Heat Treating

Heat treating is commonly employed to soften or harden steel in order to facilitate subsequent machining processes or to improve a part's performance when in service.

These operations are sometimes segregated from other manufacturing processes because the amounts of heat and smoke generated by large-scale heat-treating facilities make physical integration impractical. Smaller electric and induction furnaces, however, are commonly integrated in the machine tool or assembly area to facilitate material flow.

Heat treating softens or hardens steel by elevating the material's temperature and then reducing it at different rates of speed. (The material is never heated to a state where it becomes molten or plastic.)

Softening treatments are used to make the material easier and faster to form (in forging or stamping processes) or to machine in chip-removal processes. After manufacturing, a part may also be softened in order to make it better able to withstand the destructive effects of shocks. In softening processes, steel is raised to temperatures between 1,000°F and 1,400°F and is allowed to cool slowly over periods as long as 24 hours. This treatment relieves internal stresses that build up in the metal during severe rolling, forging, stamping, or

FIGURE 67. This heat-treating department contains five furnaces and washing facilities for cleaning gears after heat treatment. (Courtesy The A. F. Holden Company.)

machining operations which physically distort the relationship of molecules in the material.

Hardening processes are used to increase the material's resistance to penetration and its strength to as much as five times that of soft metal. Because these characteristics make forming and machining slower or impossible, hardening is commonly not performed until a part has been completely fabricated. Parts are sometimes hardened before grinding operations, however, since abrasive wheels cut hard materials efficiently. This procedure also corrects any minute distortions which occur during the hardening process. In hardening, steel is raised to temperatures between 1,400°F and 2,400°F and then cooled rapidly, often in water or oil quenches. The resulting stronger, harder, and more brittle material is sometimes reheated to approximately 800°F and cooled slowly. This moderate softening treatment

reduces the steel's internal stresses resulting from the thermal shock of quenching and increases the material's resistance to shock loadings while slightly decreasing its strength and hardness.

Furnaces and cooling facilities capable of heating and cooling forgings and castings weighing more than 50 tons can cost more than $30,000 installed, and require a crew to operate. Smaller equipment costs less than $1,000 and requires very little attention.

Some of these processes may also be used to treat only sections of parts. For example, in flame hardening, a flame is passed over the part, heating its surface. If this surface is allowed to cool slowly or is quenched, it will be made softer or harder than before, but the interior of the part will be unchanged. The depth of this treatment ranges from a few thousandths of an inch to more than half an inch depending upon how long the flame is in contact with the surface. The cost of flame-hardening machines commonly ranges from less

FIGURE 68. An operator manually loads rocker arms on eight fixtures in one section of a flame-hardening machine while those in the other section are heated. The hot pieces are automatically dropped into an oil quench, washed, and conveyed to inspection. (Courtesy Chrysler Corporation.)

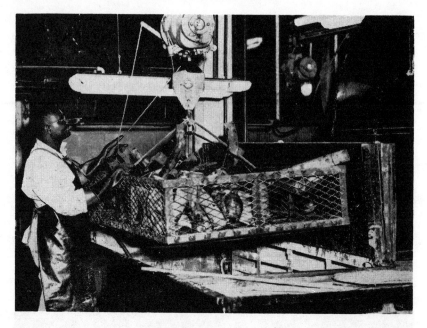

FIGURE 69. An operator is dipping a basket of parts into a cleaning solution. (Courtesy Book Division, Chilton Company, and American Airlines, Inc.)

than $1,000 to more than $5,000. In the more expensive machines, production rates exceeding 1,000 parts per hour are possible.

Cleaning

Cleaning processes are employed to remove burrs, grease, and dirt. Parts are commonly deburred and cleaned after foundry and machining processes to facilitate further operations, and before painting, preservative treatments, and packaging operations to remove harmful oil and solvents.

Dirt and grease removal is commonly performed in large tanks containing chemical solutions which are specially developed to remove particular types of impurities. Parts may be dipped separately or together on frames or in baskets. The solution commonly is heated and stirred by pumps, vibrators, or ultrasonic waves.

In other processes used to chip off scale, burrs, and implanted foreign material and to produce bright surfaces, abrasive particles are mixed with a fluid and then are sprayed on or thrown at the part being cleaned.

Wash tanks and associated apparatus as well as abrasive cleaning equipment seldom cost more than $3,000. Cleaning operations are quickly set up, since usually only the cleaning fluid or the size and type of abrasive material has to be selected and put into cleaning equipment. By batching parts in these processes, many thousands of small parts can be cleaned in an hour.

Painting

Painting is a cheap, simple, and rapid means of applying coatings which will protect parts, subassemblies, and assemblies from corrosion

FIGURE 70. An automatic spraying machine applies white enamel to refrigerator liners on an overhead conveyor. This booth uses a water curtain to trap over-spray and fumes before the air is exhausted outside. (Courtesy the DeVilbiss Company.)

TABLE B   SUMMARY OF PRODUCTION FACTORS IN ELEVEN FABRICATING

	Sand Casting Process*	Die Casting Process*	Stamping and Forming Processes*
Tool and Die Costs	*Low* as compared to dies and molds	*High*—more than for other casting methods—$200 to $5,000 or more	*High*—$400 to $2,000 for small parts, more for large
Direct Labor Costs	*High*—men needed to mold, melt, clean, snag, etc.	*Low to medium*	*Medium*—depending on size and shape
Finishing Costs	*High*—require machining, cleaning, and snagging	*Low*—little if any machining, only a simple trim	*Low*—cleaning and trimming most frequent
Choice of Materials	*Wide*—ferrous, nonferrous, light and heavy alloys	*Narrow*—aluminum, brass, magnesium, and zinc	*Wide*—includes all workable sheet metals; plastics
Complexity of Parts	*Considerable*—holes, bosses, locating pads, complex shapes	*Great*—limited only by die which can be complex	*Limited*—many restricted design rules
Maximum Size	*Large*—as large or larger than any other method	*Moderate*—about 35 lb. for zinc, about 70 lb. for aluminum†	*Large*—can be used on very large parts
Minimum Size	⅛ in. is the smallest practical section thickness	*Tiny*—from fractions of an ounce down to 0.012 inch sections	*Small*—sections as thin as 0.003 to 0.005 in. possible
Precision and Tolerances	*Low*—±⅟₁₆ in. per in. of casting except for shell molding	*High*—±0.001 to ±0.003 in. common	*High*—±0.001 in. common, closer on small parts
Surface Smoothness	*Poor*	*Good*—often obviates finishing	*High*
Getting into Production	*Moderate*—3 to 5 days for pattern to be made	*Moderate to slow*—from a week to several weeks	*Slow*—dies may require several weeks
Rate of Output	25 to 600 or more pieces per hour by using modern methods	*High*—usual range from 100 to 1,000 per hour, up to 3,500	*High*—up to several thousand pieces per hour
Remarks	Most sand castings require some machining	Among the most economical metal processes	Usually the cheapest when quantities are high enough; best for thin sections

* Theodore C. DuMond, Fabricated Materials and Parts, 1953.   Reinhold Publishing Corporation, New York.

† The Doehler-Jarvis Division of National Lead Company die cast aluminum engine blocks weighing 67 pounds in 1960.

PROCESSES

Planer and Vertical Boring Mill	Engine Lathe, Turret Lathe, and Drill Press	Milling Machine	Cylindrical and Horizontal Surface Grinders
Low—from $50 to $200 common	*Low*—from $50 to $200 common	*Low*—from $50 to $200 common	*Low*—from $50 to $200 common
High—skilled operators needed to attend each machine	*Medium*—skilled and semiskilled labor required	*Medium*—depends on the work's complexity and accuracy required	*Medium*—depends on accuracy and finish required
Low—cleaning and deburring; grinding occasionally	*Low*—cleaning and deburring	*Low*—cleaning and deburring	*Low*—cleaning and deburring
Wide—highly machinable materials best	*Wide*—highly machinable materials best	*Wide*—highly machinable materials best	*Wide*—machinable and harder materials
Limited—flat and rotational surfaces	*Limited*—rotational shapes and threads	*Considerable*—complex surfaces using special cutters	*Limited*—flat and cylindrical shapes; wheel can be dressed
Large—weighing many tons	*Medium to large*—300 lb. common	*Medium*—usually less than 300 lb.	*Medium*—usually less than 300 lb.
Moderate—more than 10 lb.	*Small*—fractions of an ounce	*Small*—fractions of an ounce	*Small*—fractions of an ounce
High—±0.001 to ±0.005 in. common	*High*—±0.003 in. common, closer on small parts	*High*—±0.001 in. common, closer possible	*High*—±0.0002 in. possible
Good	*Excellent*	*Excellent*	*Excellent*
Fast—hours or less unless fixtures must be made	*Fast*—hours or less unless fixtures must be made	*Fast*—hours or less unless fixtures must be made	*Fast*
Slow—mounting parts can require an hour per piece	*Medium*—up to 300 per hour in the turret lathe and drill press; less in the engine lathe	*Medium*—up to several hundred parts per hour for simple operations using a fixture	*Medium*—up to 300 per hour with a fixture
Several small parts may be mounted on the table and machined at the same time	Increased accuracy necessitates lower production rates, fixtures, or jigs.	The most versatile machine tool	Grinding is usually preceded by machining operations

FIGURE 71. An over-all view of a production enameling set-up shows a conveyor and ovens. (Courtesy Ferro Corporation.)

and enhance their appearance. To facilitate material flow, these operations commonly are located as close to other operations as their requirements for large drying areas or ovens will permit.

Application is usually accomplished by dipping or spraying processes. The latter are ordinarily performed in booths so that "overspray" and fumes can be exhausted from the plant. Equipment costing less than $2,000 can be used for coating a range of shapes and sizes with a variety of different paints. Racks are often used to hold the work and to facilitate painting more than 1,000 small parts per hour.

Commonly, gas-fired or electric ovens are employed to reduce drying time. In the case of enamel, this time can be reduced from four hours to half an hour. The capacity, size, and price of these ovens vary widely depending on the requirements of the part and the coating.

Recent Developments in Fabrication Technology

Fabrication processes, because of their economic importance, are an object of continual appraisal and improvement. Manufacturers and designers, in addition to making machines easier to operate, have of late concentrated on improvements which change the burden on the operator by mechanizing material handling and machine control. This section will describe examples of handling mechanization and control automation to provide some insight into the continuing development in machine-tool processes.

Transfer Machines

A transfer machine is a composite of several standard machine tools, linked by special-purpose equipment into one operating mechanism that will automatically perform a series of secondary fabrication operations. These machine tools are often made up of standard machine building blocks specially designed to be joined together to form such a unit. The linkage mechanisms are material-handling devices which extract the workpiece from one tool, reorient it if necessary, and position it under the cutting tool for the next operation. Transfer machines often include automatic inspection positions and sensing devices which indicate malfunctioning of the machine. They may include buffer inventory conveyors to adjust for different rates of flow and can include tooling for a variety of shapes of the same part. The high initial cost of these machines and the expense of retooling for product changes has restricted their use to high volume applications. The most common use of transfer machines has been by the automotive manufacturers.

Figure 72 shows a transfer machine which integrates all operations except broaching that are required to machine a cylinder block of three different horsepower capacities. This new machine consists of six sections with a total of 121 stations. Three banking conveyors are provided between appropriate sections. Sections One and Two handle most of the heavy metal removal operations. These include straddle milling the main bearings, milling the oil-slinger grooves, rough drilling the valve-lifter holes, rough boring the cylinders, rough boring the camshafts, and milling the ends of the block. In Section Three, the sides are completely machined and the accessory and engine mounting pads are milled. In Section Four, the operations in the top and bottom of the part are performed and the valve-lifter holes are finish machined. A special coolant system is employed through-

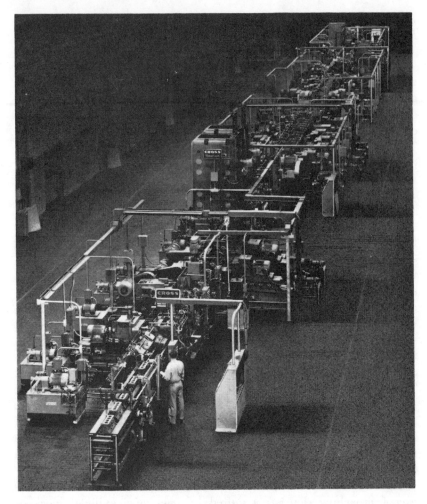

FIGURE 72. An automatic transfer machine for processing 4-cylinder blocks. (Courtesy The Cross Company.)

out Section Four. In Section Five, the block is washed and the bearing caps are assembled. In Section Six, the cam and crankboring operations and inspections are completed. At 100 per cent efficiency, production is at the rate of 109 blocks per hour.

Figure 73 is a transfer machine for producing hulls for a self-propelled army howitzer. This part is one of the largest and heaviest ever processed on a completely automatic transfer machine. The ma-

chine is 250 feet long by 50 feet wide and weighs 775,000 pounds. It has 28 heads with 231 cutting tools which complete 297 operations, including milling, boring, facing, drilling, core-drilling, reaming, chamfering, profiling, routing, and tapping.   The bulky, 10,000-pound hull weldment is securely clamped on a special self-propelled pallet type of work-holding fixture fitted on wheels on which it is transferred through the machine.   Precision indexing automatically locates the work at each of the 24 differently spaced work stations.

FIGURE 73.   An automatic transfer machine for producing self-propelled howitzers. (Courtesy The Cross Company.)

Numerically Controlled Machine Tools

One of the most important of the recent developments in secondary fabrication has been the use of electronics to control the operation of a machine tool. Control of the machine tool by a computer or other electronic device eliminates most manual tool adjustments in set-up of the machine tool and all operator intervention with the machine during the operating cycle. The electronic controls convert numerical information to electric or hydraulic impulses which drive motors, controlling cutting tools or machine tables. Thus the machine is actually controlled by numbers. This numerical information is derived from an operation plan which has been defined by a production engineer on the basis of a blueprint. Depending on the complexity of machine and part, this plan is then converted into a machine-readable format either by a flexowriter operator punching paper tape or by punching the information into cards and having a digital computer prepare the machine-tool control information on tape. The information on the tape is in the form of numbers which the machine control can interpret and transform into appropriate signals. The output of the information-processing logic is generally of two kinds: information on various auxiliary functions the machine or process must perform, such as coolant on or off and spindle retract, and information as to where a machine member, such as a drill table or hexagon turret-lathe head, is to move.

Set-up requirements for numerically controlled machines consist of loading the appropriate tools in the tool holders, attaching the holding device in a pre-determined location, and mounting or loading an input tape in the computer or control device. The operator then loads the workpiece in the holding device, secures it and starts the machine. Once started, the appropriate cutting tool moves to the first cut, makes the desired cut, and is withdrawn. Some of these machines automatically change tools if necessary and continue all succeeding operations until the desired part is completed.

Numerical control systems fall into two general classifications, point-to-point and continuous control. In point-to-point control, the input instructs the machine tool or table to move from one point to another with no concern about the path taken. For example, it would call for drilling a hole at point A and then one at point B (Figure 74). The workpiece being moved from position A to position B can follow any path because the tool is not intended to do any work until the desired position has been reached. Common point-to-point applications of numerical control include drill presses,

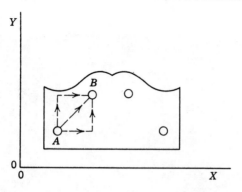

FIGURE 74. Point-to-point control causes a machine member to move from one point to another in an X and Y coordinate system so that operations can be performed at the desired points. Any path can be taken because the tool does no work during movement.

positioning tables, turret lathes, milling machines, and jig borers.

In continuous control, sometimes called contouring control, work is performed while a machine tool moves from one point to another. Consequently, a predetermined path must be followed and the machine must be under continuous control (Figure 75).

Numerical control was an insignificant part of the total machine-tool business in 1958, but by 1963 it was considered to account for 25 per cent of all machine tools sold. About 1,500 numerically controlled units had been put into operation by the end of 1961. By the end of 1962, there were about 3,000. It is anticipated that the sales rate of 1,500 machines a year will remain constant or grow for some time to come.

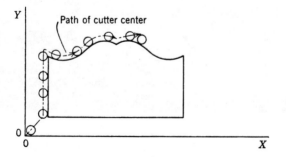

FIGURE 75. Continuous control also causes a machine member to move in X and Y coordinates. The path taken is critical, because the tool cuts as it moves.

FIGURE 76. A numerically controlled turret lathe. (Courtesy Jones and Lamson Machine Company.)

FIGURE 77. An operator starting a job held in a chuck on a numerically controlled lathe. (Courtesy R. K. LeBlond Machine Tool Company.)

FIGURE 78. The control for this lathe includes a high-speed photoelectric tape reader. All information that would normally be entered by tape can be introduced, for set-up and maintenance purposes, through the manual data input such as is evident at the upper left on the Mark-Century control. (Courtesy R. K. LeBlond Machine Tool Company.)

The increasing use of numerically controlled machine tools has been the result of several forces, most important of which are improved productivity and flexibility, reduced set-up time, ease of engineering changes, and reduction in number of jigs and special tools. The use of automatic control enables almost continuous chip removal. Most machine tools designed for numerical control also are much sturdier and remove metal at a much faster rate than other machines. This advantage, coupled with the fact that the calculation of feeds and speeds is automatic, enables most machining operations to be performed at the limit of the capability of the machine. Thus, in many

cases the machining operations are much faster than when under the control of the operator.

Figures 76–78 show examples of point-to-point, numerically controlled turret lathes. The Jones & Lampson lathe comes in two sizes, one with a collet chuck with a 2½-inch bar capacity and the other with a 4½-inch bar capacity. If the bar-feed mechanism is not used, parts up to 12 inches or 19 inches in diameter, respectively, can be mounted in a chuck or face plate. Machine accuracy is ±0.001 inch for the saddle and carriage; ±0.0005 inch for the cross slide. Two square turrets on the cross slide in addition to the hex turret on the saddle provide 14 potential tool positions. Both the carriage with the cross slide and the saddle can operate independently or in unison, and all can function simultaneously. Fully automatic, preset cutting tools are used to machine parts according to numerical information punched into standard 1-inch wide 8-channel paper or milar tape. Roughly speaking, a 2½-inch NCTL Jones & Lampson would cost about $135,000 installed.

The Milwaukee-matic (Figure 79) is a special kind of point-to-point numerically controlled machine tool. It has a single unit horizontal spindle and is capable of automatically performing milling,

FIGURE 79. The numerically controlled Milwaukee-matic. (Courtesy Kearney & Trecker Corporation.)

FIGURE 80. A Cincinnati three-spindle numerically controlled profiles milling machine. These machines are used in the aircraft industry to mill struts, spars, fittings, and other complex forms three at a time. They can also be used with two spindles or with only one for larger sized parts. (Courtesy The Cincinnati Milling Machine Company.)

drilling, reaming, tapping, and boring operations in any sequence and on several sides of a workpiece during a single set-up. Three axes of motion are controllable in the hydraulic-powered machine tool. They are provided by a laterally moving upright column, a vertically moving saddle that is mounted on this column, and a transversable, moving, machine spindle head supported by the saddle. A tool-changing assembly and a rotary tool magazine which can provide storage for 30 tools are also supported by the saddle and located adjacent to the machine head. Anticipating that set-ups for new parts will be made while the part is being machined, the worktables have been designed to accept a moveable pallet on which the workpiece is fixtured. The pallet shuttle equipment can be provided at both ends of the index table to permit automatic transfer of pallets on and off the index table. The total installed cost of a typical Milwaukee-matic is roughly $250,000.

Magna Machine Company

During recent months, production personnel of the Magna Machine Company had been visited several times by a salesman from a local firm which specialized in powder metallurgy. During these calls the salesman had urged Magna's officials to consider adopting powder metallurgy as an alternative method of manufacturing certain of the small, accurate, metal parts required as components of various items in Magna's product line.

As a result of these visits, Magna personnel were weighing the advisability of changing to the powder-metallurgy process in the manufacture of expander weights used in their firm's extensive line of tachometers (speed-counters). At the time, these weights were produced from cylindrical brass blanks which Magna purchased from screw-machine subcontractors who machined them to specifications (Exhibit 1). The blanks were then milled, drilled, and burred to the final shape and dimensions in the Magna factory (Exhibit 2).

Powder Metallurgy

Powder metallurgy is a process which forms metal objects by compressing powdered metal into dies to produce a "briquette" of desired shape and then heating the briquette to obtain a fusing of the powder, which solidifies upon cooling. The appearance of the resulting product is similar to that obtained by the melting and casting of metals. Accuracy obtainable by the powder-metallurgy process is usually comparable to that obtainable by die casting (± 0.002 inch), but with less loss of metal from oxidation and overflow. Where greater accuracy or strength is desired, the briquette can be "coined," that is, compressed by coining dies operated in powerful embossing-type presses, producing tolerances approaching ± 0.0001 inch.

Powder metallurgy can be employed successfully only with certain metals. These include aluminum, brass, bronze, copper, gold, iron, lead, nickel, silver, tin, tungsten, and zinc. There are also some limits upon the ability of compressed metal powder to hold a given shape. Within these limitations, however, an experienced manufacturer can obtain consistent quality and accuracy.

Objects produced by powder metallurgy are weaker and more porous than those machined from bar stock. In addition, they are sometimes

EXHIBIT 1   MAGNA MACHINE COMPANY

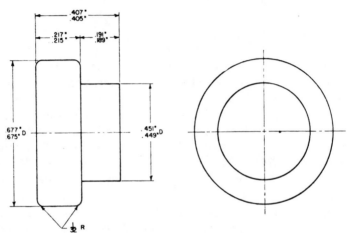

FRACTIONAL   DIMENSIONS   ON   ROUGH & CAST   SURFACES   ± $\frac{1}{16}$
FRACTIONAL   DIMENSIONS   ON   FINISHED   SURFACES   ± .010

E			TOOLS	FINISH	NAME EXPANDER WEIGHT (UNFINISHED)		
D				MAT'L BRASS SCREW STOCK	PART NO. 27 BLANK NO. REQ	SCALE 4" × 1"	
C					USED ON TACHOMETER		DWG. NO.
B					DWN N.B.S. APP.		IA-27-SM
A		CHK		HEAT TREATMENT			

more difficult to machine, thus generating a higher scrap rate than would generally be experienced if comparable parts were machined from metal stock.

Product Line

The company's line of tachometers has been manufactured as a sideline for over 50 years and presently includes 30 models with list prices ranging from $26.40 to $59.49. These units were purchased and installed by manufacturers or users of marine engines, diesel-

electric locomotives, textile machines, newspaper presses, and other forms of machinery, to permit a reading of the operating speeds (usually in shaft-revolutions per minute) of the equipment in question. Magna's principal product line consists of specially designed machinery employed by the soap-, chemical-, and textile-manufacturing industries. Certain types of ground-service equipment for military and commercial jet aircraft constitutes a second, but less sizeable, source of company sales.

EXHIBIT 2   MAGNA MACHINE COMPANY

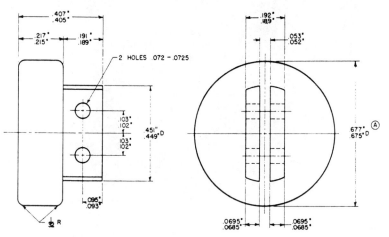

SUPERCEDES   PART   27   OF   8 – 6 – 58
FRACTIONAL   DIMENSIONS   ON   ROUGH   8   CAST   SURFACES   ± 1/16
FRACTIONAL   DIMENSIONS   ON   FINISHED   SURFACES   ± .010

E			TOOLS	FINISH	NAME EXPANDER WEIGHT			
D				MAT'L BRASS SCREW STOCK	PART NO. 27	NO REQ.	SCALE 4" • 1"	
C					USED ON TACHOMETER		DWG NO.	
B						DWN N.B.S	APP.	IA – 27
A	WAS 679'/ 676'	CHK		HEAT TREATMENT				

The design of Magna's tachometers is based upon the centrifugal-governor principle. Three of the finished weights are required in each of the various tachometer models. As the shaft of the motor or engine to which the tachometer is attached rotates, a similar rotational movement is imparted to the tachometer governor mechanism. As a result of this rotation, the tachometer expander weights and the components to which they are attached move outward under centrifugal force. The distance they move is a function of the r.p.m. of the engine or motor shaft. This outward movement of the three

EXHIBIT 3   MAGNA MACHINE COMPANY

INTERIOR COMPONENTS OF TYPICAL TACHOMETER

(Note: Two of the unit's three expander weights are visible in the right center portion of the photograph.)

weights is transmitted through a gear system to a moving needle mounted on the tachometer's calibrated dial, the position of the needle thus indicating shaft speed. Exhibit 3 shows the interior components of a typical tachometer, with two of the three tachometer weights visible.

As a result of these operating characteristics, the tolerances (and hence the weight and balance) of the weights are crucial to tachometer accuracy. Magna had long enjoyed an excellent reputation for precision manufacturing and for the quality of its entire product line. Company officials were confident that this was an important consideration behind the steady increase which had been achieved in tachometer sales over the years, climaxing in a total of over 25,000 units sold during the 12 months just completed. Sales forecasts indicated a probable continuation at least at the current level for the coming year, with perhaps a modest expansion.

Manufacture

Under the existing method of manufacturing expander weights, the brass blanks are purchased from either of two local screw-

machine manufacturers at a cost of $.062 each. Information provided by the suppliers indicates that approximately $.015 of this amount is for the brass bar stock itself, with the remainder representing the cost of the screw-machine operation, the supplier's factory overhead, other expenses, and profit.

Standard times for the remaining machining operations performed in Magna's own factory are as follows:

	Standard Minutes per Piece
1. Straddle milling	0.34
2. Mill slot	0.30
3. Drill two holes	0.16
4. Burr drilled holes	0.16

Magna officials were confident that wages in their nonunion plant compared favorably with the going rate in the local labor market. Under the company's current wage structure, milling-machine operators are paid day-rate wages of $2.40 per hour; drilling and burring operators receive $2.16 per hour.

The fixture used to hold the blanks during the milling operation was purchased from an outside supplier and had cost $190 when last replaced, about 17 months previously. At that same time a new fixture employed in the drilling operation had also been obtained from the same supplier at a cost of $75. At current rates of usage, total operating life of both types of fixtures was estimated at approximately three years.

Under Magna's accounting practices, general factory overhead (exclusive of fixture and tooling cost) is computed at the rate of 100 per cent of direct labor. The items covered by this rate include allowances for anticipated costs of inspection and also of manufacturing spoilage. Magna's experience has been that approximately 5 per cent of the bar-stock expander weights usually fail to meet specifications when inspected after the machining operations performed in the company's shop. In this event, the weights have to be discarded as scrap. Almost all such spoilage arises in connection with the two milling cuts.

One of the several questions singled out for management attention in the current study arose from the fact that the density of powdered metal parts was less than that of comparable parts produced from bar stock. If Magna were to convert to the powder-metallurgy process it would therefore be necessary to redesign the expander weight by increasing its dimensions to assure that in its finished form it would

weigh the same and also have the same balance as the finished weight currently employed. As part of his sales campaign the powder-metallurgy salesman arranged for one of his own company's design engineers to prepare a drawing of a redesigned, powdered-brass expander weight which would satisfy these demands (Exhibit 4). A check by Magna's own technical personnel verified that the specifications called for in Exhibit 4 would, in fact, result in a finished part having the same weight and balance as the bar-stock units currently employed.

The quotation submitted by the supplier's salesman indicated that the redesigned, powdered-metal blanks would cost $.045 each after Magna had invested $450 for the necessary dies. These dies would be guaranteed by the supplier to have an operating life of 50,000 pieces. The powder-metallurgy firm also would guarantee that the blanks would meet the over-all finished dimensions and specifications shown in Exhibit 4. Each weight would therefore require only drilling and burring by Magna production personnel prior to assembly.

EXHIBIT 4   MAGNA MACHINE COMPANY

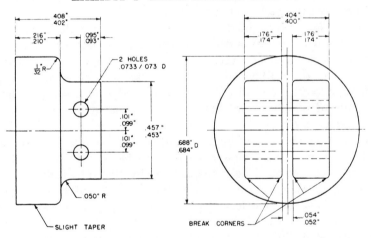

FRACTIONAL DIMENSIONS ON ROUGH & CAST SURFACES ± $\frac{1}{16}$
FRACTIONAL DIMENSIONS ON FINISHED SURFACES ± OIO

E			TOOLS	FINISH	NAME EXPANDER WEIGHT	
D				MAT'L BRASS POWDER	PART NO 27-A NO REQ	SCALE 4" = 1"
C					USED ON TACHOMETER	DWG NO.
B					DWN CHK APP	IA-27-A
A		CHK		HEAT TREATMENT		

Gross Machine Tool Company

DELLDALE DIVISION

B. F. Bocker, who recently had been promoted from another division
of the Gross Machine Tool Company to the position of assistant
superintendent of the Delldale plant, had just completed a conference
with Mark Reynolds, foreman of the Delldale assembly department.
As a result, Bocker was weighing in his mind what action, if any, he
should take in an effort to resolve, or at least to improve, an apparently long-standing atmosphere of friction between the assembly and
machining departments.

In their conversation, Reynolds had voiced his outspoken criticism
of the quality of some of the work of the machining department. He
maintained emphatically that defective workmanship on the part of
certain machinists frequently made it necessary for his assembly crews
to spend unwarranted amounts of time in various "fitting" operations,
such as filing and hand reaming on certain machined parts prior to
assembling them. At one point in the conversation, he said, "The
only explanation I can think of is that Briggs (the machine-shop
foreman) must not have any real appreciation of the complexity of
assembling heavy and intricate pieces of equipment. I'll bet I go
to him maybe a dozen times in a typical month to discuss some
specific machined part that's giving my crews headaches. And every
time he presents his one standard argument, namely that I'm unrealistic in my ideas regarding the amount of fitting that assembly personnel should reasonably be expected to do.

"Sure, a lot of the machined parts regularly come through O.K.,
and can be assembled without any fitting, or only a modest amount.
But there are just too many that don't. I'll bet a month's pay that
what really lies behind the problem is this! Briggs, simply because
he isn't able to visualize the problems it causes, doesn't maintain
tight enough control of his shop to prevent some of his less conscien-

tious machinists from sometimes taking a few short cuts or doing a little less than really first-class work. By being a little sloppy they probably save themselves a few seconds or minutes on each piece of the lot assigned to them. As a result they squeeze out a few extra pieces per hour and earn a little extra pay by the end of the day.

"But what Briggs apparently can't get through his head is that when these same sloppy parts get to assembly, one of my boys may have to spend 15 minutes, or half an hour, or sometimes even longer, playing with a part to make it fit. And if the part happens to be a critical one, it can easily develop that while one man's fitting it, maybe three or four are forced to stand idle waiting for this one stage of the assembly to be completed. This type of thing not only can throw a whole assembly job behind schedule, but to make matters worse, through no fault of their own, my assembly crews—since the men are paid on the basis of machines assembled—take home less money than otherwise. And because of the needless fitting the men actually have had to do more than the necessary amount of work in getting the machine together. Some deal!"

Reynolds closed his conversation with Bocker by saying, "Unless some way can be found to increase the percentage of decent work coming out of the machining department, I'm going to recommend that my crews be paid on a straight hourly basis. At least in this way they won't be penalized for the poor quality work of some of the machinists.

"I know that would be contrary to management's desire that all direct labor be on incentives. I know management is convinced—on the basis of our own shop experience—that by pegging pay to output we can usually count on about 10 per cent more productivity than we get with straight hourly pay. But I can't see continuing a situation in which my crews are put at an unfair disadvantage, merely because the machine shop either can't or won't regularly turn out decent parts that don't require an abnormal amount of fitting. It's bad enough for this situation to cause my department to run behind schedule so often—and for me to be made to appear ineffective as a foreman. But at least, with hourly rates, my men won't have to suffer pay losses because of the machine shop's shortcomings."

The Background

The Gross Machine Tool Company manufactures a variety of heavy, complex industrial equipment. Its production processes consist of the manufacture of the required parts and the assembly of these parts into machines. Although many parts are standard for several

different machines, the company seldom makes two machines for which the total specifications are exactly the same. This contributes to the fact that it is usually necessary to do some fitting work when a machine is assembled.

The machining department operators work from blueprints which show in detail the specifications of the part to be machined, and which also identify the machining operations to be performed. A fairly typical example of the types of parts involved, the type and accuracy of the machining demanded, and the blueprints employed, is shown in Exhibit 1.

If they request them, assembly crews are also furnished copies of the detailed blueprints of parts being assembled. This practice usually is followed, however, only in the case of parts, of which Ram Swivel DK-227 is one example, on which assembly crews find it necessary to perform what they consider unwarranted amounts of fitting. In the absence of such difficulties, the crews usually work only to assembly drawings which show the relationships between the various parts to be assembled, but not the detailed specifications of each.

Under the company's wage plan, workers in the machining department are paid on an individual, piece-work basis under which the average operator earns about $2.95 per hour. Assembly department employees, who usually work in crews, are paid on a group basis under which each member receives a standard amount for each machine assembled, with average take-home running about $2.80 per hour. The management has adopted these methods of wage payment in order to give the most skilled and productive workers an opportunity to increase their earnings. It is company policy that a wage payment once actually made to a worker will not be taken from him, that is, an equivalent amount will not be deducted from any subsequent paycheck even though the work for which the payment is made later proves of unsatisfactory quality. An employee, or a crew, however, might be required to do a job over, without any compensation for the time involved, if unsatisfactory workmanship is later discovered, which is obviously the result of operator carelessness. The company has no formal inspectors; the foremen are held responsible for both the quality and volume of work of men in their departments.

Piece rates for the machining of parts and job rates for the assembly-department crews have been determined by the company's standards department. These rates are set on the basis of standard times. In determining the standard time for an operation, the standards department studies records of times required by workers on similar operations, secures the opinion of foremen and of experienced workers, and, if

EXHIBIT 1 GROSS MACHINE TOOL CO.

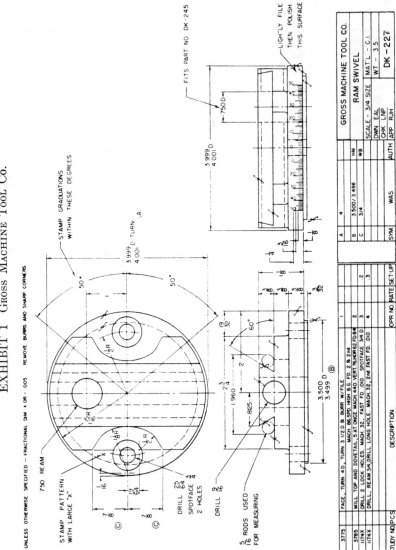

judged appropriate, makes motion and time studies of the operation.

Since the installation of piece rates in the machining department and job rates in the assembly department, questions have risen continually regarding the exact amount of fitting work which an assembly crew actually should be expected to do on machined parts when assembling a machine. To attempt to achieve great accuracy in the machining of parts in order to facilitate the subsequent assembly work obviously slows down the speed of machine operations and thus decreases earnings of workers in the machining department. On the other hand, if parts were machined less accurately, more fitting might be necessary in the assembly department, thus requiring a longer time for an assembly crew to finish its job. The company has not seen fit to establish a uniform rule regarding the amount of fitting operations that would be required. Instead, each case had been viewed as a separate matter to be determined on its own merits through conferences between the assembly- and machining-department foremen.

Brownsville Works

The Brownsville Works of International Foundry and Fabricators, Inc., produces general-purpose industrial machinery. John Olsen worked as a schedule clerk in the production control office of the Works' machine shop. Along with several other men, he scheduled production and prepared the work orders which set due dates for all work done in the shop.

On July 28, 1959 Olsen had to prepare work orders for the three parts of a reducer-adapter assembly. A lot of 120 of these requested by the order clerks was scheduled for use in the assembly department on Monday, October 12. Olsen's job was to decide the dates for the start of work and the completion of each operation in the fabrication of these parts. Those dates would then be communicated through work orders sent to the shop foremen.

In his planning Olsen used detail drawings of the parts, operation sheets for the parts, and a department load chart for the machine shop (see Exhibits 1–7). The load chart, located on a wall in the scheduling office, contained an up-to-date summary of the amount of work, in standard hours, already scheduled to be performed in each department each week. The chart was maintained by a load clerk who revised the figures daily on the basis of work orders prepared by the schedule clerks. Thus, if a job requiring ten hours on a shaper were scheduled for completion on September 9, the chart would be changed to show 230 instead of 220 hours planned for that week.

In planning the due date for an operation, the scheduling clerks ordinarily allowed five working days for the time spent processing the necessary paperwork, moving the parts from the department where work had just been completed, and waiting for a machine to become available in the next department. If the department had

140

EXHIBIT 1 BROWNSVILLE WORKS

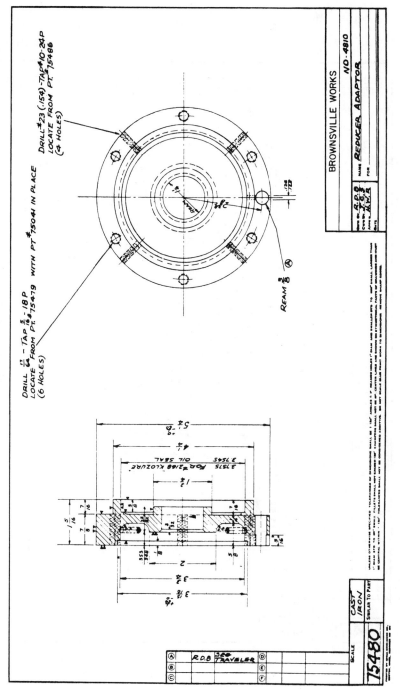

EXHIBIT 2

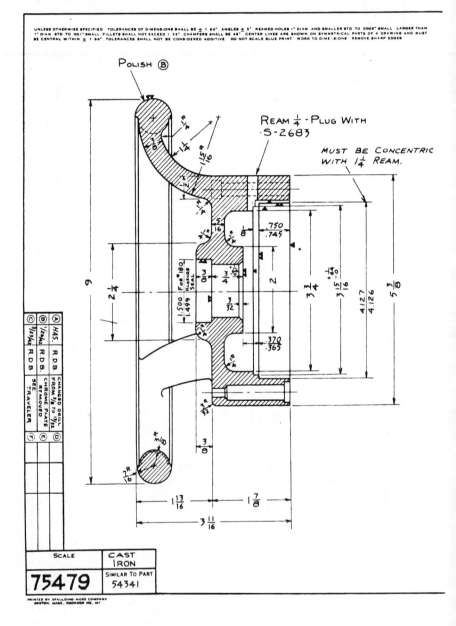

BROWNSVILLE WORKS

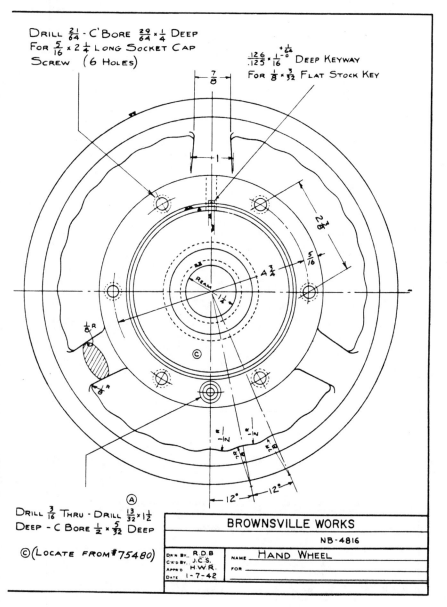

DRILL $\frac{21}{64}$ - C'BORE $\frac{29}{64} \times \frac{1}{4}$ DEEP
FOR $\frac{5}{16} \times 2\frac{1}{4}$ LONG SOCKET CAP
SCREW (6 HOLES)

$\frac{.126}{.125} \times \frac{+\frac{1}{64}}{1 - 0}$ DEEP KEYWAY
FOR $\frac{1}{8} \times \frac{3}{32}$ FLAT STOCK KEY

DRILL $\frac{3}{16}$ THRU - DRILL $\frac{13}{32} \times 1\frac{1}{2}$
DEEP - C BORE $\frac{1}{2} \times \frac{5}{32}$ DEEP

©(LOCATE FROM #75480)

DRN BY R.D.B	NAME HAND WHEEL
CK'D BY J.C.S.	
APPR'D H.W.R.	FOR
DATE 1-7-42	

BROWNSVILLE WORKS

NB-4816

EXHIBIT 3 BROWNSVILLE WORKS

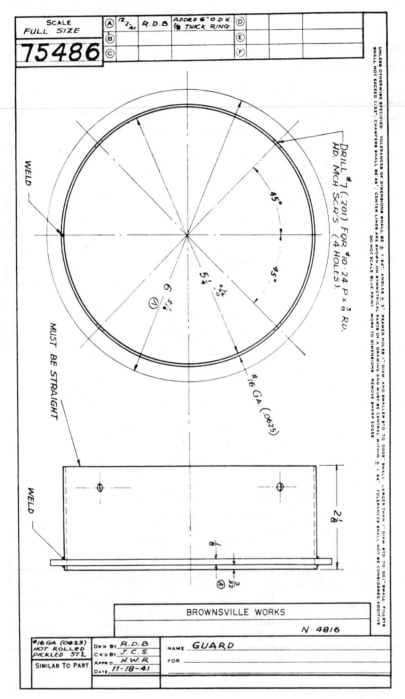

an especially light workload, or if the order were marked "rush," this time could be cut to three days.

The schedule clerks prepared two kinds of orders for these parts. The first was a foundry order, which would give the date for delivery of the necessary castings to the first machining operation. For castings of this size the foundry required three weeks' lead time. The clerk also had to set dates for completion of each machining operation. He could not, on his own authority, alter the sequence of operations shown on the operation sheet or designate an order as "rush." When he thought either action was justified he would submit the proposed schedule to the production-control supervisor along with the reasons for the exception.

EXHIBIT 4 BROWNSVILLE WORKS

OPERATION ROUTING FOR REDUCER ADAPTER 75480

Operation No.	Dept. No.	Standard Hours*
Material: C. I. Casting of Pattern 75480	Foundry	—
1. Turret Lathe	13	14.0
Drill, bore, ream, and chamfer $1\frac{1}{4}''$ hole to B/P.		
Turn, square, and bore complete to B/P.		
2. Horizontal Mill	3	6.1
Mill 0.125" slot $\frac{5}{16}''$ deep to B/P.		
3. Layout	12	2.2
Layout $\frac{3}{8}''$ reamed hole to B/P.		
4. Sensitive Drill	11	18.5
Drill and ream $\frac{3}{8}''$ hole. Drill and tap (6)		
$1\frac{7}{64}''$ holes locating from Part 75479.		
Drill $\frac{3}{16}''$ through, drill $1\frac{3}{32}''$ x $1\frac{1}{2}''$ deep, and		
counter-bore $\frac{1}{2}''$ x $\frac{5}{32}''$ deep in Part 75479.		
Drill four #23 (0.154") holes and tap locating		
from Part 75486.		
Requirements: (1) Part 75479. (1) Part 75486.		
(1) B/P Part 75479. (6) $\frac{5}{16}''$		
0.18P x $2\frac{1}{4}''$ long. Socket Cap		
Screws.		
5. Reaming	11	3.0
Hand ream $\frac{3}{8}''$ hole.		
6. Bench	11	1.0
Trim and burr completely.		

* Time required to set up and machine lot of 120 units.

EXHIBIT 5 BROWNSVILLE WORKS

OPERATION ROUTING FOR GUARD 75486

Operation No.	Dept. No.	Standard Hours*
Material: ¼ lb #11 Gauge Hot Rolled Sheet		
¾ lb #16 Gauge Hot Rolled Sheet	23	—
1. Sheet Metal	23	4.20
Make complete to B/P including drilling.		
2. Painter	26	0.50
Lacquer spray.		

* Time required to set up and produce 120 units.

EXHIBIT 6 BROWNSVILLE WORKS

OPERATION ROUTING FOR HAND WHEEL 75479

Operation No.	Dept. No.	Standard Hours*
Material C. I. Casting—Pattern #75479	Foundry	—
1. Turret Lathe	13	18.0
Drill, bore, and ream 1¼″ hole, chamfer $\frac{3}{32}$″, bore 1.500″ x ⅜″ deep, bore $3^{15}\!/_{16}$″ and 4.127″ dias to B/P. Square ¾″ and $3^{11}\!/_{16}$″ dims to high limit. Form $\frac{7}{16}$″ radius to B/P.		
2. Engine Lathe	6	13.0
Square ¾″ and $3^{11}\!/_{16}$″ dims to B/P.		
3. Layout Bench	12	4.3
Layout for drilling and reaming one ¼″ hole, and six (6) $^{21}\!/_{64}$″ holes to B/P.		
4. Sensitive Drill	11	9.1
Drill and ream ¼″ hole. Drill six (6) $^{21}\!/_{64}$″ holes and counter-bore $^{29}\!/_{64}$″ x ¼″ deep to B/P.		
5. Hand Reaming Machine	11	3.4
Hand ream one ¼″ hole.		
6. Vertical Shaper	2	3.9
Shape .126/.125 x $\frac{1}{16}$″ keyway to B/P.		
7. Bench	11	1.0
Trim and burr completely.		
8. Polisher	11	2.3
Polish to B/P.		

* Time required to set up and machine lot of 120 units.

EXHIBIT 7 BROWNSVILLE WORKS

MACHINE SHOP DEPARTMENTAL LOAD CHART*

Machine Group	Machine Hour Capacity Weekly‡	July 27	Aug. 3	Aug. 10	Aug. 17	Aug. 24	Aug. 31	Sept. 7†	Sept. 14	Sept. 21	Sept. 28	Oct. 5	Oct. 12
1. Shaper	864	864	864	864	740	680	527	220	310	149	88	111	—
2. Vertical shaper	288	288	288	273	185	212	56	93	116	84	—	44	—
3. Horizontal mill	1,872	1,872	1,872	1,872	1,872	—	1,872	1,560	1,872	1,618	1,432	418	673
4. Keyseat mill	144	27	—	—	—	—	44	57	33	28	—	—	10
5. Vertical mill	2,016	2,016	1,328	1,458	1,615	810	431	218	613	137	53	—	—
6. Engine lathe	4,320	4,320	3,579	3,348	2,763	2,185	1,216	1,198	649	337	122	—	—
7. Speed lathe	144	138	137	89	122	47	11	63	8	4	—	—	—
8. Thread grinding	288	288	288	288	288	288	273	240	243	184	162	—	14
9. Broaching	432	432	432	432	432	432	432	360	432	432	411	389	303
10. Radial drill	4,608	876	658	439	487	716	546	1,174	1,463	1,011	443	—	—
11. Sensitive drill	1,584	1,584	1,584	1,443	1,491	1,411	1,384	1,183	649	383	125	—	—
12. Layout	288	288	288	288	288	221	204	189	165	148	46	39	55
13. Turret lathe	2,736	2,736	2,736	2,736	2,736	2,736	2,736	2,126	1,548	1,799	1,243	987	1,014
14. Horizontal boring mill	2,880	2,880	2,880	2,880	2,880	2,880	2,880	2,400	2,880	2,641	2,718	2,341	1,984
15. Surface Grinder	720	720	720	720	720	720	704	600	548	548	362	141	—
16. Internal Grinder	432	432	432	432	432	388	354	360	305	328	223	204	141
17. Plain Grinder	1,728	1,728	1,728	1,728	1,480	1,292	1,113	980	746	638	319	—	89
18. Planer mill	1,296	1,296	1,296	1,296	1,296	1,296	1,296	1,080	1,296	1,247	1,190	1,016	1,142
19. Planer	5,760	5,760	5,760	5,760	5,760	5,760	5,760	4,800	4,848	5,236	3,915	3,460	3,101
20. Upright drill	1,008	612	243	111	88	46	92	104	80	161	—	93	84
21. Jig borer	144	144	144	144	144	144	144	120	126	118	97	102	64

Dates given above are Monday's. The plant works a 6-day week, except for holidays.

* Each hour of work loaded against a machine group consisted of standard operating time plus a percentage to allow for machine down time.

† Capacity this week reduced to reflect one day holiday (Labor Day).

‡ Calculated on basis of 48 hours per machine per week except in departments 10, 14, and 19, which operated 144 hours per week.

EXHIBIT 8 BROWNSVILLE WORKS

CALENDAR FOR SEPTEMBER–OCTOBER 1959

September						
S	M	T	W	T	F	S
		1	2	3	4	5
6	7	8	9	10	11	12
13	14	15	16	17	18	19
20	21	22	23	24	25	26
27	28	29	30			

October						
S	M	T	W	T	F	S
				1	2	3
4	5	6	7	8	9	10
11	12	13	14	15	16	17
18	19	20	21	22	23	24
25	26	27	28	29	30	31

O'Brien Company

On Thursday September 18, 1962, Weldon Ross, foreman of the milling-machine department (Department 15-A) of the O'Brien Company, requested the factory superintendent to approve a rush order on the company's own toolroom to rebuild the fixture currently used in Operation 14 (milling reliefs) on B-5511 bearing halves (Exhibits 1 and 2). This action arose because of difficulties which Ross believed threatened Department 15-A's ability to meet delivery schedules on Operation 14 on a lot of 5400 units (2700 pairs) of part B-5511. These were needed as components in an unusually large order of specially designed, heavy industrial machinery that O'Brien was manufacturing for overseas shipment to an important foreign customer.

The lot of 5400 B-5511 workpieces, completed through Operation 13, had been delivered to Department 15-A on schedule about midday on the preceding Friday. At the start of the first shift on Monday, Ross had assigned Bill Logan, an experienced operator of hand milling machines, to Operation 14. This required the steps described in Supplement A. At Ross's request, Logan had completed the job to which he had formerly been assigned by working two hours of overtime on Friday evening.

The Problem

Tuesday, September 16, Ross checked the B-5511 job several times and concluded that Logan had become entirely familiar with the new assignment and was working with good proficiency. At the close of Tuesday's shift Ross discovered, however, that Logan's production for the day had amounted to only 136 pairs of bearing halves. Ross found this both surprising and disturbing since it represented only about half of the volume he had expected on the basis of the information given on the Production Order Card (Exhibit 2). Yet he was

149

EXHIBIT 1 O'BRIEN COMPANY

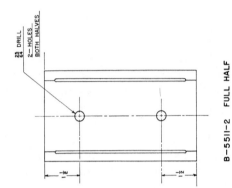

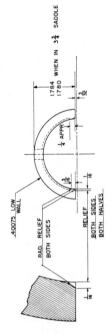

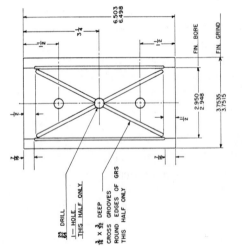

EXHIBIT 2 O'BRIEN COMPANY

PRODUCTION ORDER CARD

One cstg. = 12 lbs. (one pair)		DO NOT FOLD			write with ink	

quantity	rec'd	wanted	alloy	lot no.	order no.	part no.
2,700 pr.	8/1	10/6	27	1	96503	B-5511-1 & 2

#27 Bronze
    1 pr. = 2 hlvs.
$3\frac{3}{4}$ x $3\frac{15}{16}$ x $6\frac{1}{2}$

			Standard	
		Dept. No.	pairs per hr	
1	ro. bro. 2.922	21-B	100	
2	ro. all over	22-D	117	
3	fin. bore	25	12	
4	semi o.d. & fin. all over	22-D	117	
5	grind body	26-A	137	
6	split	15-B	22½	
7	surface	16	15½	
8	file edges	53	32½	
				ro. = rough
9	drill -2- holes	47-A	27½	
				bro. = broach
10	drill center hole -1- hole	47-A	65	
				fin. = finish
11	cosink holes i.d. to remove burr part #1 (-3- holes)	47-A	150	
				cosink = countersink
12	cosink holes (-2- holes) to remove burrs (part #2) i.d.	47-A	160	
				i.d. = inside diameter
13	file holes	53	37½	
				o.d. = outside diameter
14	mill relief	15-A	35	
				semi. = semifinish

convinced, on the basis of his own observation, that Ross was performing the job correctly, and at a good work pace.

In attempting to assess this situation Ross recalled that the Order Card specified that the entire lot of finished bearing halves should be delivered to the assembly floor for use on Monday, October 6.

EXHIBIT 3   O'BRIEN COMPANY

September

Sun.	Mon.	Tues.	Wed.	Thurs.	Fri.	Sat.
	1	2	3	4	5	6
7	8	9	10	11	12	13
14	15	16	17	18	19	20
21	22	23	24	25	26	27
28	29	30				

October

Sun.	Mon.	Tues.	Wed.	Thurs.	Fri.	Sat.
			1	2	3	4
5	6	7	8	9	10	11
12	13	14	15	16	17	18
19	20	21	22	23	24	25
26	27	28	29	30	31	

As the plant worked a five-day, 40-hour week, Ross originally concluded, after checking the calendar for September and October (Exhibit 3), that Operation 14 on the entire lot would have to be completed no later than Friday, October 3, and that this could easily be accomplished by an operator of Logan's capabilities. After learning of the results of Tuesday's operations Ross realized, however, that at a rate of 136 pairs per day it would actually take Logan about four weeks to complete the order.

Ross immediately became concerned about the possible repercussions that could arise from a failure to have the finished bearings on the assembly floor on the morning of October 6. He knew, for example, that this could delay assembly of the heavy machines for which the bearings were important components. This conceivably could necessitate rearrangement of the schedule of the entire assembly department and possibly even require the costly, inconvenient, temporary removal of a number of partially assembled machines from the floor. Ross further reasoned that delays of this sort might even result in failure to meet O'Brien's delivery promise to an extremely important customer. From prior experience Ross was aware that assembly of machines for foreign shipment had to be closely correlated with ship sailing dates. Failure to meet manufacturing deadlines,

even by a day, could sometimes lead to five or six weeks' delay in shipment.

During the morning of Wednesday, the 17th, Ross again checked Logan's work several times. This confirmed his impression that Logan was working as rapidly and proficiently as could be expected. Ross became convinced that the thirty-five "Standard Pairs per Hour" figure for Operation 14, shown on the Production Order Card (Exhibit 2) and used in setting the delivery schedule, reflected either a serious error on the part of the estimators, or a clerical mistake on the part of the typist who had prepared the card.

To verify the accuracy of this conclusion, Ross called the standards department and asked them to check Operation 14 as soon as possible. Within the hour a time-study man arrived at the department and timed Logan's performance. Late Wednesday afternoon the time-study man gave Ross the data sheet reproduced in Exhibit 4. This, coupled with the fact that Logan's Wednesday output had been only 139 pairs of bearing halves, strengthened Ross in his conviction that the problem did not lie in Logan's skill or application, but rather in the standard previously set for the operation.

A Proposal

At the start of the Thursday shift Ross consulted Logan regarding possible ways in which the job might be made less time consuming. The two men agreed that the most promising approach seemed to them to lie in employing a work-holding fixture that could be rotated 180° in a horizontal plane. This would eliminate the need to unclamp a workpiece in the present fixture, reposition it, and reclamp it after milling the first edge and prior to milling the second edge (see Exhibit 4). Instead, with a rotating fixture, a piece could be clamped into the fixture once, the roughing and finishing cuts made on the first edge, the fixture rotated, the same cuts made on the second edge, the fixture unclamped, and the piece removed.

To pursue this possibility further Ross phoned the toolroom foreman and requested that he come to Department 15-A as soon as possible. After examining the present fixture and observing the operation, the toolroom foreman agreed that the idea of employing a rotating fixture seemed entirely feasible. Furthermore, he was confident that such a move would involve only a change in, rather than a complete replacement of, the present fixture. Based on the toolroom foreman's description of the changes that could be made, both foremen and Logan agreed that with the rotating fixture the time required to rotate the fixture 180° should not exceed 0.03 minute.

EXHIBIT 4   O'BRIEN COMPANY

TIMESTUDY FORM

DESCRIPTION OF JOB _OPERATION #14 – BEARING_
HALUSS B5511 (STUDY REQUESTED BY
IS-A FOREMAN, SEPT. 17)

| ELE-MENT NO. | ELEMENTS AND TIMING POINTS | TIME IN HUNDREDTHS OF A MINUTE CYCLES | | | | | | | | | | MINUTES | | | |
		1	2	3	4	5	6	7	8	9	10	AVER-AGE	ADJ.		
FROM 1	(PRIOR) R. HITS TABLE LOAD	X	17	18	18	21	17					.181	.14		
TO 2	HAND STARTS TABLE FD ROUGH MILL	29	33	31	34	35	37					.331	.40 *		
TO 3	HAND CHANGES DIRECTION FINISH MILL	16	15	17	25	22	17					.184	.16 *		
TO 4	HAND STOPS FEED REVERSE R.	22	21	21	25	22	22					.221	.14		
TO 5	HAND STARTS TABLE FD. ROUGH MILL	36	33	39	35	30	37					.350	.40 *		
6	HAND CHANGES DIRECTION FINISH MILL	17	16	20	26	20	16					.191	.16 *		
TO 7	HAND STOPS TABLE FD. UNLOAD	10	9	8	13	12	9					.100	.07		
TO 8	R. HITS TABLE											1.56	1.47		

DETAILS:

* CALCULATED FROM SHOP STANDARD
FEED, SPEED, CUT

$480 - 71 = 409$ MIN/DAY
$409 \div 1.47 = 278$ PCS/DAY
$278 \div 8 = 34.75$ PCS/HR

(ADDITIONAL SPACE ON OTHER SIDE OF SHEET FOR NOTES ON OBSERVED ACTION, SKETCHES, CALCULATION OF STANDARD TIME PER PIECE, ETC.)

TOTAL ELEMENT TIME ADJUSTED FOR WORKER PROFICIENCY ___ _1.47_

ALLOWANCES IN MINUTES:

MACHINE ADJ.	15.0	MIN/DAY
REPAIR MAT'L.	16.0	" "
SUPERVISION	10.0	" "
REST	10.0	" "
PERSONAL	20.0	" "

TOTAL ALLOWANCES ___71___ " "

STANDARD TIME—MINUTES PER PIECE _1.71_

STANDARD OUTPUT—PIECES PER HOUR _35_
(17½ PAIRS PER HOUR)

After a few minutes of calculation, the toolroom foreman estimated that the toolroom's charges to Department 15-A for the necessary changes in the present fixture would be as follows:

Direct Labor	$ 31.00	(10 hours at $3.10 per hour)
Materials	12.50	
Overhead[1]	68.20	
	$111.70	

In response to Ross's inquiry, the toolroom foreman said that he could put an experienced toolmaker on this job at once, that the parts required to adapt the fixture could be manufactured without interrupting Logan's use of the present fixture, and that the conversion could be made in about half an hour after Logan had finished his day's work on Friday, September 19. The toolroom foreman further stated that actually he would be glad to have the job because his department temporarily was short of work. His men were all highly skilled, hourly paid workers whom he did not dare lay off because competent toolmakers were in great demand in the local labor market. There was a good possibility that if he laid off men for a week or two during a slack period he would lose some of them permanently.

Decision

After this discussion, Ross concluded that there really were only two courses of action open to him. First, he could ask Logan to work 60 hours a week,[2] starting immediately and continuing until the entire order was completed. All hours in excess of 40 hours per week would, Ross knew, involve a 50 per cent premium over Logan's regular hourly rate of $2.00 per hour. Under company practice, all overtime premiums were charged against the department in which they were incurred. Secondly, he could request the factory superintendent to approve a rush order on the tool department to rebuild the fixture.

---

[1] In estimating costs of individual jobs performed by the toolroom, the foreman followed a policy of including an amount equal to 220 per cent of direct-labor cost to cover the overhead costs of his department. This policy and the percentage to be used had been established by the plant cost department. The foreman calculated the direct-labor cost by estimating the time required to do the job and applying to that the hourly rate of the toolmaker who would be assigned to the work.

[2] Based on prior experience, Ross was convinced that 60 hours per week represented the maximum time an operator could be expected to work on this type of operation.

A third possibility—that of assigning a second operator and machine to the order—was in Ross's judgment not feasible, since his department was already working at capacity.[3]

After further study, Ross decided that the best answer would be the rebuilding of the fixture. Under standing shop practice he therefore prepared an authorization request which he marked "urgent" and submitted to the factory superintendent for approval. Since he believed the matter required an immediate decision, Ross delivered the request to the superintendent personally, explaining the situation that had developed and describing the alternatives he had considered prior to deciding to request approval of a change in the fixture.

Supplement A. Description of Operation 14

Operation 14, milling the relief on the B-5511 bearing halves, calls for the use of a W. H. Nichols hand-operated, knee-type milling machine designed for light, fast operations. For Operation 14 this machine is set up with a vertical milling attachment (held on the overarm of the machine) which permits a fixed cutter speed of 900 revolutions per minute.

A rugged fixture with a handle-operated, quick-acting spring release is mounted on the table of the machine and used to hold a bearing half in a level position while milling the relief. The table's longitudinal movement is controlled by a sensitive feed lever which the operator operates with his right hand. A simple swing of this lever feeds the table longitudinally. Another lever, controlled by the operator's left hand, is lowered or raised to position the machine's vertical milling head, thus feeding the milling cutter into, or away from, the workpiece. This head slides vertically between an adjustable bottom stop, set at the exact depth of the relief to be milled, and an adjustable top stop which allows the cutter to rise well clear of the fixture. When in the top position the head is sufficiently removed from the table to permit unobstructed loading of the part into the fixture. A counterweight keeps the milling head in this upper position until a moderate downward pressure is exerted on the left-hand lever to bring the head down to the bottom stop.

---

[3] A fourth possibility was considered briefly and discarded for lack of time. A special-form cutting tool might have speeded the process by machining both surfaces simultaneously. Such a tool would be costly, however, and would take several weeks to obtain.

The operator normally stands directly in front of the table with a lever in each hand. A large bin holding bearing halves finished through Operation 13 is positioned at the operator's left so that by reaching down he can easily pick up a bearing half. A similar large bin is located at his right to receive the bearing halves after the completion of Operation 14. A loose steel shelf is placed across the top of this bin to hold finished pieces until the inspector has time to look at them.

Operation 14 requires the removal of a very small amount of metal for a length of $5\frac{5}{8}$ inches on each of two inner edges of a bearing half through use of a special-form milling cutter. This surface does not, however, have to match with any surface on this (or any other) part. It is, therefore, necessary only that the surface be sufficiently smooth and of proper depth and shape to satisfy the inspector.

To achieve these requirements it is necessary to perform both a roughing and a finishing cut. The table is fed in one direction for the roughing cut and returned in the opposite direction for the finish cut. No resetting of the depth of cut is required on the return movement of the table. Instead, the spring of the machine away from the work during the forward roughing cut is sufficient to provide for the very shallow additional cut required to finish the surface during the return feed of the table. The design of the workpiece-holding fixture currently employed on this job is such that after the fixture is secured to the table of the milling machine, only one edge of the bearing half can be milled at a time.

Only moderate skill is required on the part of the milling-machine operator assigned to this job.

Grover Screw Machine Products Company

The Grover Screw Machine Products Company received an invitation to bid on an order from a customer for 10,000 spacers. Rudolph Holman, owner and manager, was pleased to receive the invitation to bid, because his company's workload had been reduced recently by nearly 15 per cent because of the completion of a major contract. Since Mr. Holman handled customer contacts and personally determined and quoted prices on products, he was aware of the fact that local business conditions currently were poor. Nevertheless, he felt strongly that a considerable upturn could be expected within six months.

In discussing the spacer order with Mr. Holman, the customer displayed a tentative sketch of a new gear assembly in a design stage, showing a spacer in relation to other component parts. It was apparent that each spacer was to be a cylinder of $\frac{5}{8}$-inch diameter, $\frac{1}{4}$ inch long, and that the spacer could be made out of brass or steel, solid or with a $\frac{3}{8}$-inch clearance hole, whichever was cheaper. Sketches of the spacer are in Exhibit 1.

The Choices

Mr. Holman decided that a Brown and Sharpe Automatic Screw Machine would be suitable for the job. He determined from analysis that he had six different methods of producing the spacers. He could use:

1. $\frac{5}{8}$-inch diameter B-1113 cold-drawn steel rod and drill no hole;
2. $\frac{5}{8}$-inch diameter brass rod and drill no hole;
3. $\frac{5}{8}$-inch diameter B-1113 cold-drawn steel rod and drill a $\frac{3}{8}$-inch diameter hole;
4. $\frac{5}{8}$-inch diameter brass rod and drill a $\frac{3}{8}$-inch diameter hole;

EXHIBIT 1 GROVER SCREW MACHINE PRODUCTS COMPANY

SKETCHES OF SPACER

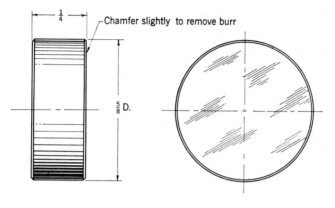

SOLID SPACER

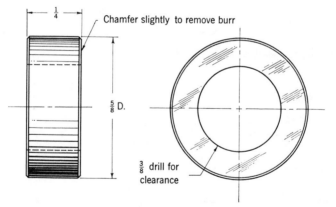

SPACER WITH 3/8 CLEARANCE HOLE

5. ⅝-inch outside diameter SAE 1020 steel tubing (with a 0.385-inch diameter hole); or

6. ⅝-inch outside diameter brass tubing (with a ⅜-inch diameter hole).

Sketches of various tool set-ups are shown in Exhibit 2. Exhibit 3 is a photograph of a Brown and Sharpe Automatic Screw Machine set up for machining spacers using ⅝-inch diameter brass rod and drilling a ⅜-inch diameter hole, and Exhibit 11 is a description of the automatic screw machine.

EXHIBIT 2 GROVER SCREW MACHINE PRODUCTS COMPANY

ALTERNATIVE TOOL SET-UPS

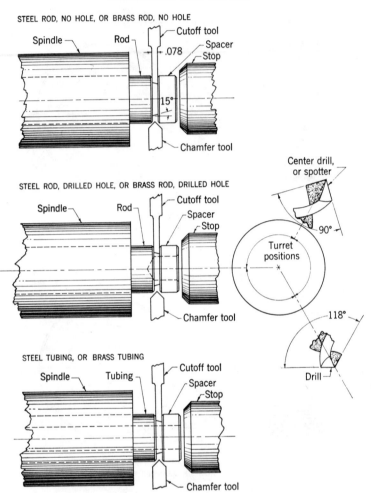

In estimating costs, Mr. Holman rounded off fractions for ease of figuring, often doing rapid-fire calculation of prices and quoting them as he talked to a customer on the telephone. In instances where products were identical or very similar to products he had produced in the past, Mr. Holman priced by "comparison"; he remembered the price on the identical or similar product and worked from it as a guide. Exhibits 4 through 9 show Mr. Holman's detailed calculations of

cost and price figures for the various methods.   Exhibit 10 is a table of feeds and speeds used by Mr. Holman.

Workers in the screw-machine department of the Grover company plant are paid hourly wages.   The company employs one set-up man who sets up the six automatic screw machines with which the department is equipped, checks their output for quality, and keeps them adjusted.   Practically all his time is devoted to set-up work.   During the night shift no set-up man is on duty.   The day shift set-up man makes sure that the machines to be run on the night shift are in good adjustment when he leaves at the end of the day shift.   The night foreman checks the work coming off the machines occasionally but does not adjust them.   If the work coming off a machine fails to meet specifications he shuts the machine down and the set-up man adjusts and starts it again when he comes on duty the next morning.

The machines are kept supplied with bar stock by one or more of several unskilled workers who do common labor work in the several departments in the shop.   Only a fraction of their time is spent in supplying the screw machines with bar stock, removing trays of finished parts, sweeping, and cleaning.

EXHIBIT 3   GROVER SCREW MACHINE PRODUCTS COMPANY

BROWN AND SHARPE AUTOMATIC SCREW MACHINE SET UP FOR MACHINING SPACERS USING ⅝″ DIAMETER BRASS ROD AND DRILLING ⅜″ DIAMETER HOLE

EXHIBIT 4 GROVER SCREW MACHINE PRODUCTS COMPANY

Detailed Calculations per 1,000 Spacers, If 10,000 Are Made, Using ⅝″-Diameter B-1113 Cold-Drawn Steel Rod, No Hole

---

Material (No Returns on Scrap)

Steel Rod Required for 1,000 Spacers	$\underline{32}$ feet
Weight of Steel Rod (1.04 lb per foot)	$\underline{32}$ lb
Cost per lb	$ .077
Total Cost of Steel Rod per 1,000	$2.46

Set-up
Estimated: 2 hr at $4.00 per hr = $8.00
$8.00 ÷ 10(000) = $.80 per 1,000

*Machining**
Cutoff:
0.330 in. (travel of cutoff blade, allowing for tool clearance and overtravel)

$$\frac{0.330 \text{ in.}}{0.001\dagger \text{ in. (feed per revolution)}} = 330 \text{ revolutions required for cutoff}$$

$$\frac{1140\dagger \text{ (rpm.)}}{60 \text{ (seconds)}} = 19 \text{ revolutions per second}$$

$$\frac{330 \text{ rev}}{19 \text{ rps}} = 17\tfrac{1}{2} \text{ sec required for cutoff}$$

Chamfering: Approx. 2 sec

Summary:
17½ sec (cutoff and chamfering done simultaneously)
 2 sec (feedout and tool-clearance time‡)
$\overline{19\tfrac{1}{2}}$ sec (total time per piece)

$$\frac{3600 \text{ sec}}{19\tfrac{1}{2} \text{ sec}} = 185 \text{ spacers per hr}$$

$$\frac{1000}{185} = 5.4 \text{ hr total machine time per 1,000 spacers}$$

5.4 × $4.55§ (machining charge per hr) = $24.57 total machining charge

---

* After the set-up man completes the tooling set-up, the operator's duties are only (1) to keep the machine supplied with rod or tubing and (2) to check the machine in order to be certain it is operating correctly.

† See Exhibit 10.

‡ Extra time per cycle to allow for tool clearance and feeding-out of stock of which the actual feeding-out time only is ⅛ second. On a very large order, a special cam would be made for this job, and the total feed out and clearance time reduced to approximately ¾ second.

§ This figure, according to Mr. Holman, is made up of an average overhead expense charge of $3.80 and a profit of $0.75/hr. The overhead charge of $3.80 includes the following, based on the previous year's costs: supervision 0.44, depreciation 0.57, indirect labor 0.30, repairs .15, supplies 0.20, tools 0.70, rent and building expenses 0.49, power 0.24, selling and administrative 0.71.

EXHIBIT 5 GROVER SCREW MACHINE PRODUCTS COMPANY

Detailed Calculations per 1,000 Spacers, If 10,000 Are Made, Using ⅝"-Diameter B-1113 Cold-Drawn Steel Rod, Drilling ⅜"-Diameter Hole

---

Material (No Returns on Scrap)

Steel Rod Required for 1,000 Spacers		32 ft
Weight of Steel Rod (1.04 lb per ft)		32 lb
Cost per lb	$ .077	
Total Cost of Steel Rod	$2.46	

Set-up

Estimated: 2.5 hr at $4.00 per hr = $10.00
$$10.00 \div 10(000) = \$1.00 \text{ per } 1,000$$

Machining

Cutoff (using one cross slide):

$$\frac{0.150 \text{ in. (travel of cutoff blade)}}{0.001^* \text{ in. (feed per rev)}}$$
$$= 150 \text{ rev reqd for cutoff}$$

$$\frac{1140^* \text{ (rpm.)}}{60 \text{ sec}} = 19 \text{ rev per second}$$

$$\frac{150 \text{ rev}}{19 \text{ rps}} = 8 \text{ sec reqd for cutoff}$$

Drilling (using turret):

$$\frac{0.150 \text{ in. (total travel for centering)}}{0.006^* \text{ in. (feed per rev)}}$$
$$= 25 \text{ rev reqd for centering}$$

$$\frac{0.328\dagger \text{ in.}}{0.006^* \text{ in.}} = 55 \text{ rev reqd for drilling}$$

$$25 \text{ rev} + 55 \text{ rev} = 80 \text{ rev total}$$

$$\frac{80 \text{ rev}}{19 \text{ rps}} = 4\frac{1}{4} \text{ sec reqd for centering and drilling}$$

Chamfering (using second cross slide): Approx. 2 sec

Summary

8 sec (cutoff, drilling, and chamfering, done simultaneously)
2 sec (feedout and tool-clearance time)
10 sec (total time per piece)

$$\frac{3600 \text{ sec}}{10 \text{ sec}} = 360 \text{ spacers per hr}$$

$$\frac{1000}{360} = 2.8 \text{ hr total machine time per 1,000 spacers}$$

2.8 × $4.55 = $12.74 total machining charge

---

* See Exhibit 10.

† 0.250 in. (width of spacer)
  0.078 in. (width of cutoff tool)
  0.328 in. (total travel for drilling)

EXHIBIT 6   GROVER SCREW MACHINE PRODUCTS COMPANY

Detailed Calculations per 1,000 Spacers, If 10,000 Are Made, Using ⅝″ O.D.
SAE 1020 Steel Tubing (with a .385″ Diameter Hole)

Material (No Returns on Scrap)

Steel Tubing Required for 1,000 Spacers	32 ft
Cost per foot	$ .225
Total Cost of Steel Tubing	$7.20

Set-up
Estimated: 2 hr at $4.00 per hr = $8.00
$8.00 ÷ 10(000) = $.80 per 1,000

Machining

Cutoff

$$\frac{0.150 \text{ in. (travel of cutoff blade)}}{0.001^* \text{ in. (feed per revolution)}} = 150 \text{ rev reqd for cutoff}$$

$$\frac{800^* \text{ rpm.}}{60 \text{ sec}} = 13\tfrac{1}{2} \text{ r.p.s.}$$

$$\frac{150 \text{ rev}}{13\tfrac{1}{2} \text{ rps}} = 11 \text{ sec reqd for cutoff}$$

Chamfering: Approx. 2 sec

Summary:
11 sec (cutoff and chamfering done simultaneously)
 2 sec (feedout and tool-clearance time)
13 sec (total time per piece)

$$\frac{3600 \text{ sec}}{13 \text{ sec}} = 277 \text{ spacers per hr}$$

$$\frac{1000}{277} = 3.6 \text{ hr total machine time per 1,000 spacers}$$

3.6 × $4.55 = $16.38 total machining charge

---

* See Exhibit 10.

EXHIBIT 7   GROVER SCREW MACHINE PRODUCTS COMPANY

Detailed Calculations per 1,000 Spacers, If 10,000 Are Made, Using ⅝"-Diameter Cold-Drawn Brass Rod, No Hole

---

Material

    Brass Rod Required for 1,000 Spacers   32 ft

    Weight of Brass Rod (1.13 lb per foot)

    Cost per lb = $.30

        Total Cost of Brass Rod $10.85

Scrap

  5 lb × $.16/lb = $.80

Set-up

  Estimated: 2 hr at $4.00 per hr = $8.00

            $8.00 ÷ 10(000) = $.80 per 1,000

Machining

  Cutoff:

    0.330 in. (travel of cutoff blade, allowing for tool clearance and overtravel)

$$\frac{0.330 \text{ in.}}{0.002 \text{ in. (feed per revolution)}} = 165 \text{ rev required for cutoff}$$

$$\frac{3600 \text{ (rpm.)}}{60 \text{ (seconds)}} = 60 \text{ rps}$$

$$\frac{165 \text{ rev}}{60 \text{ rps}} = 2.75 \text{ sec required for cutoff}$$

  Chamfering: Approx. 2 sec

Summary

  2.75 sec (cutoff and chamfering done simultaneously)

  2.00 sec (feedout and tool-clearance time)

  4.75 sec (total time per piece)

$$\frac{3600 \text{ sec}}{4.75 \text{ sec}} = 758 \text{ spacers per hr}$$

$$\frac{1000}{758} = 1.3 \text{ hr total machine time per 1,000 spacers}$$

  1.3 × $4.55 (machining charge per hr) = $5.92 total machining charge

EXHIBIT 8   GROVER SCREW MACHINE PRODUCTS COMPANY

Detailed Calculations per 1,000 Spacers, If 10,000 Are Made, Using $\frac{5}{8}''$-Diameter Cold-Drawn Brass Rod, Drilling $\frac{3}{8}''$-Diameter Hole

---

Material
  Brass Rod Required for 1,000 Spacers   __32 ft__
  Weight of Brass Rod (1.13 lb per ft)
  Cost per lb = $.30
    Total Cost of Brass Rod $10.85

Scrap
  17 lb/Thou. × $.16/lb = $2.72

Set-up
  Estimated: 2.5 hr at $4.00 per hr = $10.00
              10.00 ÷ 10(000) = $1.00 per 1,000

Machining
  Cutoff (*using one cross slide*):   Drilling (*using turret*):

  $\dfrac{0.150 \text{ in. (travel of cutoff blade)}}{0.002 \text{ in. (feed per rev)}}$ $\dfrac{0.150 \text{ in. (travel total for centering)}}{0.006 \text{ in. (feed per rev)}}$
  $= 75$ rev reqd for cutoff $= 25$ rev reqd for centering drill

  $\dfrac{3600 \text{ (rpm.)}}{60 \text{ sec}} = 60 \text{ rps}$ $\dfrac{0.328 \text{ in.}}{0.006 \text{ in.}} = 55$ rev reqd for drilling

  $\dfrac{75 \text{ rev}}{60 \text{ rps}} = 1.25 \text{ sec reqd for cutoff}$ $25 \text{ rev} + 55 \text{ rev} = 80 \text{ rev total}$

  $\dfrac{80 \text{ rev}}{60 \text{ rps}} = 1.33 \text{ sec reqd for centering and drilling}$

Chamfering (*using second cross slide*): Approx. 2 sec

Summary:
  2 sec (cutoff, drilling, and chamfering done simultaneously)
  2 sec (feedout and tool-clearance time)
  4 sec (total time per piece)

  $\dfrac{3600 \text{ sec}}{4 \text{ sec}} = 900 \text{ spacers per hr}$

  $\dfrac{1000}{900} = 1.1 \text{ hr total machine time per 1,000 spacers}$

  $1.1 \times \$4.55 = \$5.00$ total machining charge

EXHIBIT 9   GROVER SCREW MACHINE PRODUCTS COMPANY

Detailed Calculations per 1,000 Spacers, If 10,000 Are Made, Using ⅝″ O.D. Brass Tubing (with a .385″-Diameter Hole)

Material
 Brass Tubing Required for 1,000 Spacers   32 ft
 (32 ft × 0.70 lb/ft × $.52/lb = $11.65)
  Total Cost of Brass Tubing $11.65

Scrap
 1 lb × $.16/lb = $.16

Set-up
 Estimated: 2 hr at $4.00 per hr = $8.00
       $8.00 ÷ 10(000) = $.80 per 1,000

Machining
 Cutoff:

$$\frac{0.150 \text{ in. (travel of cutoff blade)}}{0.002 \text{ in. (feed per revolution)}} = 75 \text{ rev reqd for cutoff}$$

$$\frac{3600 \text{ rpm.}}{60 \text{ sec}} = 60 \text{ rps}$$

$$\frac{75 \text{ rev}}{60 \text{ rps}} = 1.25 \text{ sec reqd for cutoff}$$

 Chamfering: Approx. 1.25 sec

Summary:
 1.25 sec (cutoff and chamfering done simultaneously)
 2.00 sec (feedout and tool-clearance time)
 3.25 sec (total time per peice)

$$\frac{3600 \text{ sec}}{3.25 \text{ sec}} = 1{,}107 \text{ spacers per hr}$$

$$\frac{1000}{1107} = 0.9 \text{ hr total machine time per 1,000 spacers}$$

 0.9 × $4.55 = $4.10 total machining charge

EXHIBIT 10 GROVER SCREW MACHINE PRODUCTS COMPANY

Feeds and Speeds for Spacer Order as Selected from Table on Brown & Sharpe Automatic Screw Machine

---

Feed Per Revolution:
 (*Cutoff Tool*)
  0.001 inch* (on steel rod & steel tubing)
  0.002 inch* (brass rod & brass tubing)
 (*Drill*)
  0.006 inch (on steel rod and brass rod)

Spindle Speed:
 1140 r.p.m. (on steel rod)
  800 r.p.m. (on steel tubing—poor machinability)
 3600 r.p.m. (on brass rod and brass tubing—maximum speed of machine)

---

 * By using the above cutoff tool feeds per revolution, tool maintenance (sharpening, repair, etc.) for both steel and brass are approximately equal. The tool maintenance man makes approximately 1½ regrinds per eight-hour shift in either case. If the feed per revolution on steel is raised from 0.001″ to 0.002″, approximately 3 or 4 regrinds will be required per shift, thus increasing the "down" time of the machine. Furthermore, life of the cutoff tools would be considerably shortened.

EXHIBIT 11 GROVER SCREW MACHINE PRODUCTS COMPANY

In principle the automatic screw machine is much like a turret lathe. The Brown and Sharpe shown in Exhibit 3 is equipped with a collet chuck for holding round bar stock, a 6-face turret for mounting cutting tools and two cross slides for mounting cutting tools. Unlike the turret lathe the front and rear cross slides of the screw machine are independent of each other in action and the turret is mounted vertically instead of horizontally. A further difference is in the automatic cycling action of the automatic screw machine. Once it is set up the entire action of the machine is automatic. All tools advance to cutting position and retract automatically at the end of the cut. The rotation of the turret is automatic. The machine automatically feeds bar stock into position for cutting. The entire cycle of sequential action is automatic and the only attention required of an attendant is to keep a supply of bar stock in the machine. The setup man periodically checks parts as they come out of the machine and makes any infrequent adjustments that are necessary as the result of tool wear or other minor failure of the automatic functioning of the machine.

Kender Company

The Kender Company designs and manufactures a variety of mixing, agitating, grinding, and pulverizing equipment used in the chemicals and food-processing industries.

As a result of field reports from Kender's salesmen and customers, Kender engineers redesigned a mechanism to replace one originally installed on Kender Model C-43 mixers. This eccentric and rocker-arm assembly (Exhibit 1) was intended to give greater flexibility and control in mixing and dispensing such materials as paint pigments, batches of dough for bakery products, peanut butter, and mayonnaise. The assembly was to be used on 15 new Model C-43 mixers on order and an initial lot of 200 was to be produced and sold to replace old assemblies in use in the field. Projected demand for new and replacement assemblies was estimated at 800 units for the next two years. The Engineering Department released the design to the Production Department in November, 1958.

Process and Inspection-Planning Procedure for New Products

A. C. Karlson, Production Manager, had as his staff K. W. Brink, Production and Tool Engineer; B. H. Canton, Director of Quality Control; and B. H. Bowen, Supervisor of Production Control. Each received a set of drawings from the Engineering Department.

As a general procedure, Mr. Brink and Mr. Bowen reviewed the drawings and selected the parts to be purchased from outside suppliers. Mr. Brink often marked Mr. Bowen's drawings to assist him in specifying and buying proper weights of castings and bar stock, making allowances for material removed in machining. Mr. Canton made estimates of spoilage. In preparing operation sheets, one for each part, Mr. Brink specified the machines and tool set-ups to be used for machining the parts, and Mr. Canton the number and kinds of in-

spection operations required. Messrs. Brink and Canton often conferred with the design engineers to clarify certain specifications on the drawings. As Mr. Karlson thought most production managers' problems were traceable to operation plans, he checked and authorized all operation sheets by writing his initials, after Messrs. Brink and Bowen initialed the master stencils.

To clarify areas of responsibility and authority for quality control, Mr. Karlson, after conferring with Mr. Canton, issued a standing instruction. Excerpts are quoted below:

. . . The director of quality control is responsible for taking necessary steps to assure that at least 95 per cent of all products shipped to customers are of good quality. He shall have final authority on questions of whether products are manufactured to design specifications, and accordingly he may delegate this authority to his inspectors, as required. He may direct any process to be stopped whenever, in his opinion, the 95 per cent outgoing quality level would be jeopardized by continuing its operation.

. . . Machine and bench operators are responsible for setting up and running jobs to meet quality specifications. When recommended by the director of quality control, parts and subassemblies are to be inspected or tested by operators while performing the jobs assigned, and accordingly a time allowance for such inspection will be included in the time standard.

Explaining these instructions, Mr. Canton said,

One thing I've learned in this business of quality control is that although you guarantee the quality of performance of 100 per cent of the products shipped to customers, you have to face up to the fact that a small percentage will have faulty quality. The actual quality produced by different combinations of men, materials, and machines is naturally going to vary from one unit to the next. The 95 per cent quality level was chosen because this is the level that we think we can meet economically. With our design and manufacturing know-how, we think the 95 per cent quality level will minimize expected costs of production, inspection, and costs of repairing probable failures of our machines being used by our customers. To shoot for a 100 per cent quality level would mean we'd have to price ourselves out of the market, and we'd probably not be able to meet delivery times demanded by our customers. In a way, this is what companies in the defense-products business are facing. This 95 per cent quality level represents the degree to which we can afford to be quality conscious, and still be aware of the price and delivery obligations we have to make to our customers.

Conditions in the Shop

In the fall of 1958, Mr. Canton also said, "I've worked in a toolroom making tools and gauges; I've also had some courses in quality control. If you ask me, this job of planning inspection operations is like trying to decide what kinds of insurance policies to buy. You've got to provide inspection operations and buy the kinds of insurance

policies that'll give the greatest protection against all the risks, for the lowest cost. Inspection operations don't improve the quality; they just help to reduce the costs of being caught with bad quality." Kender's machine shop was operating on two shifts employing 45 machine operators per shift. According to Mr. Bowen, too many jobs in the department were behind schedule, and the assembly shortage list was getting longer. The average incentive wage in the Machining Department was $2.35 per standard hour; the overhead expense rate was $2.15 per direct-labor standard hour. Inspector's wages averaged $2.25 per hour, nonincentive.

Kender's union was a local of the International Association of Machinists (IAM). Machine operators' average output was 165 per cent of standard performance and ranged from 125 to 190 per cent among different jobs. The contract with the local union was to expire December 31, 1958. The business agent said that average incentive pay per hour for Kender's machine operators was at least 20 cents per hour lower than the wages for comparable jobs in the area.

Current prices for grey iron castings ranged between 15 cents and 20 cents per pound. Three to five per cent of the castings received contained sandholes and cracks which were not readily detected until after they had been machined and thoroughly cleaned.

Clearance Requirements

For the eccentric and rocker-arm assembly, one of the most critical dimensions was the clearance on the 6⅛-inch nominal diameters for the eccentric (Part 1), the eccentric strap (Part 2), and the eccentric connector (Part 5). Mr. Canton had inquired about the necessity for this small clearance. The design engineers said this clearance had to be large enough to maintain a film of lubricating oil, yet small enough to avoid a wobble and oil leakage between the eccentric and the two eccentric caps. When the mixer was operating, lubricating oil was pumped at a pressure of three pounds per square inch to lubricate and cool the three parts. Accordingly, they specified a maximum clearance of 0.003 inch and a minimum of 0.001 inch to assure a good performance of the mechanism. They said this clearance could not be made larger without a serious risk of oil leakage which would spoil the materials being mixed. Kender's chief sales engineer said that customers had complained about oil leakage and eccentric wear on the old-model eccentric assemblies which had been designed with a 0.005-inch clearance.

Mr. Canton said he was satisfied that the design clearance had to remain as specified by the Engineering Department.

To specify how these three parts were to be machined, Mr. Brink drafted the operation sheets shown as Exhibits **2**, **3**, and **4**. He did not estimate set-up and operating hours because he preferred to have Mr. Canton's comments about the quality level to be attained. Mr. Brink said, "When drafting operation sheets for certain critical parts, I usually prefer to get Canton's comments about the quality-assurance

EXHIBIT 2 KENDER COMPANY

OPERATION SHEET

Part No. __S563-1__   Material __Cast Iron 15 lbs/pc (approx.)__

Part Name __Eccentric__

Orig._____   Changes_____

Checked_____

Approved_____

	Operation	Machine	Set-up		Operate
No.	Description		Description	Hr	Hr/Unit
5	Rough & Fin. Turn & Face: 6¾" D 6⅛" D, one side reverse piece, rechuck and repeat for other side	16" Monarch Engine Lathe (Kender #122)	Univ. 4 jaw chuck on 6⅛" cast. diam.		
10	Rough & Fin. Turn, Face 3½" D eccentric boss, one side reverse piece, repeat other side. Rough & Fin. bore 2½" D hole Ream 2½" D hole	16" Monarch Engine Lathe (Kender #138)	Four jaw chuck		
15	Broach ⅝" x 5⁄16" Keyway	LaPointe Broach (Kender #310)	Gang six castings in fixture		
20	Drill 23⁄64" and tap 7⁄16" Set screw holes	L. G. Multi-Spindle Drill Press (Kender #110)			

EXHIBIT 3 KENDER COMPANY

OPERATION SHEET

Part No. __S563-2__   Material __Cast Iron 9 lbs/pc (approx.)__

Part Name __Eccentric Strap Cap Half__

Orig. _____   Changes _____

Checked _____

Approved _____

	Operation	Machine	Set-up		Operate
No.	Description		Description	Hr	Hr/Unit
5	Rough & Fin. Mill 2 Mating Surfaces	Cinc. Mill. (Kender #136)	Gang 6 castings in fixture		
10	Spotface and drill two holes $\frac{33}{64}''$ D Drill $\frac{27}{64}''$ D pipe hole; tap $\frac{1}{4}''$ pipe thread	Multi Spdle Drill Press	Piece on table Piece in 45° drill jig		
15	Rough & Fin. Bore $6\frac{1}{8}''$ D Bore $6\frac{25}{32}''$ Dia. x $\frac{3}{8}''$ wide groove	Bullard Vert. Boring Mill (Kender #335)	Clamp to Eccentric Connector Half (Part S563-5), then mount both parts in 4 jaw chuck		

level of parts machined by my proposed methods before I estimate the set-up and operating hours required. I think it's better to concentrate on quality first, because after all, if there's little or no assurance of machining to engineers' specifications, then you have no product. Estimates of time and cost are really academic until you're reasonably sure a method will meet engineering specs."

Mr. Brink put his proposed operation sheets for all S563 parts on Mr. Canton's desk with the following note attached:

Bart: 11/19/58
Re—S563 job for Model C-43 mixers
Please give me your reactions to the operation sheet for S563-1, 2 and 5, by 11/21. Castings are due in by 11/23 and we have to get this job started

as soon as possible. I think operation sheets for the other parts need just a routine consideration.

Ken

Mr. Canton said he agreed with Mr. Brink that holding tolerances and clearances on the $6\frac{1}{8}$-inch diameters would be one of the toughest problems as far as quality control was concerned.

EXHIBIT 4 KENDER COMPANY

OPERATION SHEET

Part No. __S563-5__   Material __Cast Iron 12 lbs/pc (approx.)__

Part Name __Eccentric Connector Half__

Orig._____   Changes_____

Checked_____

Approved_____

No.	Operation Description	Machine	Set-up Description	Hr	Operate Hr/Unit
5	Rough & Fin. Mill 2 Mating Surfaces	Cinc. Mill (Kender #136)	Gang 6 castings in fixture		
10	Rough & Fin. bore $6\frac{1}{8}''$ D Bore $6\frac{25}{32}''$ Dia. x $\frac{3}{8}''$ wide groove	Bullard Vert. Boring Mill (Kender #335)	Clamp to Eccentric Strap Cap. Half (Part S563-2), then mount both parts in 4 jaw chuck		
15	Mill $2\frac{13}{16}''$ Dia. boss, both sides	Cinc. Mill			
20	Drill and Ream $1\frac{15}{32}''$ D hole Drill 2 $\frac{33}{64}''$ D holes Drill $\frac{27}{64}''$ D hole Tap $\frac{1}{4}''$ pipe thread	L. G. Multi-spdle. Drill Press	Part in 45° drill jig		

Quality Performance

As a practice which he started in September, Mr. Canton had his clerk keep a record of the quality performance of the machine tools in Kender's Machining Department in order to assist him in planning quality-control procedures. Exhibit 5 is the quality performance record kept for the Bullard vertical boring mill (Exhibit 6) on which Mr. Brink had proposed to machine the 6⅛-inch diameter on parts S563-2 and S563-5. Mr. Canton had his clerk post this record every Friday, using data available from blueprints and inspection measurements recorded in the machine shop. Most machining jobs with

EXHIBIT 5 KENDER COMPANY

QUALITY PERFORMANCE RECORD,* BULLARD VERTICAL BORING MILL
Total Number of Parts Passing Inspection

| Week Ending | Under nominal size ((−) .0001 inches) | | | | | | On Spec. 0.0 | Over nominal size ((+) .0001 inches) | | | | | | Total |
	6 & under	5	4	3	2	1		1	2	3	4	5	6 & over	
6/5/58	3	27	45	54	61	78	80	76	58	51	40	30	4	607
9/12	—	3	5	8	10	16	26	18	13	12	3	3	—	117
9/19	6	3	18	33	40	53	50	58	45	37	22	4	—	369
9/29	9	14	23	29	41	46	42	40	38	30	26	15	4	357
10/3	—	5	6	18	21	28	35	30	22	14	6	6	4	195
10/17	6	22	38	48	55	63	76	74	68	50	36	25	10	571
10/24	4	8	15	32	49	51	62	58	41	40	26	15	6	407
10/31	5	13	22	36	46	50	56	53	47	32	21	17	4	402
11/7	10	17	21	19	39	53	62	60	49	35	21	10	5	401

* Notes: a. Nominal dimensions are those specified on blueprints. Presumably the boring mill is set up to produce pieces at nominal size, except when design tolerances are not symmetrical with nominal dimension. In this case, the boring mill is set up to produce a size at the middle of the tolerance. For example, if a blueprint calls for a 4.125" D + 0.005 − 0.000, then the boring mill is set up to produce 4.1275" D, and this is called "nominal," for purposes of this record.

b. Numbers in column headings are deviations from nominal dimensions in ten-thousandths of an inch (0.0001"). "Over nominal size" means the actual dimension is larger than called for on the blueprint; "under nominal size" means the actual dimension is smaller than specified on the blueprint.

c. Parts with dimensions machined *outside* acceptable (blueprint) tolerance range are *excluded* from this record. When parts were machined outside of blueprint tolerance specifications, the machining process was defined as being out of control, that is, the extreme variations outside of total blueprint tolerance range were due to assignable causes (faulty tools, materials, operator error, etc.).

Source: Mr. Canton's files.

EXHIBIT 6   KENDER COMPANY

BULLARD VERTICAL BORING MILL

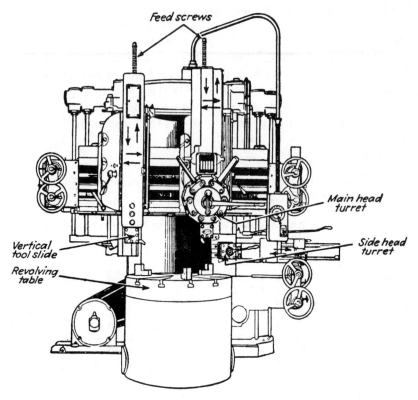

tolerances of 0.0015 inch or less were inspected by using calibrated gauges such as micrometers and dial indicators. These measurements were recorded on inspection sheets. Exceptions were in cases of lots of more than ten parts, when "go—no-go" types of gauges were often used. Mr. Canton believed the records reflected the overall pattern of precision capabilities of these machines, although he admitted that the data may have been affected by differences among skills of various operators and inspectors, by the machinability of different workpiece materials, by machine set-ups, and by conditions of gauges and tools.

In considering Mr. Brink's request, Mr. Canton reviewed the status of machine tools available and their precision capabilities. Exhibit 7 summarizes this information. Mr. Canton said, "I think another method is to cut the 6⅛-inch internal diameters on parts S563-2 and S563-5 on a vertical milling machine, using a special 6⅛-inch diam-

EXHIBIT 7 KENDER COMPANY

REPRESENTATIVE MACHINE TOOL LIST*

Machine	Kender Property No.	No. of Measurements Recorded	*Quality Capability*† 95 per cent of measurements were within a total tolerance range of:
16″ Monarch Engine Lathe	122	1,836	0.0007 inches
16″ Monarch Engine Lathe	56	312	0.0012
No. 2 W & S Turret Lathe	58	714	0.0010
48″ Reed-Prentice Eng. Lathe	45	75	0.0018
14″ Bullard Vertical Boring Mill	335		(See Exhibit 5)
6″ Landis Horiz. External Cylindrical Grinder	422	866	0.0005
14″ Cinc. Horiz. Ext. Cyl. Grinder	423	694	0.0005
18 × 36″ Cinc. Horizontal Mill	136	1,240	0.0010
14 × 36″ Bridgeport Vertical Mill	148	968	0.0008
20 × 48″ LaPointe Horiz. Broach	526	612	0.0005
36″ Cinc. Bickford Radical Drill	102	86	0.0012
18″ Leland Gifford 6 Spdle Drill	110	369	0.0015 (with jigs)

* This list does not describe every machine tool owned by Kender; it is a representative sample of the various types and sizes of machine tools owned and operated by Kender.

† Data in these columns were derived and summarized from available quality performance records, similar to Exhibit 5. These records were begun in September 1958.

eter milling cutter that would cost about $350. This probably would be less than half as fast as Brink's method; I'm not so sure we can get desired concentricity by machining one cap at a time, even though the milling machine probably can hold closer tolerances than the boring mill. Also, we don't have milling cutters this big, and it'll probably take at least two weeks to get one. Using Brink's method, I'd estimate operating time would be about five minutes for the two pieces

to be machined simultaneously, but how many castings would be spoiled? Actually, it's Brink's job to plan machining operations and my job to plan for inspection operations, so maybe I shouldn't worry about suggesting alternative machining methods."

In discussing optional methods for inspecting the eccentric assembly, Mr. Canton said, "I could consider using micrometers, measuring and recording the dimension of every piece of a lot or measuring a sample of each lot of 200 parts. It would take about 0.80 minute per piece by this method. For about $185 per gauge, I could have a set of "go—no-go" gauges made for inspecting the parts, instead of having them measured. Inspecting time using this method would probably be 0.20 minute per piece. Maybe we don't have to inspect the 6⅛-inch outside diameter on the eccentric (Part S563-1) at all. Perhaps I ought to consider some way to check the clearance on the 6⅛-inch diameter after the three parts are assembled. We might keep a Model C-43 mixer in the assembly area and check these assemblies for oil leakage and wear by operating the mix under simulated load conditions. But this would tie up a $4,500 piece of equipment that could otherwise be sold to customers."

Nolder Manufacturing Company

In the late summer of 1956, Mr. Christopher Sarle, Assistant Manager of the Electric Motor Division of the Nolder Manufacturing Company, became increasingly convinced that a change should be made in the existing methods of manufacturing stator and rotor laminations. The laminations were used in great quantities in the production of stator and rotor units, both of which were basic components in the Division's large line of electric motors.

Preliminary studies had led Mr. Sarle to conclude that the changes he contemplated probably would be fully justified at the Division's current rate of production. His enthusiasm for the changes was intensified by his knowledge that it soon might be necessary to effect a substantial increase in the volume of the Division's operations. Should this occur, it seemed probable that the changes he visualized would prove even more advantageous. Mr. Sarle therefore set aside several hours on his calendar to review again the various facts he had assembled and to prepare a memorandum to the Division Manager. In it he hoped to support the changes he wished to recommend and to describe the specific steps he would take in executing his plan if it were authorized.

Background

The Electric Motor Division is located on the outskirts of a midwestern manufacturing center. It specializes in the production of small electric motors with capacities from ¼ horsepower to 5 horsepower, in both single and three-phase models. In 1956, the workforce numbered approximately 600 persons. They worked on a one-shift basis, eight hours per day, five days per week. Machining and assembly operations were paid under a piece-rate system. Average earnings amounted to $2.18 per hour for machining

179

operations and $1.70 per hour for assembly work. Employees were represented by an independent union which maintained an informal relationship with the American Federation of Labor. In the opinion of management, dealings between the company and the union were satisfactory. Grievances were rare, and, when they occurred, were usually settled quickly and amicably.

The layout of equipment permitted an essentially straight-line process flow from one manufacturing operation to the next. Except in a few instances, materials were moved by hand or by truck, depending on the size of the workpiece and the number of pieces in a lot. Some parts were moved by a conveyor.

The Division's principal customers are manufacturers of equipment and appliances utilizing self-contained electric motors. Since the manufacture of electric motors is a highly specialized field, such firms usually purchase the motors required in their products from outside suppliers, such as the Nolder company or its competitors. In such cases, it is necessary for the performance, design, and dimensional characteristics of the motors to meet specific needs of the product manufactured by the customer. In order to satisfy the considerable variety of customer requirements, the Nolder company maintains more than 2,000 active motor models in its product line. In the opinion of the company's sales officials, competition for electric motor sales is severe. Many large and well-known concerns are in the field, seeking to win and hold customers through high product quality, reasonable price, prompt and reliable delivery, and effective in-the-field service.

The production of electric motors requires a complex series of manufacturing and assembly operations. The component parts of a typical electric motor are illustrated in Exhibit 1. Their relationship when assembled into a completed motor is shown by the cut-away view in Exhibit 2. The functions of some of the most important of these components and the processes by which they are manufactured in the Division's shops are described in Supplement A.

Existing Methods of Lamination Manufacture

In the summer of 1956, the manufacture of rotor and stator laminations was accomplished in three separate operations,[1] each of which required a press and a press operator. Within the industry, the

---

[1] See Supplement A for a description of the functions of rotor and stator laminations, and the manufacturing steps by which the rotor and stator units were formed out of the laminations.

EXHIBIT 1   NOLDER MANUFACTURING COMPANY

BASIC COMPONENTS, TYPICAL FRACTIONAL HORSEPOWER ELECTRIC MOTOR

Picture Number	Description	Picture Number	Description
1	Rotor & shaft ass'y	8	End cover—front
2	Frame, stator, & coil	9	Thermostat
3	Switch actuator		Screws
	Stationary switch		Cover
4	Ball bearing—front		Cover
5	Fan	10	Condenser
6	Lock plate	11	End frame—front
	Screws	12	End frame—rear
7	Ball bearing—rear	13	Thru bolts

EXHIBIT 2   NOLDER MANUFACTURING COMPANY

CUT-AWAY VIEW OF ASSEMBLED COMPONENTS, TYPICAL FRACTIONAL
HORSEPOWER ELECTRIC MOTOR

particular process employed was known as the "cookie method" of lamination manufacture. This terminology arose because the cutting action of the carbide dies in the press was roughly comparable to the cutting action obtained when a cookie cutter is forced through a sheet of cookie dough.

As the first step in the process, a rotor lamination blank and a stator lamination blank were stamped simultaneously out of a single 0.025-inch thick strip of silicon steel through the action of an 80-ton blanking press equipped with a carbide blanking die. The die was so designed that each time it was forced into the metal under the pressure of the press, it would simultaneously perform the three following cutting operations:

1. cut out a large circle of metal;
2. cut out a smaller, concentric circle of metal, thus forming a center hole in the large circle referred to in step 1;
3. cut out a still smaller concentric circle of metal, thus forming a center hole in the circle of metal (step 2) which had itself formed the center hole of the large circle of metal (step 1).

In this manner, three separate metal objects were formed simultaneously: a large, doughnut-shaped piece of metal which became the stator lamination blank; a smaller, doughnut-shaped piece of metal which became the rotor lamination blank; and a small, solid circle of metal which became scrap and was discarded.

On the average, a blanking die of the type required for this operation cost $3,800 and could be used for approximately ten years.

Although stamped simultaneously from the same strip, the rotor blank and the stator blank were discharged from the blanking press separately. After a sufficient number of each type of blank had been produced to fill the discharge area underneath the press, the blanking press operator loaded the blanks into tote-boxes, using separate boxes for the rotor blanks and for the stator blanks. The boxes were approximately 24 x 30 x 30 inches in size and, when full, held many thousands of the thin metal workpieces. The blanking-press operator placed the filled tote-boxes on a gravity roller conveyor. The conveyor transported the boxes to a bank of two punch presses, each of which was equipped with carbide dies and manned by a separate operator. One of these, an 80-ton press, was set up to "notch," that is, to pierce or cut out, a ring of "teeth" and a series of holes in the rotor blanks. The second press, with a capacity of 100 tons, was set up to notch teeth in the stator blanks. The stator-notching dies cost approximately $7,200; the rotor-notching dies $6,800. The productive life of each had proven to be roughly six years.[2]

When the roller conveyor deposited the full tote-boxes in the work area of the two punch presses, the operator whose press was set up for rotor laminations removed the tote-box containing rotor blanks. He unloaded the box's contents into a "magazine" attached to his press. The magazine fed the rotor blanks, one at a time, into the press for the notching and piercing operations. The operator whose press was set up for stator laminations was, at the same time, performing a similar sequence of operations on the stator blanks. The loading of both types of lamination blanks into the press magazines could be performed while the punch presses were in operation.

At the conclusion of the notching and piercing, the laminations

---

[2] In an effort to minimize die investment, lamination sizes had been standardized so that a single set of dies, that is, a blanking die, a rotor-notching die, and a stator-notching die, could produce laminations for a considerable number of different motor types. As a result of such standardization, the Nolder company was required to maintain only three different die sizes for its entire product line.

EXHIBIT 3 NOLDER MANUFACTURING COMPANY

LAMINATION MANUFACTURE

Schematic Layout and Process Sequence (simplified and not to scale)

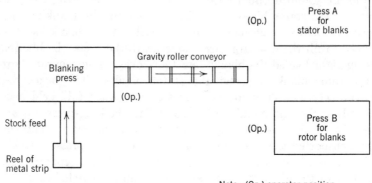

Note: (Op.) operator position.

Stage #1. (a) Raw material enters Blanking Press as a strip of .025" thick
silicon steel.
(b) Action of carbide blanking die is as follows:

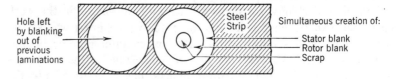

Stage #2. (a) Press A notches teeth in stator blank.

Stage #2. (b) Press B notches teeth and pierces holes in rotor blank.

were ejected automatically onto "pegs" which were mounted vertically at the rear of each of the presses. Discharge chutes from the presses were so located that the center holes in the laminations were directly over the pegs when the laminations were discharged. The laminations thus fell onto the pegs, lining up one on top of the other. The pegs were 30 inches high, and could receive approximately 1,000 laminations.[3]

When operating at normal speed, each of the presses would produce 85 notched and pierced laminations per minute. A peg would therefore be filled to the maximum allowable height in approximately 12 minutes. It then became necessary for the operator to shut down the press and spend several minutes manually removing the laminations from the pegs and placing them in tote-boxes for subsequent transporting to the degreasing and annealing operations.[4] In the interest of safety, shop rules forbade an operator to leave his press in operation during this "peg-stripping" operation.

The three press operations resulted in the creation of considerable quantities of scrap in the form of clippings and slugs. Within the industry these were known as "off-fall." The collection and removal of the scrap was the responsibility of a special crew of scrap handlers. When a scrap handler was at work in the vicinity of a press, safety considerations again made it necessary that the press be shut off. Occasionally, the scrap handlers would perform their operations at the same time the operator was removing laminations from the filled pegs. It had not proven possible to schedule the scrap handlers' activities in such a way as to assure this coordination, however. On the average, the daily halt per press for scrap removal amounted to approximately 40 minutes.

Exhibit 3 illustrates graphically the operations performed by the three presses. Exhibit 4 shows one of the punch-press operators at work.

Because of the magnitude of the manual operations, loading the magazines, removing laminations from the pegs, etc., it had been possible to assign only a single press to each operator. To meet the

---

[3] Design characteristics of the presses made it impossible to fill the pegs to their full height of 30 inches.

[4] The degreasing operation removed dirt, oil, and grease from the laminations, thus assuring that the subsequent heat-treating operation would be effective and not jeopardized by the presence of foreign matter. The annealing operation relieved the structural strains which had been created in the steel by the pressure of the press operations, and imparted optimum electrical characteristics to the laminations.

EXHIBIT 4   NOLDER MANUFACTURING COMPANY

PRESS OPERATOR AT WORK

current volume requirements of lamination production, the Division utilized 15 presses and 15 operators and employed three men as scrap handlers. The piece-rate earnings of the press operators averaged $2.00 per hour, and the scrap handlers earned $1.41 per hour on day rate.

Proposed Change

Careful study of the existing methods of lamination manufacture had convinced Mr. Sarle that the operations could lend themselves to a considerable degree of automation. The goal of such changes would be to increase the productivity of operators by reducing the amount of time now required in manual activities.

Specifically, Mr. Sarle visualized an arrangement whereby at the conclusion of the blanking operation, the laminations would be conveyed automatically to the magazines of the piercing presses. This would require the use of special "lamination chutes" leading from the blanking press to the magazines on the two piercing presses, and special conveyor equipment to transport the laminations. After the piercing operations, the laminations would be automatically stripped from the punches and blown into another chute which would lead to a conveyor belt at the rear of the presses. This belt would deposit the laminations on pegs located at its end. When a peg had been filled it would be unloaded and replaced with an empty one by the operator of the degreasing unit which would be located at the end of the conveyor belt. Mr. Sarle's study convinced him that the operations of the degreasing unit would easily allow sufficient time for the degreasing operator to take on this added job. Since the pegs would be located a considerable distance away from the presses, there would be no need to shut down the presses when the laminations were being removed by the degreasing operator.

As another feature of his plan, the scrap created by the press operations would be discharged into an oscillating conveyor to be located underneath the presses. The scrap would be carried outside the plant to a skip hoist which would automatically dump the scrap into the truck which the Division regularly used for scrap removal. The Assistant Division Manager had seen a similar oscillating-conveyor arrangement at work in another plant and had obtained the photograph shown in Exhibit 5 as an example of such a skip-hoist operation. With the scrap automatically conveyed away from the presses, the need for the three scrap handlers now required on the floor of the department would be eliminated completely.

EXHIBIT 5 NOLDER MANUFACTURING COMPANY

SCRAP REMOVAL THROUGH SKIP HOIST OPERATION

Scrap falling from machines is carried away from the work area by an oscillating conveyor which conveys it outside the plant. There the scrap is lifted by a skip hoist to a sufficient height to permit its loading into waiting trucks.

Benefits of the Proposed Change

Of even greater importance in Mr. Sarle's preliminary analysis of the problem was the belief that the proposed changes would result in substantial increases in the productivity of the presses and press operators. These would arise from the elimination of many of the time-consuming manual operations now required, particularly in load-

ing and unloading laminations into and away from the presses. Mr. Sarle's calculations led him to feel that these eliminated operations would be great enough to permit a single operator to run three presses simultaneously, in contrast to the present method. As he visualized it, with the proposed changes, each operator could man a blanking press, punch press set up to notch and pierce stator blanks, and a punch press set up to notch and pierce rotor blanks. In short, each single operator would be responsible for a complete cycle of the press operations required to produce stator and rotor laminations.

It might be assumed that the proposed change would triple the present productivity of the operators; Mr. Sarle doubted, however, that in actual practice the results would be quite this impressive. If each operator were to be responsible for three presses, it seemed likely that during each normal operating day there would be occasions when one or more of the presses would be idle while the operator was tending either or both of the other presses under his control. Furthermore, in the event of temporary breakdowns not sufficiently serious to require the attention of the Maintenance Department, the operator would have to make the repairs himself. This was in contrast to the existing system in which the operator could call for the assistance of one or both of the other operators who were "teamed" with him on the complete press cycle, and in this manner accomplish the repairs more quickly than if he worked alone.

It seemed likely that such delays would, at least in part, be offset by the fact that under the proposed system, it would not be necessary to shut down the presses and thus lose production when removing scrap or when stripping the pierced laminations from the pegs. On balance, however, Mr. Sarle felt that it would be overoptimistic to believe that the 15 presses manned by five operators would be able to match fully the rate of output achieved with the 15 presses individually manned. Instead, he felt that it would probably be necessary to acquire three additional presses for the department. If purchased new, this complete set of three presses, including magazine feeds, would cost approximately $70,000 installed, and have an estimated productive life of ten years, assuming one-shift operation. Mr. Sarle was confident that 18 presses and six operators could easily match the present rate of production, probably with a comfortable margin to spare.

Equipment Acquisition

While formulating his ideas, Mr. Sarle had been in touch with several manufacturers of conveyor equipment of the type which would

be required to accomplish the changes he visualized. From them he had ascertained that the probable cost of the necessary conveyor equipment should not exceed $35,000. This would include all the conveyors required, the chute and blower attachments for 18 presses, installation charges, and a 10 per cent allowance for contingencies. Estimates were made also that no more than three weeks would be required for the changes to be accomplished, and that during this period, it probably never would be necessary to shut down entirely the normal operations of the presses. Instead, it had been estimated that even while the conveyors were being installed, press production should remain at least 75 per cent of normal.

Mr. Sarle's inquiries had produced rather divergent views, however, on the probable life expectancy of the conveyor installation and the annual operating costs they might generate. It became obvious to him that the two considerations were interrelated: the better the maintenance the equipment received, the longer its productive life would be. Estimates from conveyor manufacturers regarding the probable life had ranged from "at least ten years" to "twenty years or more." Estimates on probable annual operating costs had ranged from "practically nil" to "not more than $500 annually."

Mr. Sarle also learned that delivery on the three new presses probably would take at least six months. There was, however, an active market in used press equipment, and Mr. Sarle believed that if it would be advantageous to do so, serviceable, reconditioned presses could be acquired in a much shorter time. Their cost would depend on the age of the presses and their probable remaining productive life. The location of three additional presses in the department would pose problems, since space was already at a premium. A check of the floor plans had convinced Mr. Sarle, however, that with a moderate amount of rearrangement, at a cost of not more than $1,500, it would be possible to accommodate the three additional presses and all the conveyor equipment.[5] Undeniably, conditions would be crowded, but Mr. Sarle was confident they would still permit efficient operations and provide complete operator safety.

Although Mr. Sarle's primary area of activity did not normally bring him into contact with accounting and financial matters, he was aware that the Division's accounting practices currently charged overhead to the lamination press department at a rate of 140 per cent

---

[5] In order to accommodate the oscillating conveyor, a "trough" 24 feet long, 2 feet wide, and 2 feet deep would have to be constructed in the floor of the press department.

of direct-labor cost. Approximately 40 per cent of the total overhead, an amount equal to 56 per cent of direct-labor cost currently charged against the department, was attributable to depreciation on the press equipment and on the other fixed assets. The remainder reflected the costs of indirect labor, supervision, heat, light, power, and the department's allocated share of the various overhead costs of the company. Mr. Sarle also knew that in anticipation of the possible expansion of the production volume, the company had been strengthening its cash position. He was confident that expenditures of the magnitude involved in his proposal could be handled without difficulty.

Mr. Sarle's examination of the possible use of conveyors in the manufacture of laminations had first been stimulated by the fact that for a number of years active consideration had been given to the possible widespread introduction of conveyors throughout the plant. Although no firm decision to move in this direction had yet been reached, there was continuing interest in such a possibility among the top management group. In fact, it seemed to Mr. Sarle that the sentiment in favor of a conveyor system was growing steadily. This reflected, in part, the impending possibility of a major plant expansion. Even were the volume of production not to be increased, several of the key production men maintained that a move should still be made to introduce an extensive conveyor system. In this way, they reasoned, it would be possible to relieve the present crowded conditions in most manufacturing areas, and to permit a more rapid and efficient process flow through the plant.

Supplement A. Function of Certain Major Motor Components and the Manufacturing Operations by Which They Are Produced and Assembled

A. END FRAME—heavy, shield-like units of cast iron or aluminum, circular in shape, forming part of the outer body of a motor, and providing support for the motor shaft. Iron end-frame castings are purchased from outside foundries. Aluminum end frames are die cast in the Division's own shops.

In the Division's Machining Department the outer diameter of each casting is turned to the required dimension and surface finish on a high-speed automatic lathe. Through a multiple tool set-up on the lathe, a housing for the motor-shaft ball bearing is rough-bored simultaneously with the turning operation. This bearing housing is then

finish-bored in a precision boring machine. To assure rigidity, proper shaft alignment, and an even distribution of thrust load in the completed motor, the final boring operation is held to a tolerance of 0.0004 inch. Two end frames, one for the front and one for the rear of the outer body, are required for each motor. Front and rear end frames differ somewhat in design, but require essentially the same series of machining operations.

B. MAIN FRAME—a steel cylinder forming the major part of the outer body of the motor and providing a housing for the motor's internal components.

Main frames are manufactured by roll-forming a length of strip metal into a hollow cylindrical shape in a special rolling machine. The right- and left-hand edges of the steel strip are brought into contact by the roll-forming, and are joined together by a seam-welding operation to form a hollow cylinder of metal. At subsequent stages of the process, after having a stator unit fitted inside it, the right- and left-hand edges of the main frame are bored and faced to length in an automatic lathe. In final assembly operations, the main frame is joined with front and rear end frames to form the complete motor body.

C. SHAFT—a cylindrical column of heavy, cold-rolled steel or of a special alloy running the length of the main frame, and passing through the end-frame bearing-housing, extending beyond the motor body at the front. Operation of the motor rotates the shaft at high speed. Belts or gears, connecting with other pieces of equipment, can be mounted securely along the exposed portion of the shaft in such a way that they rotate with it. In this manner, via the rotating shaft, the power of the motor can be transmitted to other units.

In the Division's shops, shafts automatically are cut to length from bar stock and drilled for center holes. They are then transferred to automatic lathes for rough turning. Final finish and dimensions are imparted through external-profile grinding machines. The dimensions of a shaft diameter normally vary at several different points along the shaft length. To assure concentricity along the entire length, special tooling is used on both lathes and grinders to permit machining of all diameters simultaneously in a single workpiece set-up. Shaft dimensions normally have to be accurate within a tolerance of 0.0003 inches. At later stages of manufacture, the shaft is force-fitted into the center hole of the rotor unit[1] by use of a hydraulic press.

---

[1] Described subsequently.

D. STATOR—a thick, doughnut-shaped object formed from a grouping together of many 0.025-inch thick laminations[2] of high-grade silicon steel. The completed stator unit, after having copper wire coiled around its periphery, forms the stationary electrical field of the motor. The center hole of the stator unit provides the housing for the rotor[3] unit, which constitutes the moving electrical field. Electrical forces between these two fields create energy which imparts rotating motion to the rotor unit, and through it, to the shaft of the motor.

The manufacture of the stator unit is accomplished by "weigh-counting" (with accurate scales) to ascertain the number of laminations required for a completed stator. The required number of laminations are then aligned together so that its notched teeth form slots around the inner periphery of the unit. The laminations are then compressed in a hydraulic press and riveted together with four alloy steel pins. The stator unit is cleaned and insulating materials are inserted into the slots formed by the teeth. Coils of copper wire are wound around the unit's entire periphery by the special coil-winding machines. The completed unit is then accurately fitted into a main frame. Great care is taken to assure concentricity between the bore of the stator and the surface of the main frame in which the stator is fitted.

E. ROTOR—a barrel-like object, with substantial wall thickness, formed by grouping together many 0.025-inch thick laminations of high-grade silicon steel. The completed rotor unit forms the moving electric field of the motor. In the assembled motor, the rotor unit is housed inside the stationary stator unit. The motor shaft, in turn, is housed tightly in the center hole of the rotor unit. Rotation of the rotor, created by the electrical forces between the two electrical fields, causes rotation of the motor shaft and thus permits energy transfer to other units.

Rotor units are manufactured by assembling together an appropriate number of rotor laminations, as determined by "weigh-counting." Each lamination has been pierced previously with a center hole and a series of teeth and smaller holes. They are brought into proper alignment through the assembly operation, and the entire unit is bound together into a solid mass by a "cold-chamber, high-

---

[2] The manufacture of laminations is explained in the text of the case. A typical ½ horsepower motor (two pole) would require approximately 90 stator and 90 rotor laminations.

[3] The function of the rotor and the manufacturing steps required in its manufacture are described separately in section E.

pressure, die-casting operation" in a powerful hydraulic press. The motor shaft is force-fitted into the center hole by a second hydraulic-press operation. The rotor is then machined to the proper dimensions on an automatic lathe, with the motor shaft acting as a mandrel. Tolerances of 0.002 inch are required at this stage of the operation.

As a guard against excessive motor vibration, the rotors are balanced in a special electronic machine to hold vibration of the rotor to 1/1000 of an inch when operated at full speed.

F. ROTOR AND STATOR LAMINATIONS—wafer-thin, flat, circular-shaped pieces of high-grade silicon steel which constitute the basic components in the production of rotor and stator units, respectively. The steps in lamination manufacture are described in the text of the case.

G. BALL BEARINGS—high quality ball bearings are purchased from outside suppliers. These provide support for the motor shaft and assure a minimum of friction in motor operation.

Assembly and Testing

In the assembly operations, the various components are aligned into proper relationship with each other, and the necessary electrical connections are made. The motors next pass into a testing room where they are checked for capacity, torque, and other performance characteristics. On a sampling basis, a certain number of motors receive additional quality testing of a more intensive nature. This includes a complete teardown of the motor and testing of individual components. As a result of these techniques of quality control, each Nolder motor is sold with a "quality certification."

Reliable Products Company (I)

In the fall of 1959 Mr. Arthur Drew, the Purchasing Manager of the Reliable Products Company, proposed to the Manufacturing Vice President, Mr. James Webster, that the company's full requirements of "bunched" (twisted) copper wire be purchased from the Springfield Wire Company. Mr. Drew described his recommendation as "a close decision, influenced by many factors."

The Reliable Products Company manufactures 1,500 different small wiring devices for use in the home or for installation by electricians. The products include such things as electrical wall switches, extension cords, lamp sockets, and fuses. Some of the company's products are shown in Exhibit 1. All items manufactured are selected for potential volume production, and the output of some items is well over one million units per year.

Reliable, which employs about 600 people and occupies 300,000 square feet of floor space in its own plant, is one of the largest and oldest manufacturers of small wiring devices. Since 1939, however, Reliable's share of the market had dropped and profit margins had shrunk. As part of a program to improve the company's position, the President, the Manufacturing Vice President, and other top managers at Reliable stressed the importance of a program of cost reductions. All employees, and particularly supervisory employees, were asked to scrutinize the company's operations to find ways to cut costs.

The Purchasing View

Mr. Drew, describing his department as one which contributes substantially to cost reductions, said, "Take a look at purchasing's relative importance. Fifty-three cents of every dollar Reliable receives is paid out for purchases of raw material and component parts."

EXHIBIT 1   RELIABLE PRODUCTS COMPANY

COMPANY PRODUCTS

Mr. Drew went on to say, "I see our job not simply as one of buying specified items, but rather as one of finding the best materials at a price to meet our needs. We try to dig out the many ways in which a design function can be satisfied. We have responsibility also for quality of purchased parts, for their delivery in accordance with requirement dates, and considerable responsibility for the size of the inventories of direct material.

"The company's product line is changing in some respects and this change has repercussions on the purchasing department. In the 1930's and 1940's we manufactured standard items such as pull-chain sockets and cords for electrical appliances. We still do. But now we are finding broader profit margins in what I call new items or style items. A small night-light which plugs into a wall socket is one example. Another is an outdoor light for the patio or for barbecues. Products like these must be introduced with speed, ahead of our competitors, or to keep up with them. You can surmise what effect time pressures have on the purchasing department; we must develop reliable sources, check the quality of initial runs, and procure first deliveries, all within a few weeks.

EXHIBIT 2A RELIABLE PRODUCTS COMPANY

COMPANY PRODUCTS USING CORD

Cord set

Hank of cord

EXHIBIT 2B   RELIABLE PRODUCTS COMPANY

END OF CORD SHOWING INSULATION, SEPARATE STRANDS,
AND BUNCHED (TWISTED) FINE WIRE

"Let me give you an example. The outdoor patio light, which we introduced recently, has as its largest component a hood which encloses the electrical socket and bulb. The outside of the hood serves as a shield and the inside serves as a reflecting surface. We rejected a painted metal hood because of high cost and its inability to withstand weathering. We selected a ceramic hood instead. The cost was satisfactory, the weathering qualities excellent, and potentially the hood had good style appeal. But we struck a snag on color. We needed an exterior of mottled dark brown for appearance and an interior of white for reflecting properties. We found that ceramic manufacturers could make the hood easily if it were all white but that they weren't prepared to fuse on the second, outside color to meet our requirements for quality, volume, and price. We finally got one supplier who met our needs but only after many contacts and long sessions with several ceramic manufacturers. And this was done under pressure to start manufacture at an early date."

Another problem which the purchasing manager had studied concerned the procurement and manufacture of the electrical cord used as a component of products that are among the company's large-volume items. Electrical cord is used in making extension cords and

in cords for electrical appliances. In addition, electrical cord is sold in packages of short hanks for such household uses as the rewiring of lamps. Exhibit 2A shows the 6-foot appliance cord and the 15-foot hank of cord.

Wire Twisting

Two important steps in the manufacture of the basic cord take place at the Reliable plant. Copper wire—a very fine copper wire designated as size No. 34 satisfies the great bulk of Reliable's needs—is purchased on reels. As the first step in cord manufacture, the wires from 41 reels are twisted together on a machine called a "buncher." Exhibit 3 shows a view of the five Watson bunchers used at Reliable and a plan of how the wires from many reels are fed to one buncher. Experience has shown that set-up occupies nearly 20 per cent of the time of each machine.[1] Hence one man can run five machines. After set-up, one buncher can produce twisted wire with a "one-inch lay" (one full twist per inch) at the rate of 150 feet per minute.

When filled, the reels of twisted wire are unloaded from the bunchers and moved to the second step in the manufacture of electrical cord. Here the twisted strands are coated with plastic insulation in a machine which processes two strands at a time. The plastic coating serves a dual function: it insulates each strand separately and, in a carefully controlled process, the plastic also holds the two strands together to form a cord. Exhibit 2B is the end of a cord enlarged to show the insulation, the two strands, and the bunched (twisted) fine wire.

Although Reliable bunches most of its own wire needs on the five bunchers it owns, some bunched wire is purchased from the Springfield Wire Company to meet peak demands and unusual requirements growing out of schedule changes. Exhibit 4 shows the amount of bunched wire purchased and the total amount used. Mr. Drew had found Springfield to be a reliable supplier. Deliveries were on time and quality was consistently acceptable. Further, during two periods of copper shortage, Mr. Drew felt that the Springfield sales manager had given Reliable the treatment of a preferred customer, allocating to Reliable the maximum amount of copper that Springfield's supply would permit. In addition, Springfield had helped Reliable during

---

[1] Set-up work consists of unloading the full take-up spool, installing another take-up spool, removing the empty feed spools, installing full feed spools, and threading the fine wire from the feed spools through the mechanism to the take-up spool. The wire from a set of 41 feed spools can fill five take-up spools.

an acute shortage by drawing to copper wire some rods uncovered by the Reliable purchasing manager in someone else's copper stores.

Springfield's Offer

In October 1959, the sales manager of the Springfield Wire Company offered Mr. Drew a special price for bunched wire, conditional upon Springfield's supplying all of Reliable's needs for this wire. The price was a fixed $.02 per pound above the fluctuating market price for untwisted wire. At that time the market price for No. 34 copper wire stood at $.4941 per pound, making the calculated price for bunched wire $.5141.

Reliable bought fine copper wire from three other companies. All three were big names in the copper industry and all were much larger than Springfield. These other companies, if called upon, could perform the bunching operation, but their quoted prices for bunched wire were two and three cents a pound higher than the price quoted by Springfield. The purchasing manager at Reliable explained, "The big companies are interested in volume runs and they get these on the standard, single-strand wire we buy. The smaller Springfield company wants our bunching business in order to gain the opportunity to sell us the wire, too."

Cost Factors

Mr. Drew had asked Reliable's cost accountant, Mr. William Snyder, to make a comparison of the cost of buying bunched wire from the Springfield company with the cost of bunching wire at the Reliable plant. In his calculations Mr. Snyder had worked from these facts and premises:

1. Reliable's demands for bunched wire (largely for No. 34 bunched wire) had been running at the rate of 65,000,000 feet, or 340,000 pounds,[2] for the previous 12 months. This demand fluctuated, however (Exhibit 4).
2. Reliable could continue to meet most of its demand for bunched wire by using the five bunchers it owned. Peak and unusual demands could be purchased outside.
3. Additional bunching machines could be purchased so that no demand for outside bunching service would exist. If additional machines were purchased, five machines would be bought. Five was the number of machines run by one operator.

---

[2] The weight of 1,000 feet of 41 strands of No. 34 wire was 5.23 pounds.

EXHIBIT 3 RELIABLE PRODUCTS COMPANY

BUNCHING MACHINES AND SPOOL RACK

Bunching machines

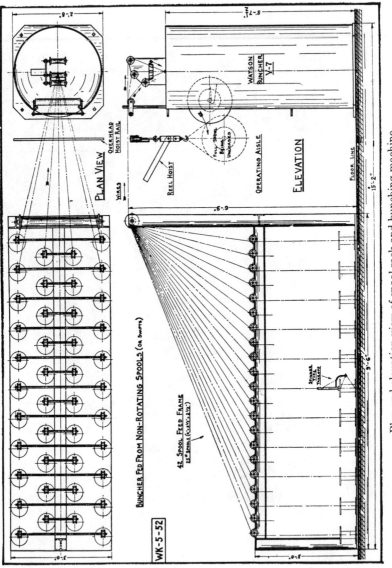

Plan and elevation view of spool rack and bunching machine

EXHIBIT 4   RELIABLE PRODUCTS COMPANY

PURCHASE, PRODUCTION AND USAGE OF BUNCHED WIRE
(All figures are thousands of pounds)

Month	Bunched Wire Purchased	Wire Bunched at the Reliable Plant	Bunched Wire Incorporated into Finished Products
1958 Sept.	8.9	23.4	31.5
Oct.	3.3	26.1	28.0
Nov.	2.8	25.3	25.8
Dec.	1.6	22.8	24.0
1959 Jan.	9.2	21.6	31.3
Feb.	6.4	27.2	30.6
March	4.1	25.5	31.0
April	7.9	20.3	28.1
May	5.0	22.7	31.2
June	5.3	22.2	30.6
July	6.4	16.8	21.2
August	4.3	19.4	26.7
	65.2	273.3	340.0

4. The factory area in which the bunchers were located was supervised, at the time, on both the first and second shifts. Accordingly,
the bunching machines could be run either one or two shifts.

5. If additional bunching machines were purchased, new machines
would be bought. The price of the Watson bunchers, V-7 model,
was $2,500 for each machine. A frame to hold the reels of wire
fed to one buncher cost an additional $1,800.

6. On the other hand, if the full supply of bunched wire were purchased from Springfield, Reliable would sell the five bunchers
which it owned. These machines had cost $2,400 each new, but
had current book value of $1,650 each. If sold as used equipment
the machines were expected to bring 40 per cent of their original
cost. Mr. Drew had received offers approximating this amount
from three of the many concerns that dealt in secondhand machinery for drawing, twisting, and coating wire. The five frames in use
had been fully depreciated. The market value for these frames in
used condition was $2,000 for all five frames.

7. In calculating savings, Mr. Snyder, the cost accountant, said that
his practice was to consider those costs that he thought would be
influenced by the decision to be made. He explained, "Ordinarily,

in deciding whether we should manufacture or buy a component, I consider only the variable costs—that is, direct labor, direct material, and the variable part of overhead expense. Here, however, I am comparing the 'full cost' of making bunched wire with the purchase cost. I use the full cost of manufacturing, which includes fixed overhead, because we have ample indication that if we sell these five bunchers the floor space now occupied will be used for other purposes."

Exhibits 5 and 6 contain the figures used by Mr. Snyder in comparing the costs of manufactured and purchased bunched wire. Exhibit 5 is the company's standard list of overhead items showing entries for charges against bunching wire. Exhibit 6 shows the calculation made by Mr. Snyder.

Other Factors

Mr. Drew identified two operating advantages that would accrue from the purchase of bunched wire instead of single-strand wire. As one advantage, he pointed out that large reels of bunched wire could be obtained. The V-7 buncher had reels with a capacity of 40,000 feet for taking up the twisted wire. Springfield, on the other hand, using larger machines, could twist wire onto rolls holding 100,000 feet. In the succeeding operation at Reliable, coating with plastic, the larger reels would permit longer runs. Changeovers from one reel to the next in the plastic-coating operation took 15 minutes. Direct labor and variable expense charges for the plastic-coating operations amounted to $4.75 per operating hour.

As a second operating advantage, Mr. Drew pointed out that the purchase of bunched wire instead of single-strand wire would permit Reliable to carry a lower inventory of raw material. In the past he had attempted to secure delivery in one month of the single-strand wire which would be bunched, coated, and incorporated into a product for shipment the following month. The cost of the wire thus appeared in one month-end inventory. Mr. Drew maintained that if bunched wire were purchased, he could schedule receipt of most of the wire needs in the same month in which it would be incorporated into a product and shipped. Hence, there would be almost no wire carried in the month-end manufacturing inventory.

Mr. Drew felt that this potential reduction in inventory was important. "Our president attaches considerable importance to turnover of working capital and to the size of inventories," Mr. Drew said. "We are under pressure to a considerable extent by the attitudes on

EXHIBIT 5 RELIABLE PRODUCTS COMPANY

OVERHEAD CHARGES FOR THE OPERATION OF FIVE BUNCHING MACHINES
JANUARY 1959

Account Charged	Total	Fixed	Variable
Supervision	$ 47	$ 47	—
Inspection	12	3	$ 9
Indirect Labor	10	3	7
Overtime Premium	—	—	—
Make-up Pay	1	—	1
Idle Time Pay	—	—	—
Training Pay	—	—	—
Night Bonus	—	—	—
Shop Vacation and Allowances	22	1	21
Employee Benefits	24	4	20
Social Security Tax	15	3	12
Workmen Compensation	2	—	2
Other Employee Benefits	1	—	1
Tools	—	—	—
Supplies	—	—	—
Tool Maintenance	—	—	—
Tool Replacement	—	—	—
Machine Maintenance	—	—	—
Water	—	—	—
Gas	—	—	—
Electricity	27	27	—
Compressed Air	—	—	—
Rearrangement	7	7	—
Transportation	—	—	—
Factory and Equipment Development	—	—	—
Telephone and Telegraph	—	—	—
Depreciation (Building)	64	64	—
Depreciation (Equipment)	126	126	—
Rent (Equipment)	—	—	—
Taxes	71	71	—
Insurance	5	5	—
Assessment for Indirect Factory Departments	86	61	25
Other Assessments	21	19	2
	$541	$441	$100

Note: Overhead per pound was computed by dividing total overhead ($541)
by total pounds of wire bunched in this month (21,640 lb.). Thus the
overhead per pound was $0.025.

EXHIBIT 6   RELIABLE PRODUCTS COMPANY

COMPARISON BETWEEN SPRINGFIELD'S OFFERED PRICE AND OUR COSTS
BASED ON OUR ACTUAL PERFORMANCE FOR BUNCHING NO. 34 WIRE

---

1. CALCULATION OF DIRECT LABOR COSTS

Theoretical Capacity of Bunchers at 100% Operation
150 ft per min x 60 min x 5 machines =
    45,000 ft per hr theoretical capacity of 5 machines, or 235.35 lb
    per hr theoretical capacity of 5 machines

Actual Production (as recorded for April, May, June, July 1959)
    During these 4 months 15,690,500 ft were bunched in 502.2 hr of oper-
ation by 1 man and 5 machines.
    This equals 31,244 ft per hr actual production or 163.4 lb per hr.

Per Cent Efficiency

$$\frac{31{,}244 \text{ ft/hr actual}}{45{,}000 \text{ ft/hr theoretical}} = 69.4\% \text{ efficiency}$$

Direct-Labor Cost per Pound

$$\frac{\$2.045 \text{ direct-labor cost/hr}}{235.35 \text{ theoretical lb output/hr}} = \$0.0087 \text{ theoretical direct-labor cost per lb}$$

$$\frac{\$2.045 \text{ direct-labor cost/hr}}{163.4 \text{ actual lb output/hr}} = \$0.0125 \text{ actual direct-labor cost per lb}$$

2. CALCULATION OF FULL COST IN OUR PLANT USING 5 MACHINES ON
ONE SHIFT

	Cost per Pound
Material (single-strand wire)	$0.4941
Labor	0.0125
Overhead (see Note, Exhibit 5)	0.0250
Total shop cost	$0.5316

3. COST FOR BUNCHED WIRE BOUGHT FROM SPRINGFIELD

	Cost per Pound
Material (at current prices)	$0.4941
Springfield's fixed charge	0.0200
Total purchase cost	$0.5141

inventories of the management at our holding company. It wants our inventories cut. In the past four years, by a careful scheduling of those incoming materials which have high value,[3] we have been able to reduce factory inventories by $500,000. We have no figure for the actual cost of carrying inventory. That's something we probably should figure, item by item. Nor do we have a figure for the cost of being out of stock on materials. If an out-of-stock situation threatens or exists we simply scramble here in the purchasing department to correct the shortage. And in the factory operations when they run out of stock, the foremen scramble, too, substituting other work, often at no recorded cost of changeover. Shortages in the factory don't happen often. If they did I think the cost consequences would shoot up sharply.... We use a figure of 15 per cent as a rule of thumb for the cost of carrying inventory."

His judgment of the many factors led the Purchasing Manager to recommend that Reliable secure all of its bunched wire from the Springfield Wire Company.

---

[3] Reliable classified all raw material and purchased components into an "A-B-C classification." Class A included 20 per cent of the items but represented 67 per cent of the cost. Class B included 30 per cent of the items, representing 21 per cent of the cost. Class C included 50 per cent of the items, representing only 12 per cent of the cost. Control was exercised on a selective basis; greatest attention was given to timing the delivery of Class A items to match actual needs.

PART 2. WORKPLACE METHODS

AND STANDARDS

Bagdad Pump Corporation

The product line of Bagdad Pump Corporation included electric compressor units manufactured in large volume under contract to makers of electric refrigerators. Each compressor was shipped from the factory in a heavy wooden crate to which it was attached by four sets of fasteners. A fastener set consisted of four items: a metal bolt one and one-half inches long, five-sixteenths of an inch in diameter, threaded along the final seven-eighths of an inch of its length; a five-eighths of an inch diameter, metal split-ring washer; a one-inch diameter metal ringwasher and a three-quarters of an inch diameter washer made of leather, rubber, or plastic, depending upon the specifications of the customer.

To make it unnecessary for the packing personnel to have access to separate supplies of all four items and to have to take time in the midst of packing to obtain each item when needed, the Bagdad company introduced a "fastener-set preassembly" operation. The job involves assembling into a single unit the four items comprising one fastener set. Supplies of these preassembled fastener units are furnished to the packers for use as required.

At present volume levels about 1,000 compressors are shipped each week. Preassembling the 4,000 fastener sets needed for one week's packing operations utilizes 16 hours of the time of the woman regularly assigned to this job. The usual arrangement is for the assembly-department foreman to schedule this work for each Thursday and Friday, and have a material handler move the preassembled fastener sets, representing the packing requirements for the ensuing week, to the packing area at the start of the first shift on Monday morning.

During the six weeks she has been assigned to the fastener-preassembly job, Rita has not been taught to use any specific work method for this operation. Instead, after being told by the foreman

in general terms what the job requires, she has been left to develop her own assembly technique. When an engineer from the Methods Department finally was assigned to set a standard[1] on the fastener preassembly, he decided that his first step should be to familiarize himself with the method that Rita herself had devised and had been using.

The methods engineer observed that Rita, who is right-handed, performs this job while seated at a workbench five feet long and three feet wide. She starts a typical work cycle by taking a handful of bolts and a handful of each of the three types of washers from stock boxes at the rear of the workbench, and depositing them on the workbench in separate piles arranged from left to right about 14 to 16 inches in front of her. She then grasps one of the bolts in her left hand and while continuing to hold it there she next grasps one of the split-ring metal washers with her right hand, carries it to the vicinity of her left hand and slides it onto the bolt she is holding. She then performs this same series of steps with one of the large metal washers and finally with one of the leather, rubber, or plastic washers. Then with her left hand Rita deposits the completed assembly in a pile adjacent to the unassembled bolts. The leather washer, put on last, has a sufficiently small inner diameter to grip the threads of the bolt firmly, thus holding the other washers on the bolt and preventing accidental disassembly. Periodically, as required, Rita renews her piles of bolts and washers from the stock boxes and deposits completed assemblies in one of the several take-away boxes also located at the rear of the bench.

From his conversation with the foreman prior to the start of his study, the methods engineer learned that a material handler was responsible for bringing the boxes of supplies to Rita's workbench, for replenishing them periodically, and for removing the take-away boxes. During his study Rita advised the engineer that she placed completed assemblies in the take-away box whenever the workbench area in front of her became sufficiently filled to impede assembly operations. She estimated that this occurred perhaps twice per hour. She also said she recalled one or two occasions since starting the job on which she had run out of parts and had had to wait perhaps 15 minutes until the foreman could arrange for the handler to replenish her supply.

---

[1] It is company policy to set standards on all tasks performed by assembly personnel. These standards are then used for production planning and scheduling, cost estimating, and, if the nature and volume of the work seem to warrant, for determining piece rates.

After observing Rita performing the preassembly for several minutes, the engineer requisitioned a supply of bolts and washers and took them to his office. Working at his desk he practiced the assembly method Rita had been using, using his wristwatch to obtain a rough timing of his performance.

After timing his own performance on the fastener preassembly method used by Rita Glenn, the methods engineer decided to experiment with other possible methods of performing this task. After several minutes' reflection he walked to the methods-study laboratory area located outside his office and got a piece of fiber board large enough to simulate the area of the workbench immediately in front of the preassembly operator. In this board he drilled two multiple-countersunk holes large enough to accommodate the washers and bolt required in the fastener preassembly operation. He then took the board back to his office to resume his experimentation.

Reference Note on Work Simplification

Prior to this point we have considered primarily the "things" of the manufacturing system—products, machines, and materials. Now let us turn to the human role; specifically, to those factors that determine the productivity of tasks performed by people, in the factory or in other operating situations. As elsewhere, we shall try to examine concrete situations that illustrate general concepts and principles.

The nature of the jobs performed in making a product or providing a service will, of course, be determined partially by the technologies of the product or service and by the available process. The steelworker's job is markedly different from the weaver's. The weaving task, in turn, will be different for the man in a modern, mechanized mill in the Carolinas from that for the man at a hand-loom in India. Within a field determined by relevant technology, however, there will be several ways of doing the job; generally the manager has room for choice on nontechnological grounds.

A complete *process* may be dissected into separate, relatively independent components called *operations*. Identification of necessary operations and determination of the sequence in which they should be performed is the function of *routing*. The determination of the detailed activities within an operation, however, is another matter; this task is known as *operation analysis* or *methods design*.

Routing and methods design are similar activities, but they are concerned with different levels of abstraction. Routing deals with the total requirements of process and product; it is composed of operations. The work method pertains to a single operation; it is composed of units we shall call *elements*. An operation is typified by such tasks as: "prepare cores for mold," "inspect stampings," "mill top surface," or "assemble bolt and washers." An element of an operation is one step more specific, such as: "pick up core and

214

place, aside," "read micrometer dial," "load workpiece on milling table," or "place bolt in fixture."

To improve the utilization of resources, management continuously tries to reduce tasks to their simplest forms. A good manager asks himself *why* things are done as they are, extending his inquiry to every aspect of the job and the surroundings in which it is performed, from the flow of paper work to the daily functioning of his subordinates. For success in improving performance, the desire for improvement must pervade every level of the organization. This is accomplished more readily when the manager encourages each individual to ask why and how each phase of his task should be done. He is expected to supply the stimulus and show that job improvement or simplification of work is not only important but also is based on common-sense questioning aimed at uncovering the easiest, most economical way of performing a job.

APPROACHES TO WORK SIMPLIFICATION

Over the years a series of principles, or "rules of thumb," as well as a number of analytical tools, such as charts, have been developed to help analyze the nature and flow of the work in a given task. The principles, tools, and illustrative applications presented here are designed to give examples of questions that may be germane to an operation, and of analytical tools that may prove useful in answering the questions. This note itself is an effort to save the time and energy of the manager. On the basis of its examples, specific questions and types of charts that best fit the particular job a manager may wish to study can be formulated. Keep in mind, however, that the cost of a study should be evaluated in relation to its potential savings.

Before discussing specific tools and principles of work simplification a few terms with special connotations for methods improvement should be defined. The definitions are as follows.

PROCESS. A process is a continuing sequence of work steps which leads to a specific result, such as the fabrication of a part or the assembly of a product.

OPERATION. An operation is a specific step in a process. It is made up of several related elements of work which, when performed in their proper sequence, will result in a physical change in a raw material, or in the conditions in which it exists, thus adding value to the product.

ELEMENT. An element is a selected part of an operation which is separated for detailed analysis. It is chosen so that its beginning

and end points are clearly defined and identifiable. An example would be the element of dialing, a specific part of the operation of making a telephone call within the process of communicating an order for supplies.

An important concept to keep in mind in a job-improvement program is the dynamic relationship between the product and the process. The starting point of most work-simplification analysis is to look at the product itself and evaluate whether it might be changed in such a way as to make it easier to produce, yet still permit it to perform the same function. The best answer, where possible, is to eliminate the job completely. As an example, in attempting to improve orange crates for easier crating, a citrus grower found it was more economical and yet fully satisfactory to use cardboard cartons into which the oranges could be poured, thus eliminating the need for crating; in considering the process of billing customers, many firms have decided it is unnecessary to mail receipts to customers who paid by check or money order, since the cancelled check or the money order stub fulfills this purpose.

After studying the product itself and making whatever changes seem appropriate, the most useful next step in a work-simplification problem often is found to be an assessment of the over-all process, and then of the individual operations or elements composing this process. The breakdown should continue as long as further analysis seems economically justifiable. In the case of some processes—such as those involved in producing 2 million light sockets—it may be economically desirable to scrutinize the operation in extremely minute detail by a micromotion study[1] including motion pictures and laboratory experiments. Other processes, such as producing a few bird houses to be put in one's back yard, may warrant only a brief glance during the planning stage.

Finally, it should be noted that a large number of job improvements based on workable ideas of how to accomplish a job better have been planned on the back of an envelope with little formal analysis. The first and most important step is to question why.

GRAPHIC AIDS

Numerous special graphic techniques have been developed to aid methods analyses. These tools do not of themselves improve the way

---

[1] See the subsequent portion of this note for a more detailed description of the techniques of micromotion study.

a task is done; only the inquiring mind and creativity of the analyst can perform this step. Nevertheless, these graphic tools do assist in the improvement process by providing a convenient manner in which to record and present information about the activity under study. Through usage and the recommendations of various professional societies, standard symbols have been established for the process charts or other graphic tools of work simplification. These symbols serve as a shorthand in recording worker activity. The following table defines the five major activity classifications.

ACTIVITY CLASSIFICATION	DEFINITION	PROCESS CHART SYMBOL	
		A.S.M.E.*	ABBREVIATED
OPERATION	A step in the process which converts a material or product to add value.	◯	◯
TRANSPORTATION	An activity in which the man being studied moves an object or the object being studied is moved.	⇨	o
INSPECTION	An activity performed to assure an acceptable quality or performance. It may be quantitative or qualitative.	☐	☐
DELAYS	An interruption of a process which prevents the performance of necessary activities.	D	▽
STORAGES	A purposeful state of storing materials. It may be temporary or permanent.	▽	

*American Society of Mechanical Engineers

Examples below of the use of these symbols in several of the commonly employed graphic tools of methods studies demonstrate their flexibility and illustrate their implementation.

Process Chart

The process or flow chart shows the activities involved in an entire process in the sequence in which they are performed. It is used to chart either the activities that an individual performs when engaged in a given task, or the steps through which a material or product passes in connection with a given process. Although the analysis may be made with respect to either the man or the material, a consistent approach must be adopted and maintained throughout the preparation of a given process chart. The nature of the investigation usually indicates whether it will be most advantageous to chart the man or the material. Regardless of whether such a chart is used to analyze

the activities performed by a man, or those performed on the material or part, the activities are classified into the same standard categories. The figure below illustrates a man process chart for the activities involved in the process of cutting out the parts of a shirt.

PROCESS FLOW CHART
CHRONOLOGICAL SEQUENCE

SHEET __1__ OF __1__ SHEETS

DEPT. NO. AND LOCATION __Cutting__   P. NAME __Shirt parts__   P. NO._____

OPERATION __Cutting cloth into shirt parts__   PRESENT-PROPOSED METHOD

_____ DATE __9/12/62__ ANALYST _____

SYMBOL	DESCRIPTION OF FUNCTION	DISTANCE TRAVELLED
x	To truck with cloth for job	18′
1	Install cloth bolt in roller at end of table	
2	Pull cloth full length of table	88′
x	Return to roller end smoothing cloth	88′
3	Cut cloth	
	—Repeat operations 2 and 3 six more times—	
4	Extract bolt core and short end of cloth and dispose	
x	To truck with cloth	6′
	—Repeat process six more times—	
	Last run only put on six layers for a total of 48 layers	
5	Aside hand truck	8′
x	Inspect order for pattern types	
x	To pattern storage	32′
6	Select patterns	12′
x	To cutting table	
7	Layout patterns on cloth	88′
x	Inspect arrangement to insure minimum waste	176′
8	Cut cloth with hand cutter	88′
x	Inspect cut parts	88′
9	Tie parts in bundles	88′
x	To truck with cloth for job	18′

Different	Total #	Summary	Travel	
9	116	Operations	4508′	
6	58	Transportation	4334′	
3	3	Inspections	264′	

The following is a material process chart portraying the various activities performed on material in the process of producing a particular type of toy. As in the man process chart, a summary of activities is again included.

Producing a Yo-Yo

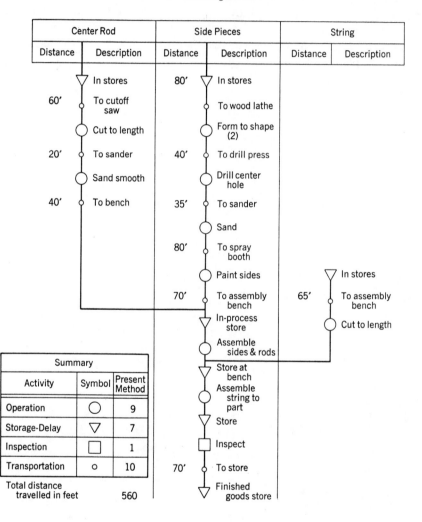

Flow Diagram

When it is desirable to picture the geographic layout in which the activity takes place, flow lines can be drawn on a plan of the area and brief descriptions of the operations can be placed in the appropriate locations to indicate what takes place where. Such a picture is called a flow diagram. Flow diagrams often are used to supplement process and activity charts to obtain a better understanding of the work flow. The figure on page 221 is a flow diagram of the assembly of a carpenter's level.

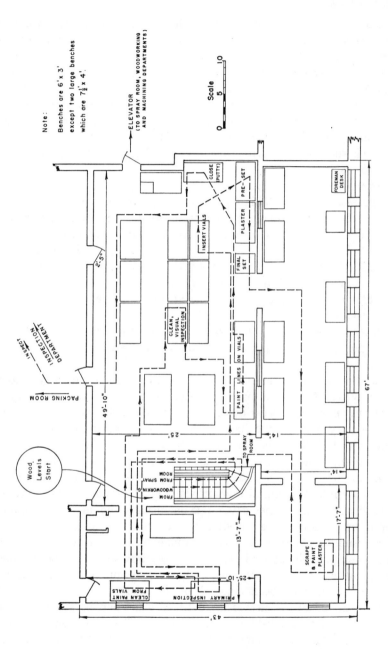

Activity Chart

The activity chart adds the dimension of *time* to a process analysis. This is accomplished by designing the chart in such a way that it provides a breakdown of process activities plotted against a time scale. The chart is particularly helpful in analyzing processes in which two or more productive inputs are employed simultaneously (for example, a job on which a group of people are working together, or a job requiring the services of one operator and one or more machines, or a job involving a group of workers and one machine). In such situations activities usually are classified into the following categories.

PRODUCTIVE. Working.

NECESSARY DELAY. This term is used to designate periods in which one of the inputs cannot be productive because of interference resulting from the activities of another input. For example, there will be periods in which a machine tool is idle because it is being unloaded or loaded by the operator. Since this type of idleness cannot be reduced without making major changes such as redesigning the equipment, it is normally assumed to be an unavoidable, or fixed, part of the process.

UNNECESSARY DELAY. This term identifies those periods of idleness resulting from the work's being unevenly distributed between the inputs.

In constructing an activity chart it is important to identify a complete cycle. A cycle normally consists of the activities necessary to perform an entire process once. The controlling factor in any process is the productive input having the longest working-plus-idle time. The total time for this input to go through its process activity once constitutes a minimum cycle time for the entire process. One can begin an activity chart at any point in the process; it usually is helpful, if possible, to begin at a point where all the inputs change activity classifications simultaneously. Also one usually should avoid graphing the initial, nonrecurring activities which occur in beginning a process. For example, setting up a drill-press machine to perform a given job, or cleaning out the ovens in a bakery, normally would not be included as operations in an activity chart. First cycles often are unrepresentative of the going process since all of the inputs are idle at the start.

An example of the use of an activity chart can be shown for the process of tumble-polishing brass jewelry. The operations for tumbling were "tumble," "blow off," and "dip clean," in that order. The manufacturer was interested in determining the feasibility of having

one man operate two tumblers and two dip tanks, as opposed to the practice of having one man operate a single tumbler and a single dip tank. The times required to perform the required elements were found to be:

Tumble	Time/Cycle (min)
1. Load tumbler with rouge	1.0
2. Load tumbler with jewelry, start machine	0.5
3. Running time (automatically stops)	6.0
4. Unload tumbler (powder and jewelry)	0.5

Blow Off	
1. Screen jewelry free from powder	0.5
2. Blow off rouge with air hose	1.0

Dip Clean	
1. Place jewelry in dip tank	0.5
2. Soaking time (minimum to clean jewelry)	3.0
3. Remove jewelry from dip tank and dump	1.0
	14.0 minutes

A trial plan of an arrangement whereby one man could operate both tumblers is shown by the activity chart on page 224.

ACTIVITY CHART

PROCESS: Tumble polishing of jewelry

Time in Minutes	Man		Tumbler 1		Tumbler 2		Dip Tank 1		Dip Tank 2	
	Unload tumbler 1	$\frac{1}{2}$								
1	Load tumbler 1 with rouge	1	Necessarily idle	2						
					Run	3	Run	3		
	Load tumbler 1 with jewelry	$\frac{1}{2}$								
2	Screen jewelry	$\frac{1}{2}$								
	Blow off rouge	1								
3							Unnecessarily idle	$\frac{1}{2}$		
4	Unload dip tank	1			Unnecessarily idle	2	Necessarily idle	$1\frac{1}{2}$		
5	Load dip tank	$\frac{1}{2}$	Run	6					Unnecessarily idle	10
	Unload tumbler 2	$\frac{1}{2}$								
6	Load tumbler 2 with rouge	1			Necessarily idle	2	Run	3		
7	Load tumbler 2 with jewelry	$\frac{1}{2}$								
	Screen jewelry	$\frac{1}{2}$								
8	Blow off rouge	1			Run	3	Unnecessarily idle	$\frac{1}{2}$		
9	Unload dip tank	1	Unnecessarily idle	2			Necessarily idle	$1\frac{1}{2}$		
10	Load dip tank	$\frac{1}{2}$								

Operation Chart

This type of chart portrays the operator's activities while performing one operation in a process. It charts the motions of the left hand and right hand of an operator and, when appropriate, leg and hand operations usually are broken down into more minute categories than those employed in a process chart, and are divided commonly into two classifications: (a) movements such as reaching for an object, or carrying an object in a hand, which are symbolized by a small circle; and (b) actions, symbolized by a large circle.

Activity Classification	Operation Chart Symbol	Examples of Activity
o	Movements	Reach for object with hand or carry object in hand
◯	Actions	Grasp, position, hold, use, or release an object; idle

The following shows an operation chart for cleaning glasses with a handkerchief.

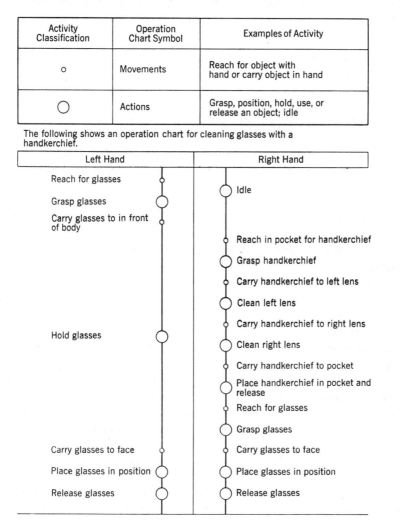

Left Hand	Right Hand
Reach for glasses	Idle
Grasp glasses	
Carry glasses to in front of body	
	Reach in pocket for handkerchief
	Grasp handkerchief
	Carry handkerchief to left lens
	Clean left lens
	Carry handkerchief to right lens
Hold glasses	Clean right lens
	Carry handkerchief to pocket
	Place handkerchief in pocket and release
	Reach for glasses
	Grasp glasses
Carry glasses to face	Carry glasses to face
Place glasses in position	Place glasses in position
Release glasses	Release glasses

MOTION PRINCIPLES

The motion-study principles stated in contemporary busi~ess literature have evolved from experience and observation in both ₁aboratory research and industrial investigations searching for the easiest way to perform manual tasks. The present principles by and large are refined common sense; it took some ingenuity to define them, however, and they serve a useful purpose as a general checklist for a work-simplification analysis. The principles in Table A can be found in most motion and time study texts. They have been developed from Gilbreth's original work in motion analysis in the 1920's.

MICROMOTION ANALYSIS

Micromotion study is a method for making a detailed motion analysis of a job. Micromotion analysis uses a motion picture of at least one cycle of a manual work operation to make a detailed analysis of the job either to improve the operation or to develop training devices to teach improved methods. Micromotion studies have been confined primarily to manual operations for large volume production because of the time and expense required to perform a complete analysis. In addition to use as an analytic technique, micromotion study also has been employed successfully to introduce method-study principles and train method engineers in their use. Another use of micromotion study is the detailed presentation of complex jobs to train individuals to perform them in a required manner. As an example, micromotion studies were made in connection with Project Mercury for use in training astronauts in the operation of the space capsule.

Micromotion was developed by Frank Gilbreth in 1920 while he was attempting to discover the best method of performing jobs and applying these methods to handicapped workers. After analyzing thousands of motion pictures of industrial operations he identified 17 basic hand-motion patterns which he believed embraced all forms of manual labor. These he termed "therbligs" (Gilbreth spelled backwards). These therbligs provided a classification system for analyzing any job in terms of the basic motion patterns required to perform it. Smooth work patterns for the job could then be developed by rearranging the essential therbligs and eliminating unnecessary or unnatural combinations of therbligs. Since some of these therbligs are minute patterns which are hard to detect, a common practice is

TABLE A   PRINCIPLES OF MOTION ECONOMY

These twenty-two rules or principles of motion economy may be profitably applied to shop and office work alike. Although not all are applicable to every operation, they do form a basis or code for improving the efficiency and reducing fatigue in manual work.

Use of the Human Body

1. The two hands should begin as well as complete their motions at the same time.
2. The two hands should not be idle at the same time except during rest periods.
3. Motions of the arms should be made in opposite and symmetrical directions, and should be made simultaneously.
4. Hand motions should be confined to the lowest classifications with which it is possible to perform the work satisfactorily.
5. Momentum should be employed to assist the worker wherever possible, and it should be reduced to a minimum if it must be overcome by muscular effort.
6. Smooth continuous motions of the hands are preferable to zigzag motions or straight-line motions involving sudden and sharp changes in direction.
7. Ballistic movements are faster, easier, and more accurate than restricted (fixation) or "controlled" movements.
8. Rhythm is essential to the smooth and automatic performance of an operation, and the work should be arranged to permit easy and natural rhythm wherever possible.

Arrangement of the Work Place

9. There should be a definite and fixed place for all tools and materials.
10. Tools, materials, and controls should be located close in and directly in front of the operator.
11. Gravity feed bins and containers should be used to deliver material close to the point of use.
12. Drop deliveries should be used wherever possible.
13. Materials and tools should be located to permit the best sequence of motions.
14. Provisions should be made for adequate conditions for seeing. Good illumination is the first requirement for satisfactory visual perception.
15. The height of the work place and the chair should preferably be arranged so that alternate sitting and standing at work are easily possible.
16. A chair of the type and height to permit good posture should be provided for every worker.

Design of Tools and Equipment

17. The hands should be relieved of all work that can be done more advantageously by a jig, a fixture, or a foot-operated device.
18. Two or more tools should be combined wherever possible.
19. Tools and materials should be prepositioned wherever possible.
20. Where each finger performs some specific movement, such as in typewriting, the load should be distributed in accordance with the inherent capacities of the fingers.
21. Handles such as those used on cranks and large screwdrivers should be designed to permit as much of the surface of the hand to come in contact with the handle as possible. This is particularly true when considerable force is exerted in using the handle. For light assembly work the screwdriver handle should be so shaped that it is smaller at the bottom than at the top.
22. Levers, crossbars, and handwheels should be located in such positions that the operator can manipulate them with the least change in body position and with the greatest mechanical advantage.

---

* Reprinted with permission from R. M. Barnes, *Motion and Time Study*, 1958, John Wiley and Sons, Inc.

to take motion pictures of the operation at high speeds and then analyze the pictures at slow speeds to observe the complete work pattern of the job under study. Quite often the motion analysis is recorded on a simultaneous-motion cycle chart referred to as a SIMO chart.

TABLE B

The following 17 fundamental hand motions or therbligs are used in micromotion and other forms of motion analysis in which a highly detailed breakdown of operations is desired.

1. *Search* (Sh). That part of the cycle during which the eyes or hands are groping for the object.
2. *Select* (St). The choice of one object from among several.
3. *Grasp* (G). Taking hold of an object, closing the fingers around it preparatory to picking it up, holding it, or manipulating it.
4. *Transport Empty* (TE). Moving the empty hand in reaching for an object.
5. *Transport Loaded* (TL). Moving an object from one place to another. The object may be carried in the hands or fingers, or it may be moved from one place to another by sliding, dragging, or pushing it along. Transport loaded also refers to moving the empty hand against resistance. Transport loaded begins when the hand begins to move an object or encounter resistance, and ends when the hand stops moving.
6. *Hold* (H). The retention of an object after it has been grasped, no movement of the object taking place. An example would be holding a pen top in one hand while assembling the pen into it with the other.
7. *Release Load* (RL). Letting go of the object. Release load begins when the object starts to leave the hand, and ends when the object has been completely separated from the hand or fingers. An example would be letting change drop into a pocket.
8. *Position* (P). Turning or locating an object in such a way that it will be properly oriented to fit into the location for which it is intended. Position begins when the hand begins to turn or locate the object, and ends when the object has been placed in the desired position or location. An example would be lining up a quarter preparatory to inserting it in a coin slot.
9. *Preposition* (PP). Locating an object in a predetermined place, or locating it in the correct position for some subsequent motion.
10. *Inspect* (I). Examining an object to determine whether it complies with standard size, shape, color, or other qualities that have been specified. Inspect is predominately a mental reaction and may occur simultaneously with other therbligs. Inspect begins when the eyes or other parts of the body begin to examine the object, and ends when the examination has been completed.

11. *Assemble* (A). Placing one object into or on another object with which it becomes an integral part.
12. *Disassemble* (DA). Separating one object from another object of which it is an integral part.
13. *Use* (U). Manipulating a tool, device, or piece of apparatus for the purpose for which it was intended. Use represents the motion for which the preceding motions have been more or less preparatory and for which the ones that follow are supplementary. It begins when the hand starts to manipulate the tool or device, and ends when the hand ceases the application.
14. *Unavoidable Delay* (UD). A delay beyond the control of the operator. Unavoidable delay may result from either of the following causes: (a) a failure or interruption in the process; (b) a delay caused by an arrangement of the operation that prevents one part of the body from working while other body members are busy.
15. *Avoidable Delay* (AD). Any delay of the operator for which he is responsible and over which he has control. This refers to delays which the operator may avoid if he wishes. Avoidable delay begins when the prescribed sequence of motions is interrupted, and ends when the standard work method is resumed.
16. *Plan* (PN). A mental reaction that precedes the physical movement, that is, the process of deciding how to proceed with the job. Plan begins at the point where the operator begins mentally to work out the next step of the operation, and ends when the procedure to be followed has been determined. An example would occur when an operator who is machining a complex part refers to the blueprint and determines which phase of the machining to do next.
17. *Rest for Overcoming Fatigue* (R). A fatigue or delay factor or allowance provided to permit the worker to recover from the fatigue incurred by his work.

A recent analysis of the assembly of chain-pull sockets by a manufacturer producing over one million sockets a year illustrates a typical micromotion study. The first step was to select an appropriate subject for filming and recording of the present method. The employee chosen was the most productive of the personnel engaged in this work, as it was assumed her performance would provide the best example of how the job was being done. A motion picture of the operator was taken at a rate of 1,000 frames per second as she worked for about 80 cycles of the assembly. The film was then analyzed frame by frame to define the therbligs used in performing the task. The therblig analysis was recorded on a SIMO chart, which was studied to eliminate waste motions, holds, or unnecessary operations by the use of better workplace layout, fixtures, automatic tools, smooth and

continuous movement of hands, use of feet, etc. This analysis detected previously unnoticed motion patterns which enabled the highly productive operator to perform the assembly work more efficiently than the other employees. These patterns were then incorporated in the new standard method for the job. The other operators were then taught the new method, with a film of the improved method serving as one of the training tools.

SIMO CHART

Sheet No. _____ Of _____   Film No. P-37

OPERATION Hand Assembly of Fuse	Date 7/27/61
	Operation No. —
Part Name Household Fuse	Part No. 72
Operator's Name and No. Weber - 7452	Chart by Ross

Left Hand Description	Sym-bol	Time	Units .001 min.	Time	Sym-bol	Right Hand Description
To glass cap	TE	14		16	TE	To plug assembly
	G	8		6	G	
To assembly area	TL	16		18	TL	To assembly area
Insure slot is under thumb	PP	2	.050	4	P	Lead strip of plug in cap
				10	A	Plug in cap
				1	RL	
				12	TE	To screw ring
				3	G	
				12	TL	To assembly area
				8	P	Ring on cap
			.100			
Hold glass cap	H	159		86	A	Screw ring on cap
			.150			
				1	RL	
				22	I	To check lead strip is properly positioned
Assembly on bench, strip up	P	8	.200	10	TE	To soldering iron
	RL	2		8	G	
To solder	TE	10		14	TL	
	G	3		7	PP	Iron to lead strip
To assembly	TL	12		13	UD	Waiting for solder
Solder upon strip	P	17	.250			
	H	26		26	U	Solder strip to ring
Aside solder	TL	9		15	TL	To soldering iron holder
	RL	1		10	PP	Iron over holder
To fuse	TE	9		2	RL	
To completed storage	TL	4	.300			
	RL	1	.304			
60.8 %	H	185		96	A	31.6 %
13.5 %	TL	41		59	TL	19.4 %
10.8 %	TE	33		38	TE	12.5 %
8.2 %	P	25		26	U	8.5 %
4.7 %	G	14		22	I	7.2 %
1.3 %	RL	4		17	G	5.6 %
7 %	PP	2		17	PP	5.6 %
				13	UD	4.3 %
				12	P	3.9 %
				4	RL	1.3 %

WORK SAMPLING

Work sampling is a technique commonly used to gather information for purposes of simplifying a job. The other analytic techniques we have discussed are based on data gathered from detailed, continuous observation of the activities being analyzed. Work sampling, in contrast, is based on observation of the functioning of employees or equipment at brief intervals over an extended period of time to obtain an over-all appraisal of a process or task. This method provides an economic means for obtaining information on how resources are being utilized in nonrepetitive, intermittent, or complex man-machine operations. Work sampling provides data which indicate the mean percentages of time devoted to defined activity classifications. Results of this sort can be very useful for planning work-simplification studies, obtaining an estimate of equipment utilization, defining actual work flow, or obtaining a measure of work-load balance.

Work sampling is similar in spirit to all techniques of work simplification in that it relies upon a thorough preparation before the study is made; the planning phase identifies the processes to be observed, defines when the observations will be made, and classifies the expected activities to be observed. The major steps in the process of work sampling are as follows.

1. Select the process to be analyzed.
2. Define the classes of activities.
3. Determine the number of observations.
4. Plan when the observations will be made.
5. Make the observations.
6. Analyze the data.
7. Draw conclusions.

The problems appropriate for study by work sampling will be discussed below. The number and identification of activity classifications is a prescription of how deep or detailed the study is intended to be. If the study is intended for rough estimates to serve as a basis for further studies, two activity classifications—such as working or idle—may be adequate. A more detailed study of a particular department may include over a dozen classifications of worker activity, such as set-up, machining, talking to foremen, reading blueprint, obtaining tools, waiting for material, and so forth. As in all sampling studies, the accuracy of the result is determined by the number of

observations. Statistical procedures have been developed to determine how many observations should be taken as a function of the variability of the process and the percentage of each classification in the over-all process.[2] The timing of the observations must be defined in advance to obtain a random sample, so that the observer's habits will not bias the data.

An engineer engaged in work sampling observes the activity of individuals or equipment at random intervals and records the observed activity each time as an occurrence of one of several predefined classes. To do this he typically follows a preset path at set intervals recording the activities of individuals or equipment under study the instant he observes them. An alternative method is to use a time-lapse motion camera which can be set to take a picture of an operation at random intervals. This provides a film sample of a long period of an operation, using a small amount of film, and eliminates the need for the on-site observer.

The analysis of the data is a straightforward statistical calculation and can be performed with a desk calculator. The results are normally presented as percentage classifications of the observed activities to provide a basis for management action. Thus, an over-all study of a shop might indicate 68 per cent working and 32 per cent idle in the assembly department, 92 per cent working, 8 per cent idle in the machine shop, etc.

One of the most common uses of work sampling is to measure the amount of delay or work interference which occurs in the normal processing of jobs in the shop. Delays such as waiting for tools or supplies, breakdown of equipment, lack of adequate jigs, or faulty materials happen at random intervals and are difficult to measure under continuous observation. A work-sampling study provides data on the total delays present as well as information by class of delay. These can then serve as the basis for determining the allowance in a standard time. The information by classes can identify possible bottlenecks, such as too few tool-crib attendants, and can provide an indication for further analysis if, for example, waiting for material proved a substantial item.

Another application of work sampling occurs in long, irregular processes which would be difficult to measure under continuous observation because of the variability or length of each job. Non-repetitive tasks, such as a maintenance or setup job, would be

---

[2] R. M. Barnes, *Work Sampling,* John Wiley and Sons, New York, 1957, pp. 21–48.

expensive to investigate with continuous observation but can be analyzed adequately at a reduced cost and little loss of information through work sampling. An example is the study of work members of a construction gang to evaluate whether they were furnished adequate amounts of equipment and whether the work load was distributed equally to crew members. The study was conducted by observing the activity of each man on the crew at random intervals of two to eighteen minutes for four work days. To aid in determining what tools should or should not be included as a standard mix for a maintenance crew, a time-lapse camera was mounted on the truck to record over a two-week period what tools were used. This afforded a basis for eliminating some of the tools never utilized and providing a greater variety for the more often used implements.

Quite often a sampling study is the first step in an over-all methods-improvement program. Its purpose then is to obtain information for making the decision as to what should come under more detailed study. Such data can provide an estimate of the alternate pay-offs for carrying out detailed work-simplification studies. An example of work sampling in connection with such a study was a continuous study of the activities of nurses in a hospital. The sampling study was conducted for two weeks by three observers to obtain some insight as to where work-improvement efforts could best assist the nursing activity and to provide a basis for job specialization.

Seneca Electric Company

On November 2, 1962, John McGregor, foreman of Seneca Electric Company's mount-assembly department, was discussing with Mary Phillips, one of his assistant foremen, the prolonged failure of one of her operators to achieve normal performance. The operator, Stella Wytoski, had been employed by Seneca for three years. All along she had been a satisfactory employee until transferred to her present job as member of a two-operator team assembling the mount parts for Type 8K2 vacuum tubes.

"Look, Mary," said McGregor, "we've got to get more production without any further delay. Stella should be up to at least 100 per cent of standard by now. We've had trouble since she and Janet started on that tube a month ago. Being experienced operators, I thought they'd need only a week or ten days to get going. The last time we ran that tube with another team about two years ago, with Alice Murphy in position two and Helen Roberts in position one, wasn't production 140 per cent of standard after the team got broken in?"

"Yes, that's what I found out when I talked to Alice Murphy," Mary Phillips replied. "Helen, you know, left the company about six months ago, but Alice has been working on the 7U6 team for the last few months. I asked her if she remembered having any trouble on the tube when they ran it. She said she recalls some difficulties getting started, but it has been so long she doesn't remember the details. She thinks the Methods Department finally came up with a breakdown of the job which worked. Alice said they made 140 per cent to 145 per cent every week once they settled down.

"Half my time this week," Mary added, "has been spent with Stella and Janet and I've done everything I can think of to increase their production. That's the only team producing 8K2's, and we're

234

not going to be able to make our schedule requirements at this rate. I think Stella's just slow. Before, when she was on the AW4 conveyor line, I heard she had trouble, even though the team's production was O.K. I know she was the last girl on a ten-operator line there, and that's a tough position, but we don't know what help the rest of the team may have been giving her."

"Have you checked how they're doing today?" McGregor asked.

"Janet's production is just about 100 per cent of standard today, but Stella is dragging her heels with only 80 per cent of standard and holding down the team's output to the same level."

In accordance with Seneca's policy, when the first member of a two-operator team produced at a rate significantly faster than her teammate, she was instructed not to pile up more than 50 units ahead of the number two operator; instead of producing more, the number one operator was to cease working and take a break to allow the second girl to catch up. Operators were paid on the basis of mounts completely assembled by the team, without regard for any individual's performance.

"John Knight from methods checked the layout for the job and ran a time study last week," Mary Phillips said. "He tells me she damages too many parts and therefore uses a lot of extra time for repairs, slowing down her output. He also said she does some double-handling of parts. We've told her about this, but she hasn't improved any. I don't think she'll make it. I'm beginning to think we should give her a written warning and tell her she's got to improve or we'll have to let her go."

After a pause, McGregor said, "I wonder if I might break the job down differently and rebalance it, just for this team. Or perhaps I should try to work out a transfer for Stella back to a conveyor. Well, I'll get whatever dope methods has on how we did this job last time, and also take a look at Knight's study. Then let's plan to get together again tomorrow morning."

The Company

The Seneca Electric Company manufactures vacuum tubes for radios, TV receivers, and the like. The company employs about 500 production workers, almost all female, with about 40 per cent of this number working in the mount department under John McGregor. The mount department is the first assembly operation following parts fabrication. After assembly the mounts are sent to another department where they are sealed in a glass bulb. The atmosphere inside the glass bulb is then exhausted and the base affixed. After an aging period the tubes

are tested, branded, and packed. Fewer than half the women in the mount department work in teams of two to four; Mary Phillips, with three supervisors, directs about 50 of these operators working in small teams. The remaining mount operators work at conveyor mounting in teams of ten to fifteen at special tables, located on a different floor of the building. The conveyors can be set at a range of speeds, depending on what the team is capable of producing without deterioration of quality.

Seneca manufactures several hundred types of tubes, but at any one time has only about 20 to 30 types going through the factory. Demand is determined mainly by the types of tube required by the ten or twelve television and radio set manufacturers who are Seneca's customers. Seneca also maintains a large finished-tube inventory to keep production runs as long as possible. Generally, the largest requirements are scheduled for conveyor mounting and the smaller requirements for two- to four-operator team mounting. Long runs are desirable because, even with experienced operators, changing to a new tube type requires four to ten days of subnormal production, depending on the differences among the tube types, while operators gain proficiency.

Mounting requires dextrous manipulation of many small parts, including threading some through small holes and cylinders. Since the location and size of holes and the size and number of the parts vary from tube type to tube type, production losses during periods of changing from one type of tube to another are significant even with experienced operators. New girls require two to three months to reach maximum proficiency. Seneca's overhead is about 150 per cent of direct labor. Profit margins on most tube types are extremely small, and the industry is highly competitive.

Seneca selects its mount operators from general applicants by means of special tests for dexterity and for 20/20, normal vision, since the work places a premium on good eyesight combined with manual dexterity. Both Stella and Janet had been hired in 1959.

Once a team has been trained in making a particular type of tube, it is to Seneca's advantage to keep the team working on that type. Moreover, the members of a team become used to working with one another, and frequently develop a team spirit. The nature of team work requires the teams to take lunch periods and rest periods (ten minutes in the morning and ten minutes in the afternoon) at the same time. Nevertheless, in order to absorb new workers, and to balance production with an ever-changing demand, McGregor has found it necessary to transfer girls continually from one team to another, and

from conveyor teams to the smaller two- to four-operator teams, or vice versa. Half a dozen utility operators are available for temporary assignments, mainly to vacancies caused by absenteeism. Seneca's Methods Department assists McGregor in determining the size of team to employ, the breakdown of work among team members, and the methods to be followed, but according to company policy it is only an advisor; Mr. McGregor can accept, reject, or modify its recommendations, as he sees fit.

In 1962, the hourly base pay rate for operators was $1.40, but operators were paid on an incentive plan, in direct proportion to their production. Utility operators earned a higher wage than the others. The mount department as a whole produced at 120 per cent of standard, resulting in an average hourly wage of about $1.70. A number of teams, however, produced as much as 140 per cent of standard output after several months of experience on a particular tube type. Operators were guaranteed their base rate of $1.40 per hour, even if their production was less than standard.

Seneca Electric Company had been organized by a local of a national electrical workers' union in 1952. Its contract with the union provides that in the event of insubordination, poor quality, low production, or abnormal absenteeism, the company has to serve a written warning to the worker, giving the worker two weeks in which to improve. At the end of that period, if no improvement takes place, the company can discharge the worker.

John McGregor had four assistant foremen, two of whom were men and two women. Both women had been highly successful operators for several years, and each had been an assistant foreman for more than eight years. Each assistant foreman was assisted by three or four supervisors, all women, who, among other general administrative duties, checked and recorded the quantity of production for each team to which she was assigned, distributed supplies of parts, and instructed operators. Seneca had no separate training organization. Each assistant foreman was held fully responsible by McGregor for meeting schedules, for maintaining quality, and for hiring, training, and disciplining all teams under his or her jurisdiction. Only the foreman could discharge a worker, and only then with the concurrence of the personnel manager.

The Mounting Procedure

Exhibit 1 shows a mount operator doing similar but not identical work to that assigned Stella Wytoski. Mount workers handle tube parts with tweezers and with their fingers, and attach parts together

EXHIBIT 1   SENECA ELECTRIC COMPANY

OPERATOR WELDING A GETTER TO A MOUNT

using simple jigs and spot welders. Welding machines are operated by means of foot pedals to keep the operators' hands free. Stella's position required her to use two welding machines, one needed for getters and the other for filaments. Exhibit 2 shows the nature of the operations involved, but the tube shown differs in design from the 8K2. The two girls on the team sat side by side at a bench. Stella's teammate, Janet, after completing her work on a mount, put it on the bench where Stella could pick it up with her left hand.

Exhibit 4 is a summary of the data appearing on John Knight's time study of Stella Wytoski. The times shown in this exhibit and those shown in Exhibit 3, the only record the Methods Department had on the earlier run, are element times. For several years the Methods Department had compiled standard data for most job elements. Standard data were used to establish production standards; time studies were used mainly to check jobs on which difficulties were encountered. Element times adjusted to 100 per cent of

normal (Exhibit 3) were utilized in balancing the work assignments of team members. In fixing standard-output figures, however, Seneca's practice was to add 12 per cent to the total element time as an allowance for rest, including scheduled rest periods and delays. In the case of two-man teams the allowance was increased to 22 per cent to recognize the difficulty of achieving closely coordinated operations.

EXHIBIT 2   SENECA ELECTRIC COMPANY

SAMPLE MOUNTING OPERATIONS

Use Workplace 509A-W-2   Job Inst. 509A-2

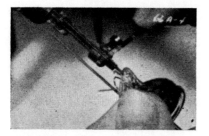

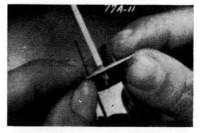

1. Weld Stops to Stem Support.
L.H. p.u. stem & position through stem support on electrode. R.H. p.u. strip of stops, assemble stop to stem. Rotate stem to weld 2nd clip stop & aside strip.

2. Assemble M.C.T. Assembly.
L.H. position stem in jig, cathode lead front. R.H. p.u. M.C.T. assembly, assemble over two stem supports, cathode tab toward operator. L.H. assist.

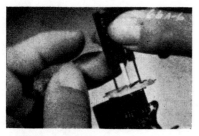

3. Assemble Plate.
R.H. p.u. plate, assemble over 2 stem supports & cathode. L.H. p.u. top mica.

4. Assemble Top Mica.
L.H. assemble top mica over 2 stem supports & cathode. R.H., when necessary, assist L.H. R.H. remove mount from jig & aside.

L.H.—Left Hand
R.H.—Right Hand
p.u.—pick up

EXHIBIT 3   SENECA ELECTRIC COMPANY

FILED DATA ON 8K2 TUBES, MOUNTING

Dated December 27, 1960

(Times in decimal parts of a minute)

Rate #153-7C
Std. 115/Hr
Rate $.871/C
2 Operators

8K2—MOUNTING

1st Position	Times at 100% of Normal*
1. P. U. & assemble two plates to jig	0.070
2. P. U. mica & assemble over four plate tabs, with tweezers bend four tabs (two at a time) and remove from jig	0.079
3. P. U. stem and assemble mica plate assembly over two stem supports	0.073
4. Position and weld glides of 1st plate to stem support (four welds) weld	0.093
5. P. U. getter, position and weld to two dummy leads and adjust on every other mount (50% × 0.116)	0.058
6. Team mark and aside	0.037
Stock	0.007
	0.417

2nd Position	
1. P. U. mount	0.015
2. Every 2nd getter, position and weld to two dummy leads and adjust (50% × 0.116)	0.058
3. P. U. and insert 1st filament through mica	0.065
4. P. U. and insert 2nd filament through mica	0.065
5. Position and weld two legs of 2nd filament to two stem leads	0.085
6. Position and weld two legs of 1st filament	0.085
7. Aside	0.010
8. Count and tray handling	0.016
Stock	0.015
Filament Reoperation	0.014
	0.428

* No allowances have been included in these element times.

EXHIBIT 4 SENECA ELECTRIC COMPANY

SUMMARY OF JOHN KNIGHT'S TIME STUDY OF STELLA WYTOSKI
ON OCTOBER 30, 1962

2d Position (44 Consecutive Cycles)

Times in decimal parts of a minute)

Stella's Workplace Layout:

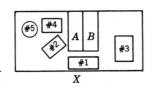

#1 Filaments on blotter—50/blotter
#2 Getters in tray—200/tray
#3 Wooden tray for completed mounts
#4 Supply of filaments—500/box
#5 Supply of getters—1,000/can
A & B Welding machine heads
X Operator #2 (seated)

1st Position   X

	Average of Observed Times
1. P. U. mount (100% of the time)	0.014
2. On half the mounts, P. U. getter, position and weld (to two dummy leads and adjust (50% × 0.152)*	0.076
3. P. U. and insert 1st filament through mica	0.070
4. P. U. and insert 2nd filament through mica	0.070
5. Position and weld two legs of 2nd filament to two stem leads	0.090
6. Position and weld two legs of 1st filament	0.090
7. Aside	0.010
8. Count and tray handling (proportion)	0.015
9. Stock replenishment (standard)	0.015
10. Filament reoperation (repairs)	

Remove filament	0.180
Insert new filament	0.070
Weld filament	0.090
	0.340

9 repairs in 44 cycles;
therefore one cycle allocated 9/44 × 0.340   0.070

Total   0.520

Rate of Output: $\left(\dfrac{60}{122\% \times 0.520}\right)$ 95 per hour

* Although the standard procedure called for each operator to attach the "getter" to every other unit, Mr. Knight's time study record showed that Stella Wytoski attached getters in only 20 of the 44 cycles he observed, or 45% of the time. Mr. McGregor believed that the first operator had attached the getter to the other 55% of the units. In making his computation, however, Mr. Knight provided time for this operation to take place every other cycle (50% × 0.152).

Reed Corporation

In June 1952, the head of the Time-Study Department of the Reed Corporation of Wareham, Massachusetts, was seeking to solve a problem which had arisen over the piece rate on a job in which one operator used four milling machines to machine an ordnance part.

The Reed Corporation normally manufactures intricate machines for use by garment makers in sewing buttonholes. The Wareham plant was completed after the end of World War II, and was laid out for maximum production efficiency. The company's equipment and productive capabilities are readily adaptable to a wide variety of precision machining operations.

In 1952, a portion of plant capacity had been allocated to defense production. Two hundred workers were employed; 150 of them, engaged in production and maintenance, were represented by the United Auto Workers, CIO. Most of the company's machine-tool operators at that time were paid on incentive rates. Conventional time study was employed to determine a standard time for each operation. An operator who failed to meet standard performance was paid at the base rate for his job. When an operator exceeded standard pace, his earnings increased in direct proportion to his base rate. For scheduling production and for balancing machine time and operator time, the company used the concept of a normal performance, which was one-third higher than the standard work pace determined by the time study. Actual experience with the incentive plan over a period of years showed that Reed operators, on the average, performed at a work pace approximately 160 per cent of standard or 120 per cent of normal. As a result, operators were able typically to earn considerable premium pay above their base rates.

Reed executives were desirous of preventing *machine interference*, that is, forced idleness while an operator waited for a machine to com-

242

plete its cutting operations, from limiting the productive effectiveness of any operator who was capable of exceeding either the standard or the normal work pace. If there were machine interference on a job, any time saved by a proficient operator on his own operations would merely result in increased idle time per cycle for the operator, rather than in increased production. To avoid this, company executives had adopted a policy of attempting to assign enough machines to each operator to prevent machine interference from curbing productivity, even if the operator were to exceed normal work pace by a considerable margin. In this way, workers were assured that, within broad limits, their ability to earn premium pay would be determined by their own capacity and willingness to maintain a premium work pace, and would not be impeded by machine interference.

When the company was operating at normal volume, sufficient numbers of various machine tools were available to permit a liberal ratio of machines to men. When the volume of production rose, however, it was necessary to hire additional operators and to effect a tighter scheduling of machine capacity. Demands on set-up men then became heavy. These were the conditions in the spring of 1952 when the company obtained subcontracts for defense work in addition to its normal production.

An Added Load

One of these subcontracts called for the manufacture of an ordnance part. Specifications required various machining operations, including four milling cuts. Because of design characteristics, all four cuts had to be made in fixed sequence, cut no. 1 before cut no. 2, etc. At the time the job was undertaken, there was considerable demand for milling-machine capacity in the shop, and the Planning Department believed that it would not be possible to assign more than four milling machines to this sequence of operations without seriously disrupting the scheduling of other work in the Milling Department. The demand for milling-machine capacity was expected to remain extremely high for some time to come, and this fact would prevent subsequent assignment of additional milling machines to the ordnance work. The four available machines were located in close proximity to each other, however, and since they were equipped for automatic feed, a single operator could run all of them simultaneously.

The method adopted for milling the four cuts on the ordnance part required that each of the four machines be set up to make one cut. Set-up time averaged approximately one hour for each milling machine, for which set-up men received a rate of $3.17 per hour.

The complete milling operation consisted of the operator's machining in sequence the required cut with each of the four milling machines. Time study data showed that the first of the four cuts was "controlling," in that it required the longest time to complete. Since each part required the first cut as the initial step in the milling process, the flow of parts at a normal work pace was limited by the 3.320-minute normal time for the first cut (Exhibit 1). For the overall operation of four cuts, the balance between machine-time and operator-time at normal pace was such that the operator would be productively engaged 96.2 per cent of the controlling cycle time of 3.320 minutes and idle only 3.8 per cent.

Because of contractual commitments, it was extremely urgent that scheduled delivery dates on the ordnance part be met. Since various other machining operations were also required on the part, these four milling operations had to be completed within rigid time deadlines. The Reed Planning Department determined, however, that if the flow of the milling cuts were maintained at the rate of one piece every 3.320 minutes, the milling operations could be completed in sufficient time, and with a narrow margin of safety. Under no circumstances, however, could the flow of milling cuts be allowed to decline below this rate.

To assure high-quality work on the milling cuts and to assure the maintenance of the required rate of flow, the foreman of the milling department assigned a particularly skilled operator, Arthur Moreno, to the job. This assignment required transferring Moreno from another job on which he had been averaging a work pace 25 per cent above normal, and, as a result, had been earning substantial premium pay. Moreno's typical weekly take-home pay on his previous job had been $74.40, of which approximately $30 was premium pay attributable to working in excess of standard pace. The foreman believed, however, that production on Moreno's former job was coming to an end and that it would make sense to transfer Moreno to the new job, which was expected to continue for at least several months.

Machine Interference

After the transfer had been made, however, a problem developed. Moreno was capable of maintaining an average work pace 25 per cent above normal and was expected to do so. Yet he found that when working at this pace on the new ordnance job, he was constantly impeded by machine interference.

In response to Moreno's protests, the head of the Time-Study Department called for the methods and the time-study data on the milling cuts. He found (Exhibit 2) that at a work pace 25 per cent

EXHIBIT 1 REED CORPORATION

STANDARD TIME, MILLING OPERATIONS, ORDNANCE PART AT NORMAL WORK PACE

(All times in minutes)

	Total Cycle Time	Machine Time	Total Operator Time*	External Time*	Internal Time*	Ratio of Total Operator Time to Controlling Cycle Time
Milling Cut No. 1	3.320†	2.600	0.825	0.720	0.105	24.8%
Milling Cut No. 2	2.760	2.220	0.720	0.540	0.180	21.7%
Milling Cut No. 3	3.058	2.420	0.900	0.638	0.262	27.1%
Milling Cut No. 4	1.558	1.118	0.750	0.440	0.310	22.6%
				Portion of *Controlling Cycle Time* operator is productively engaged		96.2%

*Total Operator Time for each milling cut was divided between "Internal Time" (i.e., the time required for operations which the operator was expected to perform during the machine cutting time) and "External Time" (i.e., the time required for operations which the operator was not expected to perform or could not perform during the machine cutting time). Load and unload operations, for example, always required External Time. Total Cycle Time equalled Machine Time plus External Time. The operator times shown above include a rest allowance of 20% of the adjusted observed times. The machines stopped automatically at the end of a cycle.

†*Controlling Cycle Time* (using four milling machines).

EXHIBIT 2   REED CORPORATION

STANDARD TIME, MILLING OPERATIONS, ORDNANCE PART AT 25% ABOVE NORMAL WORK PACE

(All times in minutes)

	Total Cycle Time	Machine Time	Total Operator Time	External Time	Internal Time	Ratio of Total Operator Time to Controlling Cycle Time
Milling Cut No. 1	3.176*	2.600	0.660†	0.576	0.084	20.8%
Milling Cut No. 2	2.652	2.220	0.576	0.432	0.144	13.1%
Milling Cut No. 3	2.930	2.420	0.720	0.510	0.210	22.7%
Milling Cut No. 4	1.472	1.118	0.600	0.354	0.246	13.8%
				Portion of *Controlling Cycle Time* operator is productively engaged		80.4%

* *Controlling Cycle Time* (using four milling machines).

† Explanation of Calculation of Total Operator Times: If an operator requires .825 minutes Total Operator Time when working at the normal work pace on Milling Cut No. 1 (see Exhibit 1), the time required on the same operation at a work pace 25% above normal is computed as follows:

$$\frac{\text{Time Required at Normal Work Pace}}{125\%} = \frac{825}{125\%} = 0.660 \text{ minutes}$$

The remaining Operator Times were derived by the same method.

above normal, the controlling cycle time was reduced to **3.176** minutes. However, when Moreno maintained this work pace on the remaining three milling cuts, all of his remaining operations could be performed before the completion of the machine-time on milling cut no. 1. As a result, when Moreno maintained the pace of which he was capable, he was productively engaged only 80.4 per cent of the controlling cycle time, and was forced to remain idle 19.6 per cent of the time. Careful study by the head of the Time-Study Department revealed that design characteristics prevented any change in the sequence of the cuts or in the method of setting up the milling machines for making the cuts.

Since the factory manager of the Reed Corporation personally supervised manufacturing operations, the matter was brought to his attention by the head of the Time-Study Department. Both men, as well as Moreno himself, were dissatisfied with the situation which had developed. Although management felt it could adopt no alternative that would endanger the flow of finished milling cuts, it was disturbed over the fact that Moreno was unable to maintain the level of earnings to which he had become accustomed. Through no fault of his own, his total weekly earnings were reduced by approximately $14.00. Moreno's attitude did not improve when it subsequently developed that the work on which he had previously been engaged did not cease, as the foreman had anticipated. Another operator, now assigned to that job, was earning the incentive pay which had previously gone to Moreno.

Careful retiming of the operation verified the accuracy of the time study. Moreno himself did not question the standard itself, but vigorously objected to the end results, less take-home pay.

In June 1952 the problem was unsolved. The head of the Time-Study Department hoped to find some solution.

Reference Note on Time Standards

Time standards are as ubiquitous, and nearly as useful, as the clock itself. A time standard is an expectation about the length of time that should be required to carry out a defined activity under specified conditions. All scheduling, whether for vast transportation networks, for delivery of products by factories, or merely for planning one's next vacation, depends upon such standards. The purpose of this note is to draw attention to the varied uses of time standards and to describe some of the ways, formal and informal, in which standards are set.

In business, standards are useful both before and after the occurrence of the activity to which they refer. They aid in preparation of plans for events to come and in evaluation of the outcome of events past. As such, they are a pervasive part of the framework of management decisions. To illustrate some of these applications:

In planning: Cost estimates based on labor time standards are used to evaluate proposals for new products or for the acquisition of new equipment; element times are used in planning the division of work on an assembly line or new methods for a single operator or machine; standard operation times are used to schedule work for men and machines, to set realistic delivery dates, and to identify bottleneck operations in a factory.

In evaluation: The standard serves as a criterion for judging the performance of departments, men, or equipment; it helps to single out the locus of low productivity so that management can search for specific causes, whether faulty material, poor training, low morale, or other such problems.

Time is the natural common unit of measure in a factory; standards make it possible to convert other diverse measures into time units. For example, if a machine has been used to produce several different products, a physical count of production by itself offers no basis for evaluation—the proverbial problem of trying to add apples and oranges is immediately encountered. If standards permit the conversion of physical production counts into "standard hours," however,

management then has a common denominator in units that are additive and directly comparable. A record that shows 38 standard hours on machine X and 43 standard hours on machine Y permits comparison of X with Y, and of either with the number of "clock hours" worked, despite the fact that the two machines may have been employed on very different products.

In short, standards are used in a wide spectrum of management judgments and decisions, in planning and scheduling, and in evaluation of operations; they make available a measure which can be applied to events still to happen, a goal for operations, and a criterion for evaluation; and, finally, they present a single unit of measure for diverse activities.

What methods are available for setting time standards? Certainly one of the most common sources of standards is the judgment of experienced personnel based on historical data from operations. Historical data, modified where necessary by informed judgment and combined with technical data for any machines involved, will serve quite usefully for many of the decisions and activities for which standards are employed. Standards so derived suffer, however, from two drawbacks: they are relatively imprecise, and they are impractical to derive for use on a large scale, for example, in setting schedules for a shop with 100 or more machines. Nevertheless, one should not underestimate the usefulness of such standards in relatively infrequent decisions such as pricing, equipment selection, and so forth.

When standards must be more precise, or be consistent across a wide scale of applications, one or more of the "scientific" techniques of work measurement should be applied. Three of these techniques will be described in this note, beginning with one in common use and known generally to the layman: stop-watch time study. The methods of implementing these techniques vary somewhat from company to company. Thus, the descriptions should be considered as examples of common, but not universal, practice in these three methods of work measurement. A fourth accepted method of measuring work is work sampling, discussed in the Reference Note on Work Simplification.

Time-Study Methods[1]

The timing of industrial tasks, like so many other so-called "modern" techniques of management, was anticipated by Charles Babbage,[2]

---

[1] Common time study terms are defined at the end of this note.

[2] See *On The Economy of Machinery and Manufactures*, 4th ed., by Charles Babbage, London, 1835. Chapter XII is entitled "On The Method of Observing

the enlightened industrial philosopher of early nineteenth-century England, and was put into practice and widely championed by Frederick W. Taylor, the father of "scientific management." Taylor first used time study in 1881 at the Midvale Steel Company. In his philosophy the stop watch was one of several instruments aimed at the creation of a wholly objective "scientific" basis for the management of labor. In the early part of the twentieth century, when trade unions struggled to maintain their very existence, the watch became a focus of agitation and a symbol of oppression. In 1914 a rider requested by the Government Employees Association was attached to a naval appropriations bill in Congress prohibiting the use of government funds for stop-watch studies in government ordnance plants. It was not until 1947 that this rider was repealed and time studies were permitted in ordnance plants.

The controversy over time studies has paralleled the development of "scientific management" and the growth of labor unions. William Gomberg has characterized the history of the relationship into four distinct periods[3]:

1. A period of unmitigated hostility between scientific management and organized labor lasting from 1911 to 1915.
2. A period of transition extending from 1915 to 1917.
3. A period of friendliness and understanding between the two until the great depression.
4. The emergence of a positive trade union philosophy of industrial engineering following the great organization drives and with the passage of New Deal legislation.

Although some of the scars of the early battles linger on, the much maligned "efficiency experts" of the twenties are accepted as "industrial engineers" in the sixties. Some labor unions have chosen now to cooperate with, rather than try to eliminate, the use of time studies. Most large unions now have sections of their research departments working on time-study problems, and maintain trained specialists in

---

Manufactories." In discussing means for measuring the output of specific tasks, Babbage comments: "If the observer stands with his watch in his hand before a person heading a pin, the workman will almost certainly increase his speed and the estimate will be too large," and continues by pointing out that "the number of operations performed in a given time may frequently be counted when the workman is quite unconscious that any person is observing him. Thus the sound made by the motion of a loom may enable the observer to count the number of strokes per minute, even though he is outside the building in which it is contained."

[3] *A Trade Union Analysis of Time Study*, by Wm. Gomberg, Prentice Hall, New York, 1955, p. 11.

the field to assist in local disputes over time studies. Since World War II, management-union controversy has focused on how time standards should be set, not on whether they should be established.

On the surface, time study techniques are relatively simple, and are applied fairly consistently from company to company. Deeper analysis, however, will disclose a morass of unresolved conflicts over the statistical, physiological, and psychological assumptions on which current practices rest. Our present concern will be to describe common practice rather than to analyze its justification.

Taking a Time Study[4]

Time study is used to set a time standard for the performance of a given operation. A useful definition of standard time is the following:

"The standard time should permit a qualified operator to work at a normal pace indefinitely without undue fatigue."[5]

The focal point in setting such a standard is the observation and timing of a worker in the performance of the operation. Given the times so obtained, a few straightforward steps of analysis and adjustment will yield the standard. Several important steps, however, must precede the actual timing of the job.

The first step, and one not so obvious as might at first appear, is to select the job to be timed. A time-study department, like many other such departments, frequently will work against a backlog of jobs which "should" be timed. Priorities must be applied to discriminate among the many jobs in a backlog. Good judgment applied at this point will influence the over-all effectiveness of a time-study program.

Given a job, with a qualified operator to perform it, the time-study man should proceed to familiarize himself with the job methods and to secure the cooperation of the worker and foreman. Accepted doctrine also calls for finding "the best method" of performing the job. In practice, this may or may not be observed, for reasons of expediency as well as the fundamental problem of identifying "the best method" on an *a priori* basis. Nevertheless, it is common for some effort to be made to improve the method. Furthermore, the job analysis which is an inherent part of time-study practice will often suggest improvements not otherwise apparent. It is essential that the job method followed during the study be described in detail and established as the standard method for the job. Description of the standard

---

[4] See *Motion and Time Study*, 4th ed., by Ralph M. Barnes, John Wiley and Sons, New York, 1958, Chapters 21, 22, and 23.

[5] *Ibid.*, page 6.

method is the main evidence when considering whether a job has changed sufficiently to invalidate an old time standard and warrant a new study.

Rather than time only the operation cycle as a whole, the time-study man will break the cycle into *elements* and time them individually. This analysis serves several purposes. When the raw time data are converted into a standard time, it will be necessary to adjust for abnormal occurrences affecting the times—for example, a worker's dropping a wrench—and for the pace and the proficiency of the operator. The separate element times facilitate this adjustment. In addition, the elements assist in describing the operation in some detail, indicating the step-by-step procedure followed during the study. Furthermore, the element times have a use in their own right. Analysis to support decisions at a later date on methods changes, acquisition of tooling, different equipment, and the like may require elemental time data.

An element is the portion of a task occurring between two timing points selected for time-study purposes. Timing points will be chosen so as to be clearly identifiable and to create elements that will be small enough to be useful in setting a standard but long enough in duration to avoid substantial errors in recording time. It is common practice to make the elements logical components of the over-all cycle. An example of elements of a drilling operation would be: reach for piece, grasp piece and remove from jig, transport to finished goods bin, release. A skilled observer using a stop watch can record elements as short as 0.10 minute with an average error of 3 to 5 per cent. For short cycles, those of a few minutes' duration, elements ranging from 0.20 to 0.60 minute are common. On longer jobs, from 10 minutes' to an hour's cycle time, elemental times may approach a whole minute or more.

In timing a worker the typical study will record element times for 5 to 30 production cycles. The actual determination of the number of cycles depends on the variability of the operator, the number and importance of noncyclical events which are part of the operation, and the length of the job. To make all standards within a company consistent, each job should be timed long enough to provide the desired statistical reliability.[6] Once a job has been timed and a normal time calculated, a statistical analysis of the variability can be made to evaluate the reliability of the new normal time.

---

[6] See *Modern Production Management,* by E. S. Buffa, John Wiley and Sons, New York, 1961, p. 528.

There are two common methods of using the stop watch, the "snap-back" and "continuous" methods. In the snapback method the watch hands are returned to zero at the end of each element, the time for the element having been observed just prior to the snapback. In continuous timing the watch runs without interruption and the elapsed time from the start of the study is recorded at the end of each element. Continuous timing is the more popular technique, despite the fact that an extra computational step is required to derive individual element times. The accuracy of the snapback method can be enhanced by using a pair of watches linked so that at the end of an element one is "frozen" while the other snaps to zero to time the next element. In this way the time for the element just completed can be read more easily on the frozen dial.

At the conclusion of time-study observations, the engineer will have a description (probably including a workplace diagram) of the task and the approved method, a listing of elements, and observed times for these elements over several cycles. The timing sheets will also contain notes describing any recurring noncyclical events, such as removing part trays or replacing tools, and other information useful in analysis of the data (Exhibit 1).

Setting a Standard

The standard time assumes "a qualified operator working at a normal pace." The timings in our study may or may not have been derived under those conditions. The next step, then, is to adjust the times actually observed so that they represent a "normal" time for doing the job. It is common to reject abnormal element times and to "rate" the worker's pace and proficiency, and then to adjust the observed times accordingly.

Abnormally high or low times for an element may be thrown out if a definite reason can be assigned for the variation. For example, the operator may have skipped or repeated a part of the element inadvertently, he may have encountered an unusually difficult piece of material, or he may have been affected by any one of a multitude of unusual circumstances. One such delay or speed-up in the relatively few cycles timed may have an effect beyond its probable long-run likelihood of occurrence. An allowance may be made in the next step of the calculation for such contingencies, but at this point they are best eliminated.

The rating factor is a significant and controversial part of time-study practice. While some plants use "unleveled" elemental data to derive standard times, that is, they assume that the observations were

EXHIBIT 1 An Example of a Timing Sheet

Opn. #14 R & F Mill relief bearing halves B-5511-1 & 2. (2,700 pair lot) W. H. Nichols & Sons hand miller with vertical milling head attachment; special form cutter; hand feed. Jig no. B-5511-1 & 2-14.

Ele-ment No.	Elements and Timing Points	Read-ing	Time in Minutes Cycles										Minutes	
			1	2	3	4	5	6	7	8	9	10	Aver-age	Se-lect
From	Piece hits bench	Cont												
1	Load	Indv	0.15	0.15	0.16	0.19	0.15	0.16	0.14	0.13	0.13	0.15	0.151	0.12‡ 0.12
To	Cutter hits work	Cont												
2	R & F mill one side	Indv	0.53	0.53	0.63	0.62	0.57	0.64	0.58	0.52	0.52	0.52	0.566	0.57† 0.57
To	Cutter leaves work	Cont												
3	Reload piece in jig	Indv	0.19	0.19	0.22	0.20	0.19	0.17	0.18	0.16	0.16	0.18	0.184	0.14‡ 0.14
To	Cutter hits work	Cont												
4	R & F mill other side	Indv	0.53	0.64	0.66	0.54	0.56	0.52	0.56	0.59	0.51	0.56	0.567	0.57† 0.57
To	Cutter leaves work	Cont												
5	Unload	Indv	0.08	0.08	0.12	0.10	0.09	0.09	0.25*	0.08	0.08	0.07	0.104	0.07‡ 0.07
To	Piece hits bench	Cont												
6	Totals	Indv	1.48	1.59	1.79	1.65	1.56	1.51	1.71	1.48	1.40	1.48	1.565	1.47

Timing Ended 10:37:00 AM
Timing Started 10:21:15 AM
Elapsed Time 15:45 or 15.75 min

Details:
* Reloaded by mistake—omit
† Calculated from shop standard feed, speeds, cut
   Rough .40
   Finish .16
   Reverse .01 (Estimated)
    Total .57
‡ Unnecessary movements

Total Element Time		1.47
Total Element Time Adusted for Worker Proficiency		1.47
Allowances in Minutes: Min per Day	480	
Machine Adjustment	15	71
		409

$$\frac{409}{1.47} = 278 \text{ pcs. per day}$$

Repile Material 16
Supervision 10

Rest 10
Personal 20
Total Allowances 71

STANDARD TIME Minutes per Piece 1.71
STANDARD OUTPUT Pieces per Hour 35
  Pairs per Hour 17½

made on an operator working at a normal pace, it is more common to level the data to reflect a presumed normal pace. Pace is measured on a percentage scale with 100 the conventional normal. Thus, a slow worker might be judged at a 90 pace, and times based on his work leveled by multiplying them by 90/100. A rapid pace might be judged as 130, and the observed times correspondingly multiplied by 130/100. The ability to arrive at consistent and fair evaluations of pace is

developed through extended training programs for time-study engineers. Where there are several men in a department, they will rate films of operators performing varying tasks and then discuss their ratings to reach some consensus of standard pace. Such rating periods are repeated at regular intervals to maintain a consistent judgment within the department. The arithmetic mean of the observed element times, disregarding the abnormal timings and adjusting for the operator's pace, represents the normal time for that element.[7]

Allowances compensate for the time required for personal purposes, to offset fatigue, and to absorb delays encountered from time to time in an operation. The magnitude of the allowance will depend on both plantwide practice and the characteristics of the particular job. The 10-minute break in morning and afternoon represents a common personal time break, and thus would be included in the job allowance. A fatigue allowance in addition to personal time might be unnecessary on many kinds of light manufacturing work, but could be as high as 40 per cent on heavy work, as in a foundry or steel mill.

Standard-Data Method

A second method for determining a normal time for a job is that of using elemental standard data derived from established time standards of the company. After a few years of operation using time study to set standards, the typical company accumulates a large backlog of standard times for various operations. Since most companies tend to specialize in particular processes and products, these times often can be categorized into common sets of operations, such as lathe operations for cylindrical parts, or assembling brackets with screws. For each set, a large number of standard times may exist from which standards for common elements can be defined. As an example, a machine shop might well have a large number of standard times for performing lathe operations. The standard times for these operations normally might be broken down into the same elements—load lathe, turn tool to work, adjust tool, etc. A prerequisite for such a system is a standard manner of breaking jobs into elements so that the elements will fit into classes.

It is often possible for an analyst to use these accumulated time data to define common standard elements by averaging the standard element times to formulate a standard that will be applicable to future jobs composed of elements similar to those performed in the

---

[7] Other measures of central tendency such as the mode or median can be used, but the mean is most common.

past. Exhibit 2 shows a typical table of standard elemental times. From such a table standards can be set for a new job entering the shop without a time study, as long as the standard method of operations is specified and the tasks are similar to former tasks. A normal time could be computed from the standard data tables by breaking the new job into the standard elements and summing the predetermined time for each element. Allowances would then be added in the same manner as a time study to obtain a standard time for the job.

Most companies using standard-data methods keep a check on the standards by taking time studies of a sample of the jobs for which standard data have been used.

Synthetic Time Data

A third method of establishing a normal time is to analyze a job into its basic motion elements, obtaining times for each element from a reference system of elemental times and totaling the predetermined times to obtain a normal time. Like the standard-data method, synthetic time data permit the computation of normal operation times without actual time study of the job in question. In all three methods, of course, allowances must be added to convert normal time to standard time.

Synthetic-data systems are really a special class of standard-data methods. As such they are distinguished by the fact that they use micromotion times which, in theory, can be added to represent the time for any manual element. The time data for these motions have been derived from detailed, stop-watch analyses of many manual operations and are available in several commercial systems. The operations are broken into microelements or therbligs such as "reach," "grasp," and "hold" and are timed as exactly as possible—in units of 0.0001 of a minute. The times for these therbligs are tabulated in accordance with parameters such as the distance for an arm movement or the difficulty of grasping the part.

A normal time for an element can be derived by analyzing the standard work method into its therbligs, noting its appropriate category; for example, a 14-inch transport empty, or 10-pound hand lift. A table is then referred to for the elemental times, which are summed for the standard. Standard allowances are added to the derived normal times. Detailed information concerning synthetic-data systems is available in: *Methods—Time Measurement,* H. B. Maynard, G. J. Stegmarten, and J. L. Schwab, McGraw-Hill Book Co., New York, 1948; *Basic Motion Time-Study,* G. B. Bailey and R. Presgrave, McGraw-Hill Book Co., New York, 1957; and The Work Factor Sys-

EXHIBIT 2 TIME STANDARD FOR DRILLING AND BURRING PINS

1/22/56   Based on C.R.S.
Below (1) Hole   Based on Hundredths of a Minute.

Drill Size →	56–52	51–44	43–36	35–29	28–23	22–17	16–10	9–4	3–1
Pin Diameter ↓									
3/32—1/8	0.48	0.46	0.45	—	—	—	—	—	—
5/32—3/16	0.50	0.48	0.46	—	—	—	—	—	—
7/32—1/4	0.51	0.50	0.48	0.53	0.54	0.55	0.56	0.57	0.58
9/32—5/16	0.53	0.51	0.50	0.56	0.58	0.58	0.59	0.60	0.60
11/32—3/8	0.54	0.53	0.51	0.58	0.59	0.60	0.61	0.62	0.63
13/32—7/16	0.56	0.55	0.53	0.60	0.61	0.62	0.62	0.63	0.64
15/32—1/2	0.58	0.56	0.54	0.61	0.62	0.63	0.64	0.65	0.66
17/32—5/8	0.64	0.62	0.62	0.63	0.64	0.65	0.66	0.66	0.67
23/32—3/4	0.70	0.67	0.66	0.67	0.68	0.69	0.70	0.70	0.72
27/32—7/8	0.77	0.70	0.69	0.72	0.75	0.77	0.78	0.78	0.80
31/32—1	0.83	0.77	0.75	0.80	0.81	0.82	0.83	0.85	0.86

BELOW FOR TWO (2) HOLES

	56–52	51–44	43–36	35–29	28–23	22–17	16–10	9–4	3–1
3/32—1/8	0.80	0.78	0.72	—	—	—	—	—	—
5/32—3/16	0.82	0.80	0.78	—	—	—	—	—	—
7/32—1/4	0.83	0.82	0.76	0.78	0.80	0.82	0.84	0.86	0.88
9/32—5/16	0.85	0.83	0.78	0.80	0.82	0.83	0.85	0.87	0.90
11/32—3/8	0.86	0.85	0.80	0.83	0.85	0.86	0.88	0.89	0.90
13/32—7/16	0.88	0.86	0.85	0.86	0.88	0.90	0.90	0.91	0.92
15/32—1/2	0.90	0.89	0.86	0.88	0.90	0.90	0.91	0.92	0.93
17/32—5/8	0.96	0.92	0.90	0.93	0.96	0.97	0.98	0.98	0.99
23/32—3/4	1.02	0.96	0.93	0.96	0.99	1.01	1.02	1.04	1.07
27/32—7/8	1.09	1.04	0.96	0.99	1.02	1.06	1.09	1.11	1.12
31/32—1	1.20	1.12	1.04	1.07	1.11	1.14	1.15	1.17	1.18

For other materials make following adjustments
Brass   Minus 20%   Bronze   Plus 20%
                            C.D.H.T.   Plus 50%

tem, by J. H. Quick, J. H. Duncan, and J. A. Malcolm, in *Work Factor Time Standards*, McGraw-Hill Book Co., New York, 1962. Exhibit 3 shows a table from the work-factor system and is typical of synthetic-data tables.

EXHIBIT 3 · WORK FACTOR MOTION TIME TABLE
for DETAILED ANALYSIS*

(A) ARM—Measured at Knuckles

DISTANCE MOVED	BASIC	WORK-FACTORS			
		1	2	3	4
1″	18	26	34	40	46
2″	20	29	37	44	50
3″	22	32	41	50	57
4″	26	38	48	58	66
5″	29	43	55	65	75
6″	32	47	60	72	83
7″	35	51	65	78	90
8″	38	54	70	84	96
9″	40	58	74	89	102
10″	42	61	78	93	107
11″	44	63	81	98	112
12″	46	65	85	102	117
13″	47	67	88	105	121
14″	49	69	90	109	125
15″	51	71	92	113	129
16″	52	73	94	115	133
17″	54	75	96	118	137
18″	55	76	98	120	140
19″	56	78	100	122	142
20″	58	80	102	124	144
22″	61	83	106	128	148
24″	63	86	109	131	152
26″	66	90	113	135	156
28″	68	93	116	139	159
30″	70	96	119	142	163
35″	76	103	128	151	171
40″	81	109	135	159	179
Weight in Lbs. Male	2	7	13	20	UP
Fem.	1	3½	6½	10	UP

(T) TRUNK—Measured at Shoulder

(L) LEG—Measured at Ankle

DISTANCE MOVED	BASIC	WORK-FACTORS			
		1	2	3	4
1″	21	30	39	46	53
2″	23	33	42	51	58
3″	26	37	48	57	65
4″	30	43	55	66	76
5″	34	49	63	75	86
6″	37	54	69	83	95
7″	40	59	75	90	103
8″	43	63	80	96	110
9″	46	66	85	102	117
10″	48	70	89	107	123
11″	50	72	94	112	129
12″	52	75	97	117	134
13″	54	77	101	121	139
14″	56	80	103	125	144
15″	58	82	106	130	149
16″	60	84	108	133	153
17″	62	86	111	135	158
18″	63	88	113	137	161
19″	65	90	115	140	164
20″	67	92	117	142	166
22″	70	96	121	147	171
24″	73	99	126	151	175
26″	75	103	130	155	179
28″	78	107	134	159	183
30″	81	110	137	163	187
35″	87	118	147	173	197
40″	93	126	155	182	206
Weight in Lbs. Male	8	42	UP	—	—
Fem.	4	21	UP	—	—

(F, H) FINGER-HAND—Measured at Finger Tip

Basic Motion Time Table (Work-Factor Units)

Distance					
1"	26	38	49	58	67
2"	29	42	53	64	73
3"	32	47	60	72	82
4"	38	55	70	84	96
5"	43	62	79	95	109
6"	47	68	87	105	120
7"	51	74	95	114	130
8"	54	79	101	121	139
9"	58	84	107	128	147
10"	61	88	113	135	155
11"	63	91	118	141	162
12"	66	94	123	147	169
13"	68	97	127	153	175
14"	71	100	130	158	182
15"	73	103	133	163	188
16"	75	105	136	167	193
17"	78	108	139	170	199
18"	80	111	142	173	203
19"	82	113	145	176	206
20"	84	116	148	179	209
Weight Male in Lbs.	11	58	UP		
Fem.	5½	29	UP		

(Ft) FOOT—Measured at Toe

Weight in Lbs.					
1"	16	23	29	35	40
2"	17	25	32	38	44
3"	19	28	36	43	49
4"	23	33	42	50	58
Weight Male	2/3	2½	4	UP	—
Fem.	1/3	1¼	2	UP	—

(Forearm Swivel — Weight in Lbs.)

Weight in Lbs.					
1"	20	29	37	44	51
2"	22	32	40	48	55
3"	24	35	45	55	63
4"	29	41	53	64	73
Weight Male	5	22	UP	—	—
Fem.	2½	11	UP	—	—

(FS) FOREARM SWIVEL—Measured at Knuckles

45°	17	22	28	32	37
90°	23	30	37	43	49
135°	28	36	44	52	58
180°	31	40	49	57	65
Torque Male Lbs. Ins.	3	13	UP	—	—
Fem.	1½	6½	UP	—	—

Work-Factor® SYMBOLS

W — Weight or Resistance
S — Directional Control (Steer)
P — Care (Precaution)
U — Change Direction
D — Definite Stop

COPYRIGHT 1952. Copyright under International Copyright Union. All rights reserved under Pan American Copyright Union 1910 by
THE Work-Factor® COMPANY, INC.

MENTAL PROCESS
(From Simplified Work-Factor)

Focus	20 units
Inspect	30 units/Pt.
React	20 units

Head Turn 45° 40, 90° 60

1 Time Unit = .006 Second
= .0001 Minute
= .00000167 Hour

WALK TIME

TYPE	30" PACES		
	1	2	OVER 2
General	Analyze from Table	260	120 + 80/Pace
Restricted		300	120 + 100/Pace

Add 100 for 120° — 180° Turn at Start or Finish

Up Steps (8" Rise — 10" Flat)	126
Down Steps	100

* Time in Work Factor Units.

DEFINITIONS OF TIME-STUDY TERMS

AVOIDABLE DELAY: An interruption of work that is within the control of the operator.

CYCLE: The set of elements performed repetitively in the same sequence, which comprises an operation.

CYCLICAL ELEMENT: An element occurring during each cycle.

DELAY ALLOWANCE: Additional time added to the normal time expected to be lost because of unavoidable delays.

ELEMENT: A portion of an operation that is separated for the purpose of analysis.

FATIGUE ALLOWANCE: Additional time added to the normal time to compensate for the rest time required periodically to recover from the physiological cost of the work.

NONCYCLICAL ELEMENT: An element that, although necessary to the operation, does not occur during each cycle. Its frequency of occurrence may be constant or variable.

NORMAL PACE: The performance level of an operator whose speed of movement is equal to a conceptual standard.

NORMAL TIME: The time required by a qualified operator, working at a normal pace, to perform an operation. It is computed by multiplying the selected time by the performance rating.

OBSERVED TIME: The actual elapsed time taken by an operator in performing a unit of work, usually an element.

PERFORMANCE RATING: A judgment by an observer of an operator's pace in comparison with a normal pace.

PERSONAL ALLOWANCE: An allowance added to the normal time to compensate for the time required by the operator for his personal needs.

SELECTED TIME: A central tendency statistic selected to represent the actual observed times taken during a time study. The most commonly used statistic is the arithmetic mean. When the arithmetic mean is used, the selected time is often termed the *"average time."*

STANDARD TIME: The time required by a qualified operator, working at a normal pace, to *perform an operation* and take full advantage of *fatigue* and of *personal* and *delay allowances*. It is computed by adding the time for all required allowances to the normal time.

UNAVOIDABLE DELAYS: An interruption of work that is outside the control of the operator. This category of delays includes such interruptions as: (*a*) talk to supervisor about job, (*b*) wait for materials, and (*c*) equipment breakdown.

Paragon Camera Company (I)

$\mathbf{M}$r. John Gregory, of the Methods Department of Paragon Camera Company, had just completed installing an improved method of assembling the shutter subassembly of the P-60 camera. The operation formerly had been part of the shutter-governor assembly operation which had proven to be a long, fatiguing task involving the assembly of 13 pieces by five hydraulic press operations. The planned production rate of 8,400 cameras per month had not been achieved, nor were the operators improving with experience on the job. A work-simplification analysis had divided the shutter-governor job into three new phases, and new methods were designed for each subassembly. The shutter subassembly consisted of aligning five small, metal parts onto a shaft and pressing the pieces onto it to form a permanent combination. This subassembly insured that the film would be drawn past the lens when the shutter was closed. A graphical representation of the parts, shaft, and sequence of assembly is shown in Exhibit 1.

Engineers in Paragon's Methods Department conducted an extensive program of work simplification and measurement to reduce costs and provide management with the time requirements of jobs for use in production planning and cost allocation. One of Mr. Gregory's functions as a member of the Methods Department was to make manual tasks easier to perform and less fatiguing to the worker. He said that less fatiguing, smooth-motion jobs resulted in higher-quality assembly work and required less time to perform than jobs not planned in accordance with the principles of motion economy. In addition to establishing methods, Mr. Gregory prepared a time standard for each job he designed.

Mr. Gregory had spent three mornings in establishing the standard method for the shutter assembly. First he prepared an operation analysis of the job, watching an operator accomplish the task in a

EXHIBIT 1 PARAGON CAMERA COMPANY (I)

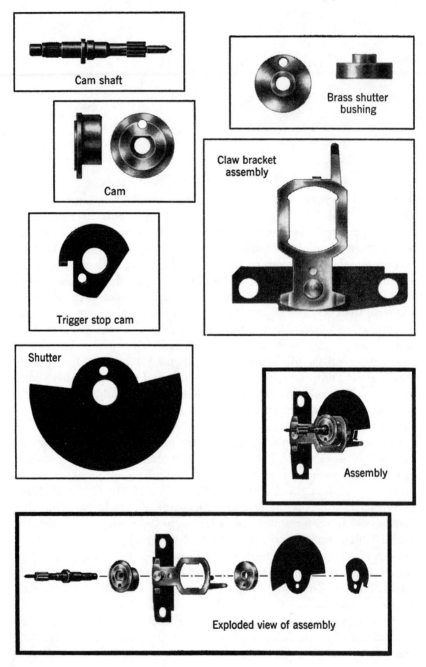

Cam shaft

Brass shutter bushing

Cam

Claw bracket assembly

Trigger stop cam

Shutter

Assembly

Exploded view of assembly

manner similar to the appropriate portion of the old work method. He noticed that to put together the shaft and cam, the flat side of the shaft had to be aligned carefully with an indentation in the cam and then assembled with pressure, since the shaft fit tightly in the cam. Because of the exact alignment and close fit, Mr. Gregory felt that the operator should position the shaft in the cam manually. The precise eye-hand coordination required seemed to limit the operation to assembling one part at a time.

Mr. Gregory's Job Design

He designed the job so that the necessary press operation was performed in two steps. The first step involved assembling the cam to the shaft, then positioning the claw-bracket subassembly, and then placing the bushing on top of the cam with the hole in the bushing in line with the hole in the cam; the bushing was then pressed on the shaft to hold the cam securely in place and lock the bracket upon the cam. This operation involved putting the shaft in a fixture and using a press part to bear on the bushing, allowing the press to exert pressure on the bushing without touching the shaft. The second press operation was to attach the shutter and trigger-stop cam to the shaft. These parts had to be placed so that the holes in the cam, bushing, shutter, and stop cam were in alignment. The press was closed and a die flattened the end of the bushing over the trigger-stop cam to provide a positive lock on the shutter and trigger-stop cam. A fixture was fabricated to hold the shaft in the press and provide a guide for positioning the hole in the cam.

It was Mr. Gregory's practice to design the job method and workplace layout at the same time, as he felt they both depended on the motion analysis. In the design of the layout he placed the bench stores of parts within forearm reach of most operators and attempted to balance the load on the hands by placing four parts on the right side and two on the left (Exhibit 2). To assist the operator in grasping parts, he provided the workplace with gravity-lip feed bins from which parts were easier to grasp than from a table. When the layout was set and the method satisfactory to him, Mr. Gregory prepared an operation card for the job (Exhibit 3). Using the card as a reference, he trained the operator in assembling the shutter subassembly by the new method. During the training period the operator was paid her average rate of $1.54 per hour.

After the operator had used the new method of assembling the shutter for one week, Mr. Gregory decided the operation was being performed in a routine enough manner to establish a time standard for

EXHIBIT 2   PARAGON CAMERA COMPANY (I)

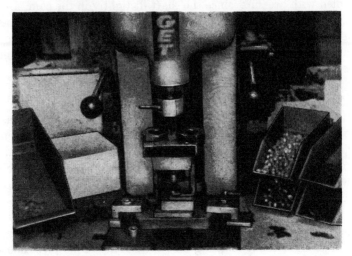

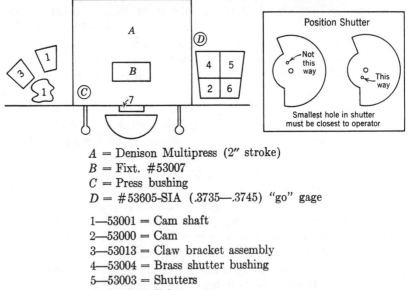

A = Denison Multipress (2″ stroke)
B = Fixt. #53007
C = Press bushing
D = #53605-SIA (.3735—.3745) "go" gage

1—53001 = Cam shaft
2—53000 = Cam
3—53013 = Claw bracket assembly
4—53004 = Brass shutter bushing
5—53003 = Shutters
6—53068 = Trigger stop cam
7—Finished pieces in box

EXHIBIT 3 PARAGON CAMERA COMPANY (I)

PART NAME P-60 Shutter Asbly   DWG. NO. 53692   OPER. NO. 53692-1

OPERATION NAME Asble Cam + Camshaft, Shutter Bushing,   CLASSIFICATION 10

CLAW BRKT. Asbly, Shutter, + Trigger Stp?   STD. PCS. PER HR.

CAM.   STD. HRS. PER 100 PIECES

Brush is carried in R.H. throughout Job

INSPECTION SPECS. Use STEP GAGE on (2) Spots of Cam. @ 1/25 pcs

OPERATION CARD—

BRIEF DESCRIPTION OF METHOD USED

L. H.	R. H.
Get Shaft - Move to Ctr	Get Cam - Move to Ctr.
	Regrasp Cam so that Counter-
	Bored Hole Faces to Left.
Hold Shaft By Pointed End +	
Posit. into Cam - Seat Shaft into	
Place Properly By Turning End of	
Shaft until it Clicks; into Place	
	Take Shaft out of LH By Regrasping
	Asbly Between Thumb + Forefinger
	Position Asbly in Fixture
Get Claw Brkt Asbly - Regrasp So	
That Cutoff Corner of Brkt is at	
Lower Right.	
	Swing Claw out to Right (Claw Tip
	Faces Bend Down.)
Posit. Claw Brkt. Asbly. in Fixture.	
Get Press Bushing	Get + Posit. Shutter Bushing in Fixt
Posit Press Bushing on Top of	
Asbly in Fixture.	
TRIP PRESS HANDLES	
Remove + Aside Press Bushing	Brush Chips off Shutter Bushing
Get + Posit. Shutter in Fixt. (See Workplace Sketch)	
	Get + Posit Trigger Stop Cam in Fixt.
TRIP PRESS HANDLES	
	Get Asbly in Fixt. - Dispose
FREQUENCY ELEMENTS	
(A) Resupply Store	
(B) Use "Go" Gage (2 Spots on Cam) @ 1/25	

NOTE: ANY APPRECIABLE CHANGE IN THE ABOVE OPERATING CONDITIONS WILL AUTOMATICALLY NULLIFY THIS STANDARD.

DATE	ANALYST	APPROVED	DEPT.
	S		

MONROE FORM 157 5M-5/61

the job. He estimated the task was taking about 30 seconds at an average pace. In considering the allowances he included two ten-minute coffee breaks in each eight-hour work day in addition to a 10 per cent fatigue and personal allowance. He estimated it would take an average of ten minutes per 1,000 pieces to obtain materials and dispose of finished parts. The press was set up by the foreman and no time was allowed for die sharpening.

Jackson Manufacturing Company

Supervisors in the Machining Department of the Jackson Manufacturing Company frequently found it possible for one man to tend two machines at a time. For example, a grinding-machine operator could start his machine cutting a part and complete a drill-press operation on another piece while the grinder was operating. In making time studies in the department, the company had followed the procedure of timing only the main operation and merely making a note of the fact that the operator performed a second task. Exhibit 1 shows the record of a time study made of a grinding-machine operator who also tended a drill press. Several timings of each operation were tabulated, and the times were summarized by main elements or subdivisions of operations, as shown in the exhibit. This exhibit gives individual times for each of the six elements during five cycles of the operation of the grinding machine. In the summary column are averages of the individual times for each element and the allowed time for each. To the sum of the individual allowed times were added a 9 per cent allowance for making tool changes and a 5 per cent allowance for contingencies.

The allowed times were set by the time-study engineer, but were based only partly on the actual or average times. The allowed time was intended to be a standard measure to be used for all employees on that job; it was expected to result in a fair measure of output to be expected from qualified operators. When he made the study, the time-study engineer observed such things as the amount of effort the worker put into the task, his skill, and general operating conditions. From the time-study records he noted how consistent the worker was in the times taken to complete each element. He considered all these things and set final allowed times that he considered fair for a satisfactory worker.

The market success of two new lines of product introduced in early

EXHIBIT 1 JACKSON MANUFACTURING COMPANY

TIMINGS OF A GRINDING MACHINE OPERATOR WHO ALSO TENDED A DRILL PRESS

OBSERVATION SHEET

Date August 16, 1960 — Part No. 888053-4
Part Name Manifold-Exhaust-Front Section — Register No. H-19012
Operation Grind Joint Face and Drill Intake Passage — Operation No. 4
Mach. No. 7650-6876 Name #1 Osterholm Auto. Disc Grinder & 24″ S.S. Cinn. Drill Press — Dept. No. M-64

Item	Detailed Description	RPM.	FPM.	Feed per Rev	1	2§	3	4	5	Summary Average	Summary Allowed
1.	Pick up piece & lay in fixture				0.12	0.11	0.11	0.11	0.08	0.106	0.07
2.	Tighten 4 clamps				0.35†	0.27	0.26	0.29	0.23	0.260‡	0.20
3.	Start mach. close guard.				0.24	0.16	0.20	0.24	0.23	0.214	0.18
*4.	GRIND	1,200		Auto	1.33	1.41	1.29	1.26	1.25	1.308	1.30
5.	Open guard, release clamps				0.19	0.17	0.17	0.13	0.14	0.160	0.12
6.	Remove piece & lay aside				0.09	0.13	0.06	0.08	0.10	0.092	0.07
*4-A	DRILL 1½″ x 2³⁄₁₆″ hole on machine 6876 during grinding time										

Fixture No. 133230
Material C.I.
Lubricant H_2O
Operators No. M-645
Helpers No.
No. of Men 1
No. of Machines 2

Total Items 2.14 — 1.94
Tool Changes 9% — .175
Contingencies 5% — .097
Set up %
Total time allowed — 2.21
Prod. per hour 27
Std. time hours .03683

* The grinding operation was performed on a machine similar to a bench or pedestal grinder except that it had a work-holding device, power feed of the work, and automatic stop at the end of the cut. The automatic stop gave sufficient accuracy for this job.

† Includes delay of 0.10.

‡ Excludes delay of 0.10 on first cycle.

§ 1.92 mins. spent to dress wheel at end of this cycle.

EXHIBIT 2 JACKSON MANUFACTURING COMPANY

TIMINGS OF THE DRILLING OPERATION CARRIED OUT DURING THE GRINDING OPERATION SHOWN IN EXHIBIT 1

OBSERVATION SHEET

Date July 11, 1961
Part Name Manifold-Exhaust-Front Section
Operation Grind Joint Face and Drill Intake Passage (Drill Press Operation Only, Shown Here)
Mach. No. 7650-6876 Name #1 Osterholm Auto. Disc Grinder and 24" S.S. Cinn. Drill Press

Part No. 888053-4
Register No. H-19012
Operation No. 4
Dept. No. M-64

Item	Detailed Description	RPM.	FPM.	Feed per Rev	1	2	3	4	5	Summary	
										Average	Allowed
1.	Turn to drill press				0.02	0.02	0.02	0.02	0.02	0.02	0.02
2.	Pick up piece & lay in jig				0.11	0.10	0.07	0.08	0.09	0.09	0.07
3.	Clamp, lower spdl, engage power feed				0.10	0.07	0.07	0.09	0.07	0.08	0.06
4.	DRILL 1½" diam. x 2 9/16" deep*	136	54'	0.0283"	0.58	0.60	0.58	0.56	0.57	0.58	0.57
5.	Raise head & release clamp				0.07	0.06	0.05	0.07	0.09	0.07	0.05
6.	Remove piece & lay aside				0.03	0.03	0.03	0.03	0.03	0.03	0.03
	Turn to grinder				0.02	0.02	0.02	0.02	0.02	0.02	0.02

Fixture No. 183230-B
Material C.I.
Lubricant
Operators No. M-645
No. of Men 1
No. of Machines 2

Total Items   0.82
Tool Changes 9%   0.074
Contingencies 5%   0.041
Set Up %
Total Time Allowed   0.935
Prod. per hour
Std. time hours

* Operator idle, waiting on automatic stop to disengage feed.

1961 placed a severe strain on the capacity of the company's manufacturing facilities. Production requirements were expected to increase even further during 1962 and 1963 as a result of additional new products and anticipated growth in existing lines. In response to this situation a special engineering task force was established to re-examine the assignment of men and machines on important operations in the machining department. The objectives of the group were to find means for increasing the utilization of manpower and machining capacity and therefore help relieve a tight delivery situation.

One of the first jobs studied was operation number 4 on the Manifold-Exhaust Front Section. To supplement the existing time-study data another study was made of the drill-press operation (Exhibit 2). The design of this part called for one grinding operation and drilling one hole $1\frac{1}{2}$ inches in diameter and $2\frac{3}{16}$ inches deep on each casting. Annual production requirements were expected to run between 120,000 and 150,000 units. During 1961 the department foreman usually employed two or three machinists on this job, each running one grinder and one drill press. Although there were seldom fewer than two men on the job, occasional peak needs might dictate the addition of a fourth man and pair of machines.

Parren Machine Works

As a part of the program to cut production costs and meet the competition in the centrifugal pump industry, C. A. Calvin, industrial engineer of the Parren Machine Works, was considering the use of one man rather than two to operate the company's two New Britain six-spindle, work-rotating, chucking machines.

The Parren Machine Works manufactures centrifugal fluid pumps. Although production is at the highest level in company history, management believes the sharp decrease in the backlog of orders during the past six months indicates that output might be reduced in the near future. All 1,000 production employees of the company are members of the International Association of Machinists.

The New Britain chuckers are used to machine the cast-iron pump end bonnet which serves as a grease retainer and liquid seal over the end of each pump shaft. A blueprint of the end bonnet is shown in Exhibit 1. The Parren Machine Works casts and machines the end bonnet in lots of 2,000 to 5,000 for parts inventory.

The Chucker

The New Britain chucker (Exhibit 2) is a type of semiautomatic lathe that has a spindle carrier equipped with six spindles, each carrying a universal chuck. Five sets of cutting tools are mounted on five sides of a hexagonal tool slide, which is fixed except for longitudinal feed toward and away from the spindles. The spindle carrier indexes 60° after every cut so that each workpiece is brought in the same sequence before each tool station. Each set of tools performs additional cutting operations on the workpiece. In this way five pieces are machined simultaneously,[1] while the sixth position is used for

---

[1] A different cut is made at each station, with the fifth station completing the machining operations on the chucker.

EXHIBIT 1 PARREN MACHINE WORKS

PUMP END BONNET

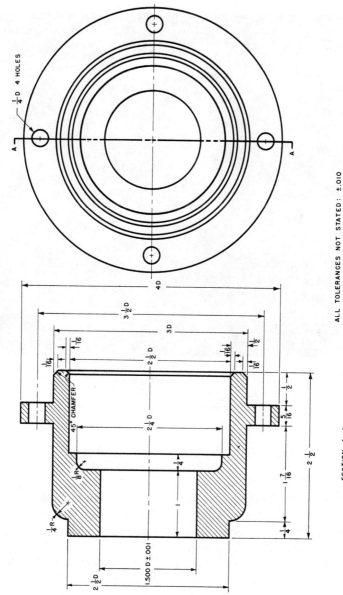

SECTION A - A

ALL TOLERANCES NOT STATED : ±.010

EXHIBIT 2   PARREN MACHINE WORKS

NEW BRITAIN SIX-SPINDLE WORK-ROTATING CHUCKING MACHINE

1. Loading and unloading position or station
2. Spindle carrier
3. Single spindle
4. Tool slide, tools not mounted

(Courtesy The New Britain Machine Company.)

unloading and loading a workpiece. After each indexing the machine stops. The operator restarts the five spindles opposite the cutting stations with a hand-control lever and replaces the finished piece on the sixth spindle with a new casting. The station cycle time per piece is the time required for machining, indexing, and restarting of the five spindles, or 0.767 minute. Machine and tool adjustments and machine maintenance are made by special set-up men after the day's production is completed.

One versus Two

To compare one-man operation with two-man operation of the chuckers, Mr. Calvin calculated the output expected from continuous operation for each method. He first listed the detailed motions of the operator's job (Exhibit 3) and attached a time to each motion from elemental time data available in the plant. As the station

EXHIBIT 3 PARREN MACHINE WORKS

OPERATOR WORK CYCLE TIME FOR MACHINING A PUMP END BONNET
ON THE NEW BRITAIN CHUCKING MACHINE

Element	Time in Minutes	
I Get a New Casting		
1. Turn toward new casting bin	0.020	
2. Walk 4 feet to stamping machine*	0.026	
3. Pick piece from supply	0.010	
4. Place piece in stamping fixture	0.031	
5. Operate air valve on stamping machine	0.026	
6. Stamp the piece	0.082	
7. Release foot from air valve	0.023	
8. Remove piece from fixture	0.018	
9. Turn toward work station	0.021	
10. Walk 4 feet to work station	0.026	
		0.282

II   Reload Machine

Left Hand	Right Hand		
1. Grasp chuck handle and start 5 spindles	1. Place new casting on machine	0.029	
2. Assist right hand	2. Remove finished piece and collar†	0.034	
3. ″ ″ ″	3. Remove collar and toss finished piece in bin	0.033	
4. ″ ″ ″	4. Place collar on new piece	0.055	
5. ″ ″ ″	5. Place new piece in chuck	0.053	
6. Operate chuck handle	6. Hold piece and collar in chuck	0.013	
			0.217
	Operator's Work Cycle Time		0.499

---

* Each pump end bonnet was stamped with a part number.

† A spacer between the pump end-bonnet flange and chuck, used to position the end bonnet accurately in the chuck.

EXHIBIT 4   PARREN MACHINE WORKS

WORKPLACE LAYOUT FOR THE NEW BRITAIN CHUCKING MACHINES

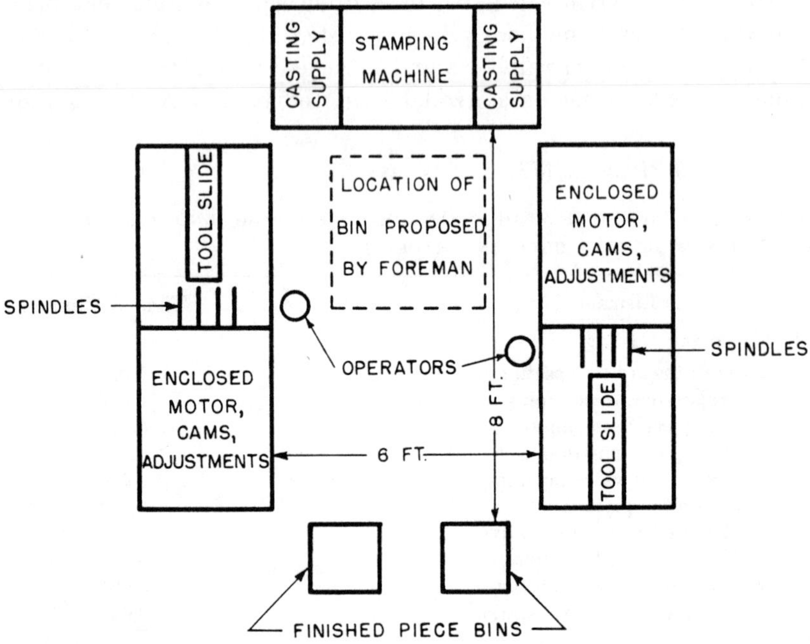

cycle time of 0.767 minute was greater than the operator's work cycle time of 0.499 minute with two-man operation, station cycle time determined machine output. With the station cycle time of 0.767 minute, Mr. Calvin determined that two-man operation of two machines in continuous operation should produce a total of 156 end bonnets per hour.[2]

With one man tending the two machines and with the same workplace layout (Exhibit 4) the operator's work cycle of 0.499 minute per machine or 0.998 minute for both machines would limit production. Therefore, Mr. Calvin concluded that one man operating two machines running continuously could produce a total of 120 pieces per hour.

In talking to the departmental foreman about the proposed change, Mr. Calvin learned that it might be difficult to gain union acceptance

---

[2] From production records Mr. Calvin learned that actual production with two-man operation of the chuckers had averaged 148 bonnets per hour over a recent seven-week period

of one-man operation.   Although multiple-machine operations were used in the department, the pump end bonnet would be the first job proposed where one machine would always be waiting for operator attention.   The foreman believed the union might complain that this condition would keep the operator under continued nervous tension, lower his morale, and decrease his output.

To obtain union acceptance of one-man operation of the chuckers, the foreman suggested a reduction in the operator's work-cycle time. He believed the reduction could be accomplished if the castings were stamped by another workman in the department and the casting supply were placed at a more convenient location.   A large steel bin, with a sloping bottom and open trough for the easy removal of castings, could be placed close to the operator's work area.   Thus, the operator could pick up a new casting from the bin trough while walking the six feet between chuckers.

The foreman estimated that the company's Maintenance Department would charge $200 as the cost for making and installing the bin and for moving the stamping machine to a new location.   As odd jobs frequently were needed to keep unskilled labor busy for an eight-hour shift, the foreman believed the stamping of castings and the refilling of the new bin could be assigned as one of the odd jobs in his department.

Mr. Calvin estimated production requirements for the next three months at 7,400 end bonnets per week.   With one-man operation the chuckers would still be used on end bonnets only and the operators would continue to be paid $1.52 per hour on either first or second shifts.   In calculating production costs, management estimated overhead at 150 per cent of the direct labor for each job.

Reliable Products Company (II)

At the end of October, 1961, Robert Rath, supervisor of methods and time-study, was concerned about whether he should set a more liberal time standard for one of the operations in assembling electrical cord sets. These are cords used to connect such things as toasters and flatirons to electrical outlets. A change in methods and an accompanying new time standard had been introduced five weeks earlier. Since that time none of the 12 women assigned to the assembly operation had achieved the standard production. All had produced "below standard," and each received make-up pay to bring her earnings up to the company's guaranteed wage minimum.

This pattern of a continued rate of performance below the new output standard had been complicated by a change in the method of setting the time standard. The old standard for assembling cord sets had been determined by stop watch; the new standard was based on a system of predetermined time values for specific hand motions.

COMPANY BACKGROUND

The cord set is but one of approximately 1,500 items manufactured by the Reliable Company. These include small electrical fuses, electrical wall outlets, electrical wall switches, lamp sockets, and a variety of other small electrical items (Exhibit 1). In the manufacture of these items, the steps employing by far the greatest number of people are the hand-assembly operations. Three-hundred and fifty of Reliable's total 600 employees are women doing hand-assembly work.

Competition in the manufacture of small electrical wiring devices is intense. It comes not only from other domestic producers, but also from foreign manufacturers, some of whom make "carbon copies" of products developed in the United States. The managers at Reliable

EXHIBIT 1 RELIABLE PRODUCTS COMPANY

SOME OF THE PRODUCTS MANUFACTURED

say that some foreign manufacturers make and ship to the United States products "every bit as good" as Reliable's, but these foreign producers pay hourly wages equivalent to only 17¢.[1]

As a consequence both of the relative importance of hand-assembly work and of the severe competition, the Reliable managers consider high labor productivity essential. Productivity standards, set by stopwatch, were used at Reliable beginning in 1936—the year of the company's founding. The women hand-assemblers, from the first, were offered incentive earnings based on actual productivity compared with a standard set for each operation.

METHODS AND STANDARDS

The responsibility for setting standards for hand-assembly and other manufacturing steps lay with Mr. Rath. Working with him were four industrial engineers trained in methods and time-study work.

---

[1] Some foreign competitors who pay low hourly wages nonetheless provide job security and other benefits, the costs of which are difficult to assess.

Mr. Rath reported to the company's manufacturing engineer who, in turn, reported to the Vice President of Manufacturing. Mr. Rath had held the position of methods and time-study supervisor for eight years, having come from a similar position at another company.

Before taking a stop-watch study and setting a standard, the men from the methods and time-study section first simplified the method of assembly. A new product scheduled for high volume production[2] received more methods attention than did shorter run jobs. Often, however, time pressures to get a long-run job into production limited the amount of methods work performed. Describing a chronic situation which also limits methods work, Mr. Rath says, "We never have the manpower to do all the work that is waiting for us."

After the methods work had been completed, the stop-watch study was taken. A time-study man took stop-watch readings, timing as many as 100 work cycles. In addition to recording the observed times, the time-study man judged the operator's work pace. He recorded this judgment using 100 per cent to indicate a "normal work pace," and a higher or lower percentage in proportion to observed work pace above or below normal. In his next step, he multiplied the average of the observed times by the percentage representing his judgment of work pace. The product was called the *graded time* or *leveled time*. To this, he added *allowed time* to compute the standard time allowance for the operation.

In 1959, standards constructed from predetermined time values began to replace standards set by stop watch at Reliable. The new system,[3] called Unit Time Standard, or U.T.S., had been developed by another company with which Reliable was associated. The U.T.S. system is based on the concept that the great bulk of bench assembly work and machine operations, when properly organized, consist of repetitious, short, hand motions to reach for and grasp a part, to position a part, or to operate a control. The industrial engineers who designed the U.T.S. system had made actual time measurements of tens of thousands of such movements with accurate recording devices. Among the recording devices were motion-picture cameras, which

---

[2] Production ran well in excess of one million units annually for some products.

[3] A number of predetermined time standard systems exist. Some of these have been developed by consulting firms and are "sold" to clients. Other systems are developed and used solely within one company. The U.T.S. system is of the latter type. The subject of predetermined time standards is treated in a number of industrial engineering and management writings including: Maynard, H. B., Editor, *Industrial Engineering Handbook*, McGraw-Hill Book Co., New York, First Edition 1956, or Second Edition 1963.

EXHIBIT 2   RELIABLE PRODUCTS COMPANY

UNIT TIME STANDARDS
FOR BASIC OPERATIONS

(Time in Minutes Per 100 Operations)

Secure

Level of Difficulty	Time/c
1. Touch	0.09
2. Grasp	0.18
3. Sliding grasp	0.54
4. Descend, grasp, lift	0.90
5. Descend, grasp, separate, lift	1.08
6. Descend, grasp, untangle, lift	1.58

Release

1. Drop release	0.07
2. Disengage release	0.14
3. Down and release	0.44
4. Preposition, down and release	0.63
5. Align, down and release	0.74
6. Align, preposition, down and release	0.93

Hand Movements

Over 0 to and including 6″	0.34
Over 6″ to and including 12″	0.42
Over 12″ to and including 18″	0.50
Over 18″ to and including 24″	0.58
Each additional 6″	0.08

Precision

	One Hand	Two Hands
Under 0.501″ to and incl. 1/4″	0.16	0.23
Under 1/4″ to and incl. 1/8″	0.32	0.47
Under 1/8″ to and incl. 1/16″	0.48	0.70
Under 1/16″ to and incl. 1/32″	0.64	0.93
Under 1/32″ to and incl. 1/64″	0.80	1.16
Under 1/64″ to and incl. 0.008″	0.95	1.40
Under 0.008″ to and incl. 0.004″	1.11	1.63
Under 0.004″ to and incl. 0.002″	1.27	1.86
Under 0.002″ to and incl. 0.000″	1.43	2.10

operated at high speeds. These were designed for accurate control of the number of "frames" (pictures) taken per second, facilitating accurate timing of the hand motions recorded.

Exhibit 2 presents the standard time data which had been developed. The designers of U.T.S. emphasized that a thorough training to under-

stand and apply these data was essential to its use. They provided, for their own industrial engineers, a five-week intensive training period. The students first used U.T.S. time values to analyze methods for putting wooden pegs into a pegboard and to set a standard for that operation. They progressed through more complex studies to a final assignment which required selecting a difficult operation from the shop, simplifying this operation through careful U.T.S. analysis of hand motions, and setting a standard based on U.T.S. values. Exhibit 3 shows the composition of a simple standard.

Speaking of the introduction of U.T.S., the Vice President for Manufacturing, John Webster, said:

> I would like to be able to say that we found this tool through a systematic search and that we changed from stop-watch standards for carefully planned reasons. In fact, we stumbled on U.T.S., even though it had been developed and used for some time by our associated company. We knew of the development, but I and others here at Reliable, without making our feelings explicit even to ourselves, had somehow resisted the idea that the hand motions of our operators were subject to analysis by predetermined standards. Then, in 1958, after we had lost some relatively profitable business and were feeling heavy competitive pressures, we inquired about predetermined time standards. The industrial engineering staff at the associated company was willing to help us. Their claim that predetermined standards had been helpful to them was convincing enough to induce me to experiment with the system.
>
> At the time we started using U.T.S., however, we had some grave doubts about our course of action. Our company has never had a union, even though there have been repeated attempts to organize our workers. As you know, the electrical industry is highly organized and this is a heavily unionized section of the country. Each time we have "sweated out" the organization drive. Each time not enough workers have responded to the union's appeal to carry the question of forming a union to a National Labor Relations Board vote.
>
> We are constantly concerned about our relationship with our workers. We try to see their point of view and make this a desirable place to work and we try to put across our point of view and the need for worker productivity. We are never quite sure of the effect of our actions. Against this background of an uncertain relationship, we started comparing a few of our stop-watch standards with the allowed times of the U.T.S. data sheet. I can remember very well a comment which our president made then. He said, "Keep in mind that a decision to use U.T.S. may bring in the union." But as I saw the situation, we faced potential trouble either way. The prospects of worker dissatisfaction threatened us, but so did the consequences of not improving our competitive position.
>
> One aspect of the decision I faced was how predetermined standards should be used. There was no question that this system offers a good tool for work simplification. We can see on this sheet (Exhibit 3) how every required hand motion must be listed and can be scrutinized closely. Further, every distance traveled is recorded, and every hindrance and interference between hands and every forced delay shows clearly.

EXHIBIT 3 RELIABLE PRODUCTS COMPANY

UNIT TIME STANDARD

APPROVED BY DATE	YEARLY PRODUCTION		100M	OPERATION	Assemble Contact Assembly
_ _ J. Hoe _ _ _ _ _ _ _ _ _ _					
_ _ R. Rath _ _ _ _ _ _ _ _ _ _	TASK /HR.	RATE /M		PART NO.	REL 54541
OPERATION				PART NAME	

LOCATION OF MATERIAL & EQUIPMENT	WORKPLACE LAYOUT	DISTANCES
LI - Clip contact		A - D = 7"
R1 - Buss Bar		D - L1 = 6"
A - Fixture		L1 - A = 6"
D - Dispose		R1 - A = 6"
O - Operator		

TIME UNIT – MIN. PER 100

	ELEMENTS		HAND MOVEMENTS	SECURE-RELEASE	PRECISION	MISC.	TOTAL
	LEFT HAND	RIGHT HAND					
1	Dispose unit A - D	Secure Buss Bar A-R1	.42	1.08			1.50
2	Secure contact D - L1	Release Buss Bar R1-A	.34+.34	1.08	.70		2.46
3	Release contact L1 - A	Unavoidable delay	.34+.34	.93	.48		2.09
4	Kick					.90	.90
5	Secure contact assembly	Unavoidable delay	.34	.18			.52
							7.47
						+ 10%	.75
							8.22

.0822/60
730 units/hour standard

EXPLANATION

The operation consists of placing a buss bar
and a clip contact in a fixture; crimping
them together using a kick-press; and removing
the fastened parts from the fixture. Time
values were taken from Exhibit 2.

Line 1 .42 min for hand movement of 6";
        and 1.08 min for securing at the fifth
        level of difficulty.
Line 2 .34 min twice for a hand movement
        which changes direction, both move-
        ments less than 6"; 1.08 min for securing
        at the fifth level of difficulty; and .70
        min for the precision required in releasing
        the buss bar.
NOTE: A smooth hand movement is given a single
        time value; a hand movement which is inter-
        rupted by a change in direction is given
        two time values.
Line 3 similar to Line 2.
Line 4 .90 min for kick.
Line 5 .34 min for hand movement; and .18 min
        to secure at the second level of difficulty.

But another question I faced was harder. Should U.T.S. become a tool to
raise the productivity of our workers? Many of our women started here
in 1948, in 1943, or even earlier. Our workers stay with us. Typically they
are more skilled in hand operations after a number of years of experience.
At the same time some of our standards, particularly some of those set dur-

ing the Korean conflict, were not very demanding. In setting new standards, should we close the gap between our standards and the greater ability of our operators? This is in part an ethical question.

I gave Bob Rath, the methods supervisor, approval to introduce U.T.S. slowly. He was placed also in a position of selling the standards to the workers and to the foremen. This "selling" of standards was something that evolved gradually; it was not a clear-cut decision at one time. For a while I asked each foreman to sign for each standard that was given to him. His signature would show that in his judgment the standard was attainable, that he would get his operators to meet it, and that labor costs in his department would reflect a corresponding level of productivity. The foremen always said to me, "I can't sign until one of my good workers tries the new standard." And they wouldn't sign. Eventually I was in the position of forcing them to sign or of giving up on signatures. I gave up.

The methods supervisor, Mr. Rath, supplied more information about the introduction of the Unit Time Standard system. He said:

When I first started using U.T.S. I used it only to aid my judgment in leveling observed stop-watch readings. The U.T.S. allowed times were uniformly well below my observed times, but I didn't dare level my readings all-the way down to what the U.T.S. values showed. I compromised.

Then I went to the company where the standards had been developed and took their five-week training program. I returned with confidence in my own ability to set a realistic standard based on U.T.S. and in the ability of operators to meet the standards. Three of my men took the course, too. Since then we have tried to see that standards were set precisely according to the actual hand motions which the operator must perform and the corresponding values contained on the U.T.S. master data sheet. This requires that in almost every case we must observe an operator go through the hand motions and carefully record exactly what her hands do before we assign time values. On a few occasions, when just a small change is made in a motion pattern, an industrial engineer can visualize the change without watching an operator. But for most changes it is necessary to record what the operator is doing and then assign the values.

I have to watch the work of one of the industrial engineers more closely than I do the work of the others. Two of the men put down time values almost the same as I do. If we were to set standards for the same operation, our standards would be very similar. But one of the men is too liberal. He is prone to put in a delay or a drift or allow a broken hand movement when in fact the hand can move directly. I check all his work. The other two men think very much as I do

EXPERIENCE WITH NEW STANDARDS

"When we first started with U.T.S.," Mr. Rath said, "every standard we set was challenged by the operators and by the foremen. Frequently I went out on the shop floor with a stop watch in order to time

an operator and prove that she *could* do the job in the time allowed.
In a few instances I found myself to be wrong, and then I changed
the standards quickly—occasionally to the company's advantage. But
most of the time we were able to convince the women and the foremen that the work could be done in the time called for by the U.T.S.
More recently we have had better acceptance of our standards, with
few calls to prove them." Mr. Rath continued:

We never have been able simply to tell the workers what to do. We have
to work with them, and we have to present standards which are in line
with what the women expect. An operator is a wonderful piece of equipment. She doesn't need oil the way a machine does, but you do have to
"baby" her. I go to all their retirement parties and other affairs. In the
assembly areas I stop to tell one worker dirty jokes. I know she likes to
hear them. To other women I speak as if I'm from Madison Avenue; they
like that approach. Some of the women have told me, "Well, I suppose we'll
have to accept this standard. It's your job. If you weren't setting these
tight standards someone else would be."

Now that we have confidence in our U.T.S. system we apply the time
values just as they come directly from the master data sheet. If our study
shows that with a small methods change a standard can be tightened 30 per
cent we make the change and tighten the standard. There is no question of
our tightening the standard by 15 per cent now and hoping that we'll get
the other 15 per cent later. We take the full 30 per cent. Our approach has
brought us a number of complaints, but this is far better than getting no
complaints. Everyone used to accept our stop-watch standards; for years
we were lying on a velvet couch. Now competition has forced us to more
realistic standards, and the complaints we receive from the operators indicate,
in part, that we're doing a better job in setting standards.

Mr. Webster and other supervisors felt that the workers' willingness
to work and their general evaluation of the company was influenced,
in part, by the favorable comparison of their incentive wages with other
wages in the community. The latest survey of wages conducted by
Reliable covered a total of 40 occupations at 45 plants. The average
throughout the community for women doing electrical hand-assembly
work was $1.44[4] per hour. The average paid at Reliable for this work
was $1.75, the highest wage reported. The survey indicated also that
the amount given in fringe benefits—vacation, accident and health
payments, pension—at Reliable was even further above the community
average than cash wages. Mr. Webster said, "From what we know
about the employees, it seems pretty clear that they consider this a
good place to work. If I were to summarize the workers' attitude
toward us—that is, to the limited extent that I understand their at-

---

[4] The community average excluding Reliable was $1.39.

EXHIBIT 4   Reliable Products Company

WEEKLY EARNINGS OF 27 WOMEN EMPLOYED AS
INCENTIVE WORKERS ON HAND-ASSEMBLY JOBS

These figures were selected by the case writer as representative of the earnings of all hand-assemblers. The variations in earnings in any one department were nowhere near as great as the variations shown here for representative workers from all departments.

Woman, Number	Piecework Earnings	Daywork Earnings	Make-up Adjustment for Earnings below Guarantee	Night-Shift Bonus	Overtime Premium	Total Earnings	Hours Worked
1	$ 33.61	$ 29.24				$ 62.85	40
2	5.05	53.93	$ 1.62			60.60	40
3	30.06	20.45	10.09			60.60	40
4	62.52	1.67			$ 5.13	69.32	37.5
5	46.93	6.97				53.90	32
6	53.64					53.64	31.9
7	64.80	2.87			6.76	74.43	40
8	81.17	15.00			6.27	102.44	46
9	89.29				5.82	95.11	46
10	63.38	3.94				67.32	40
11	57.06	8.79				65.85	40
12	60.05	8.64				68.69	40
13	95.33	3.79			6.47	105.59	46
14	105.05	.45			6.89	112.39	46
15	9.28	61.96			4.65	75.89	46
16	71.94	8.53				80.47	40
17	83.40	4.09				87.49	40
18	61.14	2.27		$ 5.34	5.01	73.76	38
19	54.46	3.18		4.99	3.90	66.53	37
20	70.09	1.82		6.17	5.10	83.18	42.3
21	48.79	3.03	5.75	4.85	4.55	66.97	38
22	29.70	22.73	17.26	6.06	4.55	80.30	46
23	56.28	4.32				60.60	40
24	59.43	1.17				60.60	40
25	42.40	18.20				60.60	40
26	103.81	5.76				109.57	40
27	60.52	7.58			1.23	69.33	41.5
	$1,599.18	$300.38	$34.72	$27.41	$66.33	$2,028.02*	1,094.2

* Total earnings excluding night-shift bonus and overtime premium were $1,934.28.

titude—I would say that they certainly don't hate us, but they do have wariness bordering on distrust about our actions."

Inspection of payroll records to determine the variations of earnings on the company average of $1.75 led to the preparation of Exhibit 4. The weekly earnings figures cover women normally assigned to hand-assembly work under incentive wages. The gross earnings and their composition (Exhibit 4) were selected as representative of earnings of all hand-assemblers.

Sets of figures were prepared by the accounting department to show over-all changes in manufacturing costs. One set of figures analyzed changes in the manufacturing costs of 30 heavy selling items for the years 1951, 1954, 1959, and 1961 (Exhibit 5). Other analyses showed that the changes in manufacturing costs for these 30 items closely approximated the changes in costs for all items. Further analyses showed that direct labor costs were 14.4 per cent of manufacturing costs in 1959 and 14.1 per cent in 1961. During that two-year period, the women doing hand-assembly work had been granted a pay increase equal to 5.06 per cent of their 1959 earnings. Given as a cost-of-living increase, this had raised all piece rates.

In analyzing changes in labor costs, Mr. Webster was not sure what part might reflect higher production standards and better work pace on the part of operators. "Many of our items," he said, "require a different set of hand motions in 1961 than they did in 1959. This comes in part as a result of our methods program to simplify assembly work. Other changes come from product redesign, which can either increase or reduce the labor content of a product. In designing a better product we may increase the labor content, but in simplifying our product design we may reduce the labor content. I have no way of measuring separately the effects on labor costs of methods changes, of products redesigns, and of changes in work pace."

MR. RATH'S PROBLEM

The situation of immediate concern to Mr. Rath in late October, 1961, was the failure of any of the 12 women to meet the five-week-old standard set by U.T.S. for assembling one of the ends of the cord sets (Exhibit 6A). The operation in question was to attach the *service block,* the end of the cord shown at the left in the picture. The parts involved in this assembly were the two halves, or "casings," of the service block and the cord with metal contacts already attached to the two wires (Exhibit 6B). The parts of the service block were located in bins near the operator's right and left hands; the cords hung from

EXHIBIT 5   RELIABLE PRODUCTS COMPANY

ANALYSIS OF CHANGING MANUFACTURING COSTS OF 30 HEAVY SELLING*
CATALOGUE ITEMS WHICH REMAINED IN THE LINE FROM 1951 TO 1961

Manufacturing Cost per Thousand

Catalogue Nos.	1951	1954	1959	1961
4320-1	$ 36.82	$ 45.48	$ 54.30	$ 51.56
4330	24.98	31.17	38.07	37.33
4367	48.70	45.52	54.82	54.23
4020	38.90	35.30	30.51	29.66
4200-2	77.14	87.02	77.31	70.74
4010	85.18	95.10	87.34	55.39
4011	117.23	114.09	116.68	113.49
4602	106.69	124.12	148.41	155.56
5009	100.94	83.40	114.49	101.64
5911-1X	122.44	138.21	123.91	124.56
5202	192.45	199.45	177.18	205.06
5310	133.65	111.39	129.05	141.43
9810-1	42.77	46.48	45.47	37.63
9810-2	60.96	59.54	59.13	48.39
6500-4	184.48	183.30	181.58	193.94
4262	169.19	168.05	178.06	181.49
3365	137.29	138.55	164.03	167.97
3780	198.87	218.27	245.38	203.90
7130	92.69	108.88	89.39	95.89
7170	173.02	143.93	169.57	142.45
9171	75.07	83.14	71.04	46.67
9828	172.22	163.81	201.91	190.81
9101	269.72	304.73	320.79	294.83
9297	446.98	394.19	422.55	395.13
2300-2	182.24	232.34	189.36	159.00
2300-4	204.92	244.99	197.87	167.29
2300-6	242.82	323.59	257.12	213.45
3636	177.67	163.69	185.30	174.43
5702-1	217.78	194.25	220.56	211.98
5703-X	290.78	274.83	322.31	299.98
	$4,422.59	$4,549.61	$4,673.49	$4,365.88

* The above items accounted for approximately 20 per cent of the annual sales volume in both 1951 and 1961.

EXHIBIT 6A Reliable Products Company

"CORD SET" USED TO CONNECT SMALL ELECTRICAL APPLIANCES, SUCH AS
TOASTERS, TO AN ELECTRICAL OUTLET. THE "SERVICE BLOCK"
IS THE END SHOWN AT THE LEFT

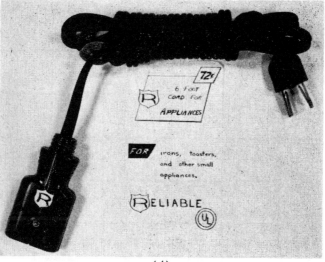

(A)

EXHIBIT 6B Reliable Products Company

THE PARTS OF THE SERVICE BLOCK AND THE CORD WIRES
WITH CONTACTS BEFORE ASSEMBLY

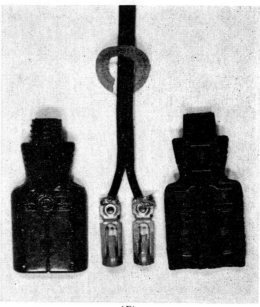

(B)

EXHIBIT 7 RELIABLE PRODUCTS COMPANY

TIME STUDY

TIME STUDY – RELIABLE PRODUCTS COMPANY

DWG. N REL 2010   APPROVED   5 SHTS SHT. NO. 1

Assemble (2) leads to service block and drive rivet

ST.	STOP RES. FIN. TOT.	DETAILS OF OPERATION	1	2	3	4	5	6	7	8	9	10	AVG.	SELECT MAN.	MCH.	% GRADE	GRADE TIME	FACTOR ALL.	ALL. TIME
		Bimanual get and place two (2) bottom sub-assembly casings in fixtures	05 05	05 43	05 74	05 1.04	05 37	05 72	06 07	05 41	04 75	05 09	0410 /2	0205		105	0215	10%	0237
		2) Right hand get and hold two (2) cord ends 2) Left hand get and assemble one (1) donut Underwriters Label to each cord	07 12	05 48	05 79	07 11	05 42	08 80	07 14	07 48	08 83	08 17	0718 /2	0359		105	0337	10%	0415
		3) Bimanual position two (2) leads of -one (1) cord in one (1) bottom casing and move slide arm to hold wires	05 17	06 54	05 84	04 15	06 48	05 85	05 19	06 54	05 88	05 22	0998 /2	0499		110	0549	10%	0604
		3) " " " " " Bimanual get and assemble two (2) top	05 22	05 59	04 88	05 20	05 53	05 90	05 24	05 59	05 93	05 27	0720 /2	0385		105	0404	10%	0444
		4) casings to bottom casings	12 34	06 65	07 95	08 28	10 63	07 97	08 32	08 67	07 3.00	07 34							
		5) Operate foot pedal to drive rivets; retard slide arms. Right hand dispose	04 38	04 69	04 99	04 32	04 67	04 2.01	04 36	04 71	04 04	04 38	0404 /2	0202		110	0222	10%	0244
																			.1944

NOTES

	TOT. MAN.	.1944
Cycle Time Per Unit	TOT. MCH.	309
Units Per Hour	TOT. CYCLE	
	TOT. S.U.	

NOTE: All time values shown are in hundredths of a minute.

Taken September 10, 1955

By J. Foss

a circular swivel rack to the right of the operator. The cords had been hung on racks after the completion of a prior operation, and the racks, on casters, stored and moved the work-in-process from operation to operation. The free ends of the cords were long enough to reach to the workplace while the other ends remained attached to the rack. The operation consisted of placing the bottom half, called *bottom casing,* into a jig; laying the two contacts of the cord in position; covering with the top half, or *top casing;* and fastening the two halves together by activating a press that drove rivets. In practice, service blocks were assembled to two cord sets at a time in order to use more efficiently both the right and left hands of the operators.

Exhibit 7 reproduces one of the stop-watch records used to set the old standard for attaching the service block. This sheet shows only 10 of the total of 80 cycles times, but gives the average time for all 80 cycles and the computation used to set the standard number of units to be assembled per hour. The time-study man had used the *continuous time* recording method. Accordingly, the figures in the lower boxes opposite each element (Exhibit 7) are the successive time readings in hundredths of a minute; the figures in the upper boxes are the calculated elapsed times between readings.

In September, 1961, a change in methods was made, consisting primarily of substituting a power-driven press for a kick-press. The operator assembled the cord to the bottom and top casings in a fixture[5] at position A–A shown in the workplace layout (Exhibit 8). Then the operator slid the fixture holding the assemblies under the press to position B–B, tripping the power press and driving rivets to fasten the casings. In addition to the installation of the power press, the only other changes repositioned supplies of parts slightly closer to the operator.

In addition to showing workplace layout, Exhibit 8 indicates how the new standard was set using U.T.S. values. One industrial engineer spent 11 hours in observing an operator and preparing this sheet.

Under the former method of assembly the women were offered $1.51 per hour for assembling the standard number of cord ends—309 assemblies per hour—and were guaranteed this same amount of $1.51. Under the old standard the women actually earned an average of $1.83 per hour, with the variation seldom more than ±$0.09. During the fifth week of operation under the new method and new standard, the

---

[5] The redesigned fixture did away with the need for "slide arms" used formerly to hold the wires in the bottom casings.

EXHIBIT 8 RELIABLE PRODUCTS COMPANY

UNIT TIME STANDARD

APPROVED BY	DATE	YEARLY PRODUCTION	5 MM		OPERATION NO.	93032
_ S. Johnson_ _ _ _ _	_8-17-61_					
_ R. Rath_ _ _ _ _ _	_8-18-61_	TASK /HR.		RATE /M	PART NO.	REL 2010
OPERATION Assemble, Service Block to Cord Set					PART NAME	Service Block

LOCATION OF MATERIAL & EQUIPMENT	WORKPLACE LAYOUT	DISTANCES
A - Work area - fixture B - In position to rivet M - Machine (Rivit) O - Operator L1 & R1 - Base Casings L2 & R2 - (empty) L3 - Donut labels (UL) R3 - Rack holding cords L4 & R4 - Cover Casings		D-R1 = 10" min 18" max D-L1 = 14" min 28" max R1&L1-A=11" min 24" max A-L3 = 10" A-R3 = 15" A-L4&R4 = 9" min 15" max A-H = 5" A-B = 5"

TIME UNIT- MIN. PER 100

ELEMENTS		HAND MOVEMENTS	SECURE- RELEASE	PRECISION	MISC.	TOTAL
LEFT HAND	RIGHT HAND					
Secure casing D-L1	Secure casing D-R1	.58	.90			1.48
Insp.& release casing L1-A	Insp. & release casing R1-A	.50	.93		1.24	2.67
Secure (2) U.L.labels A-L3	Secure cords A-R3	.50	1.08			1.58
Release one U.L.label L3-A	Hold cords R3-A	.50	.74	.16		1.40
Release one U.L.label A	Hold cords A	.34	.74	.16		1.24
Secure cord & palm A	Hold cord A	.34	.18		.28	.80
Form leads A	Hold cord A	.34	.44		.30	1.08
Release on base A	Release on base A	.34	.74	.47	.44	1.99
Unpalm cord A	Secure cord A	.34	.18		.42	.94
Form leads A	Hold cord A	.34	.44		.30	1.08
Release on base A	Release on base A	.34	.74	.47	.44	1.99
Secure cover A-L4	Secure cover A-R4	.46	.90			1.36
Insp.& release cover L4-A	Insp.& release cover R4-A	.46	.93	.70	1.24	3.33
Unavoidable delay	Secure handle A-H	.34	.18			.52
Unavoidable delay	Slide fixture in A-B	.68	(100% retarded)			.68
Machine Time					.66	.66
Unavoidable delay	Slide fixture out B-A	.34	.14			.48
Secure cord A	Secure cord A	.34	.18			.52
Insp. & dispose* A-D	Insp.& dispose* A-D	.34 + .42	.44		.44+.60	2.24
		7.84	9.88	1.96	6.36	26.04
*Note:					Divide by	
"dispose" consists of helping the free ends of					2	13.02
the cord swing back to the rack						
				Material handling		.32
				5% Rejects on covers and bases		.38
				5% Rejects (no contacts)		.15
						13.87
					+10%	15.26
.1526)	60					
	393 Pieces per Hour - Standard					

women's average hourly incentive earnings were $0.86, but these earnings were *made up* to the guaranteed amount of $1.51 per hour.

Mr. Rath said he had done everything he could to check the standard and to convince the foreman and women that it is reasonable.

I've even taken motion pictures of their work. Playing the film in slow motion, I find that the women are using the correct motion pattern and that the allowed U.T.S. values match this motion pattern. The women certainly have had more than enough time to develop the required speed. After all, these are not new women. They are some of our best operators; they have experienced only a slight job change; I think I'm dealing with a "closed corporation" there.

This is the biggest challenge we've had this year to our new system of setting standards. If I retreat on this one I feel that our entire pattern of setting standards by U.T.S. will be threatened.

PART 3. LINE FLOW PROCESSES

Reference Note on Material-Flow Processes

Material-flow processes are the sinews that unite separate fabrication, assembly, finishing, and storage operations into a complete manufacturing sequence. By creating a physical link between distant and otherwise unrelated processes they make it possible to deliver the right material to the proper location at the correct time. Within the factory, of course, the need for movement of material is not limited to transport between machines in production areas; goods also must be moved from common carriers into a receiving area, to and from in-process storage areas, and finally to a finished-goods warehouse or shipping area. To the casual observer, the most striking impression of a modern factory is one of movement—in some cases continuous movement. In fact, the conveyor, only one of the several classes of material-handling equipment, has achieved recognition as a symbol of modern mass production.

Material-handling processes can have a significant impact on the efficiency of the whole manufacturing operation. For example, they can directly affect the efficiency of individual machines and the workers operating these machines, the amount of in-process inventory required between machines, and the amount of overhead expense incurred in manufacturing (by influencing expediting, scheduling, and space requirements). To illustrate:

In one modern steel works a "mile-a-minute" cold-rolled strip mill failed at first to realize its capacity of more than 5,000 feet per minute. Actual production was limited to 3,300 feet per minute because the coils of finished strip could not be removed from the machine fast enough. Not until 80,000-pound capacity ram trucks were built for removing coils was full-capacity operation attained.

An example of space saving resulting from the selection of material-handling equipment is found in one of the largest screw-machine departments in the world. Overhead material delivery permitted 380 screw machines to be put into an area of 75,000 square feet, or only half the area traditionally required. The machines were arranged in rows with just enough room between for operators to work comfortably. The need for additional aisle and

FIGURE 1. The electric fork-lift truck in the foreground can lift a two-ton load approximately 11 feet. It travels at 6 miles per hour and costs approximately $5,000. The two-wheel truck costs approximately $20. (Courtesy Lewis Shepard Products, Inc.)

temporary-storage space (costing up to $10 per square foot in 1961) was obviated by a special overhead crane.

In addition to the effect of material-handling techniques on production efficiency, the costs of material-handling operations are significant in their own right. Material-handling labor expense for metalworking firms commonly ranges between 5 and 20 per cent of the production payroll.[1] In an extreme case, the meat-packing industry, material-handling costs amount to as much as 90 per cent of production labor costs.

Determinants of Equipment Selection

Most of more than 300 types of material-handling equipment fit into one of three general groups: vehicles, cranes, and conveyors.

---

[1] James R. Bright, *Management Guide to Productivity*, Philadelphia: Yale Material Handling Division, The Yale and Towne Manufacturing Company, 1961.

The variety of tasks which this equipment can accomplish in and around the factory is immense, and defies simple classification. The selection of particular equipment to do a given job is determined by such variables as the nature and quantity of the *material* to be moved, the structure of the existing *plant*, the nature of the *process equipment* involved, and the over-all *flow-pattern* in the factory.

The material to be moved may be solid or fluid; it may be moved in tonnage bulk or piece by piece. Even if it is not corrosive, flammable, or explosive, and thus dangerous to its environment, it may be fragile or otherwise sensitive to the environment and consequently require special care.

The structure of existing plant facilities exerts an equal influence on material-handling requirements. The necessity for considering aisle space, the distance between related-process facilities, and the number of floors in a plant is obvious.

Equipment selection is also affected by the variety of process requirements. For example, it may be necessary to link machines producing hundreds of parts per hour to others turning out only a

FIGURE 2. These two fork-lift trucks, shown storing tote boxes in a rack, have 2-ton load capacities, top speeds of 8 miles per hour, burn liquefied petroleum gas fuel, and cost more than $2,000. (Courtesy Industrial Truck Division of the Clark Equipment Company.)

few parts per hour, or to join operations producing continuously with others manufacturing in batches between periods of down time for tool changing, set-up, or adjustment. These difficulties may be compounded by processes requiring parts to be delivered individually, in particular orientations, and at exact locations.

Finally, one of the important determinants in the selection of material-handling devices is the pattern of material flow through a plant's manufacturing operations. There are two basic patterns of flow through a factory, namely, "line production" and "job shop."

Material-Flow Pattern

Line production is a pattern of material flow where work in process moves through a *fixed series* of operations at a uniform rate. The amount of work done at each operation is *balanced* in accordance with the planned rate of flow. Note that this definition does not

FIGURE 3. A two-ton capacity, electric walkie fork-lift truck is removing a scrap receptacle from beneath a stamping press's discharge chute. Stamped parts are piled in the shop boxes shown in the foreground. (Courtesy Lewis Shepard Products, Inc.)

Figure 4. A straddle truck which will carry a ten-ton load at 39 miles per hour moves unit loads of pipe in a storage yard. A cradle pallet appears in the foreground. (Courtesy Industrial Truck Division of the Clark Equipment Company.)

Figure 5. A traveling overhead bridge crane with a 104-ft. span and a 15-ton capacity serves a steel yard. The cost of these cranes varies widely, as do the load capacity, the traveling speed, the lift speed, and positioning precision. (Courtesy The Cleveland Tramrail Division of the Cleveland Crane and Engineering Company, Wickliffe, Ohio.)

imply that line operations are physically adjacent, arranged in a straight line, or even in the same building. What is implied is that a unit of product upon completion at any given work station will flow into an established sequence of subsequent operations.

An example of line flow is found in the manufacture of two products requiring stamping, turning, drilling, milling, cleaning, and packaging operations. One product is always made by moving the work sequentially through stamping, milling, drilling, and packaging machines set aside for that product. In fabricating the other product, material is always moved through stamping, drilling, turning, cleaning, and packaging operations in that order. Thus, this plant's pattern of flow is made up of one line for each product.

The antithesis of line flow is a job-shop pattern. This is common where a large number of varied products are made on the same machines. In this case, material flowing from any process may be routed to any other process in the plant. As a result, work passes through any combination of processes, in any sequence, over innumerable routes. The multiplicity of possible routes can be seen using

FIGURE 6. Four motor-driven traveling semigantry cranes work under a bridge crane in this turret-lathe assembly area. In the foreground, a worker is installing a turret. A semigantry crane with a 25-foot span and a two-ton capacity commonly costs less than $5,000 (excluding hoist and installation costs). (Courtesy The Cleveland Tramrail Division of the Cleveland Crane and Engineering Company, Wickliffe, Ohio.)

FIGURE 7. A jib crane with a 15-foot span and a one-ton capacity may cost as much as $2,000. The electric hoist may cost more than $1,000. (Courtesy The Cleveland Tramrail Division of the Cleveland Crane and Engineering Company, Wickliffe, Ohio.)

the preceding example. If the manufacturer produced 2,000 items and organized the five operations preceding packaging on a job-shop basis, there would be more than 280 possible material-flow routes. Were this company to introduce another operation before packaging, the number of possible routes would exceed 1,000.

In order to gain the simplicity of line operation and the flexibility of job-shop operation, most plants today are composed of a number of subgroups having either line-flow or job-shop patterns. Rarely are all operations organized exclusively on a line or job-shop basis.

Material-Handling Equipment

Transportation operations are performed by three basic types of equipment—vehicles, cranes, and conveyors—and by a host of miscellaneous special devices. The characteristics of these groups can only

FIGURE 8. Molten iron is transferred from a furnace in the background to a distributing ladle suspended from a monorail trolley. The distributor fills the pourer's ladle and the pourer fills the sand molds carried on a pallet conveyor. A distributor, pourer, and helper can pour more than 10 tons of iron per nine-hour day using this system. (Courtesy The Cleveland Tramrail Division of the Cleveland Crane and Engineering Company.)

be given approximately because there are so many different kinds of equipment within each group and because much of this equipment is ordinarily custom designed.

In general, the efficiency of material-handling equipment is enhanced by batching or collecting parts or raw material into "unit loads."[2] By batching small parts in tote-boxes, piling pieces on pallets, or strapping material into bundles, a large number of parts can be moved

---

[2] The phrase "unit load" is ambiguous in material-handling terminology. In the sense employed here, it refers to an assembly of parts in a load that can be moved as one pile, group, or "unit." Commonly, it is also used to distinguish between bulk material (e.g., liquid, gas, and powders) and material, like metal parts, which is composed of discrete units.

FIGURE 9. A belt conveyor is used to carry bauxite from ore ships to a depot. (Courtesy Aluminum Company of America.)

FIGURE 10. This 270-foot tow conveyor uses 125 tow carts and 15 cart trailers to move 150 tons of freight per day. Installation of this equipment reduced dock labor 30 per cent. (Courtesy Mechanical Handling Systems, Inc.)

FIGURE 11. From this shipping area orders are sent to the packaging department on a belt conveyor. Rush orders are placed in baskets and hooked to the overhead conveyor at a point where it drops down within easy reach. The baskets are removed at a similar point in the packaging area. The return side of this trolley conveyor is used to bring goods to the shipping area on tow carts. (Courtesy Mechanical Handling Systems, Inc.)

in a single transportation operation. In theory, the larger the "unit" the greater the efficiency of movement.

The advantages of fork-trucks, platform-trucks, industrial tractors, and manual two- and four-wheel trucks is their flexibility in choice of path, operating speed, and place of operation. This flexibility and the availability of many different attachments allow vehicles to fulfill random schedules and carry a variety of shapes easily. Fork and platform trucks have additional flexibility, since they can move loads vertically as well as horizontally. Some of these can raise loads more than 20 feet and can operate in aisles only 5 feet wide.

Electric fork-trucks with load capacities of 2,000 pounds cost approximately $5,000, whereas similar trucks powered by gasoline engines may cost only $2,000. The speed of indoor vehicles seldom exceeds 6 miles per hour; some trucks designed for outside use may have speeds greater than 50 miles per hour.

FIGURE 12.   Assembly fixtures are an integral part of this trolley conveyor. The fixtures hold the component parts in their required orientation as they move through the sequence of assembly operations. (Courtesy Lewis Shepard Products, Inc.)

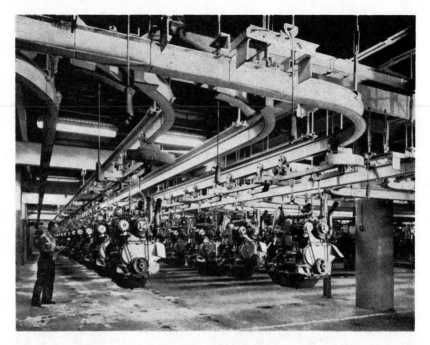

FIGURE 13. Automobile engines weighing 1,100 to 1,700 pounds are carried through assembly on a power and free conveyor system. Here they are stored on a free section of monorails. (Courtesy Mechanical Handling Systems, Inc.)

The primary advantages of cranes are that they operate above the working area and thus have access to almost any floor location and that they are capable of relatively unrestricted horizontal motion. They can carry the heaviest loads of all types of equipment, can easily move different shapes and sizes of work, and can stack material as high as the structure permits. They usually require a "rigger" on the floor to assist the crane operator.

Overhead traveling cranes, with capacities of more than 50 tons, can cost more than $200,000. Small jib, monorail, and gantry cranes, costing up to $500, are often employed underneath a larger traveling crane to keep the larger crane free for bigger workpieces and longer moves.

Conveyors are machines which transport material either continuously or in batches over a fixed path between fixed points of loading and discharging. Because they can provide precise timing, speed, and position control, conveyors may actuate production machines and

assist in production operations such as heat-treating and dipping processes. Their paths, which can pass over, under, or around obstacles, are often made more flexible by using switches, multipath installations, and portable conveyors at some places. "Power and free" conveyors permit work to be taken off the moving line, held stationary, and then replaced without stopping or slowing the main line.

The cost of conveyors varies widely, depending on the type of material handled, the precision of timing and positioning required, and the path's length and complexity. Simple gravity conveyors may cost only a few dollars, whereas a large automobile-conveyor network can cost more than a million dollars.

Special devices commonly combine the attributes of different basic types of equipment into one machine. Consequently, it is impossible to generalize about common characteristics; only examples can be given. The piggy-back trailer is an example of a device which functions as a container and as a vehicle. Stacker cranes combine the function of the lift truck and the overhead crane. Like the crane, they can move unrestricted by obstructions on the floor. On the other

FIGURE 14. A 30-ton capacity fork-lift truck is used to remove loaded truck trailers from rail cars. (Courtesy R. G. Le Tourneau, Inc.)

FIGURE 15. This stacker crane serves 12 ½-foot-deep racks on each side of an aisle 85 feet long. The bays will hold up to 1,500 tons of stock. (Courtesy The Cleveland Tramrail Division of the Cleveland Crane and Engineering Company, Wickliffe, Ohio.)

hand, they rapidly and accurately position work and require aisle space as does the fork-lift truck.

Mobile cranes are another example of the crane-and-truck combination. They combine a crane's overhead reach and access to areas not adjacent to aisles with a truck's flexibility in path and location.

Fowler Machinery Corporation

In July 1961, the factory superintendent of the Fowler Machinery Corporation was reviewing a problem which had arisen in the course of the company's efforts toward parts standardization. The part in question, an offset bracket, had been designed to serve the purposes of eight different brackets currently in use on over 50 models of machines produced by the company. An engineering drawing of the part is shown in Exhibit 1. In 1960, a survey of machine and parts designs had indicated that substantial savings in machining costs and inventories could be achieved by redesign and standardization of some parts in common use.

Requirements for the offset bracket would total approximately 20,000 units per month at the current rates of machine assembly and demand for replacement parts. In June 1961, the Manufacturing-Engineering Department had prepared an operation sheet (Exhibit 2) for the part in a routine manner. A lot size of 2,000 units was proposed at that time. All production in the Fowler plant was on a job-lot basis with parts moved from department to department in bins carried by fork-lift trucks. The engineering department pointed out that it would be impractical to move more than 2,000 units at a time or to store more than that number conveniently near a machine while the lot was being worked on. Early in July the operation sheet was submitted to the Production-Control Department, where manufacture of the first lot would be scheduled.

In establishing start and delivery dates for parts produced, the Production-Control Department commonly allowed two days between operations for moving the parts. This estimate included the time necessary for the foreman to report completion of the operation to the Production-Control Department, time to issue a move order, time required by a move man to transfer a lot to the next operation, and

309

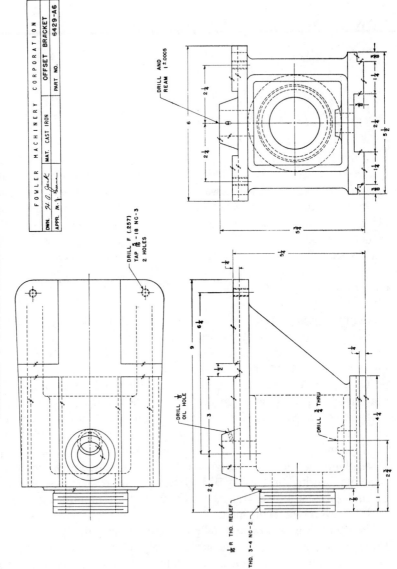

EXHIBIT 1 FOWLER MACHINERY CORPORATION

EXHIBIT 2 FOWLER MACHINERY CORPORATION

OPERATION SHEET, PART #6429-A6

Order and Number of Operations	Description of Operation	Depart-ment	Machine	Pieces per Machine per Hour
1	Drill for 1 ±0.0005	A	Drill press	20
2	Ream to 1 ±0.0005	A	Drill press	60
3	Mill carriage seat	B	Milling machine	30
4	Inspect	D	Bench	120
5	Drill and tap screw holes	A	Drill press (2-spindle)	50
6	Mill upper surface	B	Milling machine	20
7	Inspect	D	Bench	120
8	Mill groove	B	Milling machine	75
9	Drill oil hole	A	Drill press	80
10	Square shoulder	C	Engine lathe	60
11	Turn for thread	C	Engine lathe	40
12	Cut thread	C	Engine lathe	20
13	Inspection of thread	D	Bench	100
14	Drill for ¾″ stud	A	Drill press	60
15	Press in stud	E	Arbor press	80
16	Assemble with screw	F	Bench	100
17	Final inspection	D	Bench	100

time required to start work on a lot after it was received in a department or at a machine. Allowing for movement of the castings to the first operation, on the basis of an eight-hour work day, the total time allowed for moving a lot of 2,000 pieces through 17 operations was 272 hours. An additional 284 hours would be required for time spent in process while parts were being machined.[1] The total of 556 hours in process was practically 3½ working months. If each lot spent 3½ months before completion, 35 lots would have to be in process simultaneously to meet the monthly requirement of 20,000 parts. Because this amount of work in process seemed prohibitively large, the matter was referred to the factory superintendent.

---

[1] An output of 120 units per hour would be required to produce 20,000 units per month, based on 167 working hours per month. This meant the work at each operation would have to be completed in 16⅔ hours (2,000 units/120 units per hour), and that 284 hours of processing would be necessary to complete 17 operations.

Brownley Shirt Company

The Brownley Shirt Company owns and operates a group of 22 sewing plants which produce men's dress shirts,[1] sport shirts, and pajamas. The company produces 7,500,000 dress shirts annually at rates up to 44,000 per day.

All pressing operations on dress shirts are done at eight of the 22 plants. These operations are performed on five-station conveyor lines like that shown in Exhibit 1. The conveyor consists of an endless chain of shirt-holding pallets that automatically and intermittently shift from one position to the next. As shown in Exhibit 1, two conveyor lines feed a single inspection and packing station. Each of the two conveyors has five stations with an operator at each station.

EXHIBIT 1   THE BROWNLEY SHIRT COMPANY

DIAGRAM OF CONVEYOR PRESSING UNIT

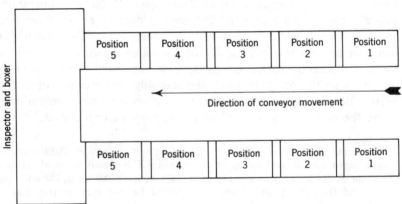

---

[1] Shirts of the type worn every day to business are termed "dress shirts."

The conveyors are intermittently in motion and at rest. When the conveyor comes to rest, a flat pallet like a small table top is in position in front of each operator, and each worker at once performs the pressing operations specified for her work station. A predetermined length of time is allowed for this work, after which the power-driven conveyor automatically moves all the pallets along to the next work station on the line. The time required for this movement is 0.02 minutes. Other timing of the conveyor operation can be adjusted by a maintenance mechanic, but the 0.02 minutes for movements from station to station is the minimum of which the conveyor is capable. The time interval during which the pallets are stationary is adjusted by the mechanic to meet the time required to perform the work of pressing a shirt when broken down into five tasks. Thus the time required to press one shirt on a double pressing line with the job breakdown shown in the left-hand part of Exhibit 6 is

$$\frac{0.44 \text{ min} \times 110\%^2 + 0.02 \text{ min}}{2} = 0.252 \text{ min}$$

In other words, a shirt comes to the inspector at the end of a double line every 0.252 minutes.

Each of the eight plants that press shirts is equipped with two double conveyor lines. These conveyors are in operation approximately 50 weeks a year. Style factors and seasonal demand peaks and lows preclude continuous operation at a steady rate. The company's 22 sewing plants normally operate on a single-shift, 40-hour-week basis. At times these plants operate less than five days a week. There is very little employment in excess of 40 hours a week since overtime pay is costly. In order to meet volume requirements, the pressing lines frequently operate two shifts of 40 hours each—less costly than overtime work. Like other workers in the industry, the sewing and pressing operators at the Brownley Company plants are accustomed to working short weeks in slack seasons and to occasional brief layoffs.

Studies at various plants show that pressing lines are in operation an average of 440 minutes per eight-hour shift. At one of the better managed plants the pressing lines are regularly shut down for five minutes each hour. The manager of that plant recommends this procedure. He says it meets the personal requirements of the workers

---

[2] In determining the speed at which a conveyor should be set, the methods engineers add 10% to the observed work time as an allowance to take care of delays at the work stations.

and gives his maintenance men opportunity to keep the conveyors in good operating condition. Over two years have passed since it was necessary to shut down one of his lines because of mechanical failure.

Recently the company initiated a methods study of all of its pressing operations and particularly of the conveyor pressing system. The engineer conducting the methods study reported the following findings:

1. All of the plants using the conveyor pressing system employ different job breakdown methods. Even the plant that operates the most nearly balanced conveyor lines has overloaded the Number 1 work station. Exhibit 2 lists the operations performed at each work station on the best balanced line observed by the methods engineer.

2. The pressing performed at the Number 3 work station could be speeded up by introducing a new type of iron (see Exhibit 3) and by changing the motions for ironing shirt fronts (Exhibit 4).

3. The time required for the two spraying operations can be reduced by 0.022 minutes on each spraying operation by installing Bengal-Gray vertical nozzle sprayers (Exhibit 5).

4. The "touch-up pressing" operation (Operation 11, Exhibit 2) could be eliminated without any apparent loss of quality. Tests of shirts that have been boxed for shipment reveal that experienced inspectors usually cannot distinguish between shirts on which Operation 11 has been performed and those upon which this operation has been omitted.

The engineer is convinced that the handling of pressed shirts when boxing them and the handling, transporting, and storage of boxed shirts prior to shipment often eliminate all of the improvement in appearance that results from touch-up pressing at Operation 11. The sales manager of the Brownley Shirt Company is not entirely convinced that the engineer is right.

Exhibit 6 presents the times observed by the methods engineer at the most efficient of the conveyor lines and the new times that would be feasible by adopting the equipment and methods changes described and then rebalancing the line. All of the operators on the pressing conveyors are paid piecework rates and the rate is set to allow the operators on a normal line to earn $1.90 per hour.

EXHIBIT 2   THE BROWNLEY SHIRT COMPANY

OPERATIONS PERFORMED AT EACH WORK STATION
ON BEST BALANCED CONVEYOR LINE

Station No. 1

Operation 1. Obtain shirt, spray, obtain iron, press patch, put iron aside.
            2. Button front and collar, lay shirt on pallet.
            3. Position cuffs and press two cuffs.

Station No. 2

Operation 4. Get pin, insert in collar front, place collar form and center pin.
            5. Place collar insert.

Station No. 3

Operation 6. Spray shirt front.
            7. Press shirt front.
            8. Remove collar form and pin, turn shirt over.

Station No. 4

Operation 9. Position packing tissue and board in shirt.
         10. Finish fold, complete.

Station No. 5

Operation 11. Touch-up pressing.
         12. Insert 2 pins, lay shirt on inspection table.

EXHIBIT 3 THE BROWNLEY SHIRT COMPANY

COMPARISON OF REGULAR IRON WITH PROPOSED IRON
FOR PRESSING AT CONVEYOR STATION NUMBER 3

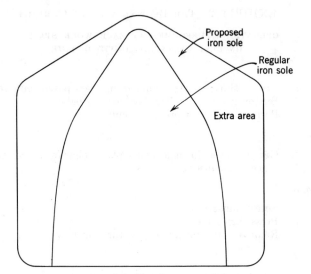

	Regular	*Proposed*
Wattage	600–1,000	1,200
Weight	6¼ lbs	6 lbs
Length	7 ³⁄₁₆ in.	7⁹⁄₁₆ in.
Width	4⅛ in.	6 in.
Sole area	21–24 sq. in.	36 sq. in.
Cost	$10.00	$20.00
Maintenance cost per year	$10.00	$10.00
Expected life	10 years	10 years

EXHIBIT 4   THE BROWNLEY SHIRT COMPANY

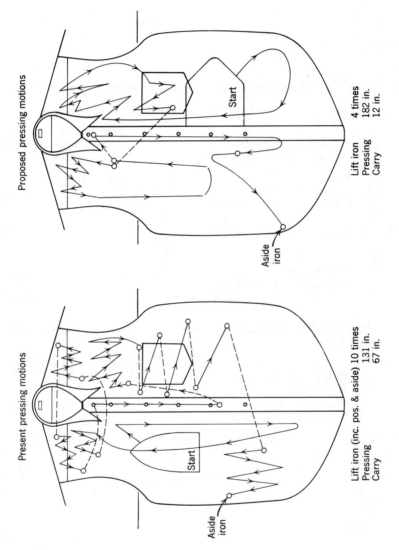

Present pressing motions

Proposed pressing motions

Start

Aside iron

Lift iron (inc. pos. & aside) 10 times
Pressing   131 in.
Carry   67 in.

Start

Aside iron

Lift iron   4 times
Pressing   182 in.
Carry   12 in.

EXHIBIT 5   THE BROWNLEY SHIRT COMPANY

ANALYSIS OF SPRAYER METHOD CHANGE

Movements Involved In Regular Sprayer Operation

○	Reach for spray nozzle and bring to work	0.011
○	Spray	0.033
○	Return nozzle to hook and hang up	0.016
		0.060 min

Movements Involved With Use of Proposed Bengal-Gray Sprayer

○	Reach for Spray Nozzle	0.004
○	Spray	0.033
○	Release	0.001
		0.038 min

Approximately 0.022 minutes saved per spraying operation with the Bengal-Gray sprayer.

	Regular	Bengal-Gray
Cost of sprayer, each	$5	$10
Expected life	15 years	15 years
Maintenance cost	$1 per year	$1 per year
Cost of installation, per sprayer	—	$15

EXHIBIT 6   THE BROWNLEY SHIRT COMPANY

ACTUAL AND PROPOSED OPERATION TIMES ON CONVEYOR PRESSING (TIMES IN MINUTES)

Operation	Present Times						Proposed Times					
	Station					Total	Station					Total
	1	2	3	4	5		1	2	3	4	5	
1. Obtain shirt, spray, obtain iron, press patch, put iron aside	0.19					0.19	0.168[a]					0.168
2. Button front and collar												
Lay shirt on pallet	0.19					0.19	0.19					0.19
3. Position cuffs and press two cuffs	0.06					0.06		0.06				0.06
4. Get pin, insert in collar front, place collar form and center pin		0.23				0.23		0.23				0.23
5. Place collar insert		0.12				0.12			0.12			0.12
6. Spray shirt front			0.06			0.06		0.038[a]				0.038
7. Press shirt front			0.26			0.26			0.22[b]			0.22
8. Remove collar form and pin, turn shirt over			0.10			0.10				0.10		0.10
9. Position packing tissue and board in shirt				0.255		0.255				0.255		0.255
10. Finish fold, complete				0.16		0.16					0.16	0.16
11. Touch-up pressing					0.18	0.18					[c]	
12. Insert 2 pins, lay shirt on inspection table					0.18	0.18					0.18	0.18
TOTAL	0.44	0.35	0.42	0.415	0.36	1.985	0.358	0.328	0.34	0.355	0.34	1.721

Notes:

a. Install spray—See Exhibit 5.

b. Purchase new type iron and follow new method—See Exhibit 4.

c. Omit this operation on basis of test.

Paragon Camera Company (II)

The Paragon Camera Company, one of the oldest manufacturers of home-movie equipment, had proven over the years to be a style leader of the industry. To maintain this market position the company conducted an aggressive marketing campaign which included the introduction of an improved 8mm camera and projector each year at the trade show held in March. A follow-up nationwide advertising campaign, aimed at stimulating demand for the new model, was conducted during the summer and fall. Paragon's sales program focused on the Christmas buying season, as this period accounted for two-thirds of its sales. A new model normally had required at least one year of design and development work before production could begin. In addition to the new models, the company continued to produce older cameras and projectors for which a demand existed. Thus, the manufacturing operation was continually developing a new product, bringing into production a prototype model, and producing several old models of cameras and projectors.

The management of Paragon was organized to provide a flexible manufacturing operation sensitive to changes in demand. The three divisions of engineering, sales, and manufacturing reported to the executive vice president who coordinated the planning stages of new models. The Engineering Division had the responsibility of developing new models and products. After engineering had developed a model, a sales forecast would be prepared by the marketing division for approval by top management. Engineering would direct the fabrication of prototype models for the new product and deliver them to manufacturing for production-planning purposes. The manufacturing division would then establish a master production schedule which would provide for the necessary facilities to produce the proposed model at the forecasted rate.

Within the manufacturing division the following departments were concerned with planning for new products: Planning, Process Engineering, Methods, Fabrication, and Assembly. The Planning Department prepared a master schedule which identified the route, quantities, and due date of all parts to be fabricated, specified which parts were to be purchased, and stated the dates they should be delivered. The Process-Engineering Department modified designs for unexpected malfunctionings, coordinated development tooling, and improved designs to produce a more economical and reliable product. The methods group worked in an advisory capacity with the line foremen to develop material-handling routines, workplace layouts, and standard methods and times for operations within departments.

Master Scheduling for the P-62 Camera

In the winter of 1961, the engineering division completed the design and development of the P-62 Camera. The marketing division intended to introduce the model at the dealers' show in March and expected it to be the prime camera of Paragon's 1962 line. On the basis of past experience with other new models, the state of the economy, and other variables, the 1962 (i.e., March through December) sales forecast for P-62s was set at 26,000 units, with an expectation that the monthly sales volume would reach 4,700 units by August. These forecasts, together with complete, detailed drawings and 12 working models of the P-62 were given to the manufacturing superintendent in January. He directed the Planning Department to prepare a schedule calling for production of 4,700 cameras a month by June, and a cumulative production total of 26,000 completed units by Thanksgiving.

In response to this assignment the Planning Department first established a master schedule for the purchase (or fabrication) of parts and their assembly into P-62 Cameras at a stable rate of 4,700 units per month. The first step was to decide the source of each part—whether to make it at the Paragon plant or buy it partially fabricated, a decision dependent upon the capabilities of the plant and the economics of the situation. Paragon had extensive punch-press, machine-screw, and metal-finishing facilities, but lacked die-casting machines and facilities for producing optical parts. Thus the camera casings and lenses invariably were purchased. A few parts, such as springs or standard screws, were cheaper purchased than fabricated and were obtained from outside suppliers.

The Planning Department then analyzed each part to specify its manufacturing requirements and to determine its routing. A part

such as a gear or a shaft started as bar stock in the receiving area; it was then forwarded to the Screw-Machine Department for fabrication, to the Finishing Department for plating, next to subassembly work stations, and then to the Final-Assembly Department. The routing of purchased parts ranged from those such as camera cases, which required extensive machining and finishing, to those such as lenses which were inspected upon receipt and forwarded immediately to the final-assembly line. The routing operation included the specification of subassemblies which were quite often standard subassemblies that had been developed over the years. For these standard subassemblies, standard data on routes and times were available.

The planning group, using the route sheets as a guide, worked backward from the final-assembly production rate to establish a time schedule on the basis of past time requirements for the processing of set part quantities. This assumed that the fabrication and assembly of the new model would not involve any unusual processes or delays. The planners allowed for two days' move time per part between departments, and included 20 per cent excess assembly time for flexibility. To reach a level of 4,700 parts per month by June, the rate was then broken into weekly target rates during the development stage.

Under the plans developed, the final-assembly line was scheduled to start up in March, and to reach a rate of 50 cameras per week by the second week in April. It was then expected to double its output each of the next four weeks to attain a rate of 800 cameras per week by the third week in May; the goal was to level out at a rate of 1,100 cameras per week the first week in June. This gradual build-up was to allow workers to be trained, material-flow and handling procedures to be worked out, and the bottlenecks that accompanied new-model introductions to be eliminated. With these final-assembly quantities established, the dates and quantities of parts and subassemblies could be specified.

Detail Scheduling of the P-62 Camera

The Planning Department's completed master schedule was given to the manufacturing superintendent the last week in January. The superintendent approved the schedule with minor changes and gave a copy, plus blueprints and, when appropriate, sample assemblies to each line foreman for detail planning. The foremen were expected to specify methods, standard times, a start date, and material requirements for each part processing for which they were responsible. The Methods Department would assist them in establishing methods

and setting the times. Tooling construction had begun concurrently with the planning stage and was expected to be completed prior to the production start-up in March.

The P-62 Camera prototype, as delivered to manufacturing by engineering for detail planning, consisted of 233 parts, the majority of which went into 12 major subassemblies before final assembly. The work stations for the subassemblies were fairly standard, as only half the subassemblies for the new camera included redesigned parts. The six subassemblies which made up the drive mechanism of the camera, for example, were unchanged from the previous year's model. Standard methods and times for these subassemblies, which included the motor, the shutter, the shutter-stop assembly, the bracket assembly for holding the motor, the drive gears, and the film footage-counter assembly, were therefore already in effect in the shop.

The majority of the remaining parts were modifications of former parts and assemblies. The methods for these stations were established primarily on a basis of past experience with similar parts, plus reliance on method principles. Old-time standards were used where applicable and, if possible, MTM[1] times were built up for new parts. When production started, a follow-up work-simplification study was made on all predetermined work methods.

Each department foreman worked with the methods analyst in defining standard operations, workplace layouts, and standard times for each of the parts assigned to him by the Planning Department. He then determined the date on which the appropriate quantities of parts should be started into production in his department in order to assure delivery to the next department in accordance with the schedule.

Designing the Final-Assembly Line of the P-62 Camera

The most complex detail-planning activity was the design of the final-assembly line. The department foreman and his two method-study assistants decided, after experimenting with the working model and using typical camera-assembly methods, that final assembly of the P-62 Camera could be accomplished in 59 steps. This total included several inspections for appearance as well as for proper functioning to insure that quality was built into the product.

Next, the standard times for these 59 steps were determined. Twenty of the steps were identical to those used in the previous year's model. For these assembly operations, the old-time standards were used. For example, the motor assembly for the P-62 was the same as

---

[1] See Exhibit 1 for an example of establishing a standard using MTM.

that of the previous year's model and was to be assembled with the crown gear in the same manner previously employed. The old standard of 0.00641 hour was applicable.

In the case of 22 steps, minor changes in design seemed to make the use of historical times inappropriate, but the motions to adapt to these changes could be readily visualized, and MTM methods were therefore used as a sole determinant of the method and time required for the operation (Exhibit 1).

Sixteen of the steps were sufficiently unique, or dissimilar to those previously employed, that Paragon personnel decided that MTM or past experience could not provide an adequate standard. The majority of these operations were inspections for which the motions were difficult to visualize. For such operations the foreman or an experienced operator performed the defined operation until he achieved some proficiency. Methods Department personnel then timed the operations to obtain an estimated standard time.

After completion of all these activities a total time of 0.178 hour per camera was established for the complete 59-step final assembly of the P-62.

The next phase of pre-production planning was to establish the number of work stations required for the line. The foreman planned for a continuous line with no duplication of stations and hand-material passing for the assembly of cameras. This method had worked successfully in the past, and the work benches were currently set up for this type of line. To determine the number of stations required, one merely obtained the total assembly time required for the planned daily production rate, and then divided by the standard, eight-hour day. The target rate of 1,100 cameras per week, or 220 per day, multiplied by the 0.178 standard hours of assembly gave 39.2 hours divided by 8, establishing the need for five stations. The line was intentionally established on the basis of the standard rate of output even though assembly workers typically maintained a rate between 110 and 145 per cent of standard. This created a certain amount of slack time which could be used by the foreman to take up unaccountable delays or changes in demand.

Balancing the P-62 Final-Assembly Line

The developmental group of foremen and methods men then began to establish the work stations on the assembly line. The group was trying to establish a perfectly balanced line; that is, an assembly line in which each work station required exactly the same amount of time to perform the elements assigned to it. Their goal was a thin,

EXHIBIT 1 PARAGON CAMERA COMPANY (II)

MTM ELEMENT ANALYSIS

MTM ELEMENT ANALYSIS

PART____*Position #1 Step 6*_____ PART NO._____ DEPT. *Final Assy*

OPERATION. *Get + Drive 2 Screws Through Claw Brkt To Mech. Plate*____ DATE *2/14*

DESCRIPTION — LEFT HAND	MOTION	TMU	MOTION	DESCRIPTION — RIGHT HAND
Get + Drive 2 screws thru Claw Brkt To Mech Plate				
	R12C	14.2	A12B	
Get 1st Screw	G4B	9.1	R2A	Get Air Screw Driver (SD)
Talk " "	G2	5.6		
	R2C	5.9		
Get 2nd Screw	G4B	9.1		
Move " " To Air Driver	M12C	15.2	H6C	
		25.3	P(2S)SD	Pos Air SD in Screw in LH
Release " "	RL1	2.0		
	R5D	9.4		
Grasp Brkt w/4 Finger	G5	0		
Push To Left	AP1	16.2		
		9.2	H5C	
		21.8	P2SD	Pos Screw into Mech Plate
		16.3	AP1	Push Down
		10.5	Drive	Screw 5 Thds
Release Brkt	RL2	0		
	R2A	6.9	H4B	Move Air SD Away
Grasp Alignment Pin in Assy	G1A	2.0		
Pull " " out of "	D1E	4.0		
	M10B	12.2		
Aside " " To Bench	RL1	2.0		
Move 2nd Screw To SD in RH	M10C	13.5	M4C	
Regrasp Screw	G5	25.3	P(2S)SD	Pos Air SD in Screw in LH
		9.0	M4C	
		21.8	P2SD	Pos Screw into Mech Plate
		16.2	AP1	Push Down
	RL2	10.5	Drive	Screw 5 Thds.
Reach To +	R4D	13.4	M12B	Aside Driver
Grasp Claw Position of Gage	G1B	3.8	R2E	
Move Gage out of Assy	D2D	11.8		
	M12B	13.4		
Aside Gage To Bench	RL1	2.0		
	TOTAL =	336.5	@ 1.13 % = .00381 hrs/pc	

SHEET_____OF_____SHEETS

fast-moving stream of parts that would minimize in-process inventory, maintain an equitable work balance within the line, and allow workers to contribute equally to the production of cameras. Various complications, however, prevented the full achievement of a perfect balance, that is, a line in which each station would have 0.0356 (0.178 ÷ 5) standard hours of work assigned to it.

The foremost limitation on dividing the 59 steps into five equal work stations was the sequence limitation on the steps required to put the camera together. The inside of the camera had to be assembled before the case could be put on; this required first the assembly of the motor and shutter assembly; the case had to be assembled in order to permit the camera front and lens to be mounted; etc. Notwithstanding such limitations, a number of alternative methods of assembly did exist, since several phases of the assembly were not limited as to sequence.

The second limiting factor was workplace layout. There was only so much work room available at each station, and large equipment would interfere with other operations. Thus, bulky inspection equipment was spread out to various stations to allow all equipment to be reached with ease from a sitting position.

A third limitation arose from the fact that in addition to attempting to obtain an even balance of times, the group endeavored to provide smooth work-method patterns for each assembly line to reduce worker fatigue and process time.

The developmental group began to set up the line by dividing the camera assembly into five general parts. They felt the shutter assembly and motor should be first; the second station would be concerned with inspection and would add the bracket for support of the motor and shutter assembly. The third station would finish assembling the working parts of the camera, add the case, and inspect the running machine. The fourth station would add the front of the camera, including the finder-lens assembly and the label. At the final station the aperture lens would be installed and miscellaneous parts added. This general grouping afforded a basis for dividing the 59 steps into five equal parts. After juggling elements around (for example, the spring clip was taken from the third station to the final station, as the third station seemed to be longer; the fourth station, which was next longest, was relieved of cleaning the lens thread, which was also shifted to the fifth position), a line was obtained which varied from 0.0389 hour per camera at station three, to 0.0328 hour at station five. The planning group anticipated changes in these times and

EXHIBIT 2 PARAGON CAMERA COMPANY (II)

PART NAME *P62 F.A. LINE*   DWG. NO. *F.A.*   OPER. NO. *Pos # 5*

OPERATION NAME *Pos # 5 of 5 Pos. LINE*

CLASSIFICATION *10*

.26
STD. PCS. PER HR.

STD. HRS. PER
100 PIECES   *3.85*

INSPECTION SPECS.

ACTUAL STD. FOR THIS POSITION IS 3.61 HOURS/HUNDRED

OPERATION CARD — I

BRIEF DESCRIPTION OF METHOD USED

L. H.	R. H.
GET CAMERA	
GUNK (2) SPOTS	
POSITION IN FIXTURE	
ASBLE TENSION PLATE SPRING ASSY + TENSION PLATE	
CHECK TENSION PLATE W/ GAGE	
DRIOS (2) CASE SCREWS TO NECK CASTING	
REMOVE FROM FIXTURE, RE-POSITION IN FIXTURE	
ASBLE CRANK SPRING CUP	
GET + FIT COVER	
BLOW OFF LENS THREADS	
GET LENS, CLEAN W/ CLOTH, POS TO CASTING + TURN IN	
APPLY LOCKTITE TO LENS THDS.	
ASIDE	
— FREQ. ELEMENTS —	
ASIDE FULL TRAY - GET EMPTY	
OPEN PKG. OF LENSES, REMOVE FROM BAGS.	
RECORD COUNT ON YELLOW SLIP.	

NOTE: ANY APPRECIABLE CHANGE IN THE ABOVE OPERATING CONDITIONS WILL AUTOMATICALLY NULLIFY THIS STANDARD.

DATE *2/17/61.*	ANALYST *PM*	APPROVED	DEPT. *CAMERA*

MONROE FORM 157 5M-5/61

felt that during the trial runs a more even flow could be obtained. An example of the rough card made to define what each trial work station should perform is shown in Exhibit 2.

Workplaces were then designed by the methods people with appropriate trays, power-driven screwdrivers, grease receptacles, inspection devices, and other items required for the tasks assigned to each station. These work stations were constructed on a long, continuous table with two to three feet between each station for temporary storage of work in process.

The initial lots of parts scheduled for fabrication and subassembly were in small batches, to allow the details of production to be worked out. Early in March enough of these parts were available to start trial assembly runs. This trial run was supervised closely by the final-assembly foreman, who had selected his five most experienced assem-

blers to work on the line. During the trial run with production parts it was seen that 11 operations not considered in the planning stages were necessary in the final assembly and five planned operations no longer were required. Eight new operations were required and five old ones eliminated because of engineering changes in the camera. Two more inspections were required and allowance had to be made for greasing two spots on the tension plate mounting. These changes resulted in station 2's actually requiring more time than originally planned. To compensate for this, three of the elements formerly assigned to station 2 were shifted to stations 3 and 4.

Definition and Evaluation of the Final-Assembly Line

After about 60 cameras had been produced and the line appeared to be balanced with a smooth work flow, a detailed operation chart was made. A copy was put at each work station showing the specific steps to be followed in carrying out the operation at that station. The detailed operation chart included a layout for each workplace, a detailed description of each step, and times, allowances, and expected delays allocated to each station (for example, taking away full trays of cameras or drawing new boxes of lenses). Exhibit 3 is the operation chart for station 3. Exhibit 4 is a pictorial view of the layout of the final-assembly line.

The line as finally evolved had 65 elements apportioned among five positions, with a maximum work-station time of 0.0388 hour. The minimum standard time required was 0.0344 hour at station 4. Exhibit 5 is a detailed description of the operations and standard times for each of the five stations.

The difference between the total time required and the sum of the standard times allowed for the separate operations was considered by the final-assembly foreman to be a reasonable measure of line efficiency. In the case of the P-62 model the total assembly time for a camera was 0.0388 hour $\times$ 5 stations = 0.1940 hour. The total of the standard hours worked was 0.0386 + 0.0388 + 0.0385 + 0.0344 + 0.0361 = 0.1864 hour. The efficiency of a line was the difference between total station and total standard time, referred to as *process allowance*, divided by the standard time. Within Paragon an effort was made to keep this figure under 10 per cent, and an assembly line was considered to be in good balance if the inefficiency was between 3 and 7 per cent. In the case of the P-62 line, the figure was

$$\frac{(0.1940 - 0.1864) \times 100}{0.1864} = 4.1 \text{ per cent.}$$

EXHIBIT 3 PARAGON CAMERA COMPANY (II)

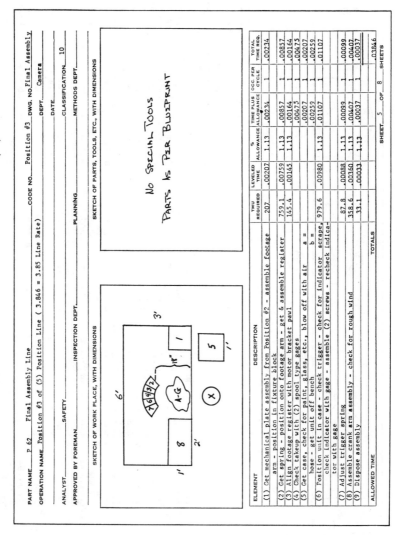

PART NAME___P 62___Final Assembly Line_____CODE NO.___Position #3___DWG. NO.__Final Assembly__

OPERATION NAME__Position #3 of (5) Position Line (3.846 = 3.85 Line Rate)_____DEPT.___Camera_____

ANALYST_____SAFETY_____INSPECTION DEPT._____PLANNING_____CLASSIFICATION__10__

APPROVED BY FOREMAN_____METHODS DEPT._____

SKETCH OF WORK PLACE, WITH DIMENSIONS

SKETCH OF PARTS, TOOLS, ETC., WITH DIMENSIONS

No Special Tools

Parts Is Per Blueprint

ELEMENT DESCRIPTION	THU REQUIRED	LEVELED TIME	% ALLOWANCE	TIME PLUS ALLOWANCE	OCC. PER CYCLE	TOTAL TIME REQ.
(1) Get mechanical plate assembly from Position #2 - assemble footage arm - position in fixture block	207	.00207	1.13	.00234	1	.00234
(2) Get spring - position onto footage arm - get & assemble register	759.1	.00759	1.13	.00857	1	.00857
(3) Align footage register with motor bracket pawl	145.4	.00145	1.13	.00164	1	.00164
(4) Check takeup with (2) spool type gages				.00475	1	.00475
(5) Get case, check for paint, glass, etc., blow off with air a =				.00207	1	.00207
hose - get unit off bench b =				.00259	1	.00259
(6) Position unit in case - check trigger - check for indicator scrape,	979.6	.00980	1.13	.01107	1	.01107
check indicator with gage - assemble (2) screws - recheck indica-						
tor with gage						
(7) Adjust trigger spring	87.8	.00088	1.13	.00099	1	.00099
(8) Assemble crank arm assembly - check for rough wind	358.6	.00360	1.13	.00407	1	.00407
(9) Dispose assembly	33.1	.00033	1.13	.00037	1	.00037
ALLOWED TIME TOTALS						.03846

SHEET__5__OF__8__SHEETS

EXHIBIT 4 PARAGON CAMERA COMPANY (II)

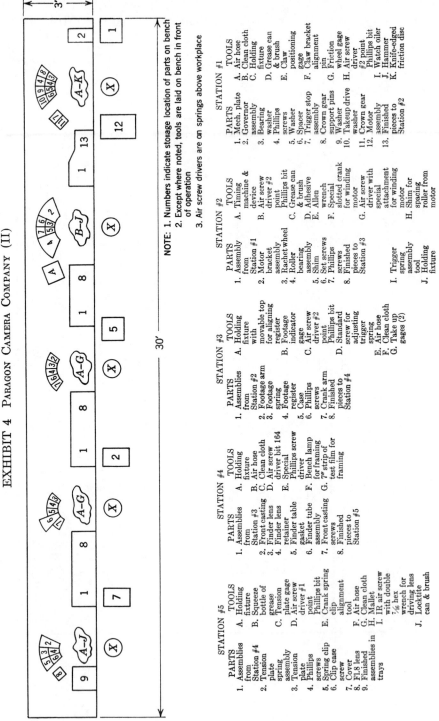

NOTE: 1. Numbers indicate storage location of parts on bench
2. Except where noted, tools are laid on bench in front of operation
3. Air screw drivers are on springs above workplace

STATION #1

PARTS
1. Mech. plate
2. Governor assembly
3. Bearing washer
4. Phillips screws
5. Washer
6. Spacer
7. Trigger stop assembly
8. Crown gear support pins
9. Washer
10. Takeup drive washer
11. Crown gear
12. Motor assembly
13. Finished pieces to Station #2

TOOLS
A. Air hose
B. Clean cloth
C. Holding fixture
D. Grease can & brush
E. Claw positioning gage
F. Claw bracket alignment pin
G. Friction wheel gage
H. Air screw driver #2 point Phillips bit
I. Watch oiler
J. Hammer
K. Knife-edged friction disc

STATION #2

PARTS
1. Assembly from Station #1
2. Motor bracket assembly
3. Rachet wheel
4. Roller bearing assembly
5. Shim
6. Set screws
7. Phillips screws
8. Finished pieces to Station #3
I. Trigger spring assembly
J. Holding fixture

TOOLS
A. Timing machine & device
B. Air screw driver #2 point Phillips bit
C. Grease can & brush
D. Adhesive
E. Allen wrench
F. Special slotted crank for winding motor
G. Air screw driver with special attachment for winding motor
H. Shim for spacing roller from motor

STATION #3

PARTS
1. Assemblies from Station #2
2. Footage arm
3. Footage spring
4. Footage register
5. Case
6. Phillips screws
7. Crank arm
8. Finished pieces to Station #4

TOOLS
A. Holding fixture with movable top for aligning register
B. Footage indicator gage
C. Air screw driver #2 point Phillips bit
D. Standard screw for adjusting trigger spring
E. Air hose
F. Clean cloth
G. Take up gages (2)

STATION #4

PARTS
1. Assemblies from Station #3
2. Front casting
3. Finder lens
4. Finder lens retainer
5. Finder table gasket
6. Finder tube assembly
7. Front casting screws
8. Finished pieces to Station #5

TOOLS
A. Holding fixture
B. Air hose
C. Clean cloth
D. Air screw driver bit 164
E. Special Phillips screw driver
F. Bench lamp for framing
G. 7" strip of test film for framing

STATION #5

PARTS
1. Assemblies from Station #4
2. Tension plate spring assembly
3. Tension plate
4. Phillips screws
5. Spring clip
6. Clip case screw
7. Cover
8. Fl.8 lens
9. Finished assemblies in trays

TOOLS
A. Holding fixture
B. Squeeze bottle of grease
C. Tension plate gage
D. Air screw driver #1 point Phillips bit
E. Crank spring clip alignment tool
F. Air hose
G. Clean cloth
H. Mallet
I. IR air screw with double 7/16 hex wrench for driving lens
J. Locktite can & brush

EXHIBIT 5 PARAGON CAMERA COMPANY (II)

PARTS ASSEMBLED AT STATION #1

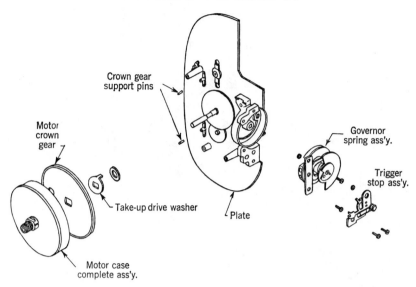

Detailed Description and Time for Station 1	Time plus Allowance
1. Get mech. plate, check, blow out governor well, wipe w/cloth	0.00304
2. Position mech.-plate assembly in fixture	0.00105
3. Get governor assembly, check, grease bracket and end of shaft, position bearing washer; position into mech. plate, check shutter and claw movement	0.00451
4. Get and position claw position gauge—align bracket assembly w/mech. plate	0.00151
5. Get and position claw bracket alignment pin	0.00071
6. Get and drive (2) screws through claw bracket to mech. plate	0.00381
7. Check up-and-down play of claw (should not stick)	0.00027
8. Assemble washer, spacer, and trigger-stop assembly	0.00831
9. Check claw and cam assembly for play—adjust	0.00129
10. Get and position friction-wheel gauge on motor post	0.00094
11. Use friction disc	0.00233
12. Remove and aside gauge	0.00034
13. Assemble (2) crown-gear support pins, grease pins and motor post	0.00304
14. Assemble washers to motor post	0.00089
15. Align friction disc	0.00036
16. Assemble crown gear to motor assembly, blow off, grease (3) spots, assemble take-up–drive washer, position to post, seat and dispose to next station	0.00641
	0.0386

EXHIBIT 5 (*Continued*)

PARTS ASSEMBLED AT STATION #2

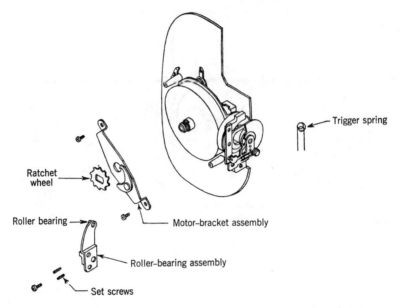

Detailed Description and Time for Station 2	Time plus Allowance
1. Get and position mech. unit in fixture	0.00125
2. Assemble motor bracket assembly and bearing-shoe–roller-bearing assembly to mech. plate	0.00646
3. Assemble ratchet wheel to motor shaft	0.00126
4. Position shim between motor and roller to insure clearance	0.00114
5. Assemble 1st set screw to bearing assembly (use Eastman 910), get 2d screw to wrench and dip in adhesive	0.00420
6. Get special slotted crank, wind unit several times	0.00178
7. Assemble 2d set screw to bearing assembly	0.00151
8. Adjust for free running w/Allen wrench	0.00308
9. Position air-driver adapter, turn to check shutter movement	0.00103
10. Wind unit w/air driver	0.00132
11. Check, and adjust for even sound	0.00493
12. Position device on take-up shaft, check timing in timing machine	0.00257
13. Get unit (after timing), check for free movement w/air-driver adapter	0.00278
14. Wind unit w/air driver	0.00172
15. Assemble trigger spring	0.00237
16. Check for continuous and single shot	0.00105
17. Dispose to station 3	0.00037
	0.0388

EXHIBIT 5 (*Continued*)

PARTS ASSEMBLED AT STATION #3

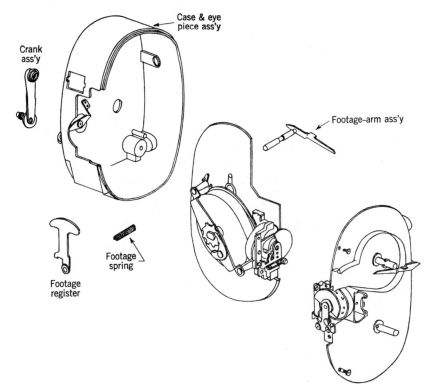

	Time plus
Detailed Description and Time for Station 3	Allowance

1. Get mech.-plate assembly from Station 2—assemble
   footage arm, position in fixture and lock   0.00234
2. Get spring—position onto footage arm—get and assemble
   register   0.00857
3. Align footage register w/motor-bracket pawl   0.00164
4. Check take-up w/(2) spool-type gauges   0.00475
5. Get case, check for paint, glass, etc., blow out w/air hose   a = 0.00207
   get unit off bench   b = 0.00259
6. Position unit in case—check trigger—check for indicator
   scrape, check indicator w/gauge—assemble (2) screws—
   recheck indicator w/gauge   0.01107
7. Adjust trigger spring   0.00099
8. Assemble crank arm—check for rough wind   0.00407
9. Dispose assembly   0.00037

     0.0385

EXHIBIT 5 (*Continued*)

PARTS ASSEMBLED AT STATION #4

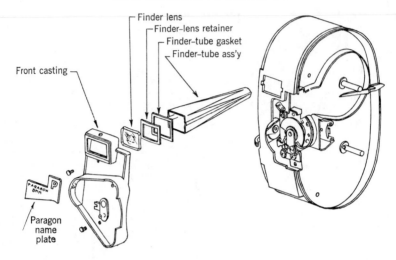

Detailed Description and Time for Station 4	Time plus Allowance
1. Get labeled front casting, blow out aperture and lens threads	a = 0.00121
Visual check for condition of paint, get and position finder lens	b = 0.00172
and retainer	c = 0.00329
2. Get unit from Station 3	0.00046
3. Assemble gasket and tube—position in case	0.00337
4. Get air hose—blow out sight tube—aside hose	0.00072
5. Position front-casting assembly onto case assembly	a = 0.00052
	b = 0.00303
6. Get, position, and drive (2) front castings to unit screws	0.00299
7. Recheck finder lens for cracking and look for hair on lens	0.00084
8. Check single shot, noise, and trigger action	0.00337
9. Frame camera	0.01193
10. Dispose	0.00037
Frequently reclean and reassemble dirty glass	0.00062
	0.0344

EXHIBIT 5 (*Continued*)

PARTS ASSEMBLED AT STATION #5

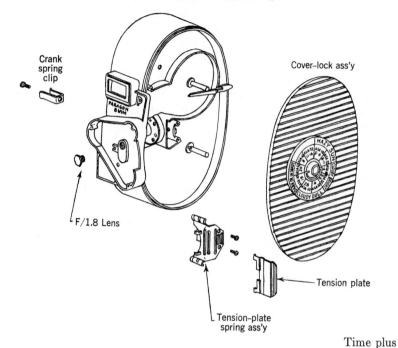

Crank spring clip

Cover–lock ass'y

F/1.8 Lens

Tension plate

Tension–plate spring ass'y

Detailed Description and Time for Station 5	Time plus Allowance
1. Get camera	0.00046
2. Grease (2) spots	0.00447
3. Position in fixture	0.00044
4. Assemble tension-plate spring assembly and tension plate	0.00665
5. Check tension-plate assembly w/gauge	0.00248
6. Drive (2) case screws to mech. plate	0.00191
7. Remove from fixture, reposition in fixture	0.00093
8. Assemble crank spring clip	0.00383
9. Get and fit cover	0.00330
10. Blow off lens threads	0.00082
11. Get lens clean w/cloth, position to front casting and turn in	0.00505
12. Apply locktite to lens threads	0.00092
13. Aside	0.00055
Frequently (1) Aside loaded tray—get empty	0.00062
(2) Open package of lenses, remove bags	0.00245
(3) Record count on yellow slip	0.00123
	0.0361

Even though this was considered quite satisfactory, a continuous effort was made by the Methods Department and the supervisors to detect further opportunities for improvements.

In late summer, after the line had been in production for over three months and had achieved its output goal of 1,100 cameras per week with ease, unexpected increases in demand created new pressures for increased output. Paragon normally planned production output of new models to allow considerable slack to take care of such increased demand. The operators on the five-station lines had been able to increase their output to 138 per cent of standard, thus producing 1,400 cameras per week. An additional hour of overtime was scheduled in July, which increased the output of the camera about 10 per cent to a production rate of 1,550 cameras per week. Notwithstanding these increases, inventories were being depleted faster than expected. The Production Department was informed by the Sales Division that the demand schedule should be revised to 8,000 per month. The manufacturing superintendent and the assembly-line foreman decided that the present five-man line could not be expected to achieve this increase nor even to maintain the present rate throughout the entire fall. A decision was made to increase the final-assembly capacity.

Art-Tone Cards

During the latter part of the past year, the Boxing Department of Art-Tone Cards experienced changes both in the manual methods for assembling and packing cards and in the personnel supervising these operations. These changes and further developments in January of the current year left what Art-Tone managers termed "unresolved problems."

Company Background

Art-Tone Cards is one of several medium-sized companies in the greeting card industry. Its plant in Detroit produces greeting cards and also a small amount of gift wrapping material. Art-Tone is an integrated producer: it designs, prints, and distributes greeting cards to retail outlets.

In recent years, Art-Tone's sales have been in excess of $10 million. Approximately half of the sales are from "seasonal cards"—those for generally recognized holidays. Christmas cards account for one-half of all the seasonal sales. The balance of sales are in "everyday cards," such as birthday and get-well cards, which display no seasonal sales pattern. The company offers 4,000 different card designs.

The predominant distribution method in the greeting card industry is direct sale to retail outlets. Like Hallmark Cards, the largest company in the industry, Art-Tone sells exclusively to retailers, who generally market the cards from display racks. It is customary for the rack spaces to be allocated to several card manfacturers, with the retailer deciding what percentage of the rack is given to each manufacturer. It is generally conceded in the industry that sales are a function of the rack space allocated to a company by retailers.

The Detroit Plant

Art-Tone's Detroit plant, employing 1,000 people, is the company's only production facility in the United States. Most employees are

members of a union. The two-story plant building, two years old, is located in a suburban area. The second floor houses the art and verse departments, the photographic department, and some of the administrative offices. Printing and other production departments and the main offices are located on the ground floor.

Card production begins in the art and verse departments, where the creative part of the process takes place. Cards are printed on offset presses, using plates prepared by a photographic process. After printing, some cards are embossed, and all the large sheets on which the cards are printed are cut to obtain the single, unfolded cards. The cards are then sorted by design and automatically folded. After folding, the cards are transported to another area where women workers apply special effects and tie ribbons where required. Throughout these operations and those that follow the operators continually inspect the cards, as they handle them, for dirt, oil smears, off-registered colors, wrinkles, process defects, and other faults.

At this point cards are packed in wooden crates, each holding about 2,000 cards, and moved to storage to be ready for final counting and packing. Envelopes are held in a separate inventory. Art-Tone's major supplier of envelopes is located nearby and can deliver envelopes of a requested size within one week after an order is placed. The envelopes are bundled by the supplier in packs of 12, fastened by a paper band.

Mr. Rorick, the Plant Manager, supervises all the production activities on the ground floor. Three subordinates report directly to him, each responsible for one part of the production process. Bert Suvalle, one of the three, was hospitalized in December with a heart attack. By early January his condition had improved enough for him to leave the hospital, but it was uncertain when he might be able to return to work. Mr. Suvalle's responsibility is the Finishing Section, which includes the operations from special effects application through final shipment. Three hundred workers, mostly women, work in the Finishing Section and are supervised by six floor ladies who report directly to Mr. Suvalle. In January they were supervised by the Plant Manager. One of these floor ladies, Miss Hudson, is in charge of the Boxing Department.

The Boxing Department

The Boxing Department prepares both everyday and seasonal cards for the Order-Filling Department. The cards are received in the Boxing Department in the wooden crates, and envelope bundles are delivered to the department in sizes corresponding to the cards to

be processed. The workers count the cards and place them in piles of 12. A bundle of envelopes is placed with each pile. The combined stack of 12 cards and 12 envelopes is then put in a container, which in turn is placed in a corrugated paper box. The corrugated boxes, called "shippers," are used for delivery to the Order-Filling Department.

When the shippers go to the Order-Filling Department they contain only one card design. The order-fillers make up shipments to customers by taking containers of card designs from various shippers as prepared by the Boxing Department and placing them in the boxes which go to the customers. Orders typically contain as many as 30 different card designs.

Because a sizable inventory of cards is kept in the Order-Filling Department, the Boxing Department seldom is required to rush through an order of a particular card. The company manufactures seasonal cards far enough ahead so that the total volume of cards through the Boxing Department is nearly constant throughout the year. This volume was expected to reach 800,000 cards per day during the current year. Forty-eight per cent of the cards processed through the Boxing Department in a year are seasonal cards; the balance is composed of everyday cards. This proportion is closely maintained throughout the year.

Because of the even volume of cards passing through the Boxing Department, the work force is held at about 43 girls and five material handlers throughout the year. In January of this year, 22 of the girls worked on everyday cards. The department worked a seven-and-one-half hour day, with two ten-minute breaks, which reduced actual production time to 430 minutes per day.

Until last July the Boxing Department used a small cardboard box as the container in which the pile of counted cards and the bundle of envelopes were placed. The boxing operation was accomplished through the use of a conveyor belt with six work positions. The first worker placed the small open box and its cover on the end of the conveyor belt. The next two workers took cards from wooden crates, counted them into stacks, and placed the stacks on the belt. The next girl on the belt placed envelopes and cards into the box and put the lid on the box. The fifth worker placed the combined pile of envelopes and cards into the box and put the lid on. The sixth worker removed the boxes from the conveyor and stacked them.

The stacks of filled boxes were then taken to another area in the department where women applied labels, indicating the number and type of cards, to the ends of the boxes. Since most orders were small, the 12-card box provided an acceptable basic shipping quantity for

one card design. The small boxes were packed into shippers for delivery to the Order-Filling Department.

The Paper Packer

In an effort to reduce costs, Art-Tone introduced a paper "packer" as a substitute for the cardboard box in which to place the everyday cards. This packer was used for all everyday cards starting in the summer of last year. The packer is a manila envelope, with a flap on the long side. One size packer, eight and one-half inches long, accommodates 90 per cent of the cards in the everyday line, and the balance of the designs fit into a second size packer, ten inches long, except for ten designs which require a box because of their unusual thickness.

By adopting the packer on everyday cards, Art-Tone was able to replace 102 sizes of the small boxes with two sizes of packers. Whereas the small boxes required 47 sizes of final shipping boxes, the packers fit into two sizes of final boxes. Art-Tone also sought savings by eliminating the hand labeling operation for everyday cards. The packers can be printed within 24 hours to meet the requirements of runs scheduled in the Boxing Department.

The packers were not introduced in the seasonal line because Art-Tone feared retailer resistance. When the dealer receives everyday cards, he withdraws the cards and envelopes from the packer, puts some in his display rack, places the balance into numbered files in rack drawers, and throws away the packer. In seasonal cards, however, the dealer purchases ahead in quantities larger than can be displayed or stored in the drawers in the display rack. The retailer can easily stack the small boxes in his storeroom, but the paper packers are more difficult to store. Hallmark introduced packers in its everyday line before the summer of last year, as had other manufacturers, but Hallmark had not experimented with packers on its seasonal line until its Father's Day cards last June. Even though Art-Tone's dealer survey indicated this innovation was successful, Art-Tone felt that Father's Day cards were too low a volume seasonal card to serve as a fair test of dealer acceptance.

When the packer was introduced in the Boxing Department last July, the method used for packing was a slight adaptation of the method used previously with the boxes. Two of the department's four conveyors were changed to accomodate the packers. The first worker on the belt inserted a bundle of envelopes into a packer and placed the packer on the belt. The next two girls counted out stacks of cards and placed them on the belt. The fourth girl placed a stack of cards into the packer and the fifth girl folded over the packer

flap, removed the packer from the belt, and put it on a table. The sixth girl took the filled packers from the table and packed them in a shipper. The work arrangement is shown in Exhibit 1.

EXHIBIT 1   ART-TONE CARDS

LAYOUT FOR THE SIX-OPERATOR BELT METHOD

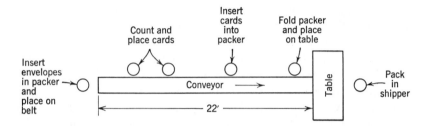

At the time the packers were introduced in the Detroit plant, Art-Tone's Canadian affiliate used the same packer in its Boxing Department. The Canadian plant averaged 175 packers per hour for each worker on the line, using the same six-operator method and layout shown in Exhibit 1. Since Art-Tone had been getting 212 boxes per hour for each of the 43 women workers before shifting to packers, and since the number of cards contained in either a box or packer was the same, Art-Tone management was concerned that increased labor costs might offset the savings in changing to the packer.

As the result of a study made by a management trainee, the plant manager authorized two measures intended to reduce costs for filling the packers. One of them was based on a simplified manual operation and the other employed a mechanical aid in filling the packers. The first measure was to assign the plant's only industrial engineer, Bob Hayes, the job of improving the six-operator belt method which was then in use with the packers. The method he developed, which will be described, is called the "single-operator method." The second measure was the placing of an order for a Tele-Sonic machine. The salesman representing the manufacturer of the Tele-Sonic machine claimed that his company could adapt it for use with the packers, and that it could produce at a rate of at least 26 packers per minute. On the basis of this claim and the experience of Art-Tone personnel with other models of the machine, one machine was ordered last July.

The Single-Operator Method

As Mr. Hayes worked to improve the packing methods, he decided to experiment with a single-operator method. In this arrangement,

each girl works at a separate table, with all materials supplied to the table by the material handlers. The material handlers also take away the finished shippers. Each operator arranges the materials on her table and then fills the packers and places them in the shipper. Packers, envelopes, and cards are placed by the material handlers in open boxes along the rear of the table. The method specifies that the worker first arrange enough packers on the table in front of her to fill one shipper. She then places the same number of envelope bundles in a loose pile on the right of the packers. She reaches under the table to get a shipper from the stack stored there and places one open shipper on the table to her left. She next reaches into the container of cards, takes a handful, counts them into stacks of 12, and places the stacks on the table beside the envelopes. She is then ready to fill the packers and pack them in the shipper. In a memo describing the operation and throughout his training of the operators, Mr. Hayes emphasized the necessity of arranging the materials on the table neatly to achieve high output.

Exhibit 2 is the Left- and Right-Hand Chart which Mr. Hayes developed for filling one packer and placing it in a shipper after the work table was arranged. Exhibit 3 is a diagram of the work table and the time standard which Mr. Hayes calculated for the filling and packing operation. The times were synthetically derived from a Methods-Time Measurement (MTM) analysis. (See footnote to Exhibit 3.)

EXHIBIT 2   ART-TONE CARDS

LEFT- AND RIGHT-HAND CHART FOR "FILL AND PACK" IN SINGLE-OPERATOR METHOD

Left Hand	Right Hand
1. Open packer	1. Reach for and grasp envelopes
2. Wait	2. Transfer envelopes to the cards
3. Wait	3. Grasp the cards with the envelopes
4. Wait	4. Transfer the envelopes and the cards to the packer
5. Aid right hand	5. Insert envelopes and cards
6. Lift, twist and close the packer	6. Wait
7. Regrasp the packer and place it into the carton	7. Repeat the cycle
8. Repeat the cycle	

EXHIBIT 3   ART-TONE CARDS

TIME STANDARD FOR FILL AND PACK USING SINGLE-OPERATOR METHOD*

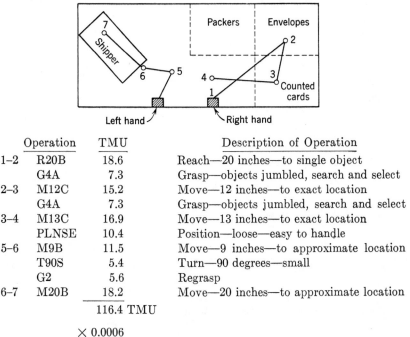

	Operation	TMU	Description of Operation
1–2	R20B	18.6	Reach—20 inches—to single object
	G4A	7.3	Grasp—objects jumbled, search and select
2–3	M12C	15.2	Move—12 inches—to exact location
	G4A	7.3	Grasp—objects jumbled, search and select
3–4	M13C	16.9	Move—13 inches—to exact location
	PLNSE	10.4	Position—loose—easy to handle
5–6	M9B	11.5	Move—9 inches—to approximate location
	T90S	5.4	Turn—90 degrees—small
	G2	5.6	Regrasp
6–7	M20B	18.2	Move—20 inches—to approximate location
		116.4 TMU	

$\times$ 0.0006

0.06984 minutes to fill one packer and place in shipper

---

* All the time standards were developed using Measured-Time Measurement (MTM). This is a method of developing synthetic time standards by breaking down the work into elements, to which predetermined times are assigned. The time unit used is a TMU, which equals six ten-thousandths of a minute. The TMU value given each work element is intended to represent the time required by an average proficient worker at a normal pace without allowance for unavoidable delay, fatigue, or personal time.

Exhibit 4 shows the MTM calculation which Mr. Hayes made for the time required by a single operator to position packers and envelopes on the table prior to the fill and pack operation. Exhibit 5 is Mr. Hayes' calculation of the total time required to fill one shipper, including the operations which were performed only once in the filling of a shipper. These times were derived from MTM standard data, in a manner similar to the calculations for getting the packer, getting the envelopes, and filling and packing.

Mr. Hayes used the standard times he calculated to set goals for the five girls he trained in the single-operator method. He began training the five girls on December 14, and each had received six hours of instruction when she began to use the single-operator method in the Boxing Department on December 21. Mr. Hayes kept no records of the girls' learning progress during the training, but he estimated that on the last day of training the slowest girl was producing at the rate of 1,000 packers per day and the fastest, 1,700 packers. The only production figures which were kept for the five girls were for December 28, 29, and 30. On those three days the average production per girl was 1,415, 1,332, and 1,610 packers per day.

EXHIBIT 4 ART-TONE CARDS

TIME STANDARDS FOR GETTING PACKERS AND ENVELOPES FOR SINGLE-OPERATOR METHOD*

Get Packers

Operation	TMU	Description of Operation
R29C	26.7	Reach—29 inches—to object jumbled with others —search, select
G4A	7.3	Grasp—object jumbled—search, select
M24B	20.6	Move—24 inches—to approximate location
RL1	2.0	Release—normal—open fingers
R5E	7.4	Reach—5 inches—to indefinite location

64.0 TMU
×0.0006
0.0384 min

Get Envelopes

Operation	TMU	Description of Operation
R30C	26.7	Reach—30 inches—to object jumbled with others —search, select
G4A	7.3	Grasp—object jumbled—search, select
M19B	18.2	Move—19 inches—to approximate location
RL1	2.0	Release—normal—open fingers
R20E	16.7	Reach—20 inches—to indefinite location

70.9 TMU
× 0.0006
0.04254 min

* See footnote to Exhibit 3.

EXHIBIT 5   ART-TONE CARDS

TIME STANDARD FOR SINGLE-OPERATOR METHOD*

Element	Element Time (min)	Frequency/Shipper	Normal Time/Shipper
1. Get packers	0.0384	1	0.0384
2. Get envelopes	0.0425	1	0.0425
3. Get shipper	0.1088	1	0.1088
4. Count cards	0.0025	360	0.9000
5. Fill and pack	0.0698	30	2.0940
6. Aside shipper	0.1088	1	0.1088
			3.2925 min/shipper

$+ 15\%$ personal and fatigue allowance

$= 3.7825$ min/shipper

divided by 30 packers/shipper

$= 0.1261$ min/packer

* See footnote to Exhibit 3.

The Tele-Sonic Machine

On December 23, the Tele-Sonic machine was delivered to the Detroit plant. The billed price to Art-Tone was $550, but the manufacturer said he would not deliver another machine for less than $1,000 because of the difficulties encountered in adapting it to take the Art-Tone packer.

The Tele-Sonic machine is a flat table, approximately three feet by four feet, under which are mounted two small fans. The air blast from the fans is directed through a tube to the top of the table. Seventy-five packers are held in a recess in the top of the table so that the packer on top of the pile is just flush with the surface of the table. The packer's open side faces the air jet. The packer is held in place by two small metal arms inserted into the packer from the open side. The blast of air holds the packer open so that, with one hand, a person can slide a stack of cards and bundle of envelopes into the open mouth of the packer. By continuing the motion, the hand can push the packer and its contents off the two

metal arms.   The other hand can then take the packer and place it on another table at the side of the Tele-Sonic machine.   As the packer leaves the two metal arms, a spring-loaded device raises the pile of packers to bring the next packer even with the metal arms.   The blast of air opens the packer and the arms again engage the edges of the packer.   The machine is thus automatically ready for another cycle.

Because Mr. Hayes worked out the layout for the Tele-Sonic machine (Exhibit 6) before the machine was delivered, he was able to start training the four operators on December 27.   The machine was put in production in the Boxing Department on December 28.   During the first three days of production the four girls on the team using the machine produced 4,065, 6,700, and 6,178 packers per day.   Although Mr. Hayes trained operators in the new methods, he did not train Miss Hudson.

Mr. Hayes calculated MTM time standards for the Tele-Sonic machine operator (Exhibit 7).   He thought the method might be improved by utilizing the idle time of the Tele-Sonic machine operator's left hand, but he did not have time to develop a better method.

Exhibit 8 shows the MTM calculation which Mr. Hayes made to determine the length of time required to place one bundle of envelopes on the conveyor in the Tele-Sonic method.   A similar calculation indicated a time of 0.03 minutes to count and place 12 cards on the conveyor.   From these calculations, Mr. Hayes decided that the first girl on the conveyor would count cards and the second girl would place envelopes.

Mr. Hayes left the company on December 30, the third working day after the last of the new methods was introduced.

EXHIBIT 6   ART-TONE CARDS

LAYOUT FOR TELE-SONIC MACHINE

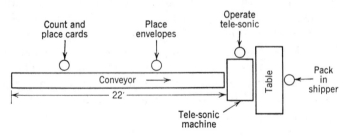

EXHIBIT 7 ART-TONE CARDS

TIME STANDARD FOR TELE-SONIC MACHINE OPERATOR*

Operation	TMU	Description of Operation
R20B	18.6	Reach—20 inches—to single object
G5	0.0	Grasp—contact or sliding grasp
M20A	19.2	Move—20 inches—against stop
PLSE	5.6	Position—loose—easy to handle
M8A	9.7	Move—8 inches—to other hand
R8E	9.3	Reach—8 inches—indefinite location
	62.4 TMU	
	× 0.0006	
	0.03744 min to fill one packer†	

* See footnote to Exhibit 3.

† Does not include time to put packer in shipper. This operation was done by another worker.

EXHIBIT 8 ART-TONE CARDS

TIME STANDARD TO PLACE ENVELOPE PACK ON CONVEYOR FOR TELE-SONIC MACHINE

Operation	TMU	Description of Operation
R10B	11.5	Reach—10 inches—to single object, inexact location
G4A	7.3	Grasp—objects jumbled, search and select
M16C	18.7	Move—16 inches—to exact location
PLNSE	16.4	Position—no pressure required—easy to handle
RL	2.0	Contact release
R16E	14.2	Reach—16 inches—indefinite location
	70.1 TMU	
	× 0.0006	
	0.04206 minutes/envelope pack	

The First Week in January

After the New Year's holiday, Miss Hudson had 12 girls working on the single-operator method. Since Mr. Hayes was gone and she felt incapable of training seven girls, she directed the five girls already trained to teach the others. The girls deviated from the method developed by Mr. Hayes, however. They used the same general hand motions, but none of the girls carefully laid out her work area as planned by Mr. Hayes. They were particularly sloppy in stacking the counted cards. Occasionally one of the piles fell over or became entangled with another stack. As a result, the girls lost time when reaching for stacks of cards.

Everyday cards were processed not only by the twelve single operators, but also by one belt running to the Tele-Sonic machine, and by a second belt used with the six-operator method. The six-operator line never exceeded production of 9,400 packers per day, and its production was as low as 6,202 packers on December 28. Average production for the belt during December was 9,100 packers per day. These three methods handled all the everyday cards for the Boxing Department. One material handler served the two belts and a second material handler supported the 12 single operators. The Boxing Department's other two belts were used for the seasonal cards. Six girls worked on each of these belts with the remaining nine girls labeling the boxes and placing them in shippers.

In January, Art-Tone managers, including the president, decided to introduce packers in the seasonal card line. Hallmark had used packers with their entire Christmas line and Art-Tone managers interpreted dealers' reactions as favorable. The Art-Tone managers anticipated that all the card manufacturers would follow Hallmark's lead to avoid mixed types of containers for the retail dealers, and the managers sought a full changeover to packers "as soon as possible and surely by June." In June the first of the Christmas cards are packed.

Mr. Rorick recently discharged Miss Hudson's assistant in the Boxing Department, and he had no replacement in mind. In the absence of Mr. Suvalle, Mr. Rorick realized he would have to continue to take responsibility for activities in the Boxing Department.

PART 4. THE PLANNING AND CONTROL OF

OPERATIONS AND OF INVENTORIES:

BASIC PROBLEMS AND CONCEPTS

Guides to Inventory Policy
1. Functions and Lot Sizes[1]

"Why are we always out of stock?" So goes the complaint of great numbers of businessmen faced with the dilemmas and frustrations of attempting simultaneously to maintain stable production operations, provide customers with adequate service, and keep investment in stocks and equipment at reasonable levels.

But this is only one of the characteristic problems business managers face in dealing with production planning, scheduling, keeping inventories in hand, and expediting. Other questions—just as perplexing and baffling when managers approach them on the basis of intuition and pencil work alone—are: How often should we reorder, or how should we adjust production, when sales are uncertain? What capacity levels should we set for job-shop operations? How do we plan production and procurement for seasonal sales? And so on, and so on.

In this series of articles, I will describe some of the technical developments which aim at giving the business manager better control over inventory and scheduling policy. While these techniques sometimes employ concepts and language foreign to the line executive, they are far from being either academic exercises or mere clerical devices. They are designed to help the business manager make better policy decisions and get his people to follow policy more closely.

As such, these techniques are worth some time and thought, commensurate with the central importance of production planning and inventory policy in business operations. Indeed, many companies have found that analysis of the functions of inventories, measurement of

---

[1] By John F. Magee. Reprinted from *Harvard Business Review*, January–February 1956, Vol. 34, No. 1, with permission from the editor.

the proper level of stocks, and development of inventory and production control systems based on the sorts of techniques described in this and following sections can be very profitable. For example:

❡ Johnson & Johnson has used these techniques for studying inventory requirements for products with seasonally changing demand, and also to set economical inventory goals balancing investment requirements against additional training and overtime costs.

❡ The American Thread Company, as a supplier to the fashion goods industry, plagued with large in-process inventories, day-to-day imbalances among production departments, labor turnover, and customer service difficulties, found these methods the key to improved scheduling and control procedures. Now these improved procedures help keep an inventory of tens of thousands of items in balance and smooth out production operations even in the face of demand showing extremely erratic fluctuations due to fashion changes.

❡ The Lamp Division of the General Electric Company has reported using these methods to survey its finished inventory functions and stock requirements in view of operating conditions and costs. This survey indicated how an improved warehouse reorder system would yield inventory cuts at both factories and warehouses, and pointed to the reorder system characteristics that were needed; it led to the installation of a new reorder and stock control system offering substantial opportunities for stock reduction. The analytic approach can also be used to show clearly what the cost in inventory investment and schedule changes is to achieve a given level of customer service.

❡ An industrial equipment manufacturer used these methods to investigate inventory and scheduling practices and to clear up policy ambiguities in this area, as a prelude to installing an electronic computer system to handle inventory control, scheduling, and purchase requisitions. In general, the analytic approach has proved a valuable help in bringing disagreements over inventory policy into the open, helping each side to recognize its own and the other's hidden assumptions, and to reach a common agreement more quickly.

❡ The Procter & Gamble Company recently described how analysis of its factory inventory functions and requirements, using these methods, has pointed out means for improved scheduling and more efficient use of finished stock. The analysis indicated how the company could take advantage of certain particular characteristics of its factories to cut stocks needed to meet sales fluctuations while still maintaining its long-standing policy of guaranteed annual employment.

These are only a few instances of applications. Numerous others could be drawn from the experience of companies ranging from moderate to large size, selling consumer goods or industrial products, with thousands of items or only a few, and distribution in highly stable, predictable markets or in erratically changing and unpredictable circumstances.

In the present article major attention will be devoted to (a) the conceptual framework of the analytic approach, including the definition of inventory function and the measurement of operational costs;

and (b) the problem of optimum lot size, with a detailed case illustration showing how the techniques are applied.

This case reveals that the appropriate order quantity and the average inventory maintained do not vary directly with sales, and that a good answer to the lot size question can be obtained with fairly crude cost data, provided that a sound analytical approach is used. The case also shows that the businessman does not need calculus to solve many inventory problems (although use has to be made of it when certain complications arise).

INVENTORY PROBLEMS

The question before management is: How big should inventories be? The answer to this is obvious—they should be just big enough. But what is big enough?

This question is made more difficult by the fact that generally each individual within a management group tends to answer the question from his own point of view. He fails to recognize costs outside his usual framework. He tends to think of inventories in isolation from other operations. The sales manager commonly says that the company must never make a customer wait; the production manager says there must be long manufacturing runs for lower costs and steady employment; the treasurer says that large inventories are draining off cash which could be used to make a profit.

Such a situation occurs all the time. The task of all production planning, scheduling, or control functions, in fact, is typically to balance conflicting objectives such as those of minimum purchase or production cost, minimum inventory investment, minimum storage and distribution cost, and maximum service to customers.

Production vs. Time

Often businessmen blame their inventory and scheduling difficulties on small orders and product diversity: "You can't keep track of 100,000 items. Forecasts mean nothing. We're just a job shop." Many businessmen seem to feel that their problems in this respect are unusual, whereas actually the problems faced by a moderate-size manufacturer with a widely diversified product line are almost typical of business today.

The fact is, simply, that under present methods of organization the costs of paper work, setup, and control, in view of the diversity of products sold, represent an extremely heavy drain on many a company's profit and a severe cost to its customers. The superficial

variety of output has often blinded management to the opportunities for more systematic production flow and for the elimination of many of the curses of job-shop operation by better organization and planning.

The problem of planning and scheduling production or inventories pervades all operations concerned with the matter of production versus time—i.e., the interaction between production, distribution, and the location and size of physical stocks. It occurs at almost every step in the production process: purchasing, production of in-process materials, finished production, distribution of finished product, and service to customers. In multiplant operations, the problem becomes compounded because decisions must be made with reference to the amount of each item to be produced in each factory; management must also specify how the warehouses should be served by the plants.

Action vs. Analysis

The questions businessmen raise in connection with management and control of inventories are basically aimed at action, not at arriving at answers. The questions are stated, unsurprisingly, in the characteristic terms of decisions to be made: "Where shall we maintain how much stock?" "Who will be responsible for it?" "What shall we do to control balances or set proper schedules?" A manager necessarily thinks of problems in production planning in terms of centers of responsibility.

However, action questions are not enough by themselves. In order to get at the answers to these questions as a basis for taking action, it is necessary to back off and ask some rather different kinds of questions: "Why do we have inventories?" "What affects the inventory balances we maintain?" "How do these effects take place?" From these questions, a picture of the inventory problem can be built up which shows the influence on inventories and costs of the various alternative decisions which the management may ultimately want to consider.

This type of analytic or functional question has been answered intuitively by businessmen with considerable success in the past. Consequently, most of the effort toward improved inventory management has been spent in other directions; it has been aimed at better means for recording, filing, or displaying information and at better ways of doing the necessary clerical work. This is all to the good, for efficient data-handling helps. However, it does not lessen the need for a more systematic approach to inventory problems that can take the place of, or at least supplement, intuition.

As business has grown, it has become more complex, and as business executives have become more and more specialized in their jobs or farther removed from direct operations, the task of achieving an economical balance intuitively has become increasingly difficult. That is why more businessmen are finding the concepts and mathematics of the growing field of inventory theory to be of direct practical help.

One of the principal difficulties in the intuitive approach is that the types and definitions of cost which influence appropriate inventory policy are not those characteristically found on the books of a company. Many costs such as setup or purchasing costs are hidden in the accounting records. Others such as inventory capital costs may never appear at all. Each cost may be clear to the operating head primarily responsible for its control; since it is a "hidden" cost, however, its importance may not be clear at all to other operating executives concerned. The resulting confusion may make it difficult to arrive at anything like a consistent policy.

In the last five years in particular, operations research teams have succeeded in using techniques of research scientists to develop a practical analytic approach to inventory questions, despite growing business size, complexity, and division of management responsibility.

INVENTORY FUNCTIONS

To understand the principles of the analytic approach, we must have some idea of the basic functions of inventories.

Fundamentally, inventories serve to uncouple successive operations in the process of making a product and getting it to consumers. For example, inventories make it possible to process a product at a distance from customers or from raw material supplies, or to do two operations at a distance from one another (perhaps only across the plant). Inventories make it unnecessary to gear production directly to consumption or, alternatively, to force consumption to adapt to the necessities of production. In these and similar ways, inventories free one stage in the production-distribution process from the next, permitting each to operate more economically.

The essential question is: At what point does the uncoupling function of inventory stop earning enough advantage to justify the investment required? To arrive at a satisfactory answer we must first distinguish between (a) inventories necessary because it takes time to complete an operation and to move the product from one stage to another; and (b) inventories employed for organizational reasons,

i.e., to let one unit schedule its operations more or less independently of another.

Movement Inventories

Inventory balances needed because of the time required to move stocks from one place to another are often not recognized, or are confused with inventories resulting from other needs—e.g., economical shipping quantities (to be discussed in a later section).

The average amount of movement inventory can be determined from the mathematical expression $I = S \times T$ in which S represents the average sales rate, T the transit time from one stage to the next, and I the movement inventory needed. For example, if it takes two weeks to move materials from the plant to a warehouse, and the warehouse sells 100 units per week, the average inventory in movement is 100 units per week times 2 weeks, or 200 units. From a different point of view, when a unit is manufactured and ready for use at the plant, it must sit idle for two weeks while being moved to the next station (the warehouse); so, on the average, stocks equal to two weeks' sales will be in movement.

Movement inventories are usually thought of in connection with movement between distant points—plant to warehouse. However, any plant may contain substantial stocks in movement from one operation to another—for example, the product moving along an assembly line. Movement stock is one component of the "float" or in-process inventory in a manufacturing operation.

The amount of movement stock changes only when sales or the time in transit is changed. Time in transit is largely a result of method of transportation, although improvements in loading or dispatching practices may cut transit time by eliminating unnecessary delays. Other somewhat more subtle influences of time in transit on total inventories will be described in connection with safety stocks.

Organization Inventories

Management's most difficult problems are with the inventories that "buy" organization in the sense that the more of them management carries between stages in the manufacturing-distribution process, the less coordination is required to keep the process running smoothly. Contrariwise, if inventories are already being used efficiently, they can be cut only at the expense of greater organization effort—e.g., greater scheduling effort to keep successive stages in balance, and greater expediting effort to work out of the difficulties which un-

foreseen disruptions at one point or another may cause in the whole process.

Despite superficial differences among businesses in the nature and characteristics of the organization inventory they maintain, the following three functions are basic:

(1) *Lot size inventories* are probably the most common in business. They are maintained wherever the user makes or purchases material in larger lots than are needed for his immediate purposes. For example, it is common practice to buy raw materials in relatively large quantities in order to obtain quantity price discounts, keep shipping costs in balance, and hold down clerical costs connected with making out requisitions, checking receipts, and handling accounts payable. Similar reasons lead to long production runs on equipment calling for expensive setup, or to sizable replenishment orders placed on factories by field warehouses.

(2) *Fluctuation stocks*, also very common in business, are held to cushion the shocks arising basically from unpredictable fluctuations in consumer demand. For example, warehouses and retail outlets maintain stocks to be able to supply consumers on demand, even when the rate of consumer demand may show quite irregular and unpredictable fluctuations. In turn, factories maintain stocks to be in a position to replenish retail and field warehouse stocks in line with customer demands.

Short-term fluctuations in the mix of orders on a plant often make it necessary to carry stocks of parts of subassemblies, in order to give assembly operations flexibility in meeting orders as they arise while freeing earlier operations (e.g., machining) from the need to make momentary adjustments in schedules to meet assembly requirements. Fluctuation stocks may also be carried in semifinished form in order to balance out the load among manufacturing departments when orders received during the current day, week, or month may put a load on individual departments which is out of balance with long-run requirements.

In most cases, anticipating all fluctuations is uneconomical, if not impossible. But a business cannot get along without some fluctuation stocks unless it is willing and able always to make its customers wait until the material needed can be purchased conveniently or until their orders can be scheduled into production conveniently. Fluctuation stocks are part of the price we pay for our general business philosophy of serving the consumers' wants (and whims!) rather than having them take what they can get. The queues before Russian retail stores illustrate a different point of view.

(3) *Anticipation stocks* are needed where goods or materials are consumed on a predictable but changing pattern through the year, and where it is desirable to absorb some of these changes by building and depleting inventories rather than by changing production rates with attendant fluctuations in employment and additional capital capacity requirements. For example, inventories may be built up in anticipation of a special sale or to fill needs during a plant shutdown.

The need for seasonal stocks may also arise where materials (e.g., agricultural products) are *produced* at seasonally fluctuating rates but where con-

sumption is reasonably uniform; here the problems connected with producing and storing tomato catsup are a prime example.[2]

Striking a Balance

The joker is that the gains which these organization inventories achieve in the way of less need for coordination and planning, less clerical effort to handle orders, and greater economies in manufacturing and shipping are not in direct proportion to the size of inventory. Even if the additional stocks are kept well balanced and properly located, the gains become smaller, while at the same time the warehouse, obsolescence, and capital costs associated with maintaining inventories rise in proportion to, or perhaps even at a faster rate than, the inventories themselves. To illustrate:

Suppose a plant needs 2,000 units of a specially machined part in a year. If these are made in runs of 100 units each, then 20 runs with attendant setup costs will be required each year.

If the production quantity were increased from 100 to 200 units, only 10 runs would be required—a 50 per cent reduction in setup costs, but a 100 per cent increase in the size of a run and in the resulting inventory balance carried.

If the runs were further increased in length to 400 units each, only 5 production runs during the year would be required—only 25 per cent more reduction in setup costs, but 200 per cent more increase in run length and inventory balances.

The basic problem of inventory policy connected with the three types of inventories which "buy" organization is to strike a balance between the increasing costs and the declining return earned from additional stocks. It is because striking this balance is easier to say than to do, and because it is a problem that defies solution through an intuitive understanding alone, that the new analytical concepts are necessary.

INVENTORY COSTS

This brings us face to face with the question of the costs that influence inventory policy, and the fact, noted earlier, that they are characteristically not those recorded, at least not in directly available form, in the usual industrial accounting system. Accounting costs are derived under principles developed over many years and strongly

---

[2] See Alexander Henderson and Robert Schlaifer, "Mathematical Programing: Better Information for Better Decision-Making," HBR May–June 1954, p. 73.

influenced by tradition. The specific methods and degree of skill and refinement may be better in particular companies, but in all of them the basic objective of accounting procedures is to provide a fair, consistent, and conservative valuation of assets and a picture of the flow of values in the business.

In contrast to the principles and search for consistency underlying accounting costs, the definition of costs for production and inventory control will vary from time to time—even in the same company—according to the circumstances and the length of the period being planned for. The following criteria apply:

(1) *The costs shall represent "out-of-pocket" expenditures, i.e., cash actually paid out or opportunities for profit foregone.* Overtime premium payments are out-of-pocket; depreciation on equipment on hand is not. To the extent that storage space is available and cannot be used for other productive purposes, no out-of-pocket cost of space is incurred; but to the extent that storage space is rented (out-of-pocket) or could be used for other productive purposes (foregone opportunity), a suitable charge is justified. The charge for investment is based on the out-of-pocket investment in inventories or added facilities, not on the "book" or accounting value of the investment.

The rate of interest charged on out-of-pocket investment may be based either on the rate paid banks (out-of-pocket) or on the rate of profit that might reasonably be earned by alternative uses of investment (foregone opportunity), depending on the financial policies of the business. In some cases, a bank rate may be used on short-term seasonal inventories and an internal rate for long-term, minimum requirements.

Obviously, much depends on the time scale in classifying a given item. In the short run, few costs are controllable out-of-pocket costs; in the long run, all are.

(2) *The costs shall represent only those out-of-pocket expenditures or foregone opportunities for profit whose magnitude is affected by the schedule or plan.* Many overhead costs, such as supervision costs, are out-of-pocket, but neither the timing nor the size is affected by the schedule. Normal material and direct labor costs are unaffected in total and so are not considered directly; however, these as well as some components of overhead cost do represent out-of-pocket investments, and accordingly enter the picture indirectly through any charge for capital.

Direct Influence

Among the costs which directly influence inventory policy are (a) costs depending on the amount ordered, (b) production costs, and (c) costs of storing and handling inventory.

COSTS THAT DEPEND ON THE AMOUNT ORDERED. These include, for example, quantity discounts offered by vendors; setup costs in internal manufacturing operations and clerical costs of making out a purchase

order; and, when capacity is pressed, the profit on production lost during downtime for setup. Shipping costs represent another factor to the extent that they influence the quantity of raw materials purchased and resulting raw stock levels, the size of intraplant or plant-warehouse shipments, or the size and the frequency of shipments to customers.

PRODUCTION COSTS. Beyond setup or change-over costs, which are included in the preceding category, there are the abnormal or non-routine costs of production whose size may be affected by the policies or control methods used. (Normal or standard raw material and direct labor costs are not significant in inventory control; these relate to the total quantity sold rather than to the amount stocked.) Overtime, shakedown, hiring, and training represent costs that have a direct bearing on inventory policy.

To illustrate, shakedown or learning costs show up wherever output during the early part of a new run is below standard in quantity or quality.[3] A cost of undercapacity operation may also be encountered—for example, where a basic labor force must be maintained regardless of volume (although sometimes this can be looked on as part of the fixed facility cost, despite the fact that it is accounted for as a directly variable labor cost).

COSTS OF HANDLING AND STORING INVENTORY. In this group of costs affected by control methods and inventory policies are expenses of handling products in and out of stock, storage costs such as rent and heat, insurance and taxes, obsolescence and spoilage costs, and capital costs (which will receive detailed examination in the next section).

Inventory obsolescence and spoilage costs may take several forms, including (1) outright spoilage after a more or less fixed period; (2) risk that a particular unit in stock or a particular product number will (a) become technologically unsalable, except perhaps at a discount or as spare parts, (b) go out of style, or (c) spoil.

Certain food and drug products, for example, have specified maximum shelf lives and must either be used within a fixed period of time or be dumped. Some kinds of style goods, such as many lines of toys, Christmas novelties, or women's clothes, may effectively "spoil" at the end of a season, with only reclaim or dump value. Some kinds of technical equipment undergo almost constant engineering change during their production life; thus component stocks may suddenly and unexpectedly be made obsolete.

---

[3] See Frank J. Andress, "The Learning Curve as a Production Tool," HBR January–February 1954, p. 87.

Capital Investment

Evaluating the effect of inventory and scheduling policy upon capital investment and the worth of capital tied up in inventories is one of the most difficult problems in resolving inventory policy questions.

Think for a moment of the amount of capital invested in inventory. This is the out-of-pocket, or avoidable, cash cost for material, labor, and overhead of goods in inventory (as distinguished from the "book" or accounting value of inventory). For example, raw materials are normally purchased in accordance with production schedules; and if the production of an item can be postponed, buying and paying for raw materials can likewise be put off.

Usually, then, the raw material cost component represents a part of the out-of-pocket inventory investment in finished goods. However, if raw materials must be purchased when available (e.g., agricultural crops) regardless of the production schedule, the raw material component of finished product cost does not represent avoidable investment and therefore should be struck from the computation of inventory value for planning purposes.

As for maintenance and similar factory overhead items, they are usually paid for the year round, regardless of the timing of production scheduled; therefore these elements of burden should not be counted as part of the product investment for planning purposes. (One exception: if, as sometimes happens, the maintenance costs actually vary directly with the production rate as, for example, in the case of supplies, they should of course be included.)

Again, supervision, at least general supervision, is usually a fixed monthly cost which the schedule will not influence, and hence should not be included. Depreciation is another type of burden item representing a charge for equipment and facilities already bought and paid for; the timing of the production schedule cannot influence these past investments and, while they represent a legitimate cost for accounting purposes, they should not be counted as part of the inventory investment for inventory and production planning purposes.

In sum, the rule is this: for production planning and inventory management purposes, the investment value of goods in inventory should be taken as the cash outlay made at the time of production that could have been delayed if the goods were not made then but at a later time, closer to the time of sale.

COST OF CAPITAL INVESTED. This item is the product of three factors: (a) the capital value of a unit of inventory, (b) the time a unit of product is in inventory, and (c) the charge or imputed interest rate

placed against a dollar of invested cash. The first factor was mentioned above. As for the second, it is fixed by management's inventory policy decisions. But these decisions can be made economically only in view of the third factor. This factor depends directly on the financial policy of the business.

Sometimes businessmen make the mistake of thinking that cash tied up in inventories costs nothing, especially if the cash to finance inventory is generated internally through profits and depreciation. However, this implies that the cash in inventories would otherwise sit idle. In fact, the cash could, at least, be invested in government bonds if not in inventories. And if it were really idle, the cash very likely should be released to stockholders for profitable investment elsewhere.

Moreover, it is dangerous to assume that, as a "short-term" investment, inventory is relatively liquid and riskless. Businessmen say, "After all, we turn our inventory investment over six times a year." But, in reality, inventory investment may or may not be short-term and riskless, depending on circumstances. No broad generalization is possible, and each case must be decided on its own merits. For example:

⁋ A great deal of inventory carried in business is as much a part of the permanent investment as the machinery and buildings. The inventory must be maintained to make operations possible as long as the business is a going concern. The cash investment released by the sale of one item from stock must be promptly reinvested in new stock, and the inventory can be liquidated only when the company is closed. How much more riskless is this than other fixed manufacturing assets?

⁋ To take an extreme case, inventory in fashion lines or other types of products having high obsolescence carries a definite risk. Its value depends wholly on the company's ability to sell it. If sales are insufficient to liquidate the inventory built up, considerable losses may result.

⁋ At the other extreme, inventory in stable product lines built up to absorb short-term seasonal fluctuations might be thought of as bearing the least risk, since this type of investment is characteristically short-term. But even in these cases there can be losses. Suppose, for instance, that peak seasonal sales do not reach anticipated levels and substantially increased costs of storage and obsolescence have to be incurred before the excess inventory can be liquidated.

Finally, it might be pointed out that the cost of the dollars invested in inventory may be underestimated if bank interest rate is used as the basis, ignoring the risk-bearing or entrepreneur's compensation. How many businessmen are actually satisfied with uses of their companies' capital funds which do not earn more than a lender's rate of

return? In choosing a truly appropriate rate—a matter of financial policy—the executive must answer some questions:

1. Where is the cash coming from—inside earnings or outside financing?
2. What else could we do with the funds, and what could we earn?
3. When can we get the investment back out, if ever?
4. How much risk of sales disappointment and obsolescence is really connected with this inventory?
5. How much of a return do we want, in view of what we could earn elsewhere or in view of the cost of money to us and the risk the inventory investment entails?

INVESTMENT IN FACILITIES. Valuation of investment in facilities is generally important only in long-run planning problems—as, for example, when increases in productive or warehouse capacity are being considered. (Where facilities already exist and are not usable for other purposes, and where planning or scheduling do not contemplate changing these existing facilities, investment is not affected.)

Facilities investment may also be important where productive capacity is taxed, and where the form of the plan or schedule will determine the amount of added capacity which must be installed, either to meet the plan itself or for alternative uses. In such cases, considerable care is necessary in defining the facilities investment in order to be consistent with the principles noted above: i.e., that facilities investment should represent out-of-pocket investment, or, alternatively, foregone opportunities to make out-of-pocket investment elsewhere.

Customer Service

An important objective in most production planning and inventory control systems is maintenance of reasonable customer service. An evaluation of the worth of customer service, or the loss suffered through poor service, is an important part of the problem of arriving at a reasonable inventory policy. This cost is typically very difficult to arrive at, including as it does the paper work costs of rehandling back orders and, usually much more important, the effect that dissatisfaction of customers may have on future profits.

In some cases it may be possible to limit consideration to the cost of producing the needed material on overtime or of purchasing it from the outside and losing the contribution to profit which it would have made. On the other hand, sometimes the possible loss of customers and their sales over a substantial time may outweigh the cost of direct loss in immediate business, and it may be necessary to arrive at a

statement of a "reasonable" level of customer service—i.e., the degree of risk of running out of stock, or perhaps the number of times a year the management is willing to run out of an item. In other cases, it may be possible to arrive at a reasonable maximum level of sales which the company is prepared to meet with 100 per cent reliability, being reconciled to have service suffer if sales exceed this level.

One of the uses of the analytic techniques described below and in following parts of this series is to help management arrive at a realistic view of the cost of poor service, or of the value of building high service, by laying out clearly what the cost in inventory investment and schedule changes is to achieve this degree of customer service. Sometimes when these costs are clearly brought home, even a 100 per cent service-minded management is willing to settle for a more realistic, "excellent" service at moderate cost, instead of striving for "perfect" service entailing extreme cost.

OPTIMUM LOT SIZE

Now, with this background, let us examine in some detail one of the inventory problems which plague businessmen the most—that of the optimum size of lot to purchase or produce for stock. This happens also to be one of the oldest problems discussed in the industrial engineering texts—but this does not lessen the fact that it is one of the most profitable for a great many companies to attack today with new analytic techniques.

Common Practices

This problem arises, as mentioned earlier, because of the need to purchase or produce in quantities greater than will be used or sold. Thus, specifically, businessmen buy raw materials in sizable quantities—carloads, or even trainloads—in order to reduce the costs connected with purchasing and control, to obtain a favorable price, and to minimize handling and transportation costs. They replenish factory in-process stocks of parts in sizable quantities to avoid, where possible, the costs of equipment setups and clerical routines. Likewise, finished stocks maintained in warehouses usually come in shipments substantially greater than the typical amount sold at once, the motive again being, in part, to avoid equipment setup and paperwork costs and, in the case of field warehouses, to minimize shipping costs.

Where the same equipment is used for a variety of items, the equipment will be devoted first to one item and then to another in sequence,

with the length of the run in any individual item to be chosen, as far as is economically possible, to minimize change-over cost from one item to another and to reduce the production time lost because of clean-out requirements during change-overs. Blocked operations of this sort are seen frequently, for example, in the petroleum industry, on packaging lines, or on assembly lines where change-over from one model to another may require adjustment in feed speeds and settings and change of components.

In all these cases, the practice of replenishing stocks in sizable quantities compared with the typical usage quantity means that inventory has to be carried; it makes it possible to spread fixed costs (e.g., setup and clerical costs) over many units and thus reduce the unit cost. However, one can carry this principle only so far, for if the replenishment orders become too large, the resulting inventories get out of line, and the capital and handling costs of carrying these inventories more than offset the possible savings in production, transportation, and clerical costs. Here is the matter, again, of striking a balance between these conflicting considerations.

Even though formulas for selecting the optimum lot size are presented in many industrial engineering texts,[4] few companies make any attempt to arrive at an explicit quantitative balance of inventory and change-over or setup costs. Why?

For one thing, the cost elements which enter into an explicit solution frequently are very difficult to measure, or are only very hazily defined. For example, it may be possible to get a fairly accurate measure of the cost of setting up a particular machine, but it may be almost impossible to derive a precise measure of the cost of making out a new production order. Again, warehouse costs may be accumulated separately on the accounting records, but these rarely show what the cost of housing an *additional* unit of material may be. In my experience the capital cost, or imputed interest cost, connected with inventory investment never appears on the company's accounting records.

Furthermore, the inventory is traditionally valued in such a way that the true incremental investment is difficult to measure for scheduling purposes. Oftentimes companies therefore attempt to strike only a qualitative balance of these costs to arrive at something like an optimum or minimum-cost reorder quantity.

Despite the difficulty in measuring costs—and indeed because of

---

[4] See, for example, Raymond E. Fairfield, *Quantity and Economy in Manufacture,* New York, D. Van Nostrand Company, Inc., 1931.

such difficulty—it is eminently worthwhile to look at the lot size problem explicitly formulated. The value of an analytic solution does not rest solely on one's ability to plug in precise cost data to get an answer. An analytic solution often helps clarify questions of principle, even with only crude data available for use. Moreover, it appears that many companies today still have not accepted the philosophy of optimum reorder quantities from the over-all company standpoint; instead, decisions are dominated from the standpoint of some particular interest such as production or traffic and transportation. Here too the analytic solution can be of help, even when the cost data are incomplete or imperfect.

Case Example

To illustrate how the lot size problem can be attacked analytically—and what some of the problems and advantages of such an attack are—let us take a fictitious example. The situation is greatly oversimplified on purpose to get quickly to the heart of the analytic approach.

ELEMENTS OF THE PROBLEM. Brown and Brown, Inc., an automotive parts supplier, produces a simple patented electric switch on long-term contracts. The covering is purchased on the outside at $0.01 each, and 1,000 are used regularly each day, 250 days per year.

The casings are made in a nearby plant, and B. and B. sends its own truck to pick them up. The cost of truck operation, maintenance, and the driver amounts to $10 per trip.

The company can send the truck once a day to bring back 1,000 casings for that day's requirements, but this makes the cost of a casing rather high. The truck can go less frequently, but this means that it has to bring back more than the company needs for its immediate day-to-day purposes.

The characteristic "saw-tooth" inventory pattern which will result is shown in Exhibit 1, where 1,000 Q casings are picked up each trip (Q being whatever number of days' supply is obtained per replenishment trip). These are used up over a period of Q days. When the inventory is depleted again, another trip is made to pick up Q days' supply or 1,000 Q casings once more, and so on.

B. and B. estimates that the cost of storing casings under properly controlled humidity conditions is $1 per 1,000 casings per year. The company wants to obtain a 10 per cent return on its inventory investment of $10 (1,000 times $0.01), which means that it should properly charge an additional $1 (10 per cent of $10), making a total inventory cost of $2 per 1,000 casings per year.

EXHIBIT 1

PATTERN OF INVENTORY BALANCE

(1,000 Q casings obtained per replenishment trip; 1,000 casings used per day)

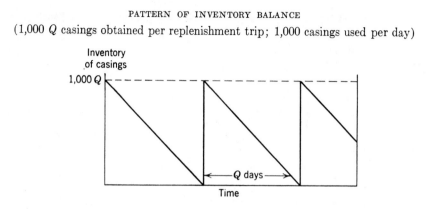

(Note that, in order to avoid undue complications, the inventory investment charge is made here only against the purchase price of the casings and not against the total delivery cost including transportation. Where transportation is a major component of total cost, it is of course possible and desirable to include it in the base for the inventory charge.)

GRAPHIC SOLUTION. Brown and Brown, Inc., can find what it should do by means of a graph (see Exhibit 2) showing the annual cost of buying, moving, and storing casings:

The broken line shows total trucking costs versus the size of the individual purchase quantity:

If 1,000 casings are purchased at a time, the total cost is $10 times 250 trips, or $2,500 per year.

If 10,000 casings are purchased at one time, only 25 trips need be made, for a total cost of $250 per year.

If 100,000 casings are purchased, only 2½ trips, on the average, have to be taken each year, for a total cost of $25.

The dotted line shows the inventory cost compared with the size of the purchased quantity:

If 10,000 casings are purchased at one time, the inventory at purchase will contain 10,000, and it will gradually be depleted until none are on hand, when a new purchase will be made. The average inventory on hand thus will be 5,000 casings. The cost per year will be $2 times 5,000 casings, or $10.

Similarly, if 100,000 casings are purchased at one time, the average inventory will be 50,000 casings, and the total inventory and storage cost will be $100.

EXHIBIT 2

ANNUAL COST OF BUYING, MOVING, AND STORING CASINGS COMPARED
WITH REORDER QUANTITY

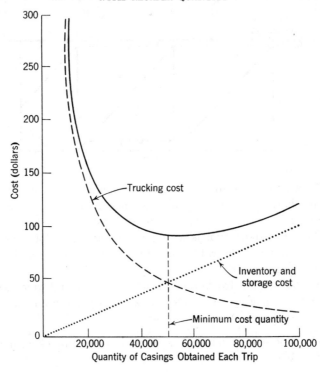

Quantity of Casings Obtained Each Trip

The solid line is the total cost, including both trucking and inventory and storage costs. The total cost is at a minimum when 50,000 casings are purchased on each trip and 5 trips are made each year, for at this point the total trucking cost and the total inventory and storage cost are equal.

The solution to B. and B.'s problem can be reached algebraically as well as graphically. Exhibit 3 shows how the approach works in this very simple case.

Similar Cases

The problem of Brown and Brown, Inc., though artificial, is not too far from the questions many businesses face in fixing reorder quantities.

Despite the simplifications introduced—for example, the assumption that usage is known in advance—the method of solution has been found widely useful in industries ranging from mail order merchan-

EXHIBIT 3   EXAMPLE OF ALGEBRAIC SOLUTION OF SAME
INVENTORY PROBLEM AS EXHIBIT 2

The total annual cost of supplying casings is equal to the sum of the direct
cost of the casings, plus the trucking cost, plus the inventory and storage cost.
Let:

> T = total annual cost
> b = unit purchase price, \$10 per 1,000 casings
> s = annual usage, 250,000 casings
> A = trucking cost, \$10 per trip
> N = number of trips per year
> i = cost of carrying casings in inventory at the annual rate
>   of \$2 per 1,000, or \$0.002 per casing
> x = size of an individual purchase ($x/2$ = average inventory)

Then the basic equation will be:

$$T = bs + AN + ix/2$$

The problem is to choose the minimum-cost value of x (or, if desired, N).
Since x is the same as s/N, N can be expressed as s/x. Substituting s/x for
N in the above equation, we get:

$$T = bs + As/x + ix/2$$

From this point on we shall use differential calculus. The derivative of
total cost, T, with respect to x will be expressed as:

$$dT/dx = -As/x^2 + i/2$$

And the minimum-cost value of x is that for which the derivative of total
cost with respect to x equals zero. This is true when:

$$x = \sqrt{2As/i}$$

Substituting the known values for A, s, and i:

$$x = \sqrt{2 \cdot 10 \cdot 250{,}000/.002} = 50{,}000 \text{ casings}$$

---

dising (replenishing staple lines) through electrical equipment manufacturing (ordering machined parts to replenish stockrooms) to shoe
manufacturing (ordering findings and other purchased supplies). In
particular, the approach has been found helpful in controlling stocks
made up of many low-value items used regularly in large quantities.

A number of realistic complications might have been introduced
into the Brown and Brown Inc., problem. For example:

❡ In determining the size of a manufacturing run, it sometimes is important
to account explicitly for the production and sales rate. In this case, the
inventory balance pattern looks like Exhibit 4 instead of the saw-tooth design
in Exhibit 1. The maximum inventory point is not equal to the amount pro-

EXHIBIT 4

INFLUENCE OF PRODUCTION AND SALES RATE ON
PRODUCTION CYCLE INVENTORY

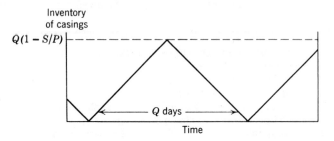

duced in an individual run, but to that quantity less the amount sold during the course of the run. The maximum inventory equals $Q\ (1 - S/P)$, where Q is the amount produced in a single run, and S and P are the daily sales and production rates respectively.

This refinement can be important, particularly if the sales rate is fairly large compared with the production rate. Thus, if the sales rate is half the production rate, then the maximum inventory is only half the quantity made in one run, and the average inventory equals only one-fourth the individual run quantity. This means that substantially more inventory can be carried—in fact, about 40 per cent more.

❨ When a number of products are made on a regular cycle, one after another, with the sequence in the cycle established by economy in change-over cost, the total cycle length can be obtained in the same way as described above. Of course, it sometimes happens that there is a periodic breach in the cycle, either to make an occasional run of a product with very low sales or to allow for planned maintenance of equipment; the very simple run-length formulas can be adjusted to allow for this.

❨ Other kinds of costs can also be included, such as different sorts of handling costs. Or the inventory cost can be defined in such a way as to include transportation, obsolescence, or even capital and storage cost as part of the unit value of the product against which a charge for capital is made. When a charge for capital is included as part of the base value in computing the cost of capital, this is equivalent to requiring that capital earnings be compounded; this can have an important bearing on decisions connected with very low volume items which might be purchased in relatively large, long-lasting quantities.

Complications such as the foregoing, while important in practice, represent changes in arithmetic rather than in basic concept.

Significant Conclusions

When the analytic approach is applied to Brown and Brown's problem and similar cases, it reveals certain relationships which are

significant and useful to executives concerned with inventory management:

(1) *The appropriate order quantity and the average inventory maintained do not vary directly with sales.* In fact, both of these quantities vary with the square root of sales. This means that with the same ordering and setup cost characteristics, the larger the volume of sales of an item, the less inventory per unit of sales is required. One of the sources of inefficiency in many inventory control systems is the rigid adoption of a rule for ordering or carrying inventory equivalent to, say, one month's sales.

(2) *The total cost in the neighborhood of the optimum order quantity is relatively insensitive to moderately small changes in the amount ordered.* Exhibit 2 illustrates this proposition. Thus, all that is needed is just to get in the "right ball park," and a good answer can be obtained even with fairly crude cost data. For example, suppose the company had estimated that its total cost of holding 1,000 casings in inventory for a year was $1 when it actually was $2 (as in our illustration). Working through the same arithmetic, the company would have arrived at an optimum order quantity of 70,000 casings instead of 50,000. Even so, the total cost would have been (using the correct $2 annual carrying cost):

3.6 trips per year @ $10	= $36
35,000 casings average inventory @ $0.002	= 70
Total annual cost	= $106

Thus, an error of a factor of 2 in one cost results in only a 6 per cent difference in total cost.

In summary, Brown and Brown's problem, despite its oversimplification, provides an introduction to the analytic approach to inventory problems.

In particular, it illustrates the first essential in such an approach—i.e., defining an inventory function. In this case the function is to permit purchase or manufacture in economical order quantities or run lengths; in other cases it may be different. The important point is that this basic function can be identified wherever it may be found—in manufacturing, purchasing, or warehouse operation.

The only way to cut inventories is to organize operations so that they are tied more closely together. For example, a company can cut its raw materials inventory by buying in smaller quantities closer to needs, but it does so at a cost; this cost results from the increased clerical operations needed to tie the purchasing function more closely to manufacturing and to keep it more fully informed of manufacturing's plans and operations. The right inventory level is reached when the cost of maintaining any additional inventory cushion offsets the saving that the additional inventory earns by permitting the plant to operate in a somewhat less fully organized fashion.

B. and B.'s problem also illustrates problems and questions connected with defining and making costs explicit. The inventory capital cost is usually not found on a company's books, but it is implied in some of the disagreements over inventory policy. Here, again, bringing the matter into the open may help each side in a discussion to recognize its own and the other's hidden assumptions, and thus more quickly to reach a common agreement.

Reference Note on Production Planning and Control

This note is an introduction to the management area of production planning and control. It also discusses the control of inventories as an important related consideration. Productive capacity is the common denominator of the management considerations examined and serves to integrate the various systems covered. Terms are defined not so much to insist on specific meanings for words as to convey underlying ideas.

At the outset, productive capacity is defined as an assemblage of all the factors of production—men, machines, materials, technological know-how, working capital—well tied together by an intelligent management group with access to an information system. Following from this definition are definitions for *production planning*, the setting of productive capacity; *production scheduling*, the basis for determining how this capacity will be used; and *inventories*, the "reservior" of productive capacity serving as a buffer between successive process steps and between the production process and the market, which generates demand. All these activities fit together and are managed within a broad information and *control system*.

Time is another useful dimension on which to sort out these activities. Production planning, working largely from market estimates, sets aggregate production rates and inventory levels for several periods in the future and assigns general responsibility for these plans to specific productive units so that decisions on such things as the size and composition of the labor force and additions to plant and capital equipment can be made. It might be said that production planning begins with a clean slate, having no long-term commitments to fixed capacity, and ends with specification of a productive capacity which

will remain quite fixed for the short term. In essence, production planning establishes long-term capacity through investments in equipment and facilities and short-term capacity through manpower and broad hours-of-work decisions.

Production scheduling begins with a relatively fixed commitment to short-term capacity determined by production planning and essentially decides how this capacity is to be used. The interval of production scheduling is quite brief (often days or weeks), and the determination of the sequence and timing of specific demands on specific process units generally involves the consideration of a large amount of detailed information. In a factory, scheduling consists of such activities as the setting of due dates or promised delivery dates for orders to be run, decisions on the routing of orders to specific machines, and the sequencing of batches or lots through various productive facilities. Outside the factory, the aircraft controller who approves flight plans can be thought of as a scheduler of productive capacity, as can the traffic supervisor who decides the number of bridge toll booths to operate at specific hours. Thus production scheduling is the activity which makes production plans "come true," and, since it can have an important impact on the utilization of specific elements of capacity and hence productivity, efficient scheduling is of great concern to production managers.

Efficient production scheduling may be extremely difficult to achieve if demands from customers impinge directly on specific units of productive capacity. By interposing inventories as buffers between demand and utilization of capacity, productivity may be increased. We are therefore led to consider inventories as an important part of production scheduling. In the longer run, inventories, as will be shown later, are also an important part of production planning.

The study of inventories broadly involves two questions: (1) which items to carry in inventory and (2) when to order and in what quantity for each inventoried item. The first of these may be thought of as inventory planning. In addition to deciding which items are to be carried, inventory planning deals with stock location—whether to locate inventory stocks in one central warehouse, at branch warehouses, or with retailers. Location decisions have an important effect on the firm's ability to control inventory levels effectively. Despite this strong relationship, most stock location decisions are made quite independently of decisions regarding the control of these inventories. The form in which the inventory is to be carried—raw materials, finished parts, subassemblies, final product—is another inventory planning decision.

The second question, when to order and how much, is referred to as inventory control. In discussing the functions of inventory and presenting introductory concepts for the control of inventories, especially the economic lot size concept, "Guides to Inventory Processing," the preceding reprint from the *Harvard Business Review*, sheds light on this subject.

Production control is the activity which "closes the loop," or obtains feedback on actual performance from process units, compares these results with plans and schedules, and takes corrective action when necessary. Actually, in many companies the production control department includes all of the functions described thus far—production planning, scheduling, inventory planning, and control—but production control will be discussed here in the narrower sense of obtaining feedback and taking corrective action to insure that plans and schedules are met.

Two categories of action may be said to be available in production control: input control and output control. Input control involves the scheduling system and the inventory control system, which together determine the total demands on productive capacity for the short-term future. When the demands on the production facility exceed the facility's capacity, adjustments must be made to slow down the input of orders. Similarly, when the productive facility runs out of work, input dates must be moved up and other adjustments made if capacity is to be fully utilized.

Output control involves the flow of work through the productive facility and can be called shop-floor control. Since the production schedules developed in many situations do not—indeed cannot—express all the details necessary for minute by minute execution of the schedule, many small decisions are made by foremen and production control personnel, and even hourly workers, the sum of which amount to output control. Examples of these decisions are: choosing the job to be run next at a particular machine, choosing an alternative method for accomplishing a task when a process unit breaks down, or deciding to move a worker from one machine to another to balance better the available capacity.

Unseen behind the busy and sometimes chaotic-appearing activity in all production facilities is an information and control network that coordinates all human and physical elements of the system. An interesting analogy between manufacturing systems and other systems is provided in an article by Morris Tanenbaum which says in part:[1]

---

[1] Morris Tanenbaum, "Changing the Factory," *International Science and Technology,* June 1967.

The view, then, is of a manufacturing system as a collection of resources whose actions are coordinated by an information network so that the desired output is produced in response to a particular stimulus or input to the system. From this viewpoint, the manufacturing system closely resembles other enterprises which we're more used to thinking of as systems. A number dialed into the telephone network produces a connection to a desired telephone; a launch command delivers a missile to the desired trajectory. The manufacturing system differs from the communications system or the missile launch system in one fundamental respect, however. The manufacturing system is much more complex. The missile system can stand only a limited deviation from its design mode before the mission aborts, and even today's sophisticated telephone switching systems have a relatively limited number of modes by which a given connection can be made. A manufacturing plant, on the other hand, can operate in a great many modes. There are many ways a cable plant can use its machinery to make a cable, and, similarly, there are many ways to deploy the personnel of a plant. This is a wide variety of unanticipated demands and internal changes such as a machine breakdown or a flu epidemic. And while this redundancy makes for greater complexity, it also permits greater tolerance in its operation than more highly mechanized systems which do not involve the activities of large numbers of people.

On the other hand, this flexibility makes it extremely difficult to determine the one operating mode that is truly optimal—that will make the most efficient use of all resources. It is even more difficult to structure this kind of a system in a completely deterministic fashion than it is a communications system.

Obviously, a manufacturing system with a well-planned, clearly defined, and well-understood information and control network will come closer to making the most efficient use of all resources than a system using informal, "seat-of-the-pants" control.

The remainder of this note is devoted to specific topics within the larger area of production planning and control.

Forecasting

In production it can be fairly said that everything begins with forecasts—many different forecasts covering different time periods and forecasting different things. An appliance manufacturer might be interested in new family formations five years hence in order to plan for new or expanded plant facilities. The same manufacturer might also be attempting to forecast consumer acceptance of avocado green refrigerators as a guide to production plans for avocado green dishwashers. An auto parts manufacturer might be concerned about forecasting the size of a major customer's production run only one week in advance.

Sales forecasts are first approximations of production plans. Clearly, their impact on future capacities and, more generally, on

the firm's ability to compete effectively is highly significant. Just as production schedules are more detailed and specific than production plans, the forecasts used in developing production schedules need to be more accurate and detailed than the forecasts used in long-range production planning. As one might expect, there are many techniques for generating the many different forecasts required, a few of which will now be listed.

EXECUTIVE EDUCATED GUESS. This technique is generally recognized as an efficient way to get reasonably good estimates on aggregate future sales. The technique consists of nothing more than polling supposedly knowledgeable executives in the company on their views regarding future sales levels. This technique is usually not good for specific breakdowns of sales forecasts by individual products or sizes, colors, or models. On the advantage side, the forecasts can be obtained in a fast, inexpensive manner, and a possible additional advantage is that the same executives who make the forecasts will have to live with the results.

MARKETING ESTIMATES. On the theory that marketing and sales people know more about what is going on in the marketplace than anyone else, the polling of marketing executives and sales personnel is a common way to generate forecasts. Although salesmen are not generally recognized as particularly good estimators, the process of combining and filtering the estimates of salesmen by sales and marketing managers often results in reasonably reliable forecasts.

CORRELATIONS WITH INDICES OF ECONOMIC ACTIVITY. It is often true that the sales of certain products show a statistically reliable relationship to an index of economic activity or to some other measure. Examples include the relationship of the sales of bathroom fixtures to new housing starts, the sales of gasoline to automobile registrations, or the sales of heating oil to long-range temperature forecasts. When such relationships are thought to exist, the statistical techniques of regression or correlation analysis may be useful in supporting such working hypotheses.

DETAILED SAMPLING OF KEY CUSTOMERS. Some firms develop detailed forecasts of sales to a few key customers and then extrapolate these results to develop sales forecasts for sales to all customers. Interviews with customers can be used or salesmen can be asked to make an extra effort to get a clear picture of expected sales from a few customers.

MATHEMATICAL METHODS FOR HISTORICAL PROJECTION. There are many techniques available for projecting historical sales patterns into the future. Perhaps the most well known of these techniques is the mov-

ing average method whereby the sales for a given number of past periods are averaged and perhaps adjusted for trend. If forecasts are developed monthly, the most recent period's sales figure is added each month and the oldest period's figure included in the previous month's forecast is dropped. Thereby the number of sales periods included in the averaging process stays the same each time a new forecast is developed. Another technique for projecting historical sales paterns is called exponential smoothing. Although exponential smoothing is also basically an averaging technique, it allows a single number to carry forward progressively the weighted average of many periods and, with consistent weights, to combine this history with a number for the most recent period. A key decision is the weights to assign. Excellent material on both moving average forecasting methods and exponential smoothing forecasting methods can be found in two books by Robert G. Brown.[2]

Since the only sure thing about most forecasts is that they will be wrong to some degree, allowances must be made for possible errors and plans for dealing with these must be made explicit. Thus a production plan must consist not only of a projected production rate and a time period for that rate to hold, but also a device for changing the rate if sales do not develop as forecasted or if sales exceed the original forecasts.

Production Planning and Facilities Planning

Previously referred to as capacity setting, long-range production planning is also known as facilities planning. Since manufacturing cost structures and capacity constraints are largely determined by available facilities, specific production plans are usually developed in retrospect of facility plans. That is, the physical facilities will be in existence and will constrain the production planning alternatives considered.

Although many production people tend to view investments in facilities from a technical or engineering point of view, concentrating on what the new facility will do or how it will improve the production process, the basic criterion by which all investments must be judged is economic: How profitable will they be? Thus facilities planning, or long-range capacity setting, becomes what many know as capital budgeting, where the basic issue is to choose among all possible invest-

---

[2] R. G. Brown, *Statistical Forecasting for Inventory Control,* McGraw-Hill New York, 1959; R. G. Brown, *Smoothing, Forecasting and Prediction of Discrete Time Series,* Prentice Hall, Englewood Cliffs, N.J., 1962.

TABLE A   PRODUCTION PLANNING EXAMPLE

ALTERNATIVE PROGRAMS FOR MEETING FORECASTED DEMAND

Month	Forecasted Demand	Cumulated Forecasted Demand	Program I Production Rate	Program I Forecasted Inventory (end of month)	Program II Production Rate	Program II Forecasted Inventory (end of month)
Beginning inventory				500		500
January	300	300	700	900	350	550
February	400	700	700	1,200	350	500
March	500	1,200	700	1,400	500†	500
April	800	2,000	700	1,300	800†	500
May	1,000	3,000	700	1,000	1,050†	550
June	1,100	4,100	700	600	1,050	500
July	700	4,800	700	600	700†	500
August	400	5,200	160*	360	400†	500
September	250	5,450	160	270	250†	500
October	100	5,550	160	330	83†	483
November	100	5,650	160	390	83	466
December	50	5,700	160	500	83	499

* One change in production rate.
† Seven changes in production rates.

ment alternatives (including many outside the production area) those alternatives which will give the firm the best return on its investment. A discussion of techniques for capital budgeting is beyond the scope of this note, but the reader is referred to two excellent books on the subject.[3]

A more frequent decision in production planning is the decision that determines production rates, inventory levels, and work force levels for the next several weeks or months. One term often used to describe this problem is "production smoothing," since many manufacturing organizations attempt to smooth out the rate of production through the year, thus avoiding large changes in work force levels and capacity. Another term for much the same thing is "production programming," since a program for meeting fluctuations in sales demands is called for. As an example of a production programming problem, consider the firm facing the demand forecast shown in Table A. This forecast shows a distinct seasonal trend, as the sales of boats might show. The last four columns of Table A and the cumula-

[3] E. L. Grant and W. G. Ireson, *Principles of Engineering Economy*, Ronald Press Company, New York, 1960; and H. Bierman and S. Smidt, *The Capital Budgeting Decision: Economic Analysis and Financing of Investment Projects*, Macmillan Company, New York, 1966.

tive lines in Figure 1 show two alternative production programs for meeting the example's forecasted demand. Production program I is an example of a program which attempts to smooth out the production rate throughout major parts of the year. An absolutely smooth or uniform production rate for the entire year would involve the creation of large inventories. Thus production program I shows one change in production rate at the end of July. Production program II is designed to hold inventory levels down to approximately 500 units throughout the year. An important point brought out by Table A and Figure 1 is the difference in the magnitude of the changes in

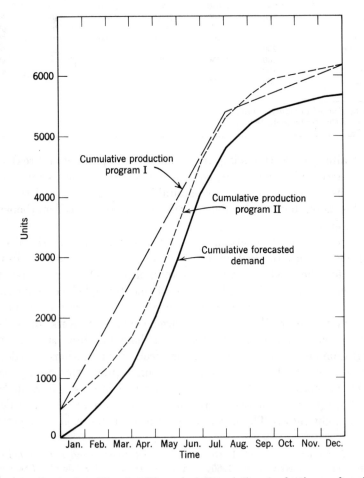

FIGURE 1. Production Planning Example. Cumulative production under alternative programs compared with cumulative forecasted demand.

the production rates required by the two programs. Program I requires only one change in production rate throughout the year, but that change is larger than any single change in program II. Program II, on the other hand, must reach a peak production rate of 1,050 units per month during the months of May and June. This peak production rate is 50 per cent higher than the highest production rate called for by program I. Program II therefore requires a capacity 50 per cent higher than that required by program I, and productive capacity, like inventory, is expensive. One might say that program I uses inventory to obtain capacity, whereas program II, by keeping inventory levels low, must have real plant capacity to meet demand.

The actual choice between these two programs depends on the measurable costs of providing capacity, changing production rates, and carrying inventory and such intangible considerations as company policy toward the labor force, the union contract, community relations, and desired customer service.

As one might expect, the general problem of production planning has been an attractive area for the application of operations research techniques. A thorough and complete quantitative study of this problem is reported by Holt, Muth, Modigliani, and Simon.[4]

Production Scheduling and Production Control

Production scheduling was defined previously as the determination of the sequence and timing of demands on specific units of productive capacity. Production control was defined as the activity that involves the constant readjustment of plans and schedules in the light of collected operating facts. The discussion turns now to several activities which take place within these broad definitions.

Perhaps the simplest production scheduling situation involves a single machine which produces a finished product. An example is a toothpick-making machine. The scheduling question is simply "Do we turn the machine on today; and if so, how long do we leave it on?" Of course, the answer to this scheduling question will lie in the sales forecast for toothpicks for the next several weeks, and in the supply of finished toothpicks already on hand (finished goods inventory). Thus the scheduling of a single-purpose machine which makes a storable product is largely an inventory control problem.

A somewhat more complex scheduling problem is faced by the company with a single producing facility on which several products are

---

[4] See C. Holt, J. Muth, F. Modigliani, and H. Simon, *Planning Production, Inventories and Work Force,* Prentice-Hall, Englewood Cliffs, N.J., 1960.

to be run. A good example is a small paint producer with one paint-mixing and blending facility. Here the question is not only "How long do you run the facility?" but also, "Which products do you run and in what sequence do you run them?"

Again, the supply of finished goods inventory on hand is an important determinant of the schedule, but now the costs of changing from one product to another also become important. For example, the cost of changing from blue to white paint might be higher than the cost of changing from blue to dark green paint. A product sequence running from very dark colors to white, then cleaning up and starting the same sequence over again, might be a desirable objective to minimize the costs of cleaning the mixing facility, but it may not be a good sequence in terms of making the colors that customers are demanding or that balance finished goods inventory.

This type of problem is not restricted to firms with only a single production facility. Paper manufacturers, for example, may have several large paper-making machines, perhaps in several different locations. A particular grade of paper can be made on more than one of the company's machines, so the problem becomes one of determining a cycle for each individual machine. It's solution necessitates taking into account a total demand larger than any one machine's capacity, the economies of producing certain products on certain machines, transportation costs, etc., as well as existing inventory levels and the costs of carrying inventory. A straightforward approach to the problem of determining production cycles is mentioned in the preceding article, "Guides to Inventory Policy," by John F. Magee and is developed further in his book.[5] Other treatments of this same problem are discussed in Hanssmann[6] and McGarrah.[7]

Many manufacturing organizations produce solely or largely to customer orders. Typically these producers have flexible, general purpose production facilities and can handle a broad range of products on a job-order basis. Often called job shops or job-order producers, such organizations can be characterized by three distinct features:

1. A high variety in the types and quantities of items produced.
2. A variety of general purpose machines and production processes.

---

[5] J. F. Magee and D. M. Boodman, *Production Planning and Inventory Control*, McGraw-Hill, New York, 1967.

[6] F. Hanssmann, *Operations Research in Production and Inventory Control*, John Wiley and Sons, New York, 1962.

[7] R. E. McGarrah, *Production and Logistics Management: Text and Cases*, John Wiley and Sons, New York, 1963.

3. A relatively low degree of short-run control over the quantity, production requirements, and often even delivery requirements on incoming orders.

Examples of manufacturing organizations which can be designated as job-shop in character are the large, captive shops which supply parts to the assembly facilities of air frame manufacturers. Smaller, more specialized shops producing such items as gears and other component parts and common machine shops producing a broad range of machined, stamped, or welded parts for a large number of customers are also job shops. In addition to these examples from manufacturing, auto repair shops can be said to have a job-shop character, as do restaurants and hospitals.

When a customer of a job shop places an order, he either specifies a desired delivery date or asks when his order will be delivered. In those few instances where the item ordered is one that is carried in inventory, there is no problem specifying a delivery date; but the basic problem still exists since a delivery date must be placed on orders for replenishment of inventory stocks. Thus in almost any job shop situation, management is frequently placed in the position of having to specify a delivery date on a new order which may not be run in the shop until several weeks or even months hence. In order to provide reasonable data for the delivery date decision, most job shops keep track of shop load by department or by machine. Shop load is nothing more than an accumulation of the hours of work already on the books which will be run on the machine or facilities in question. For example, shop load data might indicate that 32,244 hours of work for the horizontal boring mill department are on the books and have yet to be run. If the capacity of the boring mill department is 2,880 hours per week (say, 20 machines at 144 hours per week each), the backlog of work for this department is over 11 weeks. Nominally, this indicates that any new order received which requires time on the horizontal boring mill cannot be delivered in less than 11, and more likely, 12 or 13 weeks, allowing for other operations.

A major weakness of this simple loading approach for setting delivery dates is that the big block of hours representing load is not broken down by time period or by job. It is quite conceivable that a machine group with an 11-week backlog can run out of work in the third week if much of the work in the backlog does not reach the machine group until the fifth week. One remedy for this situation is to account for the accumulated load over time so that particular load on a ma-

chine group is shown in the week in which the work is expected to be accomplished. An example of such a method for keeping track of loads is shown in Exhibit 7 of the Brownsville Works case. This approach assumes an ability to estimate with reasonable accuracy the times between operations on jobs and the delays that will occur as jobs move through the shop.

Before proceeding, it is desirable to step back to examine more carefully the nature of work done in job shops. Typically, a job consists of a series of operations, each to be performed on all pieces in the lot, and each done on a different machine or with a different setup of the same machine. The sequence of operations and the machines on which they are to be performed are usually uniquely specified. The document that describes this sequence is called the operations sheet or routing sheet (see the Brownsville Works case, Exhibits 5 and 6, for examples of routing sheets). In addition to the sequence of operations, the routing sheet shows the allowed time for the performance of each operation. This time may be a gross estimate made by the production engineer who developed the routing or it may be a more precise standard time for the operation developed from standard data, time study, or synthetic standard time data. (See the Reference Note on Time Standards.) The time estimate represents the debit the operation will incur against capacity; this figure is used to build up the load data discussed earlier.

Given the existence of a routing sheet with estimated times for all jobs to be performed and a delivery date (or due date) for each job, two important tasks remain to complete the scheduling of a job shop: releasing of work to the shop, and dispatching and expediting jobs on the shop floor. Often jobs are released to the shop as soon as necessary paper work has been completed. This policy sometimes results in a large backlog of work at the initial work centers. This also means that many jobs with delivery dates still a long way off sit around on the shop floor longer than necessary. Many organizations therefore try to release work to the shop in accordance with due dates, thereby trying to reduce the number of bottlenecks in the shop and the level of in-process inventory.

Dispatching can be described simply as the activity of choosing the sequence of jobs to be run on each machine or processing unit. Jobs that have been released to the shop proceed through the shop, moving from machine to machine as the operations on the routing sheet are performed. Typically, when a lot of parts arrives at a machine, machine group, or work center, there already exists a line of jobs which arrived earlier and which are waiting for the same

machine(s). The foreman of the area, the production control man on the floor of the shop (the dispatcher), or perhaps the worker who will run the job must decide which of the waiting jobs will be run on the next available machine. The fact that many job shops have a large number of machines (500 is not unusually large) and an even larger number of jobs in process makes the problem of dispatching in an efficient manner a severely difficult one. Yet, if jobs are dispatched at random or according to an obviously nonoptimal scheme (like choosing the job carrying the highest piece rate in a shop paying by incentives), the results are likely to be poor performance against delivery promises, high in-process inventory, and idle machine time.

Operations researchers, working on the so-called "job shop scheduling problem," have developed a large number of decision rules for dispatching in job shops. Many of these rules have been tested in computer simulations of actual job shops or in smaller hypothetical simulations. Following are a few dispatching rules that have intuitive appeal.

EARLIEST DUE DATE. Select among the jobs waiting for an available machine that job which has the earliest due date. Use of this rule insures that due dates will be met reasonably well, but in-process inventory levels and machine idle time may be high.

FIRST COME-FIRST SERVED. Select among the jobs waiting for an available machine that job which arrived first in the waiting line. As might be expected, use of this rule means that due dates will not be met as well as with the first rule, but this rule does insure that no job will wait too long in any waiting line. Thus the statistical variance of flow time is lower with this rule than with almost any other rule, where flow time is the time from the start to the finish of the job.

SHORTEST PROCESSING TIME. Select among the jobs waiting for an available machine that job which has the shortest processing time for the present operation. This rule essentially picks the job that can get through the present work center the fastest. Since it gets through the fastest, it gets to the next operation the fastest, which is desirable if the next work center is idle and waiting for work. Use of this rule results in low average flow time, low in-process inventory levels, and usually good performance on due dates. (Even though the rule does not consider due dates, it moves work fast so that most jobs get done on time.) The major difficulty in using this rule becomes evident when a job with long running operations does not come out of the shop on time. This kind of job sits and

sits in a waiting line while all short-running jobs go ahead of it. This means that a few of the late jobs will be very late and a few jobs will have extremely long flow times.

Other simple rules have been proposed and tested, and a large number of complex rules have been designed for specific situations. A series of articles in the *Journal of Industrial Engineering* is an excellent reference for further material on dispatching rules and their properties.[8]

Recently a few large-scale computer systems for job shop scheduling and dispatching have been developed. (See "The Computer as a Manufacturing Tool" in this book.) Surely in the next few years many more of these systems will appear.

Until the time that efficient and inexpensive computer systems are developed for a wide variety of scheduling situations, the expediter will be an important man in most job shops. Expediting is the fire-fighting arm of the production control department. Expediters are charged with the responsibility for locating and "pushing" jobs that are behind schedule. Because a sizable fraction of the total load of many job shops is behind schedule, the actual scheduling of many large job shops is accomplished by a loosely knit process of negotiation, persuasion, and analysis. Armed with "hot lists" or "priority lists" of jobs behind schedule, expediters seek to have their jobs run next. Two or three expediters may try to get different jobs run on a single machine. The foreman, trying to keep his department's machine utilization up, wants to sequence jobs to minimize set-up times and to balance the skills of his men with the requirements of the jobs to be done. The worker, if given a chance to express a preference on the job to be run next, will probably choose the job with which he is most familiar, the one that pays the most, or the one that is easiest to run.

The important management tasks to be accomplished in such an environment are to develop and communicate the decision rules by which the shop is to be scheduled and controlled and to check periodically the validity of the rules. If such rules and guidelines are not made explicit, the decisions made independently on the floor of the

---

[8] R. W. Conway, B. W. Johnson, and W. L. Maxwell, "An Experimental Investigation of Priority Dispatching," *Journal of Industrial Engineering,* May–June 1960; R. W. Conway, "Priority Dispatching and Job Lateness in a Job Shop," *Journal of Industrial Engineering,* July–August 1965; R. W. Conway, "Priority Dispatching and Work In-Process Inventory in a Job Shop," *Journal of Industrial Engineering,* March–April 1965.

shop may result in schedules at cross purposes with managements objectives.

Inventory Control

Two important management objectives of most inventory systems can be expressed in terms of two desired results: an acceptable customer service level and a low total investment in inventory. That these two objectives are antithetical should be quite clear. The general problem of inventory management can be described simply as maintaining that supply of stock which provides acceptable customer service but which does not tie up an excessive amount of capital. This simple notion, easy to state, is very difficult to apply in operating situations. One reason for difficulty is that almost all of the available tools and techniques for inventory control involve item inventories, or the analysis and control of individual parts, products, or raw materials. The management problem and the objectives to be met involve aggregate inventories and larger considerations, including total investment in inventories. Managers therefore face a large, general problem armed with small, rather specific tools.

This note will go on to discuss a few concepts of item inventory control which were not covered in the article by Magee and will attempt to place these in somewhat larger perspective at the end.

Magee's "Guides to Inventory Policy" assumes an inventory situation for the development of an economic lot size formula, as shown in Figure 2. This "saw-tooth" diagram assumes a uniform, constant usage rate and instantaneous replenishment. If we relax the replenishment assumption and assume that it takes 20 days to get delivery after placing the replenishment order, the saw-tooth diagram remains

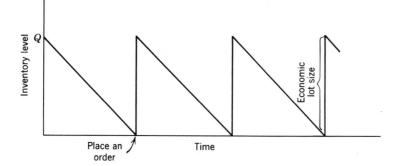

FIGURE 2. Inventory pattern with constant demand and instantaneous replenishment.

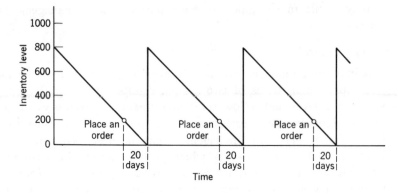

FIGURE 3. Inventory pattern with constant demand and fixed lead time.

unchanged except that orders are placed 20 days before the stock is expected to run out, as shown in Figure 3. In this example, demand is 10 units per day so the reorder point is 200 units; an order is placed every time the stock on hand gets down to 200 units. The assumption is made in these examples that the economic lot size is 800 units.

If the constant usage assumption is relaxed, the situation is as shown in Figure 4. Here the reorder point is not constant at 200 units, but the concept of setting the reorder point remained the same. An order is placed when 20 days' supply, calculated at the most recent usage rate, is on hand. There are two ways that the system shown in Figure 4 can go afoul: if the demand after placing a replenishment order is higher than the expected demand on which the reorder point was based, or if the delivery time is longer than expected—longer

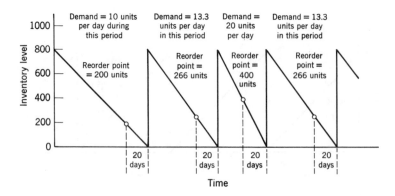

FIGURE 4. Inventory pattern with variable reorder point based on recent demand.

than 20 days in this example. If either situation develops, a stock-out will occur. Since both the demand rate and the replenishment lead time are, in fact, uncertain phenomena in most real-world situations, the inventory model must be able to handle them. To do so, the concept of safety stock, an amount of inventory to protect against random fluctuations in demand rate and delivery lead time, is introduced. Figure 5 shows an inventory pattern similar to that shown in Figure 4, but with a fluctuating demand rate. A fixed 20-day lead time for replenishment is still assumed, and provision is made for safety stock. The first cycle of the diagram gives an example of how safety stock is useful. The reorder point is set at 400 units (200 units safety stock plus 200 units of expected demand during the replenishment lead time). The expectation may be that the replenishment order will arrive just as inventory on hand reaches 200 units, but it is practical to recognize that there is a 50–50 chance or 0.5 probability that demand during the lead time will exceed 10 units per day, thereby requiring safety stock to prevent a stock-out. In the first cycle on Figure 5, demand averages 14 units per day during the replenishment lead time, so 80 units of safety stock are used. In the second cycle, the demand during the lead time averages less than the expected amount so the replenishment order arrives before inventory on hand reaches the safety stock level.

In these examples the assumption has been made that the reorder point is a variable which is recalculated frequently. More commonly, the reorder point is considered fixed and the safety stock is used

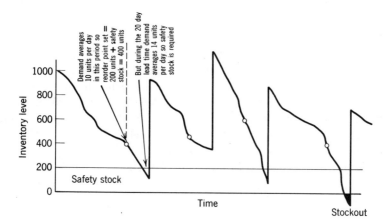

FIGURE 5. Inventory pattern with variable demand, variable reorder point, and safety stock.

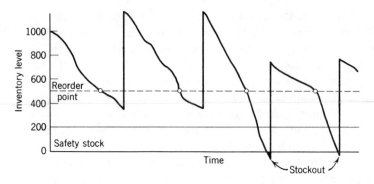

FIGURE 6. Inventory pattern with variable demand, fixed reorder point, and safety stock.

to absorb more of the demand uncertainty. Figure 6 shows the same demand pattern as Figure 5, but with a fixed reorder point based on a forecasted average demand of 15 units per day. It is interesting to compare cycles 1 and 3 in Figures 5 and 6, keeping in mind that the reorder point is variable in Figure 5 and fixed (at 500 units) in Figure 6. On the first cycle the fixed reorder point system does not use safety stock because the fixed reorder point calculated on the basis of forecasted average demand is higher than the reorder point calculated on the basis of recent demand. On cycle 3, however, the recent high demand rate yields a high reorder point in Figure 5, which, despite the very high demand during lead time, prevents a stock-out. In Figure 6 the same high demand rate causes a stock-out when the fixed reorder point is used.

Magee[9] suggests a method for determining the safety stock level for a fixed reorder point and fixed order quantity system like that shown in Figure 6. Basically, the reorder point is set equal to the "reasonable maximum usage" during the replenishment lead time. As an example of this method, assume the demand pattern shown in Figure 6 and assume further that a demand rate of 25 units per day or greater has a probability of 0.05. If the company is willing to accept a one-in-twenty chance of a stock-out during lead time, the reasonable maximum usage is set equal to 25 units per day and the reorder point equals (25 units per day times 20 days) 500 units. Actually, during an average lead time, the demand will be only (15 units per day times 20 days) 300 units so that the safety stock is

---

[9] J. F. Magee and D. M. Boodman, *Production Planning and Inventory Control*, McGraw-Hill, New York, 1967.

200 units.   Stated another way, 300 units of the 500 units in stock when a reorder is placed are to cover the expected demand during the lead time.   The other 200 units are to provide insurance against a stock-out if the demand is higher than expected.

The foregoing has presented only one rather straightforward system of inventory control—a fixed quantity or fixed order system with certain lead time.   Clearly, if lead time is uncertain, safety stock will have to protect against variations in both demand rate and lead time, and the method for determining safety stock levels becomes more complex.   There are, further, other models which can be used for inventory control.   One such model is the fixed reorder cycle with a variable order quantity system.   Here stock levels are reviewed on a fixed cycle (e.g., every month) and a replenishment order is placed based on the amount used since the last review.   Considerable research has been reported on a model of this latter type called the (s,S) model, wherein if, upon review at fixed intervals, the stock on hand plus on order has fallen to a level $x \leq s$ then the amount $(S - x)$ is ordered.[10]

Many excellent references are available on the subject of inventory control.   Although some of the treatments are highly quantitative and theoretical, there are several books that discuss quite straightforward approaches which can be applied in many operating situations.[11]

The tools and techniques discussed here and in the previous article deal, as noted, with the control of item inventories.   The aggregate results from the use of such tools might not be in concert with management's larger objectives for inventories, reordering frequency, investment, or customer service.   The straightforward application of an economic order quantity (EOQ) may, for example, lead to a considerably greater investment in inventories than management is willing to accept.   The problem then becomes one of making changes or adjustments in the rules for controlling item inventories so that

[10] An exhaustive quantitative study of (s,S) inventory systems is reported in H. M. Wagner, *Statistical Management of Inventory Systems,* John Wiley and Sons, New York, 1962.

[11] See, for example, J. F. Magee and D. M. Boodman, *Production Planning and Inventory Control,* McGraw-Hill, New York, 1967; J. W. Prichard and R. A. Eagle, *Modern Inventory Management,* John Wiley and Sons, New York, 1965; M. K. Starr and D. W. Miller, *Inventory Control: Theory and Practice,* Prentice-Hall, Englewood Cliffs, N.J., 1962; R. G. Brown, *Decision Rules for Inventory Management,* Holt, Rinehart and Winston, New York, 1967; R. B. Fetter and W. C. Dalleck, *Decision Models for Inventory Management,* Richard D. Irwin, Homewood, Illinois, 1961.

the aggregate results become acceptable. Such adjustments usually involve changing the data used to derive order quantities, reorder points, and safety stocks rather than changing the structure of the model itself. To bring the total investment in inventory down, for example, the cost of carrying the inventory might be increased in the EOQ formula. This would have the effect of lowering the quantities ordered, but increasing the frequency with which orders are placed. Such a move might be reasonable if the reason for the over-all limit on inventory investment were a general tightening of funds. The increased carrying charge would reflect the relatively high cost of borrowing additional funds to support high inventory levels. If application of an EOQ system resulted in more inventory than could be stored in existing warehouse facilities, an increased carrying cost in the EOQ formula, reflecting the higher cost of outside warehousing, would tend to bring inventory levels down.

Another problem which often arises stems from the independence of the inventory control system and the production planning system. It is not unusual for an EOQ system to trigger more replenishment orders in a short period of time than the producing facility is able to handle (here we are assuming replenishment orders are placed with a production facility of the same company). One researcher[12] has suggested that when this occurs a company should attempt to lower reorder points and make safety stocks carry the short-term demand rather than lower economic order quantities.

Conclusion

In conclusion, first a look back and then a look forward. In the opening paragraph of this note the definition of terms was given a role secondary to the conveying of basic ideas. In keeping with that, similar terms have been introduced for a single concept, and both the specific and general meanings of terms have been given. For the operating manager, it is pointless to insist on single meanings— practice does not respect precise definitions. What is important is to come to grips with the ideas underlying the words. Looking forward, the task of conceptualizing about production planning and control requires more work, and, particularly, the task of making ideas operational represents a challenge.

---

[12] P. R. Winters, "Constrained Inventory Rules for Production Smoothing," *Management Science,* Volume VIII, No. 4.

Space Constructors, Inc.

Space Constructors, Inc., (SCI) had received a fixed price contract
to construct a missile launching site for a government agency. Work
was nearly complete on the main launch site; however, it was apparent
that work on a special remote control building would have to be
finished earlier than originally planned if the contract were to be
completed on time.

James Alison, field construction supervisor for SCI, had arranged
a meeting with Henry Phillips, SCI's project engineer, to restudy
the arrow diagram of their Critical Path Schedule for the construction
of the remote control building in an effort to determine the shortest
possible time in which the job could be done without spending more
money than necessary.

The Critical Path Method, sometimes referred to as "the latest
and most powerful management technique for planning, scheduling,
and controlling large projects," is intended to provide improved project
planning and scheduling and a diagrammed display of all project
activities. On the typical diagram, arrows of any convenient length
are drawn to represent a single pertinent project element or activity.
These arrows, indicating time progression only, terminate at junc-
tions (or "nodes") indicated by circles signifying the beginning or
termination of activities. Arrows *originating* at a junction indicate
activities that can begin only after all activities (arrows) *terminating*
at that junction have been completed. When combined with a Cost
Table, the diagram indicates the possibility and cost of speeding up
a given activity. The sequence of activities requiring the longest
time to complete before the end of the project is known as the "critical
path" for that project. The path is considered "critical" because
any delay in the particular sequence will delay the completion of
the entire project.

EXHIBIT 1

CRITICAL PATH DIAGRAM FOR REMOTE CONTROL BUILDING PROJECT

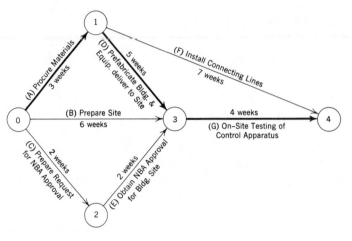

Note: Heavy arrows indicate critical path.

EXHIBIT 2   COST TABLE FOR REMOTE CONTROL BUILDING PROJECT

Activity	Normal		Crash*		Cost Slope, Dollars/Week
	Weeks	Dollars	Weeks	Dollars	
A	3	$ 5,000	2	$ 10,000	$5,000†
B	6	14,000	4	26,000	6,000
C	2	2,500	1	5,000	2,500
D	5	10,000	3	18,000	4,000
E	2	8,000	2	8,000	—
F	7	11,500	5	17,500	3,000
G	4	10,000	2	24,000	7,000
Total		$61,000		$108,500	

* Crash weeks shown represent the minimum possible time for the given activity.

† This is the cost of gaining one week over the normal time by use of "crash" methods.

Mr. Alison had the original arrow diagram for the remote control building project (Exhibit 1) in his office. It was, of course, considerably simpler than the similar diagram for the control of the entire missile site construction job.

Using the data provided by the Cost Table for this project (Exhibit 2), Mr. Alison saw that the critical path for this project followed the sequence of activities A-D-G and would require 12 weeks. The original project cost was estimated at $61,000. Mr. Alison could also see that the sequence of activities along one path, C-E-G could lag as much as four weeks behind schedule without affecting the planned time for the completion of the project. This available slack time is known as "float."

Although a computer was necessary for the rapid solution of critical path problems in larger projects, Mr. Phillips had manually worked

EXHIBIT 3

CRITICAL PATH DIAGRAM OF REVISED SCHEDULE
FOR REMOTE CONTROL BUILDING PROJECT

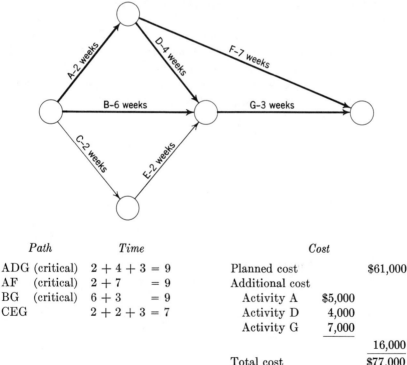

Path	Time	Cost		
ADG (critical)	2 + 4 + 3 = 9	Planned cost		$61,000
AF (critical)	2 + 7 = 9	Additional cost		
BG (critical)	6 + 3 = 9	Activity A	$5,000	
CEG	2 + 2 + 3 = 7	Activity D	4,000	
		Activity G	7,000	
				16,000
		Total cost		$77,000

out a schedule for this project which indicated that the job could be completed in nine weeks at a total cost of $77,000. The additional cost of $16,000 was largely attributable to the cost of extra shift operations necessitated by a "crash" program. It will be noticed that in his revised schedule (Exhibit 3) three paths had become critical to completion of the project as rescheduled.

In their conference, Messrs. Alison and Phillips concluded that a further speedup of the job was both necessary and possible.

Required

1. Reduce total project duration as much as possible without unnecessary additional costs. Indicate the new critical path or paths. Show how much slack time or "float" remains in the noncritical paths.
2. Assume that the situation proves to be less urgent than it seems to Messrs. Alison and Phillips. Revise the schedule in order to complete the job within ten weeks. Indicate the new cost and critical path or paths.
3. Suppose SCI were proceeding on the ten-week schedule and it became obvious that it would take not two but five weeks to prepare the necessary data for the request for government approval and that this step alone would now cost $7,000. What steps would you take to keep on schedule? What would be your new critical path or paths? What would happen to project costs?
4. Does CPM resemble any other planning techniques with which you are familiar (e.g., budgeting, break-even analysis)?

Arrow Diagramming Exercise

A major firm in the field of industrial machinery fabrication is planning to launch a campaign to promote the sale of a recently developed item of industrial hardware. You are asked to prepare the arrow diagram from which schedules for the campaign preparation can be developed. You have available the information listed in the following paragraphs. The number in parentheses following the description of each activity indicates the estimated time in weeks required for its accomplishment.

In general, the project may be broken down into three major categories:

a. The training of sales personnel.
b. Consultation with and training of marketing personnel.
c. Preparation of the necessary advertising and instruction material for the campaign.

TRAINING OF SALES PERSONNEL

In order to save time on the sales side, it has been decided to:

Prepare phase 1 of the training program for salesmen (8),

at the same time that the sales managers are selecting the sales personnel who are to be trained (2).

Both of these activities will therefore begin at the start of the project.

Following their selection, the chosen sales personnel must be relieved of their responsibilities in their areas and sent to the company's training center in the home office (4).

Obviously, it would be foolish for the salesmen to arrive before phase 1 of the training program is ready for them. When phase 1 of the

program is prepared, the salesmen will be trained in this part of the program (10).

While the salesmen are being trained in phase 1 of the program, phase 2 will be prepared (9).

As soon as the salesmen's training in the first phase is completed and phase 2 of the program has been approved,[1] sales training in the second phase can commence. The second part of the program will take (12).

At the conclusion of the two major phases of their training, the sales personnel will be issued "Customers Instruction Manuals" on the new machine and will spend time at the home office becoming familiar with them (5).

When the salesmen are familiar with the manuals, they will return to their respective territories ready to begin their effort simultaneously with the national advertising campaign. Getting back to their territories should take (1).

TRAINING OF MARKETING PERSONNEL

The first step in the project for the marketing side will be the determination of the general marketing approach (10).

When this has been arranged, the necessary marketing personnel will be selected (4) and brought into the home office (2).

Following the determination of the general marketing approach, and while the marketing trainees are being selected and brought in, specific training plans for the marketing personnel will be consolidated (2).

After these plans are consolidated, a familiarization course for these personnel will be designed (8).

When personnel and course are ready, the training of marketing personnel will proceed. It is estimated to take (8).

PREPARATION OF ADVERTISING

Immediately after the general marketing approach has been determined, advertising plans must be consolidated (6).

When this consolidation is complete, a paper is to be prepared (6) and printed in a professional journal (8).

---

[1] Approval cannot be given until the General Marketing Approach (see "Training of Marketing Personnel") has been determined.

Also immediately following consolidation of advertising plans, national advertising must be prepared (10), approved (4), and distributed to the proper media (2).

Not until the marketing people are trained, the professional paper published, and the advertising distributed will the national advertising be released and carried by the media involved. The release and preparation to carry the national advertising will take about (2).

It is not planned to proceed further with the national advertising campaign until the salesmen have returned to their territories.

As soon as the advertising plans are consolidated (the first step under "Preparation of Advertising"), a general brochure will be drafted and approved (4).

Following the approval of the brochure, a layout must be designed (5) and the brochure printed (3).

As soon as the brochure is approved, a "Customers Instruction Manual" will be prepared (3).

The "Customers Instruction Manual" in its turn must be approved (1) and printed (2).

Copies of the "Customers Instruction Manual" alone will be sent to the training center (1), where the manual will be utilized in completing the training of the salesmen.

As soon as both the brochure and manual are printed, they will be packaged together and delivered to marketing for general distribution. This activity should take about (8).

Actual implementation of the campaign, which may be regarded as the termination of this project, cannot begin until the salesmen are in their territories, the national advertising compaign is released, and the proper brochures and manuals are distributed.

Required

Prepare the arrow diagram for this project and select the critical path or paths. You will probably show from 30 to 35 activities including dummies, and from 20 to 25 events.

Chase Brass & Copper Company

In November 1965, the Chase Brass & Copper Company, a subsidiary of Kennecott Copper Company, opened a new brass rod plant in Williams County, Ohio. Costing $8 million, the plant was designed to produce 50 million pounds per year of a patented, free-cutting brass alloy particularly suited to high-speed metal working, especially on automatic screw machines. The design and operation of this installation represented significant departures from the traditional methods of brass manufacture.

A "brass" mill usually consists of a number of facilities, including a casting shop and several metal processing and finishing installations, each with its own manager. These mills process the many different alloys of brass, copper, and occasionally aluminum to order in the casting shops and produce a broad line of products including rod, tubing, wire, and sheet. The Williams County mill is designed to produce only the one alloy in an integrated process from casting to finishing. Scrap brass chips are the basic raw material; it is estimated that customers will directly return about 40 per cent of the mill's shipments as scrap. The process requires unusually close composition and temperature control, but the new mill is considerably simplified from older, multipurpose plants. Exhibit 1 compares the old and new brass production methods used by Chase and describes the steps in the new process.

In an interview printed in the October 7, 1965, issue of *Iron Age*, Glenn Bakken, President of Chase, commented that the Williams County mill was a systems laboratory to prove out company-wide computer control techniques. "What we have done," Mr. Bakken said, "is to put a roof over a machine. From that machine we expect to push out free-machining brass rod in a continuous process."

Startup Problems

The new, simplified process incorporates sufficient departures from traditional brass rod manufacturing techniques to require a considerable experimentation and development effort. The mill includes many features novel to the industry:

Single-alloy, rod-only processes without annealing.
Continuous-melt, semicontinuous-pour furnace.
Computerized inventory control of extrusion billets.
Largest brass extrusion rod press installed in the U.S.
On-line process control computer.
Computer control of finished goods inventory location.

The process control system was built and installed by the Foxboro Company. The central processor was a Digital Equipment Corporation PDP-4 digital computer to which Foxboro linked censors, instruments, controls, teletypewriters, and other peripheral equipment.

During the initial startup of the plant, many adjustments were made in the equipment and the process. Most changes were minor and were made quickly, but it became evident that major equipment modifications would be required in the casting shop. Even prior to the formal opening of the plant, the designers realized that the technical problems in the casting shop would seriously limit over-all production. Casting production in November 1965 was about 15 per cent of design capacity. The most difficult problems involved the movement of molten brass. Material flowing from the three melting furnaces to the holding (pouring) furnace froze in the passages between the furnaces. The flow through the manifold or "distributor" which connected the holding furnace and the four semicontinuous casting molds was also unsatisfactory.

The casting shop contains four furnaces: two identical chip melting furnaces, a solids melting furnace, and the larger holding furnace. The weight of any charge can be monitored continuously by load cells and power monitors that feed data to the process control computer. The basic raw material, brass scrap, is crushed and fed continouously through a degreasing unit (a small chemical cleaning plant) into the chip melting furnaces, each with a 24,000 pound capacity. Molten brass continuously overflows down from these furnaces into the 78,000-pound capacity holding furnace. Samples are taken regularly from these furnaces and analyzed for 16 elements on an X-ray spectrometer that is connected on-line to the process control system. If the analyses from the holding and chip melting furnaces indicate a deviation from the metal compositions required to yield

New Production Methods

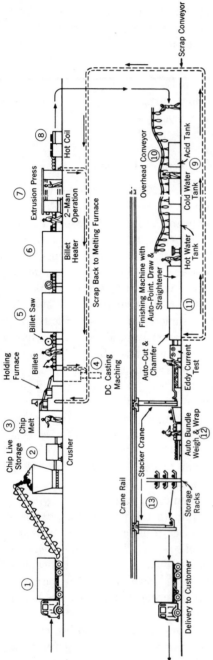

KEY TO NUMBERS ON FLOW DIAGRAM: (1) *Truck Dumper and Computerized Scale.* Entire truckloads of brass chips are up-ended and dumped into the below-floor hopper. The weight of the delivered materials is automatically calculated by the computer. Brass chips immediately needed for the plant's casting operations are blown into large piles by pneumatic conveyor. (2) *Brass Chip Processing System.* Brass chips dumped into the hopper are carried up the inclined conveyor and dumped into the storage bins. As they are needed by the furnaces, they are crushed to uniform size and then chemically degreased and cleaned. As the brass chips are vibrated up spiral towers, grease and dirt are removed by trichlorethylene vapors and fluid. They then are blown by pneumatic conveyor to the large chip bins over the melting furnaces. (3) *Continuous Feed Chip Melting Furnaces.* Chips are fed into melting furnaces by gravity in a continuous stream. (4) *Billet Casting Center.* From this vantage point (Exhibit 5) one can see the chip and solids melting furnaces, the central holding furnace, the casting machine, the casting controls, and, near the far wall, the automatic billet saw. (5) *Billet Storage Conveyors.* After they are moved by conveyor from the automatic billet, the 10-inch billets are stored on live conveyor tracks until they are called for by the extrusion press operator. (6) *Billet Heater.* The billets are moved from the conveyor tracks through a gas-fired heater bringing them to a red hot temperature before they are fed into the extrusion press at the other end. (7) *Extrusion Press.* A completely automatic 4,000-ton press pushes the red hot billets through a die, forming long strings of brass rod. The entire operation is accomplished by pushing a single button. (8) *Automatic Rod Coiler.* Brass rod that is 1¾ inches in diameter or smaller is extruded directly into this automatic rod coiling machine. After the extrusion cycle is complete, the coils of rod are conveyed automatically through cooling and pickling steps. *Extrusion Rod Run-Out Table.* Brass rod 1¾ inches in diameter or larger is pushed out of the extrusion press directly onto the automatic run-out table conveyor in lengths up to 100 feet. Once on the run-out table the rod

is automatically cooled and positioned to be picked up by the pickling crane. The crane then dips it into successive acid and water baths to complete the pickling operation. (9) *Automatic Coil Pickling System*. The coils of small-diameter brass rods are automatically placed on hooks which will dip them into successive acid and water baths in a completely automatic pickling process. (10) *Coil Storage on Conveyor Hooks*. Leaving the pickling system the coils of brass rod are automatically transferred to the "C" hook conveyor system. This complex of conveyors then moves the coils into the proper storage tracks behind the finishing machines according to computer's instructions. (11) *Rod Finishing Equipment*. Each of these finishing lines takes the coils of brass rod, then straightens and draws them to precise dimensions. As the brass rod is going through the finishing line, every inch is checked by an electronic eddy current tester, which checks for flaws or imperfections. Any material that does not meet quality standards is automatically rejected. This equipment also polishes the rod surface, cuts the rod to select lengths, chamfers the ends and stacks them in the conveyor cradle. (12) *Bundling and Wrapping Station*. The bundles of finished brass rod are wrapped and banded for storage and shipping. Here, the computer gives each bundle a storage "address" card. (13) *Computer-Directed Stacker Crane*. The crane operator punches the three-digit code from the storage "address" card into the stacker crane's control panel. The unmanned stacker crane then automatically places the bundles in the tree rack storage area according to the computer's instructions.

Old Production Methods

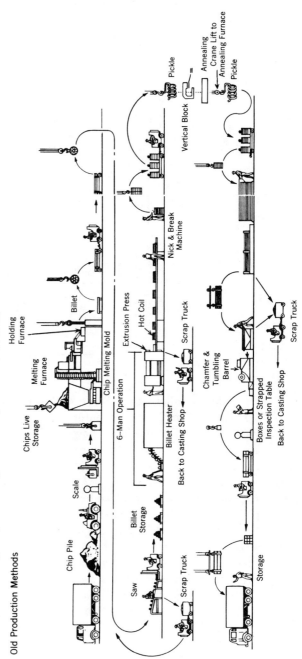

EXHIBIT 2 CHASE BRASS & COPPER COMPANY

CASTING SHOP LAYOUT

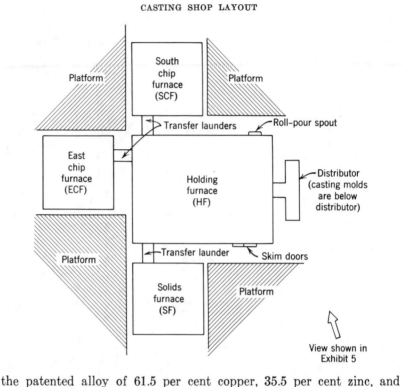

View shown in
Exhibit 5

the patented alloy of 61.5 per cent copper, 35.5 per cent zinc, and 3.0 per cent lead, the computer program prints instructions for the furnace operator on a teletypewriter in the casting shop, telling him to add specific materials to the solids melting furnace. The program checks the analyses of the solid brass scrap in inventory and prints out the weight and type of the material to be added. In some instances virgin zinc is added rather than brass scrap. The operator places the additional material in the solids melting furnace, which heats the material rapidly. When the metal reaches the molten state, it is dumped down into the holding furnace. Exhibit 2 contains a sketch of the locations of the four furnaces.

All four furnaces in the casting shop are induction-type, in which electricity is used to heat the metal. Theoretically, there were to be no chemical changes in materials. Actually, however, a chemical change often did occur and this change was responsible for most of the problems that plagued the casting shop. At the temperatures used in the holding furnace the zinc in the brass had a tendency

to oxidize in the presence of air. The new system was designed to operate with a blanket of inert gas (nitrogen) over the pool of molten brass in the holding furnace, but, nonetheless, some oxidation took place. As the molten brass flowed from furnace to furnace through the channels of firebrick and ceramic, it cooled and zinc oxide crystals precipitated out onto the walls of the channels, finally disrupting the flow of metal and forcing frequent shutdowns. Poor heat distribution in the channels contributed to these problems.

The company's engineers decided that it was necessary to redesign and rebuild the channels, called transfer launders, that linked the three melting furnaces to the holding furnace. These modifications included installation of channels with much larger cross sections and orifices and the addition of electrical heating units called inductors. The modifications to the transfer launders were so extensive that the work had to be done at the manufacturer's factory. A decision was made in November, 1965 to operate for a while with only one chip melting furnace. The south chip furnace (SCF) was shut down immediately, and its transfer launder was disconnected and returned to the manufacturer.

Despite all these problems, a limited supply of billets of the patented alloy was produced in the casting shop. An emergency supply of additional billets was prepared by conventional methods at the company's Waterbury, Connecticut mill and shipped in for further processing. This entailed added freight from Waterbury to the Williams County mill, which was located near the Ohio-Indiana line. The manufacture of billets at Waterbury also consumed more raw materials and yielded a product that was more difficult to extrude through the Williams County mill's press. During shutdowns at Williams County, a chip inventory worth more than a half-million dollars was immobilized at a time when scrap was in short supply and customers would gladly take at firm prices all the brass that could be produced.

Billets produced elsewhere were also something of a problem, because assays of metal content were not automatically recorded by the X-ray diffraction and process control computer system at the time of casting. Some customers specified that these assays were to be supplied as part of their orders and received them free of charge in accordance with industry practice. At the old mill, this meant exception handling of orders requesting assays from the casting shop through shipping or, alternatively, last minute special analyses of samples cut from the rod just before shipment. In the new mill, the inventory control system utilized the memory and tapes of the

PDP-4 computer to keep track of the assay of each billet and control the movement of billets and bundles of rods from operation to operation and into inventory. Thus, when the console in the shipping department printed out shipping papers and location in inventory of the material to be shipped, it also could print out at virtually no additional cost the correct assay for each bundle of rods.

Preparing for the Shutdown

The Williams County mill had been designed in the Central Engineering Department at Chase's Cleveland headquarters. Engineers from this group also supervised the startup, the debugging of the equipment, and the training of the operators. Only the plant manager and the administrative director had been transferred from existing Chase plants. The general foreman was hired from a nearby bread plant and the shipping room foreman from an egg packaging plant. The balance of the 60 plant employees were recruited from nearby farming communities. Only three of the blue collar workers were over age 29. Three engineers from the Central Engineering Department remained at the plant most of the last half of 1965. One of these, Joseph Goodell, became responsible for scheduling the shutdown and modification of the casting shop. He had joined the company in August, 1965 and had been assigned to help with the startup of

EXHIBIT 3 CHASE BRASS & COPPER COMPANY

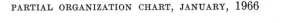

PARTIAL ORGANIZATION CHART, JANUARY, 1966

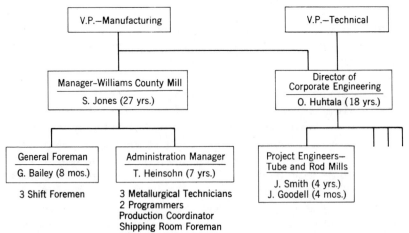

( ) Indicates period of experience at Chase.

the equipment and the training of the operators. A partial organization chart appears in Exhibit 3.

Mr. Goodell's supervisor in the Central Engineering Department had asked him to develop a critical path schedule for the casting shop project. During his several years as a field cost control supervisor for a large heavy construction firm, Mr. Goodell had observed the widespread use of critical path schedules. He had never, however, received any formal instruction concerning PERT or CPM during his undergraduate engineering studies nor in the Harvard Business School MBA Program from which he had graduated in 1961, but he was aware that maintenance shutdowns had been among the earliest and most successful applications of these techniques.

A meeting to develop a schedule was arranged that included both Chase personnel and representatives of the furnace manufacturer. The first step in formulating the schedule was to establish the sequence of work. After the sequence had been agreed upon, time and manpower estimates were added. Mr. Goodell felt that the meeting had proven quite successful. "My startup responsibilities," he commented, "did not involve the casting shop, so I had very little knowledge of what work was entailed. This proved to be a blessing, since my elementary questions often stimulated a new approach to a task."

After the meeting he drew up a rough schedule. While he worked on this, a number of ideas and questions occurred to him. A second meeting resulted in a revised and significantly shorter schedule. "At this point I made an analysis of the manpower requirements," he said. "I wanted to see how many men from the various trades (ironworkers, cement masons, welders, etc.) were required on each shift. This was done by making up a chart with the shifts across the top and the trades down the side. This revealed a few problems, only one of which was serious. Only one man, who was to be supplied by the furnace manufacturer, would have the skill to burn out the refractory brick to enlarge the furnace's inlets, an extremely hot and exacting task. We could not expect that man to work on this task for one and one-half shifts continuously. Five and a half shifts were added to the schedule at that point." Inasmuch as the whole plant could not operate effectively without the output of the casting shop, there was no question of the desirability of paying for overtime.

The final critical path schedule is shown in Exhibit 4. Since Mr. Goodell had had no formal training in CPM, he developed his own symbols. Under the line segment denoting each activity he placed two numbers representing, respectively, the number of men required on the crew and the number of eight-hour shifts required. In the

circles at the beginning of each activity he placed the total time in shifts required before that activity could start. Dummy activities were represented by dotted lines, and over each the slack time in shifts was marked in a triangle.

Once the critical path schedule was completed and checked with the parties involved, a number of other actions were taken. A quick check was made to determine how many cutting torches and welding outfits were required. Materials were ordered and drawings were completed. The transfer launder for the south chip furnace was already at the manufacturer's plant. February 1 was chosen as the date for the complete shutdown of the casting shop.

The Shutdown Plan

The modifications required a number of changes in and around the furnaces. Exhibit 5 pictures the work area. Careful planning was required to allow removal of the right amounts of hot metal in order that the furnace modifications might go forward and still maintain a small pool of hot metal in the bottom of the furnaces. If the furnaces were emptied completely, they would cool down,

EXHIBIT 5   CHASE BRASS & COPPER COMPANY

VIEW OF CASTING SHOP SHOWING REMOVAL OF SEMICONTINUOUS
CAST BILLETS AFTER A POUR

requiring several shifts to heat them again. Complete cooling and reheating might also damage the furnace linings and electrical heating elements and force another shutdown. The procedure started with the draining of metal from the active east chip furnace (ECF) into a heated ladle for transfer to the solids furnace (SF) from which it immediately was poured into the holding furnace (HF) and cast into billets in the usual fashion.

Casting was accomplished by increasing the nitrogen gas pressure in the holding furnace to force the metal out through an opening into the distributor and down into the four semicontinuous casting molds. In order to work on the nearly empty holding furnace it was necessary to release the nitrogen pressure. This threatened to allow oxidation of the metal remaining in the furnace. Therefore special "skim doors" at the side of the furnace were opened and graphite beads were spread over the metal surface to blanket it against the air.

Once the graphite beads had been inserted into the holding furnace it was possible to remove the platforms and catwalks around the furnaces, roll the barrel-shaped holding furnace, and pour more metal into the ladle. The ladle could be emptied into the east chip and solids furnaces after each had been plugged to prevent flows into the holding furnace. The south chip furnace had been cold for weeks while its transfer launder was being modified.

At this point it was possible to remove the distributor and the remaining launder and start modifying the holding furnace. These modifications were quite involved and critical. The openings in the holding furnace that received hot metal were to be equipped with external pockets to which the transfer launders were attached by flanges. Exhibit 6 illustrates the construction of a typical furnace opening. After the transfer launders were taken out it was necessary to remove the flanges at the furnace openings. The original design included no pockets. To enlarge these openings it was necessary to chip and burn out old firebrick and ceramic. Then new openings and pockets were built with larger openings and channels. This required cement masons skilled in molding and curing ceramics to assure smooth channels for metal flows and to contain the various heating elements such as inductors and glow bars.

Other changes were planned during the shutdown. The inert gas generator was to be modified. So were the distributor and the metal tubes leading to it from the holding furnace. Because the holding furnace was not wearing well under the operating conditions of heat and abrasion, a new, tougher alloy tubing was to be installed. The

EXHIBIT 6   CHASE BRASS & COPPER COMPANY

ELEVATION VIEW OF CHIP FURNACE TRANSFER LAUNDER

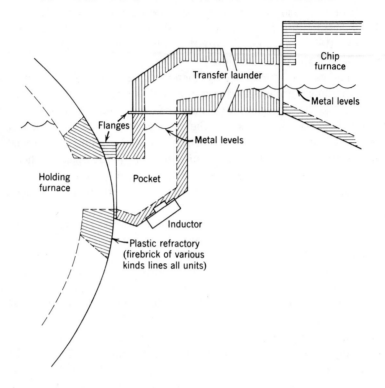

solids furnace transfer launder was to be replaced with one of a modified design. The transfer launders for the chip furnaces required extensive rebuilding, which could not be handled by local facilities and personnel. The plan therefore was to remove the old transfer launder from the east chip furnace, install the rebuilt one originally assigned to the south chip furnace, and send the old one back to the factory. Thus the schedule called for a return to 50 per cent of casting shop capacity in about nine calendar days and to full production in about eighteen calendar days. It had been decided that placing the south chip furnace in operation was relatively not urgent and should follow satisfactory operation of the east chip furnace.

Early Shutdown

On the morning of December 30 the launders suddenly froze up. Mr. Goodell was asked if everything was on hand to permit a shut-

down on January 3, 1966, instead of February 1. Since all of the required materials were listed on the critical path schedule a check was easily made. Missing components were located and rushed out from the manufacturer's plant some 300 miles away. Most of the materials for revisions of the inert gas generator were not available, so that this work was eliminated from the January 3 plans. (A method was worked out for making those revisions later without a complete shutdown of the casting shop.)

Arrangements were made with the steelworking, plumbing, electrical, and cement masonry contractors and with the furnace manufacturer to have the men report at the times at which they were required according to the critical path schedule. The Chase men were to report at 6 A.M. on January 3 to start emptying the furnaces. The crews were scheduled so that work would continue around the clock.

Mr. Goodell had the critical pah schedule (Exhibit 4) reproduced on a 3-foot × 5-foot sheet and posted on the wall of an office just outside the casting shop. When the men reported on the morning of January 3, he called them into the office and explained the schedule on the wall. He instructed Jack Bailey, the Chase general foreman, to write the time that each activity was completed on the schedule in colored pencil.

Every two or three hours Mr. Goodell checked the schedule and the shop to make sure that everything was proceeding according to plan. On the first day, the emptying of the furnaces moved ahead much faster than expected. Mr. Goodell left the plant well after midnight. When he returned the following morning at 8, he checked the schedule and found that the transfers of hot metal had been completed and that the skim doors, distributor cover, and distributor all had been removed. Then he went out to the shop to check over the work done by the third shift. It seemed satisfactory.

Assessing the Results

Mr. Bailey reported enthusiastically that everything was under control. "That schedule seems to be a big help," he observed. "I know just where to put the eight Chase men. We are getting that distributor apart and done, so we won't have to worry about it anymore. The ironworkers arrived ahead of time today, so I put them to work on the skim door modification over in the maintenance shop. Then that will be out of the way. By the end of the day shift both Chase and ironworker crews will get around to the rest of the platforms and flanges on the holding furnace and east chip furnace. Everything will be ready for the man from the furnace company when he gets in tonight."

Mr. Goodell continued to look over the work being done. He noted that three Chase men were at work breaking out the lining of the distributor. Two men were busy on the cover of the distributor, removing tubes and glow bars and the cover lining. Three others were placing the graphite beads over the hot metal in the holding furnace and cleaning the holding furnace refractory. Two cement masons were busy casting the pocket for the holding furnace intake from the solids furnace transfer launder.

After his inspection trip Mr. Goodell went to the office containing the critical path schedule to check what he had seen against the schedule and decide what to do next.

Davis Tool and Die Company (I)

In May 1954, Frank Sisco, production manager of the Davis Tool and Die Company, became concerned with the fact that the company's Machine Department was unable to meet promised delivery dates. This Department had been expanding rapidly and, as soon as he could, Mr. Sisco planned to add more men to its workforce, since Davis cylindrical thread-rolling machines made in this Department were gaining customer acceptance at a rapid rate.

Products Manufactured

Until 1953, the Davis Tool and Die Company realized practically all its revenues from the sale of dies used to form threads by a cold-rolling process. Both flat and cylindrical dies were manufactured for machines made by a variety of other companies. Because of its pioneer work and technical competence the Davis company attained a commanding position in flat-die manufacturing and was consulted as an authority, not only by die users, but also by the manufacturers of thread-rolling machines.

During the latter part of World War II, the company started to develop and manufacture thread-rolling machines using its own cylindrical dies. Davis machines were designed not for manufacturing standard fasteners but rather for threading high-production parts such as spark plugs, primarily for the aircraft and automotive industries. Through 1952, however, the sales of these machines were negligible compared to its other product lines. Early in 1953 Davis increased its machine sales effort and orders increased rapidly. By May 1954, the cylindrical thread-rolling machines represented roughly one-third of the company's annual sales, with the remainder divided about evenly between flat and cylindrical dies.

EXHIBIT 1 THE DAVIS TOOL AND DIE COMPANY (I)

THE NATURE OF THE THREAD-ROLLING PROCESS

Exhibit 1 shows the nature of the thread-rolling process and some of the products threaded by these methods. Exhibit 2 shows the company's three standard thread-rolling machines, the designs for which had not changed materially from the original designs. Early redesigns of these machines were not contemplated. The A-22 machine sold for $8,000, the horizontal A-23 for $10,000, and the large A-32 horizontal machine for $20,000. In about half the cases, however, machines required a substantial amount of custom work, either re-design of some basic parts or design of special attachments or both. Such machines, termed "specials," sold for $2,000 to $5,000 above the price of standard machines. Each machine comprised about 200 different parts, most of them being manufactured rather than pur-chased.

EXHIBIT 2   THE DAVIS TOOL AND DIE COMPANY (I)

THE COMPANY'S THREE STANDARD MACHINES

Organization of the Machine Department

The following chart shows the organization of the Machine Department in May 1954:

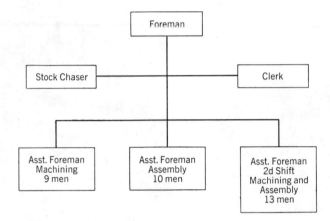

The first shift worked from 7 A.M. to 3:40 P.M., and the second shift from 3:40 P.M. to 12:10 A.M. The second-shift assistant foreman was responsible for all activities in the Machine Department; the second shift throughout the plant was under the supervision of a general foreman, who was, in effect, the plant's superintendent at night.

Preliminary Processing of a New Order

For the most part, orders originated from manufacturers' agents. As customers invariably required a cost quotation before entering a machine order, the quotation was worked out by the "inside" salesman (a sales engineer) with assistance as required from the Engineering Department and the Machine Department foreman. Sometimes the item was quite different from standard machines, and compiling data for quoting required considerable coordination; on other occasions, however, the job was as simple as "Make the same kind as we made for *X* company."

When an order was received, the "inside" salesman for thread-rolling machines made out a form called "Customer's Order." Machines were serially numbered and a separate order form was made out for each machine. This showed an order number and a promised delivery date. The promised delivery date was based on a schedule estimated by the foreman's clerk (described later), but the inside salesman also verified the proposed delivery date with the Machine Department

foreman and the Engineering Department. For standard machines, the Engineering Department had little to do beyond duplicating existing documents, but for special machines the time required for engineering sometimes amounted to as much as a month.

In any event, before production on a shop order began, the Engineering Department prepared and delivered to the Machine Department foreman's clerk both a complete set of prints and a "schedule" or bill of materials which listed the individual parts and quantities required. The unit schedule for each subassembly distinguished purchased parts by means of an asterisk. Exhibit 3 is an example of a unit schedule.

Transactions between the inside salesman, the Machine Department, and the Engineering Department were informal, without following the "chain of command." Each of the other two product lines similarly had an inside salesman who worked directly with the foreman in charge of the Department making his product line and with appropriate engineering personnel.

After Engineering had completed the blueprints and the schedules, Mr. Sisco believed that for efficient manufacturing the shop needed a minimum of eight weeks' lead time for a standard machine and twelve weeks for a special machine. When the shop's backlog was less than two months' production, or if, in spite of two months' backlog, Davis promised a customer delivery in less than two months, Mr. Sisco believed that high-cost production resulted and too many things went wrong with both the rush order and other orders in the shop. Difficulty was experienced in getting quick deliveries on some purchased parts, notably castings and welded pieces. The foreman was unable to make the best distribution of work among his men, and inevitably work on some orders in process had to be stopped to try to meet the rush-order delivery date. In spite of such efforts, Mr. Sisco's experience had been that a few parts would be missing at final assembly and cause further disruption of the shop in an effort to expedite or replace them.

Scheduling by the Foreman's Clerk

For over-all purposes, the foreman's clerk scheduled each order on the basis of estimated total direct-labor dollars. To compute the direct-labor dollars in each machine order, the scheduling clerk multiplied the sales price by 15 per cent, which historically had been the average relationship between direct-labor dollars and thread-rolling machine sales. This percentage figure had remained stable in the last few years. The estimated direct-labor cost in the order was

EXHIBIT 3 DAVIS TOOL AND DIE COMPANY (I)

UNIT SCHEDULE

Name	4B-13 Die Holder Assembly—1⅝ Die Face		Our Order No._____
	Splined Spindle		Cust. Order No._____
	A-22 Machine		Quantity_____
Date	3/11/54		_____

Part or Unit No.	Draw Size	Part or Unit Name	Quan. Req'd.	Material	Cost
	D	See 70-U-3B-13-5 Die Holder Assembly			Due 9/15
C-9564		4B-13 Die Holder	1	Spec. 3—Blank C-2256	
B-3821		Die Blank	1	Spec. 4A	
C-1653*		Die Holder Bolt	1	Spec. 9	
—		#304 Woodruff Key	1	$\frac{3}{32}$ x ½	
A-1654*		Bottom Lock	1	No. 12 Hill Alloy Bronze	
A-1655*		Bolt Latch	1	Steel	
A-1666*		Latch Spring	1	Purchase	
A-1792		Bolt Nut	2	½–13 Semifinished Check Nuts	
C-1659*		Link	1	Bronze Casting	
C-4382*		Splined Spindle	1	Spec. 19	
B-9577		Steel Bushing	2	Spec. 9	
B-5986*		Top & Bottom Bronze Bushing	2	Spec. 20	
A-3414*		Washer	1	Spec. 9	
C-6178*		1¾ Splined Top Univ. Fork	1	Spec. 15	
A-4386*		Spindle Pin	1	Spec. 16	
A-4315		Spindle Pin Retainer	1	0626 Music Wire— Purchase	
C-7305*		1¾ Univ. Solid Connector	1	Spec. 15	
B-6194*		1¾ Univ. Center Block	2	Spec. 19	
B-9954-1*		1¾ Univ. Rivet	2	Purchase	
A-6192*		1¾ Univ. Pin (Short)	4	Spec. 19	
A-6193*		1¾ Univ. Pin (Long)	2	Spec. 19	
C-6984*		Top Die Matching Gear	1	Spec. 15	
A-6991		Ring Gear Cap	1	C.R.S.	

balanced against the current payroll for the Machine Department. For instance, if the estimated direct-labor content of orders already scheduled totaled $25,000, then with the approximately $500 per day direct-labor payroll ($2,500 per week) being disbursed in May 1954, the earliest a new order could be started would be ten weeks from the date the scheduling was being done. If the new order was for an A-32 machine selling for $20,000, the estimated direct-labor cost was $3,000 (15 per cent × $20,000). Since $3,000 was about six days' payroll (at $500 per day), the estimated shipping date would be set ten weeks plus six working days hence. This process of scheduling by estimated direct-labor dollars was useful mainly in working with the inside salesman to give customers estimated delivery dates on quotations.

Upon receiving a "Customer's Order" the foreman's clerk sent a purchase request to the Purchasing Agent for each purchased part, specifying a delivery date two weeks before assembly of the machine was to begin. He checked the raw material required for manufactured parts and, if the raw material was not in stock, placed purchase requests for these items too. Stocks of a few purchased parts, such as screws and bolts, and of a variety of bar-stock metals were maintained. The foreman's clerk then placed one copy of each unit schedule (Exhibit 3), marked with the order number, in a loose-leaf binder for follow-up purposes, and placed the "Customer's Order" form in a tickler file by its promised delivery date. Finally, the clerk filled out certain information on a shop card (Exhibit 4) for each manufactured part: the part number, nomenclature, number of finished parts required, and a required completion date, by which the parts would have to be completed so that assembly would have enough time to do its job and still meet the estimated delivery date for the completed machine. The foreman's clerk tried to get all manufactured parts completed two weeks before the machine's estimated shipping date, in order to give the assembly group more than adequate time to put each machine together. Based upon his experience, the foreman's clerk entered on each card the date when the part should be started through the manufacturing process in order to be completed two weeks before the promised shipping date for the machine. He then filed each card in an "active" file by chronological order according to the starting date.

Assigning work to the men and filling out the list of operations on the shop card were the responsibility of the foreman. When a man finished one job, he came to the foreman, who consulted the "active" file and assigned him the job represented by the first shop card in

EXHIBIT 4   THE DAVIS TOOL AND DIE COMPANY (I)

SAMPLE SHOP CARD

PART: 4 B-13 Die Holder #C-9564

NUMBER: 1   DUE DATE: 9/15

                   START: 9/5

Radial Drill
Mill
Saw
Drill
Mill
Grind
* Heat treat & sandblast
Polish
Hone
Grind
Hone
Insp.

the file, if it was within the capability of the operator. Six of the nine men in the machining group on the first shift were all-around experienced machinists who could take a job through several machining operations on one or more machines and complete the workpieces required. Often, however, a workman would be assigned only part of the operations required to produce a workpiece. Most of these men maintained rough notes in a little black notebook of key points in setting up and machining jobs they found to be repeated. Mr. Sisco believed that each man regarded his notebook as his personal property. Three men could not operate all the machines in the shop and were often assigned to do part of a job, rather than a complete one. Usually, they also required more help in making set-ups than did the all-around machinists. In any event, the foreman listed the principal steps required to make the workpiece on the shop card before turning

over the job with the shop card and the appropriate blueprints to the workman.

In addition to the "active" file of shop cards, the foreman was also guided by a checklist, prepared by his clerk, of work scheduled for completion during the week. This list included delinquent orders and orders representing a parts shortage at assembly, as well as the parts due during the current week according to the clerk's follow-up copies of the unit schedules not yet completed. Using these data and his general knowledge, the foreman juggled and balanced man and machine assignments in the face of daily changes in demands.

Equipment included several lathes, horizontal and vertical milling machines, a horizontal boring mill, a vertical turret lathe, a cylindrical grinder, two small surface grinders, two gear shapers, a horizontal turret lathe, a four-spindle drill press, and two radial drills.[1] The assembly group utilized the two radial drills together with hand tools. Sometimes two men, each with different shop cards, wanted to use the same machine at the same time; in this case they called the foreman, who decided which man had priority. The foreman also decided what the other man was to do until a machine was available for him to complete the job he had begun.

When a workman completed a job, he noted this on the shop card and returned the card to the foreman, who gave it to the shop clerk. The shop clerk recorded completion of the parts in the column headed "Cost" on the appropriate unit schedule in his follow-up notebook and filled out a travel card authorizing the stock chaser to take the parts to the storeroom, where they would be held until withdrawn by the assembly group as needed for construction of the machine. Shop cards were filed and destroyed periodically to keep the ₁pace occupied by such files within bounds.

The Machine Department in Operation

The Machine Department foreman, appointed to his job in 1947, was a trade-school graduate, aged 35, who was formerly a machine operator. He not only assigned work to his men; he also drew on his memory to tell the workmen whether or not any jigs or fixtures were available for each job and, if so, to which parts of the job they applied. He listed on the shop card in sequence the machines to which

---

[1] The other two departments, flat die and cylindrical die, by and large had more specialized machines, gear hobbers and thread grinders, and were laid out in a "line" arrangement.

the operator should move. He maintained a log in a notebook to show the location of all jobs at all times. When large parts had to be moved from one machine to another, or when work was transferred to another department, the foreman told the stock chaser to move them. The foreman and assistant foreman were responsible for suggesting whatever new jigs or fixtures might be useful; jigs and fixtures were made up in a central toolroom for all departments.

In observing the Machine Department in operation, Mr. Sisco found that the Assembly Department, despite customer demands for more machines, sometimes had one or more idle men who had to be assigned odd jobs other than assembly just to keep them busy. These occasions were the result of a lack of one or more parts required to proceed further on the assembling of a particular machine. Usually it was a manufactured part that was missing. The assistant foreman in charge of the assembly group, Mr. Sisco found, tried not to start assembly operations on a machine until the clerk's follow-up file showed all parts to be available; on some occasions, however, he was forced to begin assembly of a machine with some missing parts, in the hope that the missing parts would become available before they actually had to be assembled. Occasionally, a machine could be completed except for one or two subassemblies; in this event, the machine was left on the shop floor until the missing parts became available, and in the interim the men were assigned another machine on which to begin assembly operations.

Mr. Sisco also observed that when the Department foreman was particularly pressed for time, he did not write out the sequence of operations on shop cards but merely gave the workman verbal instructions. In Mr. Sisco's opinion, verbal orders were likely to be misunderstood and to result in spoiled workpieces, criticism of the worker for failure to carry out instructions, or criticism of the foreman for failing to tell the worker what to do. At the same time, Mr. Sisco fully appreciated the pressures on the Machine Department foreman growing out of the increasing demand for thread-rolling machines and the gradual addition of new men to his workforce (Exhibit 5).

Mr. Sisco discovered that the transfer of a partially complete job from one shift to the next was often a source of delay and confusion. Some jobs could be successfully completed by two or more methods, or by a different sequence of operations. Although either method or sequence might be acceptable, problems arose when a piece half-finished by Method A was transferred to a man on the next shift who preferred to do it by Method B.

EXHIBIT 5   DAVIS TOOL AND DIE COMPANY (I)

SALES (SHIPMENTS) OF MACHINE DEPARTMENT 1/1/53 THROUGH 4/30/54
AND ORDER BACKLOG AS OF 4/30/54

		Total Sales	Number of Machines Sold		
1953			A-22	A-23	A-32
	Jan.	$ 23,751	1	1	—
	Feb.	20,077	2	—	—
	Mar.	35,432	1	2	—
	Apr.	29,341	2	1	—
	May	21,076	1	1	—
	June	18,788	2	—	—
	July	43,929	2	—	1
	Aug.	52,314	3	2	—
	Sept.	57,798	1	—	2
	Oct.	54,742	3	2	—
	Nov.	58,337	2	3	—
	Dec.	61,722	5	1	—
Total 1953		$477,307	25	13	3
1954					
	Jan.	$ 67,224	6	1	—
	Feb.	70,302	1	3	1
	Mar.	74,362	4	3	—
	Apr.	71,008	6	1	—

Backlog of orders on hand, 4/30/54:
    Model A-22   13
            A-23   4
            A-32   —

Selling price of special attachments for machines in the backlog:
    $26,000 (estimated)

NOTE: Manufactured parts, all of which were made for a specific machine order, were stored in a central storeroom (also used to store finished flat and cylindrical dies) pending withdrawal from stores by the assembly department.

At the time Mr. Sisco was studying this problem, the Machine Department foreman reported to Mr. Sisco that a radial-drill operator on the second shift had gone home one night only two hours after reporting for work. According to the Machine Department foreman, this operator, a new employee, had been assigned a job involving 24 drilling and tapping operations and a rather complex set-up. The operator had not done the job before and it developed that the second-shift assistant foreman did not know enough about the job to help the operator get the initial set-up correct. None of the other workmen on the shift had ever done this particular job, so after unsuccessfully attempting it himself, the radial-drill operator finally said that he simply gave up trying to figure out how to start the job and went home.

It seemed fairly clear to Mr. Sisco that the Machine Department foreman did not have enough time to do a good job of supervising his Department and that this fact underlay much of the difficulty of meeting production schedules. With the prospects for even greater demand on this Department in the months ahead, Mr. Sisco decided that it was imperative for him to take action that would substantially improve the situation as quickly as possible.

Knobel Manufacturing Company

During the past year, the Knobel Manufacturing Company had repeatedly failed to meet promised delivery dates on its orders. Henry Sellmeyer, hired recently as factory superintendent, investigated the difficulty.

Production Categories

The company letterhead describes the product line as brass and wire goods. Actually the products are distinctly separated as to market and as to manufacture, falling roughly into about five classes: screw-machine products; bent-wire products, such as paper clips; stampings, such as talcum-can tops; upholstery tacks and thumb tacks; and small, special, wire springs.

Large production runs and highly automatic machinery characterize all of the company's manufacturing operations. The 75 to 100 screw machines are mostly under five years old, capable of combining many diverse machining operations simultaneously, automatically, and very rapidly on small parts. There are small, inclined, open-back punch presses equipped with roll feed for rapid production of simple stampings from coils of strip stock. Complicated stampings, such as talcum-can tops, are produced complete from coiled strip in eyelet machines, which are essentially high-speed, automatic punch presses having six to ten plungers which operate complicated progressive dies. Upholstery tacks are produced on high-speed, fully automatic nail machines which blank and form various-shaped heads and attach them to the wire points. Fine-wire springs of special shape are made on "coilers" and "winders," which are high-speed, fully automatic machines designed and produced by the company's own engineers in association with local machinery makers. Bent-wire products are produced on "four-slides," which are also high-speed, fully automatic machines.

The factory is organized into 15 production departments. These departments are segregated into those performing the first, or so-called primary, operation on the product and those performing secondary operations. Primary operations are automatic, eyelet, press, spring, fabric, chain, clip, and nail. Secondary operations are buffing, plating, rolling, assembling, hardening, lacquering, and packing. Some of the primary departments contain additional equipment to perform such secondary operations as drilling, slotting, and grinding.

The plant layout, on four floors and in four buildings, is such that considerable movement of the material in process is required. This circumstance grew out of the way in which the company developed. The Knobel Manufacturing Company had been founded about 50 years earlier by Frederick Knobel and an associate in Waterbury, Connecticut. The first factory building was a three-story brick building. Buildings 2 and 3 were built just before and during World War II and were of similar construction. Building 4 was the final major addition, and housed the Hardening and Lacquering Departments. Paralleling the plant expansion, the number of plant employees had grown to 407.

Products

One half of the company's sales volume has consisted of products classified as standard-stock items. The firm's first product was of steel wire linked in the rectangular pattern commonly used for bed springs in hospital cots. This product was called "fabric." Other standard-stock products include paper clips, paper-binder clamps, jewelry chains, chair glides, thumb tacks, and upholstery tacks.

Several years earlier, the company had maintained inventories of the standard products and filled all orders for standard products from stock. However, a period of heavy demand had wiped out these inventories, and management had never returned to the former practice of filling orders for standard products from stock.

The remaining half of the company's business has consisted of the production of special "contract" items. As an example of this business, the company has made parts for lipstick containers in accordance with customer specifications. Other contract items have been special kinds of springs, metal inserts for plastics manufacturers, electrical parts, and different types of wire goods. These contract products have been chiefly made of brass, but some items were also made of steel, phosphor bronze, aluminum, or stainless steel, and some have been plated in nickel, cadmium, zinc, copper, or brass. Exhibit 1 is the working drawing of a product of the

EXHIBIT 1 KNOBEL MANUFACTURING COMPANY

WORKING DRAWING

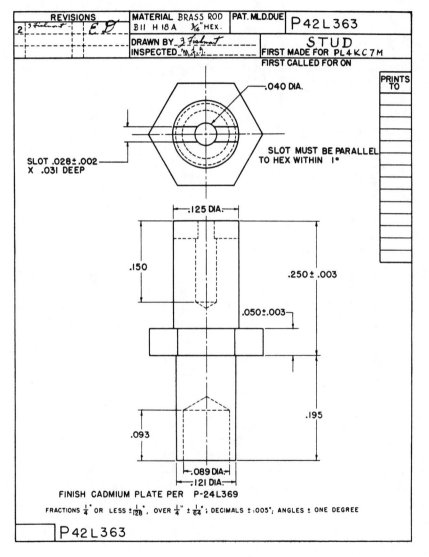

REVISIONS			MATERIAL BRASS ROD BII H 18A 3/16"HEX.	PAT. MLD.DUE	P42L363
2	3 *Fishmt*	*E.D.*	DRAWN BY *3 Fishmt*		STUD
			INSPECTED *M.S.R.*		FIRST MADE FOR PL4KC7M

FIRST CALLED FOR ON

PRINTS TO

.040 DIA.

SLOT .028±.002
X .031 DEEP

SLOT MUST BE PARALLEL
TO HEX WITHIN 1°

.125 DIA.

.150

.250±.003

.050±.003

.195

.093

.089 DIA.

.121 DIA.

FINISH CADMIUM PLATE PER   P-24L369

FRACTIONS ¼" OR LESS ± 1/128", OVER ¼" ± 1/64"; DECIMALS ±.005"; ANGLES ± ONE DEGREE

P42L363

EXHIBIT 2 KNOBEL MANUFACTURING COMPANY

ORGANIZATION CHART

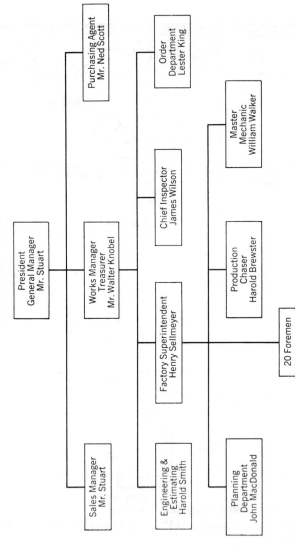

contract-order type on which the primary operation is done on an automatic screw machine. Most contract orders require processing in more than one department.

Management Shifts

About six months before Mr. Sellmeyer joined the Knobel company the firm experienced a shift in top-management personnel. The organization chart of the firm (Exhibit 2) did not accurately reflect these changes because the reorganization resulted in a shift of responsibilities from Alan Stuart to Walter Knobel, son of the founder, but not a change in titles. At the time of Frederick Knobel's death, Mr. Stuart had assumed the duties of president and general manager in addition to his regular duties as sales manager. During the years that followed, Mr. Stuart kept in constant contact with all phases of the company's operation and made most of the day-by-day detail decisions himself. Upon reorganization, Mr. Knobel had become, in fact, operating head of the firm while still retaining his duties as treasurer. Mr. Stuart restricted his activities to his duties as sales manager. One of Mr. Knobel's first moves was to employ Mr. Sellmeyer as factory superintendent. Sellmeyer replaced Ned Scott, who was promoted to the newly created position of purchasing agent.

Production Procedure

Mr. Sellmeyer's investigations revealed that the production-scheduling system used for orders was not highly formalized. The Sales Department made delivery promises to customers at the time a bid was submitted on a prospective order. When an order was received, the Sales Department notified the Purchasing, Tool, and Order Departments. Upon receipt of the order information, the Purchasing Department placed orders for the required amount of raw material, the Tool Department commenced work on the necessary tools and gauges, and the Order Department made out the manufacturing order. Exhibit 3 is the manufacturing order for the part shown in Exhibit 1. One copy of the manufacturing order was routed to the Planning Department and a second copy to the foreman in charge of that department in which the first, or primary, operation on the order was to be performed. A record was kept in the Planning Department of the availability status of the raw material, tools, and gauges required by each order.

When all the necessary elements for commencing production were on hand, the Planning Department filled out the upper half of the machine-assignment slip (Exhibit 4) and sent it to the foreman in

EXHIBIT 3 KNOBEL MANUFACTURING COMPANY

MANUFACTURING ORDER

MANUFACTURING ORDER

DEPT. *L I J*	DATE *10-7*	QUANTITY *100,000*	ARTICLE NAME *Studs*	ARTICLE NO. *S-486-1735*

DESCRIPTION *P#2L363 Studs, our S-486-1735 made from 3/16" hex. Brass Rod, Cadmium Plated Finish. To B/P we have .090 hole to be burred.*

PART NO. _____   M. O. NO. *46-8210*

RAW MATERIAL *3/16" hex. Brass Rod – Our Spec. A*   S. O. NO. *4687*

R. W. LBS. PER M *5.3*	LBS. REQUIRED *530*	LBS. IN STOCK *1535*	LBS. AVAILABLE

MACHINE TYPE *COES*   MACHINE NO. *1787*

Op. No.	DATE	MADE	Est. Prod. Per Hr.	TOTAL	Op. No.	DATE	MADE	Est. Prod. Per Hr.	TOTAL	Op. No.	DATE	MADE	Est. Prod. Per Hr.	TOTAL
	Prod	*1 hr. 420*												

RAW MATERIAL REC'D IN DEPT.
DATE   LBS.   TOTAL

RETURNED TO REC. DEPT
DATE   LBS.   TOTAL

NET LBS. USED

O. K.

FOREMAN

CHECKED BY

S. O.   MASTER REC.

EXHIBIT 4 KNOBEL MANUFACTURING COMPANY

MACHINE-ASSIGNMENT SLIP

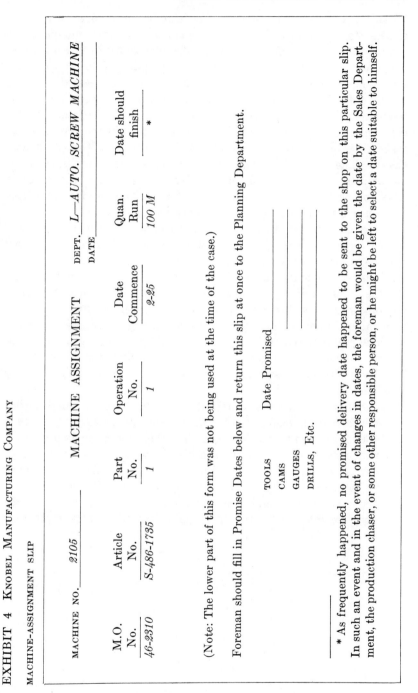

MACHINE NO. _2105_   MACHINE ASSIGNMENT   DEPT. _L—AUTO. SCREW MACHINE_

DATE

M.O. No.	Article No.	Part No.	Operation No.	Date Commence	Quan. Run	Date should finish
_46-2310_	_S-486-1735_	_1_	_1_	_2-25_	_100 M_	_*_

(Note: The lower part of this form was not being used at the time of the case.)

Foreman should fill in Promise Dates below and return this slip at once to the Planning Department.

Date Promised _____

TOOLS _____

CAMS _____

GAUGES _____

DRILLS, Etc. _____

* As frequently happened, no promised delivery date happened to be sent to the shop on this particular slip. In such an event and in the event of changes in dates, the foreman would be given the date by the Sales Department, the production chaser, or some other responsible person, or he might be left to select a date suitable to himself.

the primary department concerned as a directive to commence operations on the specified order. The foreman carried out the manufacturing operations in conformance with the blueprints furnished by the Engineering Department. Each foreman prepared a daily production sheet showing by article number the quantity processed by each machine in his department. Once an order had been started in production in this manner, each foreman routed the work to the department he thought should follow, and this further routing and scheduling of the order was also followed up by the production chaser. The production chaser was constantly in touch with the Sales Department and at its direction attempted to finish the order in time to meet promised-delivery schedules. The production chaser also served as foreman of the Shipping Department.

In actual practice the system described above was not followed very closely. Personnel of the Sales Department often felt that it was necessary to make direct contact with the foreman in suggesting machine assignments on specific orders. Also it was not unusual for the foreman in a primary department to commence production on some orders on his own initiative without the authorization of a machine-assignment slip. Thus, the actual assignment to a particular machine was ignored in many cases. Another irregularity from the above procedure was the practice of "borrowing" raw material that had been purchased and allocated for a given order and diverting it to another order.

Mr. Sellmeyer also discovered that the backlog of orders varied considerably from one primary department to another. Whenever, for lack of orders, idle-machine time began to be evident in a primary department, the salesmen were usually able, within a matter of weeks, to secure a volume of orders sufficient to bring the department back to full capacity. In the meantime, the backlog of orders in other primary departments might be running low; and in response to the shortage, the salesmen would once again shift their sales efforts.

Evers Machinery Company

In July 1962 Tom Shay joined the Evers Machinery Company as manager of the Repair Parts Department. The Evers Machinery Company, which employed about 2,500 people, manufactured a line of industrial machinery. The life of Evers major items of equipment usually ranged from 15 years upward, and many users still had Evers machines over 25 years old. As a result, the Repair Parts Department constituted an appreciable part of the company's total annual sales and represented an even more important portion of total profits, particularly in years when sales of new equipment declined. Evers equipment items were subject to wide cyclical swings in demand.

The Repair Parts Department received from 600 to 750 customer orders per week; since there were 3.4 items, on the average, per order, this meant requirements for 2,000 to 2,600 items each week. It maintained a stock of about 5,000 parts for old-model machines. Evers no longer manufactured these models of machines, which were either discontinued or, in most instances, had been supplanted by new designs. In addition to the stock items, there were several times as many nonstock parts which were made only upon customer order. It was a policy of Evers that it would make a replacement for any part of its machines which a customer wanted; Evers reserved the right, however, to charge the customer on a cost plus normal-profit-margin basis for producing the part.

The Repair Parts Department also maintained stocks of parts currently used in the manufacture of new machine designs, about 15,000 parts. For these parts the Department did not make the decision on the quantity to be ordered into production but, instead, simply notified the order section of the Manufacturing Department of its expected annual consumption rate. The ordering section of the Manu-

facturing Department determined the expected requirements for new construction and added this figure to the estimated consumption of repair parts to get the total annual expected consumption of the part. The order section used this total to make a decision on lot size. The Repair Parts Department and the order section maintained separate Kardex inventory records. Each set of records pertained only to the transactions of that department.

Evers' plant is located in New Jersey. The Repair Parts Department maintains its headquarters in a separate warehouse near the plant. A second Repair Parts Department warehouse is located in Chicago. Each of these warehouses serves about one-half of Evers' customers, who are divided into two divisions, the eastern and the western. There had been some trend towards faster growth in the western division's sales in the years just preceding 1962. Since the availability of quick parts service is an important factor in competition on new machinery sales, both warehouses maintain stocks of all stock parts, both for old designs and for current models of machines. The home plant's stock records in the Repair Parts Department show the number of each item available at the home plant's warehouse and the number available in Chicago. Evers maintains a teletype circuit between the eastern and the western division office, where they are posted to the home-office Kardex records. The home-office stock records also show whether the customer's plant is in the eastern or the western division. All nonstock parts, of course, are manufactured and shipped from New Jersey.

Some of the parts used in both the production of new models and their repair sales were stored without segregation in the Production Department's storeroom. Therefore, the Cost Accounting Department had been unable to compile periodic reports on the dollar value of the Repair Parts Department's inventories. Mr. Shay knew, however, that accounting procedures were being developed by Al Clark, the controller, to try to identify his Department's items in the future. When this occurred, he knew that Ralph Lewis, manager of Manufacturing, might ask for explanations if the Repair Parts Department's total inventories ran over a million dollars.

About six months after starting with Evers, Mr. Shay turned his attention to the question of economic-lot size. The existing practice was to order one to two years' anticipated supply of each item, depending on the judgment of the stock-control clerk. In Mr. Shay's opinion, ordering in economic-lot size would probably improve the profit position of his Department. In response to his inquiry, a trade association to which Evers belonged sent him a supply of nomographs (Exhibit 1) which permitted the application of the economic-lot-size

formula shown on the form. The economic-lot size could be calculated by utilizing the formula directly, but the nomograph permitted the determination of the economic-lot size for parts without using arithmetic. Mr. Shay believed that the nomograph would therefore permit much easier calculations of economic lots by John Thompson, his assistant, who directly supervised the stock control section, comprised of three stock clerks.

EXHIBIT 1 EVERS MACHINERY COMPANY*

NOMOGRAPH

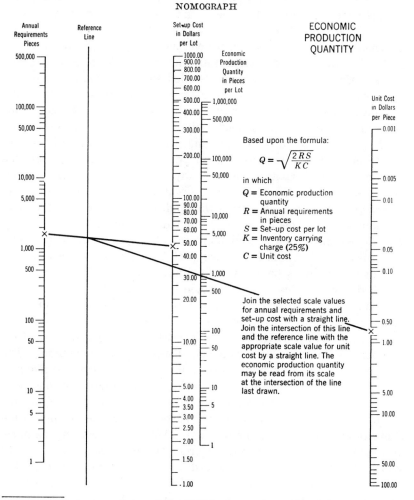

* Reprinted by permission from "IBM Accounting—Manufacturing Control, No. 4, Production Planning and Control," Form No. 320-6031-2.(c) by International Business Machines Corporation.

Development of Formula Data

Mr. Shay arranged for the company's Cost Accounting Department to furnish an IBM tabulation showing for each part the standard direct-labor cost, the standard material cost, and the total set-up cost for all operations required on it. The typical part required about ten operations, almost all of which had set-up costs. In addition, Mr. Shay asked the Cost Accounting Department to add $15 to the set-up cost for each part to reflect the clerical and other costs of handling an order. The $15 figure had been established by the Cost Accounting Department as a result of a recent survey of paperwork costs.

Mr. Shay realized that the results of the formula were significantly influenced by the "K" factor, which the nomograph fixed at 25 per cent. He therefore discussed this factor with Messrs. Lewis and Clark. Mr. Clark had made no detailed study of storage or obsolescence costs, but he felt that the 25 per cent figure was appropriate for the kind of parts Mr. Shay was dealing with. Over the years, according to Mr. Clark, the charge-off of obsolete parts had been quite small. Mr. Lewis, on the other hand, was of the opinion that use of the formula would probably result in larger inventories, requiring more capital and exposing the company to greater risks. As a result of this conference, however, it was decided to lower the quantity to be ordered by 10 per cent from that indicated by the application of the nomograph. This device was adopted as a rough but satisfactory way of obtaining results equivalent to a "K" factor of 33 per cent. Mr. Shay and Mr. Clark realized that this was not a very precise way of doing things but they believed that with all the uncertainty involved anyway, this approach would be completely satisfactory.

In conference with Mr. Lewis, Mr. Shay established minimum and maximum levels for all repair parts at 18 weeks and one and one-half years, respectively. Mr. Shay believed that it might be expedient occasionally to exceed the one and one-half year maximum. The minimum was based on the shop's estimate that it currently required nine weeks of lead time to deliver an item after a shop order had been written. Mr. Shay added an additional nine weeks as a safety factor because actual deliveries of many parts showed the planned nine weeks to be too short. At present only about 70 per cent of the parts were delivered in nine weeks; all orders were on hand after the 18 weeks allowed. Mr. Shay planned to vary the minimum as the shop's ability to deliver changed. It was standard practice for the shop to tell both the Sales Department and the Repair Sales Department periodically its lead time requirements.

Procedures for the Stock Control Section

Mr. Shay decided that the order quantity should be fixed by Mr. Thompson. When a shipment was posted to the Kardex which caused the balance of that item on hand to fall below the minimum, the stock clerk would pull the card and give it to Mr. Thompson. Mr. Thompson might then decide to reorder the part, and in this event he would fix the quantity to be ordered; or he might turn the card back to the stock clerk and postpone reordering until another entry had to be made on the card.

In discussing economic-lot-size calculations with Mr. Thompson, Mr. Shay decided that the proper period for averaging past consumption was the previous two or sometimes three years. But he emphasized that Mr. Thompson was to apply his judgment and take into account trends, design changes, and other information in making his estimate of future annual consumption rates. Mr. Shay believed that the economic-lot formula had to be applied on the basis of "half figures and half hunch." Specifically, he believed that decisions had to be made taking into account whether the part or the end item might become obsolete.

An Illustration of the Application of the Formula and Nomograph

To test the application of the procedures developed, Mr. Shay and Mr. Thompson determined the ordering quantity for the 10 x 5 gear used on several models of a very popular item of equipment which had been manufactured by the Evers company until 1957. Each machine using this part required from 18 to 24 of this type of gear, and relatively frequent replacement was made because of the wear in use.

Exhibit 2 shows the unit sales of this item, tabulated from the Kardex on file on this part. Mr. Shay decided to use the average for the last two years, 1961 and 1962, as a basis for estimating the annual demand: 1,236 plus 1,934 divided by 2, or 1,585, which he rounded to 1,600 for convenience in handling.

The Cost Accounting Department advised Mr. Shay that the total set-up costs, including a $15 order-handling charge, for the 10 x 5 gears was $46.80. The part went through eight operations, and the total set-up cost was obtained by multiplying the set-up hours required by $6, a figure which represented the total hourly labor cost, and adding an overhead charge of 150 per cent and the $15 order-handling charge. The Cost Accounting Department also furnished Mr. Shay with the following unit-cost breakdown on this part: direct labor, $0.395; material, $0.310; and overhead, $0.59 (150 per cent x $0.395).

EXHIBIT 2   EVERS MACHINERY COMPANY

SHIPMENTS OF 10 x 5 GEARS
January 1959–January 1963

	1959	1960	1961	1962	1963
January	31	76	0	72	195
February	498	24	36	322	
March	25	190	24	258	
April	125	139	72	144	
May	92	24	36	24	
June	111	404	220	384	
July	24	12	74	25	
August	112	88	174	183	
September	97	36	136	89	
October	60	209	27	120	
November	203	222	129	128	
December	36	123	308	185	
Total	1,414	1,547	1,236	1,934	

Weight 1.13 pounds each.
Selling price 6/60: $1.91 each.

Based on their understanding of the instruction sent by the trade association, Messrs. Shay and Thompson omitted the $0.59 overhead item in determining "C," the unit cost for purposes of calculating the economic-lot size. The overhead charge was utilized, however, in determining the set-up costs.

To make his calculation of the economic lot, Mr. Shay showed Mr. Thompson how to plot the following data on the nomograph (Exhibit 1): annual requirements, 1,600 pieces; set-up costs, $47; and unit cost, $0.70. He joined the first two points by a straight line, and then joined the point where that line crossed the reference line with the $0.70 point on the "Unit Cost" scale. He then read off the economic-lot size at the point where this last line crossed the scale headed "Economic Production Quantity in Pieces per Lot." This he read as about 950. Finally, he reduced this last figure by 10 per cent, or to 855. He rounded this quantity to 900 to establish the number of items to be ordered. Since the current minimums were to be equal to 18 weeks' consumption, he set the minimum at 550.

A Second Illustration

The next day, Mr. Thompson came to Mr. Shay's office and asked for advice on determining the quantity of 40 inch rolls, Model No. 5,

to order from production. He showed Mr. Shay the Kardex file (Exhibit 3) on this part, as maintained by Miss Mary LeMay, the stock clerk in charge of this class of item.

This part was used on a very popular machine which had been manufactured by the company for more than 15 years without drastic design changes. The roll design had not changed at all during this period and Mr. Thompson estimated that there were about 2,000 to 3,000 machines in use by Evers' customers. Mr. Shay knew, however, that a new-model antifriction roll had just been adopted as standard for new machines to be manufactured by Evers. Customers with equipment of the old design could convert to the new antifriction rolls at a conversion cost of $800 per machine plus the cost of the new roll, one of which was required per machine. If a customer converted an old machine to using antifriction rolls, there would be an increase of productivity which would enable the customer to lay off one worker for every four machines of this type in its plant. Customers typically had 3 to 15 of this type of machine in their plant.

Messrs. Shay and Thompson agreed that some customers with equipment of the old design would change to the antifriction rolls in lieu of the Model No. 5 rolls within the next two to three years; other customers would change over the subsequent 10 years or so, and a significant minority, they believed, would never change because of the conversion cost. Both the Model No. 5 roll and the antifriction roll had a life in use of seven to fifteen years.

Mr. Shay found that the selling price of the new antifriction rolls would be only $112 each, compared with $148.50 for the Model No. 5 rolls, because the antifriction rolls could be manufactured by a cheaper process. The Model No. 5 roll was seven and one-half inches in diameter and five feet long. It was stacked vertically in racks in the repair-parts warehouse.

The Cost Accounting Department told Mr. Shay that the total set-up cost including a $15 order-handling charge for Model No. 5 rolls was $630. The part went through 11 separate operations, and the set-up cost was computed by multiplying total set-up labor hours for all these by $6 an hour. The Cost Accounting Department informed Mr. Shay that the standard cost for a Model No. 5 roll included material costs of $57.01 and direct-labor costs of $43.41.

Explanation of Notation on Kardex

The designations such as X-444 are "X-contracts" or shop orders placed to replenish the supply of an item. When there is a delivery under one of the top orders, a large D precedes the entry as "2/22/61,

EXHIBIT 3 EVERS MACHINERY COMPANY

REPAIR PARTS DEPARTMENT

Kardex Records, Model 5 Rolls   Page 1 of 3

DESCRIPTION: 40" Model 5 Rolls

PART OR ASSEMBLY NO.: 19-14722-5

MATERIAL:

PRODUCT CODE:

SECT.: Bay   BIN: 3

B.C.P. 1   S.C.P. 2   B.S.D. 3   C.S.D. 4

OUT

STOCK ITEM / PAST MODEL

UNIT MEASURE: EA.   WEIGHT 320   LBS. PER EA.

PRICE PER: EA.   1/10/59 $148.50

	JULY	AUG.	SEPT.	OCT.	NOV.	DEC.	JAN.	FEB.	MAR.	APR.	MAY	JUNE	TOTAL
MONTHLY ACTIVITY TO JULY 1, 1960	1	4	2	1	5	0	0	1	2	1	0	1	
MONTHLY ACTIVITY TO JULY 1, 1961	0	2	1										

DATE	REFERENCE NUMBER	CUSTOMER	MILL ORDER E/W	HOME/B PLANT	CHICAGO	TOTAL	QUANTITY AVAILABLE	ORDERED OR RECEIVED	W/K	BALANCE DUE ON ORDER	PAST 12 MOS.	PAST 3 MOS.	WEEKLY AVERAGE	ORDER POINT (MIN.)
7/1		Forwarded (1960)												
10/27	Dx388			1	3	4	6	2		2	13	4	.3	5
		Inventory 10/10/60		3	3	6	6							
11/3	21779	Savoy Mfg.	W 2	3	1	4	4							
11/27	21901	Lee & Baker	E 1	2	1	3	3				12	4	.3	5
12/11	X-444	Oakview	W 1	2	0	2	2	3		3				
12/23	22422		E 2	0	0	0	5	3	K	3				
28	22501	Hopper	E	0	0	0	3	4		4				
12/31	X-450						7	4		7	15	6	.4	6

1951																		
1/14	206	T+J Monson	W	1	Ox	0	(1)	6	4									
1/20	531	Hopper	E	2	Ox	0	(3)	4										
1/29	X-464							10	6	19	13							
1/29	2190	Western #1	W	1	Ox	0	(4)	9				19	9	6	9			
2/23	Dx-444				3	0	(1)	9	3	10								
	Dx-450				7	0	3	9	4	6								
	206	FLR-1			6													
	531	-2			4													
	2190	-1			3	3	3	9										
3/23	6707	Hopper	E	1	2	0	2	8				15	5	4	6			
4/12	Dx-464				8	0	8	8	6	0								
4/12		Trans 4-T#159 Comp 4/23			4	0	8	8										
4/23	T-159	Comp			4	4	8	8										
6/6	6707	Mill Return 683			4	5	9	9										
10/31		Trans. To Prod. - X464			2	5	7	9		2								
		Inventory 10/29/61			2	5	7											

REPAIR PARTS DEPT. — ACTIVITY — STORES RECORD

EXHIBIT 3 EVERS MACHINERY COMPANY

REPAIR PARTS DEPARTMENT

Kardex Records, Model 5 Rolls   Page 2 of 3

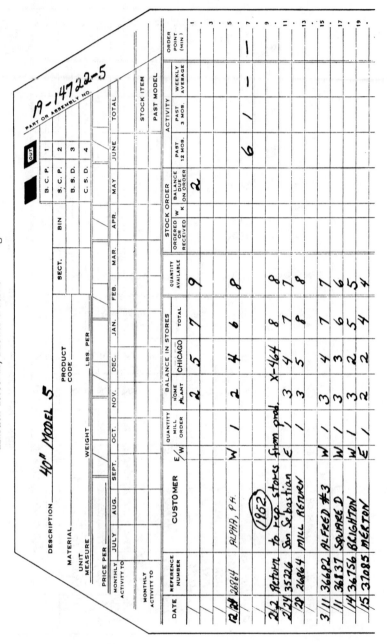

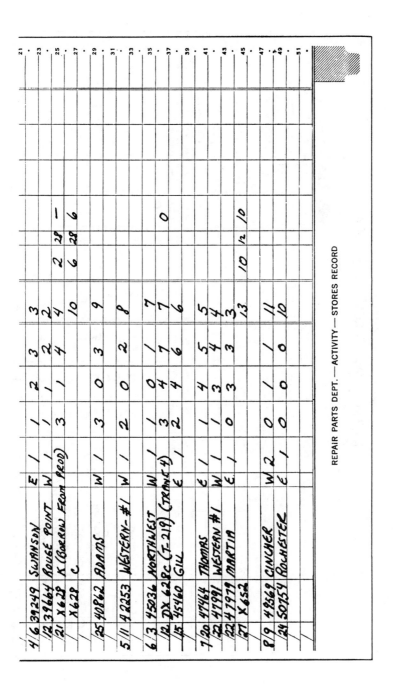

REPAIR PARTS DEPT.—ACTIVITY—STORES RECORD

EXHIBIT 3 EVERS MACHINERY COMPANY

REPAIR PARTS DEPARTMENT

Kardex Records, Model 5 Rolls   Page 3 of 3

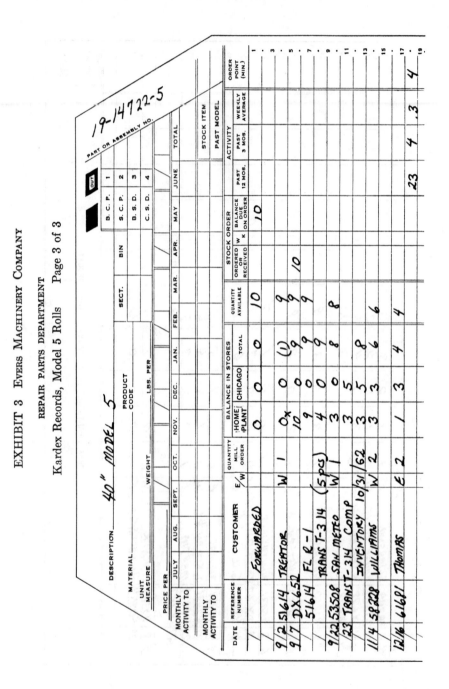

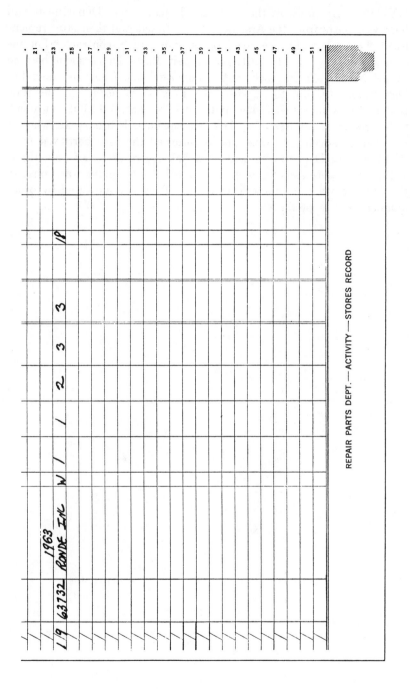

REPAIR PARTS DEPT. — ACTIVITY — STORES RECORD

DX-444." At times in the past, the Repair Parts Department had borrowed parts from the Assembly Department and then later replenished them when they received parts under an X-contract. For instance, on January 14, 1961, the Repair Parts Department had no Model No. 5 rolls in stock, but it borrowed one from the Assembly Department to ship to its customer T. & J. Monson. At the time Repair Parts had seven due under two X-contracts, but continued to borrow from the Assembly Department until February 22, when it received all seven. At this time it returned the four borrowed from the Assembly Department, leaving a balance in stores of only three.

Transfers were sometimes made from the home-plant warehouse to the Chicago warehouse and vice versa. They are indicated by order numbers with a prefix T.

Davis Tool and Die Company (II)

On January 15, 1953, the executives of Davis Tool and Die Company assembled in the company's conference room to discuss ways and means of leveling out production, so as to minimize the amount of hiring and lay-off of production workers. The meeting had been called by Alden Davis, founder and president of the company.

At a management meeting three weeks earlier, Mr. Davis had pointed out that the company had sharply cut back its production workforce in September 1952, only to turn around two months later and significantly increase the number of production workers on its payroll; furthermore, that the same thing had happened before, in the fall of 1951, and again in the spring of 1952. In Mr. Davis' opinion, such irregular employment imposed financial strains on the workers and made it more difficult for the company to hire good men when they were needed. A large percentage of the better workers in a group laid off did not return to Davis Tool and Die Company since they quickly found other jobs and were not available when the company began hiring again. Furthermore, Mr. Davis believed that the extensive training of many new workers considerably impaired production efficiency and thus lowered the company's profits. Frank Sisco, production manager, concurred fully with Mr. Davis' opinion, although since the company had virtually no cost-accounting system, there was no tangible evidence to demonstrate just how costly the absorption of new workers might be.

At the earlier meeting Mr. Davis had requested that Mr. Sisco look into the problem. Mr. Davis called the January 15 meeting after Mr. Sisco reported he believed he had developed a specific proposal that would result in more stable employment.

Products Manufactured

Davis Tool and Die Company specializes in making flat dies which form threads by a cold-rolling process. Flat dies, in 1952, accounted for about 60 per cent of dollar sales. Exhibit 1 shows the basic features of the thread-rolling process; Exhibit 2 shows typical flat dies and illustrates the variety of products threaded by cold rolling. Because of its pioneering work and technical competence, the Davis Company has held a commanding position in flat-die manufacturing and was consulted as an authority not only by customers but also by manufacturers of thread-rolling machines.

EXHIBIT 1   DAVIS TOOL AND DIE COMPANY (II)

ILLUSTRATIONS OF THE THREAD-ROLLING PROCESS

EXHIBIT 2 Davis Tool and Die Company (II)

EXAMPLES OF DIES AND PRODUCTS

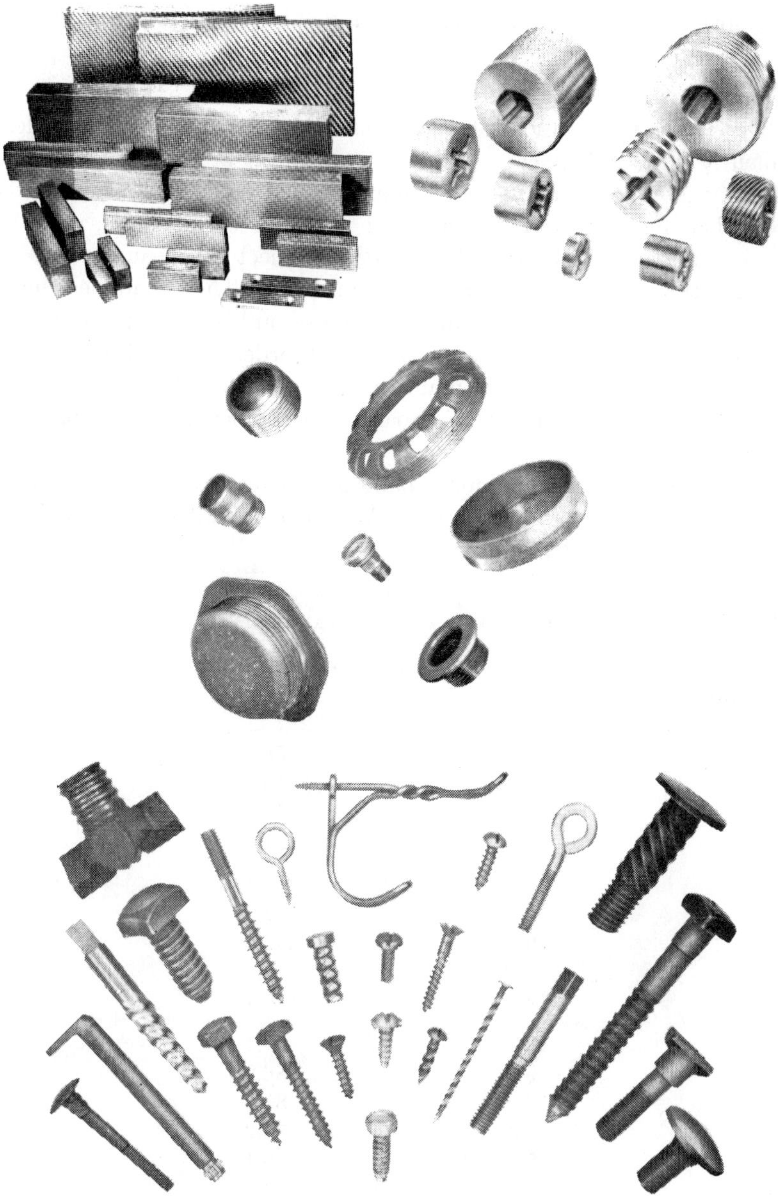

Cylindrical dies, introduced in 1940, had grown to 40 per cent of dollar sales. These dies could be used on cylindrical machines of all manufacturers. Exhibit 2 illustrates the cylindrical dies. The manufacture of dies required considerable numbers of milling machines and special thread grinders, as well as heat-treating equipment.

Demand

The Davis Company's total sales usually fluctuated somewhat less violently than did machine-tool sales. Exhibit 3 shows an index of monthly average machine-tool shipments, 1937–1951. World War II created a huge demand for threaded fasteners of all types, and the Davis Company had expanded greatly to meet the requirements of manufacturers of trucks, tanks, and aircraft. There had been cutbacks as the war concluded, but the defense build-up beginning in the middle of 1950 had brought floods of new orders. The Davis Company started building a new plant in 1951 and moved into it in 1952. Exhibit 4 shows the Davis Company's December 31, 1952, balance sheet.

Typical die orders ran a dozen pairs or less for flat dies and a dozen units or less for cylindrical dies. An order for 20 or 30 pairs (or units) was considered large.

EXHIBIT 3 Davis Tool and Die Company (II)

INDEX OF MONTHLY AVERAGE MACHINE TOOL SHIPMENTS, TOTAL INDUSTRY 1937–1951 (1945–1947 = 100)

1937	55.0
1938	40.9
1939	56.4
1940	124.0
1941	218.4
1942	372.5
1943	332.6
1944	140.2
1945	119.4
1946	94.4
1947	86.2
1948	81.3
1949	70.2
1950	86.1
1951	178.2

EXHIBIT 4 DAVIS TOOL AND DIE COMPANY (II)

BALANCE SHEET, DECEMBER 31, 1952

(Dollar Figures in Thousands)

Cash	$ 249	Accounts Payable and	
Accounts Receivable	383	Accrued Expenses	$ 232
Inventories	449	Notes Payable	315
Total Current Assets	$1,081	Accrued Federal Income	
		Taxes	201
		Total Current Liabilities	$ 748
Fixed Assets (Net)	629	Mortgage	205
Miscellaneous Assets	85	Common Stock	209
Total	$1,795	Surplus	633
		Total	$1,795

Net Sales: $3,165

Flat dies were sold principally to the fastener industry—companies making bolts, screws, nail screws, etc.—and to automobile, aircraft, and appliance manufacturers. To meet basic variables, there were several thousand different flat dies that a customer might order. Different dies were required for different diameters, for different forms of thread, and for different makes, sizes, and designs of machines using the dies.

Cylindrical dies, which also included a wide variety of designs, were sold to a variety of metalworking shops of all types, including automobile, aircraft, and appliance manufacturers. Sales were largely to high-volume manufacturers, because thread-rolling was economical only when long runs of identical threaded parts were required. Thread-rolling machines produced from 40 to 170 pieces per minute.

Mr. Sisco's Plan

Mr. Sisco began by relating that Robert Jordan, the company's sales manager, had told him that ten weeks constituted the maximum time which customers would accept between placing an order and its delivery without many of them seeking actively to channel part of their business to a second source of supply. Mr. Sisco believed that efficient production scheduling required a minimum backlog six times the current average weekly output. In computing the "average weekly output" Mr. Sisco minimized the effects of random variations by using the average weekly production during the preceding six

weeks. Mr. Sisco proposed that these two limits—six weeks' and ten weeks' order backlogs—be used to control production. When the backlog of unfilled orders approached ten times the current average weekly output, he would increase production; when the backlog dropped close to six times the current average weekly output, he would decrease production.

The proposal provided that at the end of each accounting period, Mr. Sisco, Mr. Jordan, and Henry Gompers, the treasurer, should study the trend of orders—and especially the average weekly orders received in the preceding six weeks—along with the current backlog, the company's inventory position, and the predicted sales. After discussion, the group would then make a decision as to the level of operations for the following accounting period, six or seven weeks, as the case might be.[1] Since Mr. Sisco planned to have a minimum order backlog at all times equivalent to six weeks' work, only moderate accuracy in forecasting would be required.

Mr. Sisco planned to minimize layoffs by changing work hours and by manufacturing for stock. He believed that the company's three-shift operations made 51 hours per worker a maximum and that work available in other local plants employing similar workers made 40 hours a minimum. Mr. Sisco believed that items constituting 45 per cent of annual sales could be stocked. He said that currently the company stocked some flat dies and a few cylindrical dies, items constituting about 25 to 30 per cent of annual sales. The Davis Company had adequate finished-goods storage facilities.

Theoretical Application of Plan to 1950–1952

Mr. Sisco reported that he had tested his plan by assuming that it had been in effect for some time prior to 1950, and that his backlog of unfilled orders at January 1, 1950 was midway between the six weeks' and ten weeks' limit, or eight weeks' production at the actual average weekly output at that time. Using orders the Davis Company had actually received and the January 1, 1950 inventory, Mr. Sisco had worked out the theoretical production which the company would have maintained if his plan had been in effect for the three years, 1950–1952. At the end of each successive accounting period, Mr. Sisco decided on the level of production for the subsequent accounting period.

---

[1] The company's fiscal year was divided into eight accounting periods, the first of which was always seven weeks long and the remaining periods alternately six and seven weeks long.

Mr. Sisco said he had tried to avoid "second guessing" by ignoring the actual trend of orders received in the subsequent period. In general, as the backlog of orders approached the ten-week top limit, he increased production first by extending the work week toward 51 hours, and after that limit had been reached, by adding new employees. As the backlog of orders dropped toward six weeks' production at the current average-weekly-production rate, he cut back the work week. Since Mr. Sisco estimated that the Davis Company could stock items constituting 45 per cent of total annual sales, he assumed that in any accounting period in which new orders exceeded production, 45 per cent of the excess of new orders over production was filled by drawing down inventory; the remaining 55 per cent of the excess was added to the backlog. On the other hand, when new orders received during an accounting period were less than production, he added 45 per cent of the excess of production over new orders to inventory and applied 55 per cent of the excess to reducing the order backlog.

In order to make this theoretical application of his plan, Mr. Sisco expressed production and inventory figures in terms of selling prices, rather than cost values; the Davis Company's selling prices averaged 180 per cent of cost. When a sizeable increase in the workforce occurred, Mr. Sisco assumed a less than proportional increase in production for the immediately following weeks. For instance, during the sixth period of 1950, when the workforce jumped from 60 to 90 workers, he assumed it would take two full accounting periods before the 90-man workforce would reach full productivity.

To show the results of this test of his plan, Mr. Sisco placed three exhibits before the other executives. Exhibit 5 compares actual and theoretical backlogs at the end of each period, 1950–1952. Mr. Sisco called attention to the reduction of order backlogs which would have taken place at the end of 1951 and in early 1952 with consequent acceleration of the Davis Company's deliveries to customers. Exhibit 6 shows the finished-goods inventories at selling prices both actual and theoretical. Exhibit 7 shows the elimination of layoffs that would have resulted from his proposal.

Personnel Problems Raised by Mr. Sisco's Plan

To meet variations in demand for individual products while maintaining steady employment, Mr. Sisco believed it would be necessary to shift people from one department to the other. Each of the two product types was made in a different department; these departments had modified production lines.

EXHIBIT 5   DAVIS TOOL AND DIE COMPANY (II)

ACTUAL AND THEORETICAL BACKLOGS OF ORDERS AT THE END OF EACH ACCOUNTING PERIOD,
1950–1952, AND MAXIMUM[1] AND MINIMUM[2] LIMITS AT CURRENT PRODUCTION

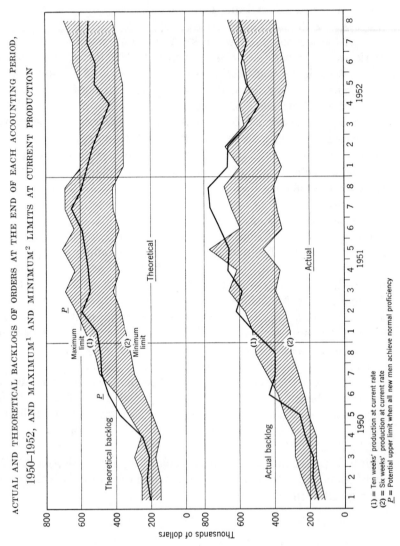

(1) = Ten weeks' production at current rate
(2) = Six weeks' production at current rate
$\underline{P}$ = Potential upper limit when all new men achieve normal proficiency

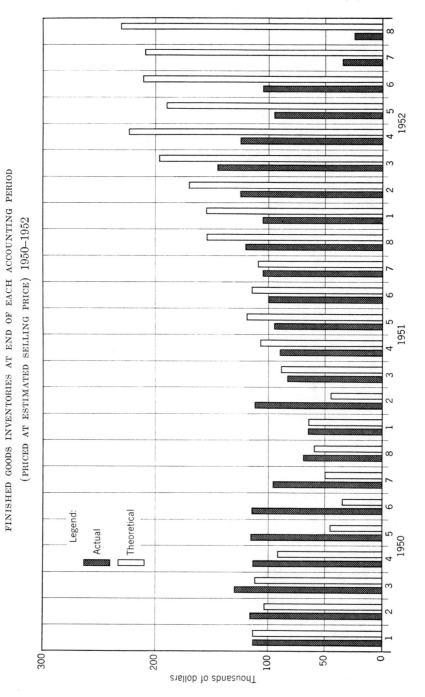

EXHIBIT 6 DAVIS TOOL AND DIE COMPANY (II)

FINISHED GOODS INVENTORIES AT END OF EACH ACCOUNTING PERIOD

(PRICED AT ESTIMATED SELLING PRICE) 1950–1952

EXHIBIT 7 DAVIS TOOL AND DIE COMPANY (II)

ACTUAL AND THEORETICAL EMPLOYMENT

	Accounting Period*	Average Number of Production Employees		Average Hours Worked per Week	
		Actual	Theoretical	Actual	Theoretical
1950	1	58	60	40	40
	2	65	60	40	40
	3	69	60	40	46½
	4	71	60	42½	40
	5	70	60	45	51
	6	81	90	45	51
	7	96	90	46	51
	8	96	105	46	46½
1951	1	137	105	46	51
	2	157	140	46	51
	3	121	140	46	51
	4	120	140	46	42½
	5	138	140	46	46½
	6	91	140	46	42½
	7	124	140	46	46½
	8	125	140	46	46½
1952	1	128	140	46	40
	2	132	140	46	40
	3	120	140	46	40
	4	120	140	45	40
	5	122	140	42½	40
	6	115	140	46½	42½
	7	124	140	46½	42½
	8	140	140	49½	46½

* The Davis Company's calendar year was divided into eight periods for accounting purposes.

EXHIBIT 8   DAVIS TOOL AND DIE COMPANY (II)

SIX WEEKS MOVING AVERAGE OF ORDERS RECEIVED
(Thousands of Dollars)

Week	1950	1951	1952	Week	1950	1951	1952
1	25	53	47	27	36	60	50
2	24	53	48	28	36	70	49
3	26	58	51	29	40	62	50
4	27	59	55	30	40	64	50
5	30	61	59	31	45	65	60
6	23	61	65	32	49	66	62
7	27	76	65	33	47	53	66
8	31	78	60	34	48	55	69
9	29	76	56	35	47	53	69
10	31	76	54	36	50	54	60
11	30	74	56	37	49	50	56
12	29	80	52	38	48	61	64
13	29	65	53	39	50	70	65
14	27	70	55	40	50	82	66
15	30	68	54	41	52	89	75
16	29	66	57	42	52	86	76
17	27	66	51	43	54	82	72
18	27	61	52	44	51	71	71
19	26	63	55	45	50	77	71
20	26	59	55	46	52	68	72
21	30	65	53	47	50	64	70
22	31	64	49	48	53	64	69
23	32	64	49	49	49	67	73
24	33	66	56	50	50	67	66
25	36	65	54	51	53	56	69
26	37	73	52	52	54	47	N.A.

The alternative of operating one department fewer hours than the other in order to meet the varying demands for products would be doubly unacceptable to the workers, Mr. Sisco pointed out, because of the possible distortion of their individual bonuses. Quarterly, the Davis Company paid to its workers a bonus of 50 per cent of its estimated annual profits,[2] distributed in direct proportion to each man's

[2] The management retained the privilege of holding back part of the bonus otherwise payable in the event the sum represented more than would probably be available on the basis of the full year's operations.

gross earnings, straight time plus overtime and shift differentials.[3] Therefore, if one department worked an average of 44 hours while the other department worked only 40, the men working 44 hours would receive not only greater straight-time earnings, but also a proportionally higher bonus. In some years the bonus had reached as much as 16 per cent of a worker's earnings.

Mr. Sisco therefore proposed the creation of a pool of specialists, trained in operating key machines in both departments and willing to work on any shift required. He suggested that such men be paid a premium of 15 cents per hour above the current rate for machine operators; they would also be eligible for night-shift and overtime premiums. Although he was not entirely certain just how many of these men ultimately would be needed, he believed they might comprise as much as 20 to 30 per cent of the company's total plant employees.

At the end of 1952, the Davis Company had 140 production workers. About 60 of these were "old-timers" with more than five years' service with the company; many had 15 years or more of service. In spite of shift differentials the old-timers, almost to a man, preferred to work the first shift, and under company practice their seniority allowed them to choose their shift. There was no union in the company, but the workers were represented by an elected "workers committee." Members of this committee were almost invariably old-timers.

---

[3] Wages currently averaged $1.75 per hour, exclusive of the bonus, plus a second- and third-shift differential of 10 cents and 15 cents, respectively.

Perkins Associates, Inc.

On April 9, 1954 William Grebler, manager of production planning and control for Perkins Associates, Inc., received a copy of the letter shown in Exhibit 1. This letter was not the first indication Mr. Grebler had of difficulties in the Press Department. About a month earlier, Allan Phillips, one of his assistants who prepared production schedules for the Press Department, had advised him that the Department foreman had complained about the volume of small repeat orders. Mr. Phillips quoted him to the effect that his equipment was out of production about 50 per cent of the time because of the many set-ups, and that the Department was having trouble meeting its production schedules.

Although the memorandum was addressed to John MacDonald, Mr. Grebler, along with each of the other persons listed, received a copy. Mr. Grebler did not report to Mr. MacDonald, but to Robert Leslie, vice president, planning and procurement. (Exhibit 2 is a partial organization chart of Perkins Associates, Inc.) Mr. Grebler realized that the executives of both the production organization and the planning organization would probably schedule a meeting within the next week or ten days to try to find some means of improving the situation in the Press Department.

Company Background

Perkins Associates, Inc. had been founded in 1937 by Henry Perkins. With the great surge in demand for electronic items as a result of World War II, and as a result of Perkins' outstanding technical ability, the organization expanded rapidly. Postwar cutbacks in defense needs drastically reduced the scale of operations, but the sales volume again increased sharply with the Korean emergency. With the end of the Korean fighting, the company's backlog began to

EXHIBIT 1   PERKINS ASSOCIATES, INC.

TO: Mr. John MacDonald

FROM: Mr. Harold Franklin

SUBJECT: Parts Inventory Program for
         Press Department Parts   April 9, 1954

In an effort to overcome the present difficulties existing in the Press Department due to the numerous orders for small quantities of parts, we wish to
make the following recommendations:

(1) A minimum and maximum inventory should be established for all parts.
(2) An expediter, employed by the Press Department, should be stationed
    in the Department to maintain inventories. This expediter will be
    responsible for requesting shop orders from production planning and
    control when the inventory reaches the minimum figure.

Small orders for die parts are very costly, in that each set-up may necessitate the regrinding of the die, involving from one to six hours direct-labor
expense. The important fact, however, is that the life of the die is frequently reduced by as much as 30 per cent, amounting to an average loss of
from $60 to $200.

We feel it will considerably reduce costs, and add to the efficiency of the
Department, if the above program is adopted, and recommend that same be
put into effect as promptly as possible.

Superintendent, Parts Mfg. Department

Harold Franklin

HF/bcs
Copies to:
Robert Leslie
William Grebler
Allan Phillips
Otto Rogers

---

shrink, and orders diminished in size; nevertheless, the principal effect
on the company had been only the elimination of third-shift operations; throughout 1953 and early 1954 the backlog of orders had
remained at eight months' current production.

Save for the Press Department, Perkins' offices and plants are at
one metropolitan location. Its employees are all unionized and in
mid-1954 totaled some 800 persons, of whom about 40 per cent were
women. The Press Department is located in a separate building,
about one-half mile from the main plant.

More than 90 per cent of Perkins Associates' sales were then ac-

EXHIBIT 2 PERKINS ASSOCIATES, INC.

PARTIAL ORGANIZATION CHART

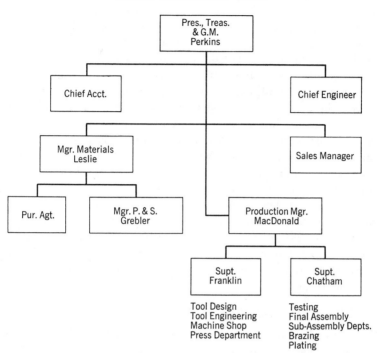

counted for by one electromechanical product which, however, had a wide range of sizes and electric characteristics. The company had some 60 models of this product and was adding to this number through its own research and development at the rate of about five or six designs a year. This product was a principal component of equipment used almost exclusively by the armed forces; sale for civilian use was nominal, although the company desired to find ways of increasing sales to the civilian market, if this could be done. The management believed, however, that civilian demand in the foreseeable future would probably not exceed 15 per cent of the total sales, a proportion which civilian sales did not then approach. Some sales were made directly to other manufacturers; other sales were made directly to the government, which supplied the Perkins product to other manufacturers as Government Furnished Material; and some sales were to the government as replacement parts for equipment that the government had acquired several years earlier. The company did not maintain

a breakdown of sales by the intended use of the product, and in a majority of instances had no information stating how a customer intended to use the products he was buying.

The Perkins product varied in price from $150 to $1,500 each; the average price was probably $400 to $500 per unit. Typically, the sales of a new design reached a peak within one or two years after its introduction, although some designs never seemed to "get off the ground." After the first couple of years, sales usually tended to decrease rapidly, ultimately reaching nominal proportions. Often, however, there were unexpected increases in demand for old models and every once in a while the company received orders for a few items of a model brought out in 1939, 1940, or 1941. Exhibit 3 shows the annual unit sales of selected models. Customer orders were accumulated until a minimum production run had been reached; this minimum was flexible depending on how hard business was to get, and was sometimes as low as 50 units. The typical run, however, was above 500 units. Because of certain bottleneck equipment used in assembly and testing, the company rarely produced more than 100 units per day of any end item; likewise, it was uneconomical to make fewer than 15 items per day. Typical production was between 30 and 60 end items per day.

Over-All Manufacturing Process

The over-all manufacturing process included both the fabrication of parts and assembly of subassemblies and completed units. Many of the major parts used in the final-assembly process were themselves the products of earlier assembly as well as machining operations. For instance, one of the most important components of a typical Perkins product was constructed from laminations produced in the

EXHIBIT 3 PERKINS ASSOCIATES, INC.

ANNUAL UNIT SALES OF SELECTED MODELS

Model	1945	1946	1947	1948	1949	1950	1951	1952	1953
2M	220	61	71	52	206	103	259	218	207
5L	—	—	—	—	762	4,856	17,242	13,841	4,869
7K	—	530	54	65	109	65	46	79	52
15C	—	—	9	3	5	372	118	209	287
17K	—	—	—	—	—	—	2,622	3,085	818
20F	2,988	985	479	1,038	1,017	3,112	13,183	5,110	8,460
22B	5,521	150	102	95	76	97	142	116	133
25C	—	—	—	—	1,404	—	2,370	2,745	568

Press Department on punch presses. These laminations were stacked together and brazed (a form of soldering) in a furnace to form a solid workpiece. This workpiece was subsequently machined, after which other pressed parts were added, brazed, and finish-machined. This method of construction, using laminations, was developed to avoid otherwise extremely difficult machining in manufacturing intricate parts to close tolerances.

After all parts had been purchased or manufactured, they were assembled progressively in the Assembly Department by a series of operations, many of which were performed by hand using simple jigs and fixtures, and others of which required large, complex machinery. The flow of parts through the various manufacturing operations had at one time been classified into 12 consecutive stages of manufacturing in connection with certain production-control activities. While bills of material still carried these "group" designators, the designators themselves were no longer used for any other purpose.

The Press Department

In mid-1954 the Press Department personnel included the foreman, Otto Rogers; a group leader and three tool and die makers; a group leader and seven press operators; and a tool-crib attendant. Unlike the rest of the plant, the Press Department operated only one shift. Although union rules prohibited the tool-crib attendant from taking on clerical duties, the company management had persuaded the union to allow him to act as timekeeper. The union, however, had refused permission for him to write out "move tickets." As a result, all paperwork connected with the Press Department was performed by Mr. Phillips, who was located in the main building with Mr. Grebler. Mr. Phillips was also responsible for supplying whatever raw material was required for whatever orders he scheduled to the Press Department. Initiating requisitions for raw material to be used by the Department was the responsibility of Mr. Phillips, who maintained them on a max-min basis. (Raw material stocks were kept at the main building.)

Exhibit 4 is a list of the equipment in the Press Department. By and large, the 35- and 50-ton presses were interchangeable; Mr. Phillips had a list of parts which required the use of these pieces of equipment. Also, the 15-, 17-, and 20-ton presses were interchangeable for most jobs, while the smaller presses from 5 to 12 tons in capacity formed a third interchangeable group. No progressive dies were used; when a part needed more than one operation a separate press had to be set up for each operation. About 70 per cent of the

EXHIBIT 4   PERKINS ASSOCIATES, INC.

EQUIPMENT IN PRESS DEPARTMENT

1	50-ton	these three presses by and large interchangeable
2	35-ton	
6	20-ton	
1	17-ton	usually interchangeable
2	15-ton	
1	12-ton	usually can be used interchangeably, but some parts cannot
2	10-ton	be done on some presses in this group
3	5-ton	

EXHIBIT 5   PERKINS ASSOCIATES, INC.

PRODUCTION RATES, MATERIAL COSTS AND DIE COSTS, SELECTED PARTS

Part No.	Pieces per Hour Each Operation	Operations per Part	Material Cost per Part	Die Cost*
14770	100	3	$1.56	$1,251
15838	60	5	0.24	427
17932	1,000	1	0.0003	234
53214	500	1	0.04	293
58193	6,000	1	0.003	22
58801	1,750	1	0.02	178
58819	1,750	1	0.01	264
60879	2,000	1	0.001	369
61267	1,850	1	0.02	844
62752	2,000	1	0.02	437
62716	3,000	1	0.0004	326
62725	110	3	0.09	2,143
62925	4,000	1	0.01	210
63190	1,000	1	0.0001	361
63262	1,000	1	0.04	320

* Mr. Rogers estimated that typically a die was good for about 30 "grinds" (or sharpenings). In order to avoid "burrs" and to preserve the close tolerances required, the dies were usually ground for each lot. The company's cost-accounting system amortized die costs over the first year of production (or the first order if it covered a different time period).

jobs currently being run required only one set-up; others required two, three, or, rarely, even four or five separate machine set-ups. Set-up time for any one press might take from 15 minutes to an hour, with the average taking approximately one-half hour.

Exhibit 5 lists some typical parts and shows the operations required per part, the rate at which the part was pressed out in pieces per hour, and the cost of the dies used. Exhibit 6 shows two parts representative of the types made in the Press Department. One of these parts is relatively simple and the other is an example of one of the more complex parts made here. Over the period of a year, the Department

EXHIBIT 6 PERKINS ASSOCIATES, INC.

BLUEPRINTS OF REPRESENTATIVE PRESS PARTS

APERTURE   A 59270

WASHER   A 7418

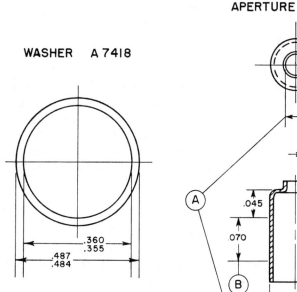

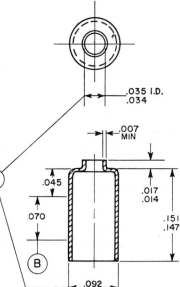

MATERIAL:
ELECTROLYTIC CU .005-.006 X ½
R5 - 42

MATERIAL:
OFHC CU .010 X ⁷⁄₁₆ R5 - 26

NOTES:
A–THESE DIAMETERS TO BE CONCENTRIC
    WITHIN .001
B–O.D. AT ANY POINT IN THIS AREA MUST
    NOT BE LESS THAN THE O.D. AT ANY
    POINT ABOVE THIS AREA

made between 450 and 500 different parts, some, of course, being run several times during the year.

General Production Planning

Perkins did not manufacture any end items or parts for stock; all manufacturing was for orders "released" to production by Mr. Grebler, who accumulated individual customer orders by model numbers until an economical manufacturing quantity was reached. Some individual government orders were so large that they were several times the minimum size desired, and these orders were manufactured in a single continuous run at fairly even daily production rates for periods of six to twelve months or more. Other orders from commercial firms were often for one to five units and had to be consolidated with government or other commercial orders for the same item to permit their manufacture. There were also many orders falling between these extremes. Whenever unreleased customers' orders for a particular model reached the minimum size Mr. Grebler believed was required, he released the quantities to the ordering section, which proceeded to write shop orders for parts, subassemblies, and final assemblies required. On some days Mr. Grebler would make one to three releases to the ordering section; on other occasions, as much as a week or more might elapse before the accumulated requirements for any model warranted a release to the ordering section. When a part was to be purchased rather than manufactured, the ordering section originated a purchase request and forwarded it to the purchasing agent.

Existing Order Procedures

The ordering section, under the supervision of Albert Wilson, determined for each release the quantity of each part to be manufactured in order to complete the number of end items released. The number of parts required was determined by the number of end items called for by the release, the quantity of the particular part used in each item, and the expected scrap loss during production.

The release showed the gross number of end items to be manufactured, Mr. Grebler having added an appropriate allowance for shrinkage during final testing of completed units. Many models had high rates of shrinkage upon final test, sometimes as high as three end items being produced to yield one acceptable item. Typically, the initial shrinkage upon first starting to produce an item ran very high —five to one—and diminished gradually as more items were produced. It rarely fell below 1.33 to 1, even after many months of continuous

production.   Blueprint copies of the bill of materials for each model showed the subassemblies required and then listed (Exhibit 7) for each subassembly the parts needed by part number and nomenclature, as well as the number of each part needed per subassembly.   In the case of about two-thirds of the Press Department parts, a specific part was designed to be used in only one end item, but some parts were used in several models, occasionally in up to four or five models.   In a majority of cases only one of the press parts was used per end item, but some subassemblies required two or more of the same part, and a few subassemblies required as many as 12 to 15 of the same part. The bill of materials for each subassembly also showed the expected rate of shrinkage for each part in manufacturing the subassembly, and for the subassembly in manufacturing assemblies.

The following example of establishing requirements for a washer manufactured by the Press Department will show how shrinkage estimates affected the determination of requirements by the ordering clerk.

Customers' requirements	1,000 end items
Expected item shrinkage rate	1 (good) for 2.5 (produced)
Number of end items to be manufactured to yield 1,000 for shipment. (This was the quantity released by Mr. Grebler to the ordering section, and was the quantity appearing on the shop order for the assembly of the end items.)	2,500 end items
Number of subassemblies (using the washer) needed per end item	1
Estimated shrinkage of subassemblies in manufacturing end items	1 for 1.05
Number of subassemblies required (1.05 × 2,500). This quantity, rounded, appeared on the shop order for this subassembly	2,700
Number of washers used in making each of this subassembly	2
Estimated shrinkage in washers during process of manufacturing subassemblies	1 for 1.10
Number of washers required (2,700 × 2 × 1.10). This quantity, rounded, was the number of washers needed to complete the 2,500 end items ordered into production	6,000

Having determined requirements as above, the ordering clerk checked a Kardex file maintained for each part upon which were listed the quantity called for on all shop orders written, and the requirements of uncompleted orders for the subassembly, or sometimes

EXHIBIT 7 PERKINS ASSOCIATES, INC.

SAMPLE BILL OF MATERIALS

REF TO DEPT.	PART TO BE ISSUED	TITLE	REFERENCE DRAWING NUMBER	FROM DEPT.	S.O. QUANTITY 2200 / REQUIRED QUANTITY	COMBINED LOSS FACTOR	UNIT	PARTS LOSS FACTOR	QTY/PC	PURCHASE ORDER NO.	MATERIAL CODE	DESCRIPTION	GR.
		SUB ASSEMBLY 61852-G-2X DESCRIPTION Mount Assem			SUB. ASSY LOSS FACTOR 1.05						RAW MATERIAL		
10	17932	Washer	2X	AD2 3352	5000	1.10	2	1.10	.0026		602/003	.003 x 1½ Brass	40
11	65509	Pot Cup Assem (Plated)	62808 G2Y	AD3 3430	2420	1.16	1	1.10			62549		
		Cyl. Pole Turn Assem		3832 MD2			1						
10	62978	Washer	2X	AD2 3252	2500	1.16	1	1.10	.0026		602/003	.003 x 1½ Nickel	40
X	62803	Pot Turn Assem		AD2 3831	2250	1.07	1	1.02					
X	62761	Cyl. Assem (Wound)		AD2 3831	2250	1.07	1	1.02					

two or more subassemblies, using the part. As parts were issued, they were deducted from both the inventory available and from the obligations first set up. If the balance on hand and due under outstanding shop orders (termed "due in") for a part were greater than remaining unfilled obligations (termed "due out"), the ordering clerk deducted the quantity available from his calculated requirements to fix the order quantity. For instance, if the Kardex for the washer used in the foregoing illustration showed an unobligated balance of 2,000 washers above and beyond the estimated unfilled requirements for orders already written, he would deduct this 2,000 already available from the gross requirements of 6,000 and write a shop order for 4,000 washers. If there was no excess of "due in" over "due out," then the clerk would order the full 6,000, or, in the event of a deficit, he would increase the 6,000 figure sufficiently to cover the deficit.

Deficits or surpluses occurred when actual consumption exceeded or fell short of estimates. The main storeroom's issues of a part to production were tallied against each authorizing shop order, and the actual average consumption of a part in making a subassembly was reviewed when the shop order for the subassembly was completed and "closed," prior to sending it to the Accounting Department. If actual issue to production was materially different from the estimate used in calculating requirements, the anticipated shrinkage figure on the bill of materials might be changed. Each instance of a proposed change was reviewed personally by Mr. Wilson. Thus "over issues" or "under issues" caused by a particular parts shop order created an excess of "due in's" over "due out's," or vice versa. A change in the actual shrinkage of subassemblies themselves or, even more importantly, in the shrinkage of final assembles, similarly affected actual consumption of parts. In Mr. Grebler's opinion, actual consumption was quite likely to vary substantially from estimates by as much as 10 per cent for an undetermined but substantial proportion of all parts, subassemblies, and final assemblies. He also believed that the secret of effective production control at Perkins was reliable information on the shrinkage of parts, subassemblies, and final assemblies.

After making his calculations, an order clerk to whom the release was assigned handwrote an "order request," from which a typist prepared a "shop-order" form (Exhibit 8). Copies of the shop orders were distributed to each manufacturing department concerned, and, in the case of shop orders for press parts, were used to prepare a schedule for operation of the Press Department.

EXHIBIT 8 PERKINS ASSOCIATES, INC.

SAMPLE SHOP ORDER

T-515-PCC REV. 1-2-46 SHOP ORDER NO. 31071	TITLE WASHER 17 K		
DATE 11/24/53	QUANTITY 6000	DWG. OR TOOL NO.	ACCT. NO. 433
	COST SUMMARY		ROUTING—DEPT. NO.
	MATERIAL 6021003		10
DEPT. 10	LABOR		DELIVER TO
MANUFACTURE 6000 WASHERS MODEL 17K PART # 17932			MAIN STOREROOM
	OVERHEAD		
MATERIAL: 17# .003 X 1½ BRASS STRIP (RAW MTL. STOREROOM)	TOTAL		REQUESTED BY MR. WILSON
			AUTHORIZED BY MR. GREBLER
	ESTIMATE: DIR. LABOR MATERIAL		REQUESTED DATE
COPIES TO MR. ROGERS – 2 MR. CHATHAM		METHODS ACCOUNTING PAYROLL	RATING

Scheduling the Press Department

Scheduling the Press Department was one of the responsibilities assigned to Mr. Phillips. He also maintained Kardex records on raw materials and expedited all purchase requests with the Purchasing Department. In addition, Mr. Phillips checked production of the Press Department, which was temporarily stored on the receiving platform until he had checked the shipment. After he made out the necessary papers, the materials were passed on to the Inspection Department en route to the main storeroom. Mr. Phillips credited the appropriate shop orders with the quantity of the receipt. The daily production of the Press Department was likely to be well under two cubic feet in bulk, and consisted of 8 to 15 items on the average.

At the end of every month, Mr. Phillips made up a schedule of items to be manufactured during the succeeding month. He began with the next assembly schedule for end items (Exhibit 9), prepared monthly for two months in advance by Mr. Grebler, and for each end item listed the parts to be used which were made in the Press Department. His next step was to compute the quantity of each part required by multiplying the number of end items scheduled for the period by the number needed per end item and a factor to cover the expected scrap

EXHIBIT 9 PERKINS ASSOCIATES, INC.

SAMPLE PAGES FROM END-ITEM ASSEMBLY SCHEDULE

		End-Item Assembly Schedule December, 1953				Page 1 of 7
Date	2M	5L	17K	20F	22B	25C
1		75				60
2		75				60
3		75				60
6	50	75			50	60
7	50	75			50	60
8	50	75			50	60
28	50	75		40		60
29	50	75		40		60
30	50	75		40		60
31				40		60
		End-Item Assembly Schedule January, 1954				Page 3 of 7
	2M	5L	17K	20F	22B	25C
3		75	100	40		60
4		75	100	40		60
5		75	100	40		60
6		75	100	40		60
7		75	100	40		60
10		75	100	40		
11		75	100	40		
26		75	100	40		
27		75	100	40		
28		75	100	40		
31		75	100	40		

loss both in making subassemblies and in making assemblies using this subassembly. In preparing the end-item production schedule Mr. Grebler took into account the scrap loss expected in testing the final end items, revising loss factors in the light of experience whenever he considered it advisable to do so.

Mr. Phillips' computations yielded a list of parts required and the quantities of each expected to be consumed during the month being scheduled. Mr. Phillips calculated the expected consumption of each part per week as well as the total so that Mr. Rogers might split the run of a part, if he needed to do so in order to make his schedule on

other parts, and still be sure to make enough to keep the assembly operations supplied.

Mr. Phillips' next step was to deduct the quantity of each part actually on hand at the main storeroom as shown by the Kardex on the item. He adjusted the "on hand" figure upwards by the amount, if any, of a part in transit between the Press Department and the Inspection Department or between the Inspection Department and the main storeroom.

Finally, Mr. Phillips established the first week during which production would have to begin. First he deducted three weeks' consumption of the part from the quantity on hand to allow a safety margin. He then determined when the excess on hand above three weeks' consumption would be exhausted by existing schedules and called for Mr. Rogers to begin making the part during that week. If there was no stock of the item on hand, Mr. Phillips simply set his estimated consumption schedule ahead by three weeks to permit a three weeks' supply of the item to accumulate at the main storeroom before the assembly operation required any of the part.

The following is an example of the procedure. The item is a washer used only in end-item model 17K which was scheduled for final assembly at the rate of 100 per day and 500 per week. Final assembly was to have begun January 3, and continue at the same rate for five consecutive weeks until 2,600 in total had been made, the number of end items authorized by this particular shop order.

Number of washers per end item	2
Estimated shrinkage of subassemblies in manufacturing end items	1 good for 1.05 produced
Estimated shrinkage of washers in making this subassembly	1 good for 1.10 produced
Composite shrinkage: $1.10 \times 1.05 = 1.16$	1 good for 1.16 produced
Number required: Total: $2 \times 1.16 \times 2,500 = 5,800$ Per week: $6,000 \div 5 = 1,250$/week	6,000 total (rounded) 1,250/week
Quantity on hand	none

Production schedule for washer:

Begin week of 12/13 and produce 6,000
(weekly production rate: 1,250 minimum)

Except in emergencies, Mr. Rogers was unlikely to have split so small an order as this, which would have taken only two or three hours to run off after the press had been set up.

Exhibit 10 shows a part of a completed schedule as Mr. Phillips sent it to Mr. Rogers. Although it shows requirements for some items based on Mr. Grebler's end-item assembly schedules, which would have been needed during the period beyond the succeeding month, only the schedule for the coming month was firm. Changes took the form of additional orders, cancelled or reduced orders, and changes in the time for final assembly of a particular order. When emergency requirements occurred during the month, as they often did, Mr. Phillips telephoned Mr. Rogers and arranged for them to be handled. Sometimes overtime was the only solution; in many instances, however, Mr. Phillips freed the necessary press time by instructing Mr. Rogers to defer a particular order already scheduled until the next week, thus lowering the safety margin on that item to two weeks' supply.

Other Complaints about the Present System

Mr. Grebler knew not only that Mr. Rogers was somewhat bitter in his criticism of the ordering and scheduling procedures, but also that John MacDonald, the production manager, had "blown his top" on several occasions when lack of a Rogers part had created an emergency situation in one of the subassembly departments. At times it had been necessary to send some workers home when it had proved impossible to find other models or even other jobs for them to work on. Even when other work had been found the foremen complained of the loss in efficiency which occurred. As the order backlog declined and as monthly schedules carried more models but shorter average runs, these complaints had become more frequent. Mr. Phillips, in discussing such incidents with Mr. Grebler, explained, "Usually production just consumes more material than we estimated, and we have to arrange with Rogers to make some more on an emergency basis— which gets him mad, too. In other cases, especially at the beginning of a run, it looks as though we just don't schedule some parts early enough. The Department 17A expediter came in yesterday and asked me where was his supply of part number 16458. I checked and told him I'd scheduled it three weeks ahead of final assembly, and it wasn't due for two weeks yet. He said that was fine, but Department 17A needs that part five weeks before final assembly, and they were planning to start using that part next Monday. I asked him if his schedule had been moved up on that item, but he said it hadn't, that this was the original schedule. He showed me his schedule to prove it."

In the background of Mr. Grebler's thinking was a top-management

EXHIBIT 10 PERKINS ASSOCIATES, INC.

PRESS DEPARTMENT SCHEDULE

(Completed by Mr. Phillips about November 25)

	12/29 12/3	12/6 12/10	12/13 12/17	12/20 12/24	12/27 12/31	1/3 1/7	1/10 1/14	1/17 1/21	1/24 1/28	1/31 2/4	2/7 2/11	2/14 2/18	2/21 2/25
17932 Washer 17K			6,000 (1,250)										
58193 Paddles, Inner 17K					20,000 (775)								
58194 Paddles, Outer 17K					20,000 (775)								
62725 Connector 17K			5,000 (250)										
53214 Support 20F					12,500 (250)								
62925 Washer 20F							8,000 (275)						

Note: For each item, the large figure shows the total estimated requirements for the part and the figure in parentheses shows the estimated weekly consumption rate once assembly operations begin using the part.

drive to reduce inventories which had taken place about eight months earlier. As a result of this pressure, Mr. Grebler had instructed his ordering people to order only what was needed; to reduce production or procurement lead-time allowances, in the case of Press Department items, from six weeks to three weeks; and to be more careful in "rounding off" order quantities. The drive had resulted in a reduction of over $1 million in inventories; most of the reduction was in the raw-material inventory, in which Perkins carried sizeable stocks of nonstandard metals.

Exhibit 11 is a distribution of items by cost, prepared at Mr. Grebler's request. Unit costs as of November 1 were used because these were the latest cost figures available. Most of the missing items were parts put into production after November 1, on which cost data had not yet been accumulated, while on other items the Cost Department simply had no recent reliable costs. Mr. Grebler believed the cost distribution was representative, however, for all parts made by the Press Department.

EXHIBIT 11   PERKINS ASSOCIATES, INC.

COST OF PRESS DEPARTMENT PARTS
(Prices as of November 1, 1954)

Cost* Class	Number in Cost Class	Cumulative Total
To 0.005 (inclusive)	132	132
$0.005 to $.01	50	182
0.01 to .02	18	200
0.02 to .03	10	210
0.03 to .04	25	235
0.04 to .05	22	257
0.05 to .10	39	296
0.10 to .20	20	316
0.20 to .50	21	337
0.50 to 1.00	2	339
1.01 and over	6	345
	345	

* Cost determined on the basis of direct labor at $1.60 per hour; material per standard (i.e., "Material Cost per Part" column on Exhibit 5); and factory overhead at 200% of direct labor cost. The 200% burden rate was the average burden rate for the whole plant; departmental rates were not calculated.

Specialty Metal Products, Inc.

On November 2, Gene Fiske reported for his first day's work as production control supervisor for Specialty Metal Products, Inc. Howard Reynolds, vice president in charge of production, had hired him to perform two jobs: first, to supervise personally production control in the Walden Mill, the larger of two mill buildings, and second, to assume general responsibility for all production-control activities in the company.

Mr. Fiske understood that Mr. Reynolds expected him to improve the whole production organization's performance in meeting delivery promises and manufacturing schedules. He knew that the former production-control supervisor for the Walden Mill had been transferred recently to an assistant foreman's job because the plant had not made good on these assignments. He believed that the problems facing him were difficult ones, proven by the fact that seven different persons had held the Walden Mill production-control job over the preceding 15 years.

When Mr. Fiske discussed the problems of production control with his superior, Bernard Cole, assistant superintendent in charge of services, Mr. Cole commented as follows.

The big problems we have had have been failure to make deliveries to customers as promised and failure to live up to the production schedules for each department. I believe that at least a part of our trouble has been making promises for deliveries that, although we didn't know it, we couldn't possibly fulfill.

We have had these two problems for some time, but with the increase in volume taking place during the past year, the situation with respect to deliveries and schedules has been aggravated. As you know, Mr. Reynolds joined the company about a year ago. He told me that he considers an improvement in production control to be the number one problem facing the production organization at this time. Furthermore, he believes that this is the place

to start in trying to make the production organization generally much more efficient than it has been of late. This is a growing company, and of course, growth always brings problems and changes.

One of the things that I have noticed in particular—and I mention it only because I have seen it happen and not because it necessarily is the biggest deficiency—is the frequency with which we have gotten in trouble with Parts Department orders. I have noticed this happening. There have been several cases where the Sales Department would start expediting an order for a customer and it would develop that the Parts Department production-control supervisor had promised delivery for a date which didn't allow the toolroom enough time to make up the special tools required for the order.

Mr. Fiske, 35 years old, had just been released from the Navy. Prior to duty he had been head of production control for a medium-sized manufacturer of industrial machinery. He had started with that company as an engine-lathe operator, and worked up to a position in the production-control organization. He became head of the production-control unit two years before joining the Navy. Upon his release from the Navy, rather than ask for his old job back, or for another one in the same company, Mr. Fiske decided to see what might be available elsewhere.

General Information about Specialty Metal Products, Inc.

The principal business of Specialty Metal Products, Inc., has been manufacturing strips and coils of solid precious metal, precious-clad base metals, and composite base metals, that is, copper-clad steel used in electrical parts and kitchen utensils. Precious metals and precious-clad base metals are sold mostly to jewelry manufacturers and constitute a majority of the company's sales. Demand for composite base metals had recently grown for a variety of uses relating to national defense products (Exhibit 1).

The large majority of dollar shipments of the Walden Mill has been to jewelry manufacturers. Almost all of these manufacturers are small, family-owned firms, and a majority are located within 100 miles of Specialty Metals. Because their capital is limited and the cost of precious metals is high, these jewelry manufacturers tend to carry only nominal stocks of raw materials, relying on the vendors, such as Specialty Metals, in effect, to carry inventories for them. In the opinion of Specialty Metals' management, little can be done to reduce rush orders, or to avoid a customer's expediting an existing order, when the customer finds himself—as he frequently does—out of a raw material needed to complete an unexpected order for one of the items in his line of merchandise.

EXHIBIT 1 SPECIALTY METAL PRODUCTS, INC.

EXAMPLES OF WALDEN MILL PRODUCTS

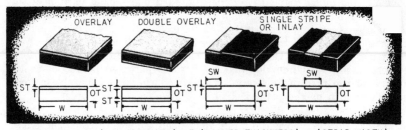

DIMENSIONS: SW (SILVER WIDTH) ST (SILVER THICKNESS) W (STRIP WIDTH)
OT (OVERALL THICKNESS — SILVER PLUS BASE METAL)

Types of Inlaid Flat Stock

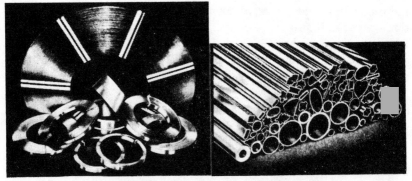

Flat Stock in Coils   **Tubular Shapes**

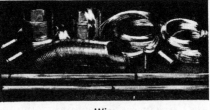

Wire

A newer and growing supplement to Specialty's primary activities was its Parts Department, engaged in fabricating thermostat metal parts and assemblies, electrical contacts, and other small parts and assemblies used mainly in electrical products, such as switches. The number of orders for the Parts Department constituted about 25 per cent of all incoming orders, but the dollar sales of the Parts Department were a much lower percentage of total sales because of the high

EXHIBIT 1 (*Continued*)

Copper
Steel
Copper
Copper
Steel

Copper on steel

Copper
Magnesium

Copper on magnesium

Silver
Beryllium copper

Silver on beryllium copper

Sample Metal Combination

EXAMPLES OF PARTS DEPARTMENT PRODUCTS

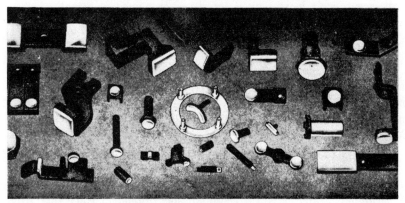

Typical Contact Assemblies

value of the precious metals involved in the products of other departments (Exhibit 1).

All manufacturing, including the Parts Department, is to customers' order only. For all departments, including parts, material costs amount to about 60 per cent; labor 10 per cent; and overhead, administrative expenses, and profits, 30 per cent of sales. In November the Production Department employed about 800 persons, the total having

increased about 150 during the year. About 500 of these worked in the Walden Mill and 300 in the Parts Department. The workforce of the Metals Department, referred to as the Walden Mill, had grown at about the same rate as the workforce of the Parts Department in that period.

Specialty Metal Products had one larger and three smaller competitors in the metals field. There were numerous businesses throughout the country which were comparable in equipment and type of product to the Parts Department. The Sales Department, headed by a vice president, included 15 salesmen located throughout the country and an inside sales force of five men. All salesmen were engineers and in many cases worked closely with a customer's design and production organizations in developing the appropriate materials for the customer's product.

Specialty Metal Products had been established by one family prior to 1920 and was still closely held. It had enjoyed steady growth over the years as the company's research organization had developed new uses for existing products and new products based on bonded bi-metal materials.

Samuel Walden, one of the founders and still the company president, took great pride in employee activities, organized principally by an active Employee Association. The company was not unionized.

Production Organization and Processes

The production organization was headed by Howard Reynolds, to whom a plant superintendent reported. Two assistant superintendents in turn headed the two principal production departments, each located in a separate building, and another assistant superintendent, to whom Mr. Fiske reported, was designated assistant superintendent in charge of services. This latter assistant superintendent, Mr. Cole, was responsible for production control, for shipping and receiving, and for storing nonprecious metals. Mr. Cole was also assistant to the plant superintendent and acted for the plant superintendent when the latter was absent. Mr. Fiske's position had the same status and salary as a foreman's job had in the operating departments.

The remainder of the production-staff organization consisted principally of a Methods Department. This department of seven engineers and a supervisor was engaged primarily in improving the various processes in each department and in determining the process for making new products. The unit was also responsible for selecting new equipment and for all plant layout work. The supervisor was John Walden, nephew of the president.

EXHIBIT 2 SPECIALTY METAL PRODUCTS, INC.

Departments and Products

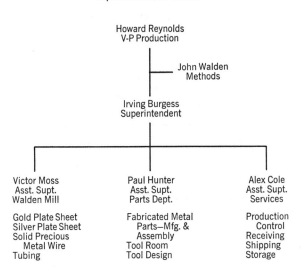

Samuel Walden believed in a policy of having no organization charts and only a minimum of titles. To clarify his own understanding, however, Mr. Fiske sketched out the data shown as Exhibit 2, which indicates the principal product lines manufactured, services provided, or both, by each department. The Walden Mill not only occupied the larger building but also had the larger workforce. Mr. Fiske gathered data on the foremen in the Walden Mill and in the Parts Department as shown in Exhibit 3.

Supplement A describes the basic steps in the production process and illustrates some of the principal pieces of equipment.

Existing Production-Control Organization

During his first few days on his new job, Mr. Fiske spent most of his time finding out how the production-control function was being carried out. Production control had been organized on a decentralized basis with two planning and scheduling supervisors, one in the Walden Mill and the other in the Parts Department. The planning and scheduling supervisor in the Walden Mill was assisted by one scheduling clerk and two expediters. The Parts Department planning and scheduling supervisor had one expediter and two recording clerks.

Both production-control supervisors had reported to two persons: the assistant superintendent in whose department they worked, and

EXHIBIT 3   SPECIALTY METAL PRODUCTS, INC.

DEPARTMENTAL ORGANIZATIONS

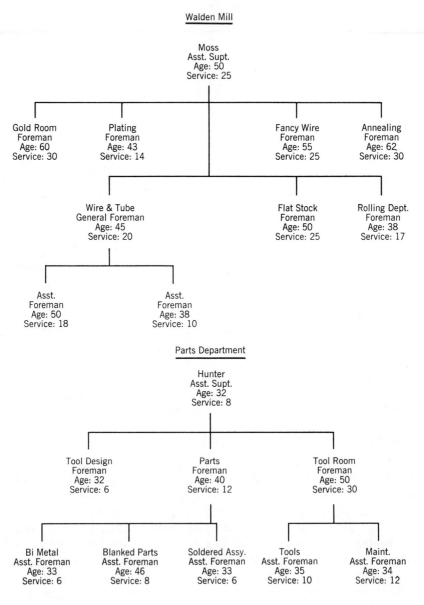

Walden Mill

Moss
Asst. Supt.
Age: 50
Service: 25

Gold Room
Foreman
Age: 60
Service: 30

Plating
Foreman
Age: 43
Service: 14

Fancy Wire
Foreman
Age: 55
Service: 25

Annealing
Foreman
Age: 62
Service: 30

Wire & Tube
General Foreman
Age: 45
Service: 20

Flat Stock
Foreman
Age: 50
Service: 25

Rolling Dept.
Foreman
Age: 38
Service: 17

Asst.
Foreman
Age: 50
Service: 18

Asst.
Foreman
Age: 38
Service: 10

Parts Department

Hunter
Asst. Supt.
Age: 32
Service: 8

Tool Design
Foreman
Age: 32
Service: 6

Parts
Foreman
Age: 40
Service: 12

Tool Room
Foreman
Age: 50
Service: 30

Bi Metal
Asst. Foreman
Age: 33
Service: 6

Blanked Parts
Asst. Foreman
Age: 46
Service: 8

Soldered Assy.
Asst. Foreman
Age: 33
Service: 6

Tools
Asst. Foreman
Age: 35
Service: 10

Maint.
Asst. Foreman
Age: 34
Service: 12

Mr. Cole, assistant superintendent in charge of services. Each supervisor was responsible for two functions, scheduling and expediting. In addition, the Walden Mill planning and scheduling supervisor maintained inventory control over a stock of base-metal raw material. Precious-metal stocks were kept in the "Gold Room" and were controlled by the Gold Room foreman.

Processing of Customers' Orders before Receipt by Production Control

A customer's order, or request for quotation, was sent by the Sales Department to the Pricing Department of the treasurer's office. Mr. Fiske interviewed Barry Horton of the Pricing Department to determine that group's part in the processing of new orders before receipt by production control. Mr. Horton explained:

To begin with, if the item has been made before, we simply follow the previous manufacturing order in making out the new manufacturing order, in four copies, which we send to the production-control supervisor in the mill building in which that product was made—in other words, to you in the Walden Mill or to Koons in the Parts Department.

If the item ordered, however, has not been made before in the required material, size, or shape, the customer invariably requires a quotation, and Jimmy Fields (supervisor of the cost-estimating section of the Pricing Department) estimates the costs of both tooling and manufacturing in any such cases before any manufacturing order is made up. In the estimating process, material costs are computed, yields are estimated, and tooling costs are obtained from the toolroom and the tool-design section, based on the customer's drawings and specifications. In the estimating process, Jimmy or his cost estimators deal not only with the toolroom and the tool-design section but also with the assistant superintendents and the various foremen to the extent necessary to find out the steps by which the customer's order will be manufactured. The cost estimators, you understand, draw heavily on their own experience and the experience of the plant foremen. When their investigations are completed, they return estimates to the Sales Department.

If the customer confirms the order after receiving the estimate, or if the item had been made before making a new estimate unnecessary, the order entry section of my group makes up a manufacturing order, showing the job to be done and stating the customer's delivery requirements or the completion date promised, if any, by the Sales Department, as the case might be. At the bottom of the form the cost estimator notes anything special about the order. For instance, if the estimating procedure develops the need for unusual outside processing, the name or names of an appropriate vendor would be noted.

Here's a typical manufacturing order (Exhibit 4).

"What about an order that requires new tooling?" asked Mr. Fiske.

If special tooling is required on a new order, the man estimating the job will make up a tooling order on a similar form and dispatch it directly to the

EXHIBIT 4 SPECIALTY METAL PRODUCTS, INC.

MANUFACTURING ORDER

| 1 | 2 | 3 | 4 | 5 | 6 | 7 | 8 | 9 | 10 | 11 | 12 | 13 | 14 | 15 | 16 | 17 | 18 | 19 | 20 | 21 | 22 | 23 | 24 | 25 | 26 |

SPECIALTY METAL PRODUCTS, INC.

OUR ORDER No. E26508				DELIVERY DATE *At once upon Receipt of Material Week of 7/2*	

CUSTOMER ORDER NO.	DATE ENTERED	SALE	ACT	MATERIAL CODE	FACTORY FOLLOW UP
R 20107	6/20/62	6	NR	100000 100900	
					GOLD ROOM *1*
					SILVER ROOM
SOLD TO Same				*S.O. to Miller 6/20*	
					PLATERS
SHIP TO Sanford & Esser Co. 1721 Main Street Plainville, Delaware					DEPT. 54 *6/22*
					DEPT. 5

F.O.B. COLLECT ☐ PREPAID ☐ F.O.B. DESTINATION ☐	ROUND WIRE
	FANCY WIRE

QUANTITY ORDERED	DESCRIPTION	
		TUBING
15 Lbs.	To Copper Clad, Roll and Slit <u>Your</u> Allegheny #2 Relay Steel	
		INSP.
	From: 3/16" thick X 3" wide	
	To: .0625 ± .002 X 5/8" Overall (with .002 + .000 − .00075 Copper Cladding one side)	PTS MAT'L. SCHEDULE
		PARTS SCHEDULE
	Temper as Rolled Coiled	ASSEMBLY SCHEDULE

A	PRODUCTION SCHEDULE	JL 1	PRECIOUS METAL ORDER CONTROL	

INSTRUCTIONS: CUSTOMER #446	F.S.C.
QUANTITY 15 Lbs. See R. Armstrong for Cust mat'l—Note: Use enough Allegheny #2 Relay Steel to cover 15 Lbs. on order from 121-1/2 Lb. cust. material rec'd—5 pcs. 3/16" X 3" X 10-3/4 Ft. and 16 Ft.—Use our Copper—Work to be done by Ed Miller in Gil Clarke's Dept.—ship At Once upon receipt of material—Via Truck—Assoc. Transport—Cleveland—Coordinated Transport	O.P.
	2

tool-design section. This order authorizes the detail design by the design section and the manufacture by the toolroom of tools according to the specifications attached.

Oh, by the way, in the case of either first orders for small quantities or small repeat orders, the Pricing Department routes the manufacturing order to the Short Order Department, which, as you probably know, is one of the activities reporting to the vice president for research and development. In such cases, none of the Production Department personnel become involved and you won't get any papers at all.

In further conversation with Mr. Horton, Mr. Fiske learned that Mr. Horton had worked in the plant in various production jobs for over 20 years before he became a cost estimator and, subsequently, head of the Pricing Department. This department was responsible for pricing, billing, and invoicing, as well as for order entry and estimating. Mr. Horton's assistant, James Fields, with the aid of two estimators, comprised the cost estimating section. Mr. Fields, Mr. Fiske discovered, had earlier worked in the Gold Room and in the Tubing Department of the Walden Mill. The two estimators who worked for Mr. Fields likewise had some shop experience.

Scheduling—Walden Mill

When he started on his new job, Mr. Fiske immediately assumed the responsibilities of the former production-control supervisor of the Walden Mill. Since the Walden Mill seemed to present the most complex problems, Mr. Fiske's first step was to learn the scheduling procedures being followed. Upon receipt of a manufacturing order from the Pricing Department, the scheduler, Miss Helen McCain, a middle-aged woman who had been on this job for over 10 years, first checked to determine whether raw material was available. The stage of fabrication in which the raw material was available governed the amount of processing required and importantly affected the scheduler's estimate of the time required to finish the order.

Some common sizes of strips and plates of both precious-metal alloys and base metal were kept in stock and occasionally met the customer's requirements, permitting immediate shipment of the order. Sometimes the appropriate strip or plate required only fabrication into tubing, wire, or other shape. More often, the customer's requirement was for a stock alloy but for a dimension different from the company's stock items; in this event, strip or plate would have to be routed to the appropriate departments (precious or base metal) for rolling down and slitting to the proper size before shipment as flat stock or before further processing into various shapes, tubing, or wire if one of these was the customer's need. On other orders requiring special alloys of base or precious metals, or both, the scheduler routed the order to the Gold Room for compounding of the raw materials, which were subsequently melted in an electric furnace and poured into one or more ingots. Before rolling, an ingot was "scalped" on a large shaper to remove the hard, outside surfaces of the metal.

Miss McCain determined the status of the required raw material by consulting the Gold Room foreman directly in the case of precious

metals—about 40 per cent of the orders—and by consulting a Kardex file in the case of base-metal raw materials. The Gold Room kept no perpetual records, but maintained inventory control by visual inspection. Precious metals were stored in a vault adjacent to the Gold Room. Miss McCain herself maintained the base-metal Kardex file, which showed only the description of each item, dates of inventory changes, and the amounts of issues, receipts, and running balance on hand. (Exhibit 8 shows a Kardex record for one item.) Periodically, the balance on hand of each item was brought into agreement with a physical inventory.

In describing her handling of an order, Miss McCain told Mr. Fiske,

After finding out the status of the raw materials needed, I fix a completion date for the order. This will be the same as the customer's requested delivery date if the existing backlog of work isn't too great. Unless our backlog gets unusually high, I set the completion date for gold plate seven to ten days after the date I get the manufacturing order from pricing. I use seven days for "hot" orders and ten days for the routine ones. On silver or base-plate and sheet orders, I use two and a half and three and a half weeks from the date I get the order. If a customer wants earlier delivery, I'll phone the foreman of the department involved to find out if he can do it, and then I'll staple a red RUSH ticket to the copy of the manufacturing order I send him.

On wire orders, I check with the Gold Room to see if they have "shell" stock on hand from which the wire needed can be drawn. If they do, I schedule completion two weeks later. If there are no "shells," and they have to be made by the Rolling Department, we may not be able to make delivery for three or four weeks. In these cases, I check with the Wire Department foreman to get his estimate of the completion date.

Mr. Fiske learned that Miss McCain kept certain scheduling records, and he asked her to explain them to him.

"Well," began Miss McCain, "I make one combined schedule for gold, silver, and base rolled orders; one schedule for round wire; and one schedule for tubing. The Gold Room, Fancy Wire, and Plating Departments are left entirely up to the foreman involved. I do no scheduling at all, just send him a copy of the manufacturing order.

"This (Exhibit 5) is my schedule for the rolled products. I keep a cumulative schedule in ounces and use 125,000 ounces per week as the approximate limit of rolling capacity."

"How did you get the figure 125,000 ounces?" Mr. Fiske asked.

"That's the most they've ever produced when we were working 50 hours a week," Miss McCain replied. "When we drop back to, say, 40 hours a week, I cut the capacity back proportionately. Right now we're working 50 hours a week."

EXHIBIT 5 SPECIALTY METAL PRODUCTS, INC.

SCHEDULING WORK SHEET

Gold Plate Sheet—November

Date Order Received	Remarks	Cumulative Ounces Scheduled				
		Week of Nov. 1	Week of Nov. 8	Week of Nov. 15	Week of Nov. 22	Week of Nov. 29
8/23			883 (4)			
8/26		274 (3)				
9/4		296 (4)	861 (3)			
9/4		1157 (7)				
9/30					100 (1)	
10/7	Mays—E12358 (2d & 3d posted)	21157 (8)		1200 (1)		
10/11		21557 (9)				
10/14					900 (3)	
10/15		26557 (10)			1400 (4)	
10/18		27257 (12)	700 (3)			
10/18	2d repl. E10986	27336 (13)				
10/19		28497 (15)				
10/20		32896 (22)				
10/21		37404 (32)				
10/22		37754 (35)				
10/23		37854 (36)			1900 (5)	
10/23		37865 (38)				
10/25		38256 (42)	1408 (6)			
10/25		44667 (54)				
10/26		52971 (63)	7700 (12)			
10/27		56086 (66)				
10/27		57286 (73)	8300 (13)			
10/27	repl. E12762	57337 (74)	17800 (20)			
10/27	repl. E11594 (3d repl.)	57352 (75)				
10/28	reduction E13335 & E13356	56432 (75)				
10/28		56734 (77)				
10/28		62199 (79)				
10/28		68799 (86)	18015 (23)			
10/28	corrected loading	78729 (97)	18933 (31)			
10/28					2100 (6)	
10/29			19068 (32)			
10/29	reschedule E12833		19568 (33)		1600 (5)	
10/29			31968 (35)			
10/29			34368 (40)			
11/1			34748 (42)			
11/1	repl. E11618		35198 (43)			
11/1	repl. E12651		35428 (44)			
11/1	repl. E13171		35559 (45)			
11/1	repl. E13167		36045 (46)			
11/1			36670 (48)			
11/1	repl. E12757		36706 (49)			
11/1			37938 (52)		1700 (6)	
11/2			38029 (53)	12211 (3)		

EXHIBIT 5 (*Continued*) SPECIALTY METAL PRODUCTS, INC.

SCHEDULING WORK SHEET

Silver Plate Sheet—November

Date Order Received	Remarks	Cumulative Ounces Scheduled				
		Week of Nov. 1	Week of Nov. 8	Week of Nov. 15	Week of Nov. 22	Week of Nov. 29
8/27		752 (2)				
9/1	(3d repl.)	1543 (7)	1400 (1)			
9/1	repl. E10471	1596 (8)				
9/4						7500 (1)
10/2		12433 (10)	6432 (2)			
10/5		15791 (13)			1200 (1)	
10/7						
10/8		21442 (14)		339 (1)		
10/13	repl. E11211	21766 (15)				
10/13	repl. E11379 & E11365	30096 (17)				
10/15		35211 (20)			1722 (3)	
10/17			7641 (5)			
10/21				1211 (3)		
10/22		39293 (24)	18141 (6)	3429 (5)		
10/24		41007 (29)	21432 (9)			
10/25		45773 (33)		10429 (6)		
10/28	repl. E13472	46386 (39)				
10/29	repl. E13201	51275 (40)	25799 (12)			
10/29	repl. E12887	52384 (41)	25843 (13)			
10/29			29221 (17)		3542 (4)	
11/1	(2d repl.)		32347 (25)			
11/1	repl. 12432		32544 (26)			
11/1	repl. 13777		32921 (27)			
11/1	repl. 12844		33079 (28)			
11/1	repl. 13398		33792 (29)			

Notes: Weekly figures (i.e., 52,384, the last figure under the Week of Nov. 1 column) are the cumulative number of ounces scheduled for that week; the figures in parentheses represent the cumulative number of orders involved, i.e., 41 orders were involved in the 52,384 ounces of silver plate scheduled for the week of Nov. 1 on 10/29.

Mr. Fiske had already learned that rolling equipment could be used alternately on gold, silver, or base metals, if necessary. A change in material required a change in rolls, however, since gold rolls were ground to a much higher surface than rolls used on silver or base material. It required about 40 minutes to change rollers.

"I also keep track of the cumulative number of orders scheduled for each week," Miss McCain continued, "because some of the operations, like the Gold Room operations, need almost as much time for a small order, like 100 ounces, as for a large order, say of 1,500 ounces. Therefore, I try to schedule no more than 75 manufacturing orders in total for completion by the two rolling departments in any one week. As you can see from my schedule (Exhibit 5), I'm a little heavier than

that right now but I've just had some unexpected reruns where the first lot of material was spoiled in processing."

Mr. Fiske learned that the figures in parentheses on Exhibit 5 showed the cumulative number of orders scheduled for that week, and the column of figures under each week was the cumulative number of ounces of materials in the orders scheduled for that week. Most of the entries under "Remarks" indicated orders replacing earlier ones spoiled during the manufacturing process. Miss McCain kept similar schedules for round wire and tubing.

In commenting on nontypical orders, Miss McCain explained, "When I get a new order, or an unusual one, I call up the foremen. They'll draw on their experience with similar orders in the past, and I know a few foremen keep personal records of how they handled out-of-the-ordinary orders which pass through their departments."

After scheduling, Miss McCain told Mr. Fiske, she distributed the four copies of the manufacturing order she had received from the Pricing Department as follows: One copy was returned to the Sales Department to inform it of the expected completion date; this promised delivery date was in turn communicated to the customer. A second copy was filed, by serial number of the manufacturing order, in the production-control "Master File" and was used for follow-up purposes. Each foreman turned in daily lists of all orders completed, showing the department to which each had been sent. The scheduler posted this progress report to the Master File copy.

Miss McCain deposited a third copy in a "tickler" file according to scheduled completion (shipment) date. Each Tuesday she used this file to list by department delinquent orders and all orders due for shipment during the following week. Copies of this list were sent to the Walden Mill assistant superintendent and to each foreman, to assist them in planning the next week's operations. Exhibit 6 shows such a list for the Tubing Department.

The fourth copy of the manufacturing order was designated as the "Shop Order" and was sent to the appropriate storeroom for issuance of the required raw material and for transportation to the first Production Department. Miss McCain did not indicate any routing on the Shop Order. Routing for an order was handwritten by the foreman of each department on a Routing Form (Exhibit 7). The foreman determined how the work was to be done in his department. The foreman might do the job in one of a half-dozen ways, depending on the form in which the material was furnished, the workload on various machines, and the skill and availability of the various workmen in his department. He drew on his prior experience with the same or

EXHIBIT 6 SPECIALTY METAL PRODUCTS, INC.

LIST OF ORDERS DUE

November 24

TO: I. Burgess   J. O'Reilly
     G. Fiske   T. Murphy
     V. Moss   L. McCain
     A. Cole

SUBJECT: Tubing—Overdue

Order No.	Part No.	Description
LO 75707		10/15 Yel #71 on L.C. Nickel Tubing
E32429 shipped 11/24 p.m.		.001 P.N. on 10% N.S. Tubing
E32695		13½K Yel #4F Gold Corrugated Tubing
E33591	94	Fine Silver Tubes
E33615 Bal		Sterling Silver Tubing

TUBING—Week of 11/23

E28945 1000 Oz		10/10 Jones #4 Int on P&A #20 Base Tubing
E33092 800 Oz		10/20 Wh #199 on L.C. Nickel Base Tubing
E34239		14K Yel #47 Gold Tubing
E34527		9½K Yel #20N Gold Aluminum Filled Tubing

TUBING—Week of 11/30

E33645		12/10 Yel #20N Not Int on 18% N.S. Tubing
E33646		12/10 Yel #20N Not Int on 18% N.S. Tubing
E33680		Fine Silver Lined Brass Rectangular Wave. Tubing
E33681		Fine Silver Lined Brass Rectangular Wave. Tubing
E33765 75 ft		CP Alloy IID Tubing
E32487	Ex 788	Fine Silver Collectoro Rings
E34387		13½K Yel #20N Gold Rectangular Tubing
E34615		10K Yel #20N Gold Tubing
E34663	1515	Coin Silver Tubes
E34725		13½K Wh #199 Gold Tubing

EXHIBIT 7   SPECIALTY METAL PRODUCTS, INC.

ROUTING FORM

ORDER NO. E 3 6 0 1 1 DATE 12-13 WRITTEN BY PET AMOUNT OZS. 3 1 5				
NO. INGOTS 1 pc. - .600 x 5 Soft CHECKED BY (ru) LOT NO.				
MATERIAL Coin Silver Contacts				
Roll - .060 +.001 -.002 Slit .860 +.015 .000				
Vick - 140-160				
ROLLING SCHEDULE	ROLLED BY	ANNEALING SCHEDULE	FURNACE NO.	WASHED BY
5"				
Roll - 16 x 24 -.350	105	Soft	26N	108²
Roll - 16 x 24 -.100	105	HD		
6x10 Fin - 3 Hi	328	HD		
Slit	196			
Kiss Pass Barb (ru)	162	V-150 SPK		
REMARKS OTHER SIDE PR 649				

Notes: (1) "V-150" and "Vick-140–160" refer to a hardness test for the finished materials, which were to be within the range of 140 to 160. Tests showed the hardness of the finished materials to be 150.

(2) "16 x 24" refers to the size of the rolling mill, and ".350" refers to the thickness to which the piece was to be reduced by this operation (from an original thickness of .600 inches). Each rolling operation was followed by an annealing operation, as shown under "Annealing Schedule." Following the three rolling and three annealing operations, this order was slit to width (.860 inches) and "kiss passed" under a rolling mill to eliminate barbs resulting from the slitting cutters.

similar orders, routing it the same way, or, if he believed the previous processing could be improved, modifying the previous routing. In rolling, for instance, the frequency of annealing and the amount of reduction in thickness of stock between anneals might be varied by the foreman in an effort to make a better product or to reduce spoilage. The foreman, Mr. Fiske learned, determined what work had to be done by other departments; the large majority of orders, however, were completed within each department, save for the Gold Room, which served all departments.

The shop copy of the manufacturing order did not show the promised delivery date. Foremen were expected to process orders by "date entered "—6/20 on Exhibit 4—the oldest date first, except when a red "RUSH" sticker was attached, indicating first priority. They were also guided by the weekly list of orders due (Exhibit 6) which contained not only delinquent orders but also all orders due out during the following calendar week.

Scheduling—Parts Department

Mr. Fiske discovered that Robert Koons, the production-control supervisor of the Parts Department, did not maintain a work-load record such as Miss McCain's scheduling work sheet (Exhibit 5). Mr. Koons established promised shipping dates by adding two weeks to the date of each order; red tickets attached to rush orders signaled the foremen to give such orders priority. Mr. Koons made up weekly overdue-order lists, similar to Miss McCain's, from his tickler file of manufacturing orders. He maintained no materials records and therefore had nothing to check before scheduling orders. Occasionally, before scheduling an important or an especially large parts order, Mr. Koons telephoned Miss McCain to determine whether the required raw material was in Walden's finished stock, and if not, the day by which the Walden Mill could manufacture and deliver the item. Save for a relatively small amount of purchased components, the raw materials required by the Parts Department were manufactured by the Walden Mill; ten of the most active sizes and shapes were carried in finished stocks by the Walden Mill, but a majority of Parts Department orders required raw materials which the Walden Mill produced only on order. Even for purchased parts, the Parts Department simply filled out a requisition, marked it "Purchase," and sent it to the Walden Mill scheduler, who made out and forwarded a purchase request to the Purchasing Department.

Mr. Koons' activities had nothing to do directly with the toolroom or the tool-design section, which worked closely with one another. Otto Chapman, foreman of the toolroom, was about 50 years old and had held that position for 17 years; before that, he had been a tool-and-die maker for Specialty. He had worked 30 years in total for the company. When a customer's order required dies or other tools to be made up, the tool-design group received a tool-manufacturing order directly from the order-entry section of the Pricing Department. The order form was a different color and had no column headed "Factory Follow-Up" but was otherwise identical with Exhibit 4.

After drawing the tool to be made, the tool-design supervisor delivered the tool order and drawings to Mr. Chapman, whose clerk kept them filed by the date the order had been entered by the order-entry section—"6/20" on Exhibit 4. He also examined the order for indications of priority, such as "Rush" or "Emergency" or "Customer Must Have by 5/27," and filed such orders in a special group, to be done as soon as the appropriate machines or toolmakers were free. Some orders not marked to indicate priority when Mr. Chapman received them acquired it by subsequent expediting action.

There were some 50 men in the toolroom, ranging from a few apprentices to fully qualified toolmakers. Mr. Chapman tried to rotate the kind of jobs he assigned toolmakers so as to give them as broad experience as possible. Some men, however, were specialists, such as the jig-borer and jig-grinder operators.

Expediting

The Walden Mill and the Parts Department each expedited its own manufacturing orders. The expediter's function consisted of checking on orders to answer a customer's query as to whether the initial delivery promise would actually be met, or to see whether delivery of an order could be advanced from the date originally promised. The expediters consulted the Master File copy of the manufacturing order to determine its status and location. They also consulted the scheduler and the foreman or foremen involved. Mr. Fiske found that in most cases, the expediting action was for the second reason, with a customer requesting earlier delivery as a result of higher sales of his products, or for other reasons. Mr. Fiske had the expediters keep a tally of expediting requests for a month; he found that they totaled nearly 500. A few orders were expedited more than once before they were shipped, but it was Mr. Fiske's impression that such repeated expediting was unusual. Since orders were being received at the rate of about 1,500 per month, Mr. Fiske concluded that expediting action was required on about one-third of all orders received. He knew that the rate of receipt of incoming orders had risen recently, and he believed that the rate would continue to grow in the foreseeable future.

Raw Material Control—Walden Mill

Mr. Fiske also examined the procedures followed by Miss McCain in posting to the Kardex file on base-metal raw materials (Exhibit 8). When the Receiving Department accepted a shipment of an item, a copy of the inspection report was delivered to Miss McCain, and when

EXHIBIT 8 SPECIALTY METAL PRODUCTS, INC.
KARDEX-BASE RAW MATERIALS *

FRONT OF KARDEX FORM

ITEM S-20(#312) ALLOY PLATER BARS						ITEM NO 1 X 3-1/2 X 20 PLANED			ACCOUNT NO UNIT					
						BEST ORDER QUANTITIES			LOCATION					
			DWG. OR SPEC. NO			2000	5000	10,000	LEAD TIME **4 - 5 WEEKS**					
VEN. DORS	1. REVERE COPPER & BRASS INC.					3								
	2. AMERICAN BRASS CO.					4								

PURCHASE REQUISITIONS						PURCHASE ORDERS							USAGE		
DATE	QUAN.	DEL.Y TO START	RATE PER MO.	DELIVER TO	APP'D	DATE	VEN.	P O NO	DEL.Y TO START	DATE COMP	TOTAL QUAN	UNIT COST	MO	19 61	19 62
7/30/61	3000#	Oct. 61			wg	8/1/61	1	65832	10/27/61	2767#	.6518/#		1		12½
10/9/61	2000#	Mar 62			wg	10/10/61	1	70166	3/31/62	1914#			2		15
12/29/61	2000#	Apr 62			wg	12/30/61	1	76284	2/27/62	1791#			3		16
2/9/62	2000#	Oct. 62			wg	2/13/62	2	7975o	11/27/62	2251#			4		1½
2/9/62	2000#	May 62			wg	2/13/62	1	79771	5/18/62	2070#			5		1
													6		18½
													7		5½
													8		33½
													9		41
													10		6
													11	8½	-
													12	35	5
													YR		
	ORDER POINT: 134 bars (3000 #)														

PURCHASE REQUISITION RECORD	METALS & CONTROLS CORPORATION	FORM NO. PR 581

* Quantities were recorded in pounds on the front of the card and in number of bars on the reverse.

one of the operating departments withdrew some base-metal stock, she received a copy of the stores requisition. From these documents she posted the Kardex file. Mr. Fiske found that the former Walden Mill production-control supervisor had personally determined whether a raw material would be stocked or purchased as needed by reviewing each manufacturing order received which required nonstock material. In the case of either stock replenishment or special orders, Miss McCain sent a purchase request to the Purchasing Department as authority to buy the item.

As he became more familiar with existing procedures, Mr. Fiske also found that the former supervisor of the Walden Mill had also established the ordering quantity for each stock raw material personally and arbitrarily, emphasizing the size of the quantity discounts offered by the supplier. Generally, the supervisor had chosen an ordering quantity for which the unit price, after quantity discounts, tended to "break" (or level off), although he had established a policy of buying no more than five years' supply of an item, even though the price "break" had not been achieved.

Mr. Fiske ascertained that the following schedule of quantity discounts and premiums from base prices applied to an item ordered from a mill.

EXHIBIT 8 SPECIALTY METAL PRODUCTS, INC.

KARDEX-BASE RAW MATERIALS

REVERSE OF KARDEX FORM

ITEM S-20 (# 312) ALLOY PLATER BARS						STOCK RECORD 1 X 3-1/2 X 20 PLANED					22.47 #		
QUAN. REC'D	BAL. ON ORDER	DATE	REFERENCE	QUAN. ISSUED	CUM. ISSUES	BAL. ON HAND	QUAN. REC'D	BAL. ON ORDER	DATE	REFERENCE	QUAN. ISSUED	CUM. ISSUES	BAL. ON HAND
		9/14/62		11		216½			8/16		2		272½
		9/14		4		212½			9/13		18		254½
		9/16		3½		209							
		9/16		1½		207½							
		9/24		2		205½							
		9/25		½		205							
		9/25		3		202							
		9/25		3		199							
		10/7		4		195							
		10/26		2		193							
		10/27	79750	100		293							
		11/30	Physical Inventory			291½							
		12/3		5		286½							
5 Gold Room		12/7				291½							
		1/10/63		1		290½							
		3/15		2		288½							
		4/12		1		287½							
		4/15		4		283½							
		4/16		2		281½							
		5/17		7		274½							

881- REMINGTON RAND INC.-11 RRHP. - 4788 (408)

Size of Order (pounds)	Premium or Discount (per pound)
300–500	+$.13
500–1,000	+ .075
1,000–2,000	+ .05
2,000–5,000	+ .02
5,000–10,000	base price
10,000–20,000	— .0025
20,000–30,000	— .0050

For instance, if Specialty were ordering a particular copper alloy from a mill on which the quoted base price was $.78 per pound, an order for 350 pounds would cost $.91 per pound ($.78 plus $.13); an order of 600 pounds $.855; an order of 2,500 pounds $.80; and so on, until base price was reached for an order of 5,000 pounds. The time required to receive a shipment of a base primary metal from a supplier, once an order had been placed, varied from six weeks to six months, depending largely on general economic conditions.

Mr. Fiske's predecessor in the Walden Mill had established a policy that an item would be reordered when withdrawals had reduced the balance on hand to an amount equal to the "ordering quantity" described above. Miss McCain made out a purchase request when an

item fell below this minimum as a result of her posting; the former supervisor, however, initialed each purchase request before it was sent to the Purchasing Department. He also periodically reviewed all, or at least the important parts, of the Kardex files, especially during times of short supply for the raw materials involved. The principal base used by the Walden Mill was copper.

Finished Stocks—Walden Mill

The Walden Mill maintained a stock of ten of its most commonly demanded products, such as reels of copper and brass strip stock in popular widths and thicknesses and copper wire in frequently used sizes. The requirements of customers, however, varied so greatly with respect to material, shapes, and dimensions that the large majority of orders were custom made. By far the principal user of this relatively small stock of finished goods was the company's own Parts Department. A finished-stock Kardex file identical in form with Exhibit 8 (raw-material item) was posted by Miss McCain. The previous production-control supervisor had established minimum stocks of each finished-goods item and had instructed Miss McCain to prepare a manufacturing order equal to the amount withdrawn every time she posted a requisition, a form which indicated a foreman had withdrawn some of the item from the Stores Department. For instance, if the stock level on a type of copper strip had been set at 2,000 pounds and Miss McCain received a requisition indicating the Parts Department had withdrawn 500 pounds of this item, she posted the withdrawal, computed the balance (1,500 pounds), and then made out a manufacturing order for 500 pounds of the item which, when completed, would bring the stock level back again to 2,000 pounds. As far as Mr. Fiske could determine, the minimum stock levels (2,000 pounds) had been arbitrarily fixed.

Parts Department Material Control

The Parts Department did not maintain a raw-material storeroom but relied on the Walden Mill's finished-materials storeroom for materials produced in the Walden Mill. The relatively small amount of outside purchased items, mainly component parts, were immediately turned over upon receipt to the appropriate Parts Department foreman; they were not kept in the Walden Mill Stores Department because of lack of space. Since the Parts Department had no storeroom, its purchased parts, and also fabricated parts awaiting other parts for assembly, were simply stored on the open floor in any space available in the Parts Department.

Accidental overruns of some completed products made by the Parts Department were stacked in a corner of the Walden Mill Shipping Department, in the hopes of being salable on a subsequent reorder from the same customer, or for use in filling another order for the same part from a different customer. A few Parts Department products were sold to more than one customer.

As he began to think of steps which he might take to improve the situation, Mr. Fiske recalled something else Mr. Cole had said: "If orders don't get out on time it is *your* responsibility. Don't try to pass the buck to the foremen. At the same time, remember that we are a service organization without line authority, only the power to make recommendations. If overtime needs to be authorized to get an order out on time, it's your job to get the foremen or assistant superintendent responsible to ask the superintendent for authorization."

Supplement A. Manufacturing Processes

The Walden Mill

The Gold Room maintains custody of all precious metals and their alloys, except when other departments are processing material. The Gold Room foreman, who has learned the technical aspects of his job through experience, is responsible for compounding all alloys, standard (18 karat gold) or special, according to a customer's order. For many orders, the required alloy can be produced in several different ways, depending on the materials on hand. Adjacent to the Gold Room proper are two electric furnaces for melting metals. After melting, metals are cast into ingots. Ingots are prepared for use by scalping, or removing the outer crust, on a shaper.

To manufacture "flat stock," the scalped ingot is rolled to the proper thickness and width, or, for smaller sizes, rolled and then slit to the desired width, ending up in either case as a roll of strip metal. Sometimes a large piece of stock rather than an ingot is reduced to smaller dimensions by rolling and then slitting. Depending on the metal involved, either the Gold Rolling or the Silver and Base Metal Rolling Department performs the rolling and slitting operations. Both departments have rolling and slitting equipment in a wide variety of sizes, the difference being primarily in the final rolling operations. Gold rolling is done in an air-conditioned room. To impart a high surface finish, the rolls used in the Gold Rolling Department are ground in the adjacent Roll Grinding Department to finer tolerances and to a higher

EXHIBIT A-1   SPECIALTY

WALDEN MILL

Gold-rolling mill

METAL PRODUCTS, INC.

EQUIPMENT

One of the furnaces used for bonding composite metals

One of several metal gang slitters

EXHIBIT A-2 SPECIALTY

PARTS DEPARTMENT

Knuckle presses used for producing electrical contacts

A battery of cold headers in electrical contact department

METAL PRODUCTS, INC.

EQUIPMENT

A view of the general toolroom

Department for fabrication of stamped metal parts

A row of surface grinders

EXHIBIT A-2 *(Continued)* SPECIALTY METAL PRODUCTS, INC.

PARTS DEPARTMENT EQUIPMENT

Mill rolls after refinishing

Part of cylindrical-grinding department

A bay of lathes in tool department

finish than the rolls used in the Silver and Base Metal Rolling Department. Rolls for the gold rolling equipment are ground to a tolerance of three-tenths of one-millionth of an inch.

By drawing through dies, various shapes—round, rectangular, special-shaped solid, or hollow—of precious, base, or composite metals are produced to close tolerances in the Wire, Fancy Wire, and Tube Departments. Composite metals are first bonded, however, by brazing in a furnace; likewise, billets are reduced in section and lengthened by rolling prior to the drawing operations for forming various shapes.

The annealing equipment is used to bond composite metals prior to rolling and drawing, and by all Rolling and Drawing Departments between operations. By annealing the workpieces in the furnace, stresses created by rolling and drawing are relieved. The workpieces are softer and therefore easier to process after annealing. The Plating Department utilizes only precious metals (gold and silver), mostly depositing gold on a base metal which is then rolled and slit by the Gold Rolling Department.

The following is a typical list of operations required to manufacture flat-rolled stock; the example is a precious metal bonded to a base metal (silver and copper): Melt silver and cast into ingot. Roll ingot into a billet to fit base metal. Cut rolled silver to size of base metal. Bond by brazing in a furnace. Wash and scrub composite billet. Rough roll, that is, reduce to about one and one-half inches thick, with one or more anneals, as required. Intermediate roll to about half-inch thick, annealing as required. Slit on slitting machine to width required. Pack and ship. As a rule, thinner gauges of material require more frequent annealing than the medium and larger thicknesses.

On the whole the set-up time between rolling jobs is negligible, provided the rolling mill is not being changed from gold to silver material, or vice versa, in which event the rolls in the rolling mill need to be changed. Slitting machines require considerable set-up time and may take from 20 minutes to an hour.

The illustrations (Exhibit A-1) show some of the principal items of equipment.

Parts Department

The two principal activities of the Parts Department are parts fabrication and assembly, and tool-and-die design, manufacture, and repair.

Parts fabrication is performed by punch presses, cold-heading machines, multislides, coil winders, and other types of metal-forming

equipment utilizing coils of flat stock or wire. The majority of parts orders are single, complete units, but some orders require two or more component parts to be assembled. Assembly is accomplished manually, and parts are fastened together by welding, soldering, and staking.

Set-up times for the Parts Department equipment average about an hour per order. About 10 per cent of the orders run for 40 hours or more on a single machine; the large majority run for one to eight hours after being set up on a machine. Some 5 to 10 per cent of the orders run less than an hour after being set up, occasionally as little as 20 minutes.

The toolroom manufactures and repairs dies for the Parts Department presses, using a variety of lathes, milling machines, drill presses and grinders, as well as special precision equipment such as two jig borers and a jig grinder. The tool-design section of 12 men and a supervisor designs dies and fixtures used in the Parts Department.

The illustrations (Exhibit A-2) show some of the principal items of equipment in the Parts Department and two views of the toolroom.

Pittsfield Manufacturing Company

George Brown, Controller of the Pittsfield Manufacturing Company, said, "We have too much money tied up in inventory. Worse yet, despite the millions of dollars invested we lack some of the parts needed to assemble the machines shown on our manufacturing schedule." Company sales and year-end inventory position for the years 1951–1964 and six months of 1965 are shown in the following table.

Year	Sales	Index Number for Sales (Avg. 1951–1964 = 100)	Inventory on Dec. 31	Index Number for Inventory (Avg. 1951–1964 = 100)	Inventory as a Per Cent of Sales
	(000)		(000)		
1951	$16,269	68	$11,548	144	71.0
1952	38,631	161	10,986	137	28.4
1953	34,466	143	8,908	111	25.8
1954	19,182	80	6,091	76	31.8
1955	19,084	79	6,179	77	32.4
1956	25,217	105	6,919	87	27.4
1957	22,447	93	6,634	83	29.6
1958	13,050	54	4,958	62	38.0
1959	21,934	91	6,989	87	31.9
1960	22,099	92	8,465	106	38.3
1961	22,602	94	7,502	94	33.2
1962	26,708	111	8,605	108	32.2
1963	26,580	111	9,693	121	36.5
1964	28,287	118	8,456	106	30.0
1965	15,671 (6 mo.)		9,988 (June 30)		

Company Background

The Pittsfield Manufacturing Company is the direct descendant of a manufacturer of machine tools started in Pittsfield in 1880. Milling machines, grinding machines, and lathes have from the start constituted the company's main product lines. Over the years, the company has been highly regarded for the design and performance of its machines, with its small milling machines receiving particularly favorable acceptance since 1935. Numerically controlled machine tools, a recent addition to the company's line, are selling at an increasing rate. Like other manufacturers of machine tools, however, the company has gone through great swings in business activity, and the managers consider themselves to be in a highly competitive business.

The Physical System

The physical system for manufacturing machine tools consists of two major steps. First the necessary parts are formed with high precision from either castings or bar stock. Additional parts such as hardware and electrical motors are purchased. The second step is the assembly of the required parts into machines. Twelve thousand different parts (excluding hardware) are used in 40 different machines.

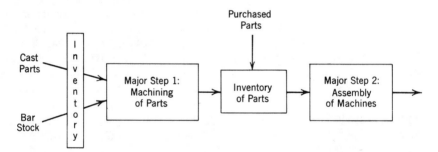

This simplified diagram of the two-step process shows the heart of the manufacturing operation. But the system is wholly dependent on a number of other activities, including the designing of the machine tools, the planning of manufacturing capacity, the hiring, training, and supervision of workers for precision work, the advance ordering of bar stock, castings, and other components, the control of quality, and the scheduling of work through the shop.

The Control System

In the judgment of the Pittsfield managers, the plan followed in the scheduling of work through the machining operations (Major Step

1) has substantial influence on both the size of inventories and the availability of parts for assembly. The plan in use for many years, the "allotment system," was largely replaced, starting in 1961, by the "economic order quantity system." Both systems will be described.

The "allotment system" tied the manufacture of parts to the assembly of specific lots of machines. For example, to meet expected sales it was decided to assemble 18 milling machines, type K4, in the third quarter of 1960. Working from parts lists, clerks "exploded" the requirement of 18 machines into a list of the necessary parts showing the needed quantity of each. Working from lead times, the clerks calculated the dates to start manufacture of each part for the lot of 18 machines. They added the requirements for identical parts to be used in other machine models and needed at about the same time. Thus every part being machined, with the exception of allowances for scrap, was destined for a particular lot of machines scheduled for assembly.

The "allotment system" had two drawbacks: (1) Since lead time ran as high as nine months, it was necessary to schedule the manufacture of parts well in advance of assembly, but it was difficult to forecast sales this far ahead. (2) The orders for lots of parts tended to hit the factory in bunches. The resulting overload and alternate underload had the most impact on the first machine operations: stock cutoff and turret lathe.

The New System

To overcome these difficulties, managers at Pittsfield decided to manufacture parts in advance and to stock these. The revised system called for the manufacture of parts in economic order quantities (hence the name "economic order quantity" given to the whole system) and the maintaining of an inventory from which parts were withdrawn for the assembly of machines. The company continued to manufacture infrequently sold products, prototype machines, and first-production lots under the "allotment system." One manager explained, "Since first-production lots are always followed by many design changes, we make only what's needed."

As the new system went into operation the following decision rules were developed.

RULE 1. Lot size is determined by the formula

$$Q = \sqrt{AMR}$$

in which:

Q = Economic order quantity

A = "Accounting information" = $\dfrac{2}{K}$

K = 0.25 the annual charge for carrying inventory, comprising:
    0.18 the opportunity cost for the use of money
    0.04 taxes
    0.02 insurance
    0.01 obsolescence

M = "Manufacturing information" = $\dfrac{S}{C}$

S = Set-up cost per lot

C = Cost of one part

R = Annual usage rate

RULE 2.   Every four months the Sales Department projects sales by machine type for a twelve-month period.   At the same times, but independently, Frank March, Director of Production Planning and Control, projects his twelve-month estimates of sales using (1) his knowledge of factory capacities, observed trends in factory load, and anticipated plans for changes such as design changes, and (2) an exponential smoothing model applied to past sales. The form of the model, in which "period" may equal a month, four months, or a year, is:

Forecast for next period =
$$\alpha \text{ (demand in last period)} + (1 - \alpha) \text{ (prior forecast)}$$

The value used for α (alpha) was 0.3.

Next comes the reconciliation of the forecasts (the Sales Department's figures and Mr. March's projections); the Sales Manager, the Division Manager, and Mr. March meet to arrive at one set of figures.   Each man judges the reasons for variations.   Much depends on both the explanation for differences and how strongly a man feels about his figures.   For instance, in their latest meeting, the Sales Manager had substantiated one low figure on the basis of his knowledge of good trade acceptance of a competing machine and one high figure on the basis of strongly favorable trade reaction to a new Pittsfield machine.   The Director of Production Planning and Control had supported one high figure with his knowledge that increased out-

put had enabled the factory to catch up with demand. The figures agreed upon become the forecast.

RULE 3. A clerk takes the average of five figures consisting of the forecast by machine type arrived at through the procedure of Rule 2 and the corresponding actual sales for each of the last four years. She then calculates limits 20 per cent above this average and 20 per cent below. If the forecast (Rule 2) lies outside of these limits, the forecast is reduced (or raised) so that it does not exceed (or fall below) the five-number average plus or minus 20 per cent. This figure for each type of machine becomes the expected sales.

RULE 4. The figures for expected sales by machine type (Rule 3) are "exploded" to determine parts requirements, and requirements for identical parts are combined. This figure becomes the value of R to be used in the lot size formula, Rule 1.

RULE 5. George Brown said, "If we are in error on the lot-size figure, we are in no great trouble; but if we are in error on our reorder point, we can be in serious difficulty. We'll run out of parts needed to meet our assembly schedule or, equally bad, we'll be carrying an unnecessary inventory of parts."

The reorder point formula is

$$P = U + SS$$

where

P = Reorder point

U = Expected usage of the part during the lead time required to manufacture the part. (See Rules 6 and 7 for the calculation of U.)

SS = Safety stock, which is set at 2.4 $\sqrt{U}$ under the assumption that this will prevent out-of-stock conditions in 99 per cent of all cases. The basic assumption is made that demand actually follows a Poisson distribution but that distribution of demand is sufficiently close to the normal distribution to allow the use of a table of areas under the normal curve in calculating probabilities.

Substituting, the reorder point equation is written as

$$P = U + 2.4 \sqrt{U}$$

Because of the importance attached to the reorder point, U is recalculated three times a year in the light of revised lead times and the latest forecast of sales as determined in Rule 2. (For use here, the forecast obtained by Rule 2 is not modified by Rule 3.)

RULE 6. Lead time, in days, for each part is calculated as the sum of five items:

Item a: One day for each move between work stations (three days for the move from the foundry to the first work station).

Item b: The sum of the set-up times in hours for all required operations ÷ 12 (12 = hours per day).

Item c: The sum of the allowed work times in hours to machine one part × the number of parts in the lot (Q) ÷ 12 (12 = hours per day).

Item d: The sum of the queueing time for each operation as set by experience, and ranging from zero days for bench work such as burring through two days for operations such as light milling machine work and three days for boring, which involved tape-controlled machines, which were heavily loaded, and up to as high as ten days (an extreme case of queueing allowance for the automatic screw machines to allow extra time for the grouping of similar work to take advantage of partial setups).

Item e: Fifteen days for the processing of necessary paperwork.

RULE 7. Expected usage during lead time (the U of Rule 5) is determined as follows:

Equation 1

$$\frac{\text{Forecasted annual requirement (from Rule 2)}}{\text{Number of work days in the year (240)}} = \left(\begin{matrix} \text{Daily} \\ \text{requirement} \\ \text{rate} \end{matrix} \right)$$

Equation 2

$$\left(\begin{matrix} \text{Expected usage} \\ \text{during lead time} \end{matrix} \right) = \left(\begin{matrix} \text{Daily} \\ \text{requirement} \\ \text{rate} \end{matrix} \right) \times \left(\begin{matrix} \text{Lead time} \\ \text{in days} \end{matrix} \right)$$

RULE 8. An order for parts of quantity Q (Rule 1) is issued when the inventory of parts in the stockroom plus the quantity of parts on order minus back orders are equal to or less than the reorder point P (Rule 5).

RULE 9. Orders for parts are issued as if the manufacturing capacity were unlimited. Only three machine tools used in the factory are scheduled with specific demand against capacity. All three are large, numerically controlled boring machines which perform many operations in long cycles. The rest of the manufacturing capacity, including a number of smaller numerically controlled machines, is not scheduled. Mr. March said, "We studied the situation and found that

in our decisions to release orders for manufacture we would act no differently with or without knowledge of machine loading. Where necessary, we seek to increase capacity, not to cancel or postpone business. We do, of course, plan in advance for subcontracting or other means to close the gap between our forecasted demand and our projected in-house capacity."

Another executive said, "If we were to load against capacity, we would have to know what our capacity is. How do you measure capacity? I'm sure that capacity is not equal to available machine hours or even clock-hours of labor input. We have found that the productivity of our labor force increases whenever the percentage of our jobs on incentives increases.[1] And just as you would expect, when we introduce new models or add substantially to our labor force, productivity per man declines. Capacity is influenced by floor space, particularly in assembly. We have allowed ten weeks to assemble and test our A42 machines, of which we have sold two a month. A ten-week period has been realistic for the high quality job needed, but now despite limited floor space we seek to raise output to four a month. If you asked me what one thing determines capacity the most, I would say that it is the capacity of bottleneck operations. The two boring machines which work exclusively and full time on the tables of our small milling machines determine the effective capacity of all preceding and subsequent operations. In short, capacity is a most difficult thing to measure."

RULE 10. If the calculated lot size Q is greater than the forecasted yearly usage, the lot size is reduced to equal the amount forecasted. This practice is the opposite of that followed in a sister company, the Pittsfield Tap and Die Company, where the full quantity Q is invariably manufactured even if, as in extreme cases, $Q =$ three years' requirements.

RULE 11. The rate at which machines are assembled is based on the twelve-month forecast of sales as revised each four months (Rule 2). The plan calls for the assembly of the fast-selling machines "on speculation." For example, if the rate of sales lives up to the forecast, it is expected that three surface grinders will be completed each month and orders will be received for these three machines. The plan allows a small storage space for machines completed ahead of orders, and

---

[1] Another manager estimated that a worker's output doubled when he went on incentives. To take advantage of this gain, Pittsfield used incentives based on stop-watch standards for most jobs and based on estimated standards for short-run jobs.

when orders temporarily run ahead of production, the plan anticipates that customers may wait for a month. The lot sizes in which parts are withdrawn from inventory and machines assembled are based on the twelve-month forecasted rate of sales, according to the formula in the following table.

(A) Twelve-Month Forecast of Sales in Units	(B) Number of Assembly Lots per Year	(C) Lot Size	(D) Frequency of Issuing Lot Orders (D = weeks or months in a year ÷ B)
over 90	8	over 11	6 weeks
41 to 90	4	10 to 23	3 months
26 to 40	3	8 to 14	4 months
6 to 25	2	3 to 13	6 months
up to 5	1	up to 5	12 months

The number of lots per year is set in order to balance two considerations: (1) to achieve withdrawal of parts from stock on a fairly regular basis to avoid undue fluctuations in the rate of withdrawal, and (2) to avoid undue loads on the men withdrawing parts from stock as would be the case if lots were substantially smaller than shown in column C. It is felt also that once parts have been issued from stock to the assembly floor there is less control, and hence less certain inventory position, on these parts.

Experience in 1963–1964

Exhibit 1 contains information taken from the order cards of four representative parts, showing how the rules were applied.

In 1963 and 1964 the new system (economic lot size and inventory of parts) satisfied the objectives sought. The load on the primary operations—stock cutoff and turret lathe—was smoothed out, and the stock of parts allowed a reduction in the lead time for the assembly of machines. Other advantages accrued from the increase in lot size: (1) total time required for setups was reduced, and (2) with longer runs of some parts, foremen felt that they could afford to invest more time in methods studies preceding the setting of time standards. (Machinists were on incentive wages.)

EXHIBIT 1 PITTSFIELD MANUFACTURING COMPANY

INFORMATION TAKEN FROM FOUR ORDER CARDS

Part number	852–1,–2,–3		3914–1		4948–1		17651–1	
Part name	Table		Gear Washer		Driving Shaft		Feed Lever	
Order history (date and	Date	Qty.	Date	Qty.	Date	Qty.	Date	Qty
quantity of parts ordered								
to be machined)	5–11–60	58	5–18–62	50	2– 7–61	15	2–13–59	159
	4–18–61	36	3– 5–63	35	3–17–61	90	9–17–59	95
	Changed to		6– 7–63	25	5–16–61	110	11–18–59	100
	EOQ System		Changed to		11– 2–61	80	2–16–60	120
	3–29–63	14	EOQ System		1–12–62	115	3–23–61	25
	5–22–63	14	12– 5–63	62	4–10–62	95	9–11–61	105
	1–17–64	14	6–17–65	62	Changed to		1–30–62	95
	3–25–64	14			EOQ System		Changed to	
	5–20–64	14			6– 7–62	156	EOQ System	
	9– 1–64	14			10–25–62	156	4–16–62	82
	11– 4–64	16			6–21–63	142	7–18–63	79
	2–24–65	23			10–11–63	142	11– 4–63	79
	6– 3–65	20			1– 8–64	142	5–18–64	79
	6–29–65	20			7–16–64	142	12– 1–64	79
	7–30–65	20			12–16–64	152	3–23–65	77
	9–29–65	20			4– 2–65	145	6–29–65	73
					9–21–65	148		
Order information as of								
August, 1965:								
Twelve-month forecast	124		59		434		327	
Costs:								
Setup (labor only)	$ 98.70		$ 2.40		$28.29		$18.30	
Paperwork charge	12.25		12.25		12.25		12.25	
Labor per piece	69.66		0.05		3.46		4.71	
Material per piece	475.58		0.05		2.59		4.42	
Lead time, days	95		28		98		49	
Lead time stock, units	49		7		177		67	
Safety stock, units	17		6		32		20	
Reorder point, units	66		13		209		87	
EOQ	14		59		148		85	

During 1963 and three quarters of 1964, sales forecasts for the ensuing four-month periods lay within ten per cent of the subsequent actual demand.

Experience in 1965

During the first seven months of 1965, the experience under the new system was complicated by a sharp upturn in orders received. The first indication of increased volume came in October 1964 when orders exceeded forecasts by 20 per cent. This upturn was thought to be a response to a 30-day advance notice of an increase in prices, and this interpretation seemed to be confirmed in November 1964 when orders fell to expected levels. In December 1964, however,

orders rose again 25 per cent above forecasts. This higher rate of bookings, with some fluctuations, continued through the first seven months of 1965.

There was a pronounced effect on inventory. At first the protective inventory stock afforded a welcome reservoir of parts to help the Assembly Department meet the higher rate of output. By August 1965, however, the stocks of a majority of the most-required parts were depleted. The inventory was in an unbalanced position, with good quantities of many parts on hand, but with out-of-stock running as high as 40 per cent of the parts needed for some assemblies. The shortage of parts was not accompanied by a reduction in the dollar value of inventory (see figures in the first table of this case).

Shortages led to the expediting of parts. The supervisor of stock said, "When we try to fill a bill-of-materials for assembly and find shortages—and we do find shortages in a majority of cases—we expedite the parts. Typically, this may mean breaking ten parts loose from a lot of 40 already in the shop and rushing these to each of the remaining operations, where they are placed at the front of the queue. Of course, this means delaying the end of the queue. It's not at all unusual to see parts that have waited over 60 days for one machine operation. Right now I can count on getting expedited parts within three weeks." In July 1965, five men worked to expedite parts for the assembly of small milling machines, whereas this function previously had required only one part-time expeditor. One supervisor commented, "Keep in mind that expeditors don't machine parts."

The foreman of heavy-parts machining thought that adherence to the economic lot sizes severely restricted flexibility. He cited the steel forging, machined to close tolerances to hold tools in the Pittsfield turret lathe. The complex operation for drilling and boring holes in this part required nearly two hours machining time per part after a lengthy setup. Consequently, the run of a full economic lot size tied up a unique machine tool for 93 hours. If work on the steel forging was not interrupted, a large queue of short-cycle jobs accumulated, none of which could be "expedited" through this work station.

In response to the demands of heavy sales, Pittsfield placed more assembly and machining sections on a two-shift basis and increased the hours worked variously to as high as 45 and 55 hours per week (55 hours = five eleven-hour work days). Mr. March's production control operation increased the rate at which work was released to the shop to 19,000 standard hours per week. Held back by both the inability to hire needed men and the reduced efficiency under sudden heavy loads, the shop succeeded in liquidating the load at

EXHIBIT 2   Pittsfield Manufacturing Company

cumulative work load for 1965
(Updated July, 1965)

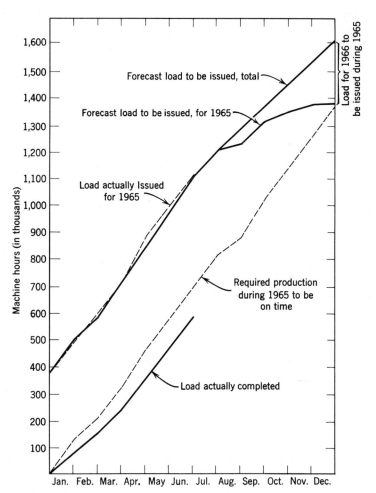

a rate of only 17,000 standard hours per week. Actual and planned work input and work output for 1965 are shown in Exhibit 2. As soon as it became apparent that the plant could not meet demand, Pittsfield increased the rate of subcontracting with results that varied all the way from quality parts delivered on time to parts which arrived weeks late only to be rejected for failure to meet specifications.

During the first six months of 1965, deliveries of Pittsfield machines lengthened from 6 to 12 weeks.

Comments by Executives

Three Pittsfield executives commented on inventory in July 1965. Mr. Brown said, "We compare our inventory turnover with that of our 'target competitors.'[2] Here are some comparable 1964 figures for both inventory turnover and return on investment:

	Turnover*	Return on Investment† (per cent)
Brown and Sharpe Manufacturing Co.	3.3	7.25
The Cincinnati Milling Machine Co.	3.8	8.27
Ex-Cell-O Corp.	3.5	10.67
Gisholt Machine Co.	2.9	5.24
Kearney & Trecker Corp.	3.2	6.10
The Monarch Machine Tool Co.	3.4	11.77
The National Acme Co.	2.6	14.37
New Britain Machine Co.	2.8	9.09
PITTSFIELD MANUFACTURING CO.	3.3	7.08
Sundstrand Corp.	2.3	7.89
The Warner & Swasey Co.	3.3	20.37

$$* \text{ Turnover} = \frac{\text{Dollar Sales}}{\text{Year-End Dollar Value of Inventory}}$$

$$\dagger \begin{matrix} \text{Return on} \\ \text{Investment} \end{matrix} = \left(\text{Sales} \div \begin{matrix} \text{Total} \\ \text{Investment} \\ \text{in Working} \\ \text{Capital and} \\ \text{Fixed Assets} \end{matrix} \right) \times \left(\begin{matrix} \text{Earnings} \\ \text{Before} \\ \text{Taxes} \end{matrix} \div \text{Sales} \right) \times 100$$

"In my judgment, we can substantially improve our inventory turnover. Please don't misunderstand me, however. I don't seek turnover as an end objective. No ratio has importance unless it contributes to profit."

Mr. March said, "Accountability for inventory turnover rests more

---

[2] Pittsfield executives selected other companies with which they competed for sales and analyzed published financial statements to determine key ratios for purposes of comparison.

directly with me than with anyone else in the organization. It takes roughly three months to manufacture our 'average' part, if there is such a thing, and another three weeks to assemble an 'average' machine. Call if four months from start to shipment. And on this rough basis I think we ought to achieve an inventory turnover of three. But I wonder if there isn't a more scientific way to determine what inventory turnover should be from our rules for scheduling and inventory."

Ralph Adams, President, said, "Perhaps this period of sudden up-turn in business is not the best time to ask for a reduction of inventory, but I am particularly concerned about the size of our inventory relative to sales if business falls off. Our periods of heavy sales have always been followed by slack periods.

"At best, forecasting is something short of perfect, but we can make sure that we apply the best possible decision rules to our forecasts. And I'm not sure that we are using the best rules."

Conclusion

When reading the case before its release, Mr. Brown and Mr. March said to the case writer, "Your description presents our method of operation in an accurate, logical way. But we find one thing under-stated, and that is the extreme complexity of dealing with thousands of high precision parts and hundreds of machines and men when the whole system is subject to interruptions, changes in priority, human error, engineering changes, and the demands of sharply increasing volume. Still, if our jobs were otherwise they would not represent the same challenge."

PART 5. THE PLANNING AND CONTROL OF

OPERATIONS AND OF INVENTORIES:

ANALYTICAL TECHNIQUES AND

INFORMATION SYSTEMS

Reference Note on Quantitative Methods
for Production Management

This note briefly discusses a number of mathematical approaches which have proven useful in the solution of common production management problems. The focus of this book on cases does not permit a broad treatment of mathematical tools and their application. However, the introductory treatment here is not meant to imply that such tools are not important in production management. They are, and they are becoming increasingly more important. Indeed, production managers in the future will rely, in part, on a basic grasp of mathematical techniques and will find themselves placing increasing emphasis on these tools and on the staff specialists, operations researchers, and management scientists, who are intimately familiar with them.

Some of the cases in this book lend themselves to analysis with one or more quantitative techniques. In others, an understanding of quantitative approaches will shed light on the problems raised in the case even though complete data are not available to support the full development of mathematical models.

Simulation[1]

In any tally of the mathematical approaches useful in production management, simulation must surely be reckoned as one of the most powerful and widely used. Successful applications of simulation have been reported in fields as widely diverse as military logistics, mainte-

---

[1] The section on simulation is adapted from "Simulation" by W. K. Holstein and W. R. Soukup, Institute Paper 23, Institute for Quantitative Research in Economics and Management, School of Industrial Administration, Purdue University.

nance, economics, and sociology. Seldom has a technique received so much attention in so little time from both industry and the academic community. Undoubtedly, the recent widespread availability of computers, usually required in simulation studies, is largely responsible for this "explosion" of simulation.

Simulation has not, however, been accepted everywhere as a *new* approach to problems. If it is true that a simulation is anything that "represents reality," as a map represents a land mass, then simulation is certainly not new. Pencil and paper representations of geometric figures, blueprints and floor plans, atomic structures, and chemical reaction equations are all in a sense simulation. Webster says that simulation is a representation of reality, and, in fact, all of these examples represent reality in one way or another. They all have a common ingredient in that each of the illustrations uses some kind of a model—either abstract of physical—to represent reality.

On this basis it might be said that simulation occurs whenever a model of any sort is employed. The real difficulty with this statement is that no matter how true it is, it does not focus attention on the level of simulation of interest here: the use of mathematical expressions and equations which closely approximate random fluctuations in the simulated system and which are often so complex that it is impossible to solve them without the aid of electronic computers. This note describes this form of simulation and provides a framework for distinguishing between what appear to be two distinctly different kinds of simulation. It also presents a detailed example of a simulation model.

It can be said that a mathematical model is a mathematical expression (one or more equations or inequalities, for example) which to some degree represents an actual system or set of phenomena. This mathematical expression can be used either to (1) predict the value of significant variables or (2) determine the value of the significant variables such that some predetermined function[2] is optimized. The first is called a *predictive* model, the second an *optimizing* model. The differences between the two models can be shown by considering an example of each.

A predictive model might be used to estimate next month's rainfall. Here the significant variable, inches of rainfall, is one over which there is no control but whose value is sought. The model might do nothing more than average the rainfall data for the past several

---

[2] The function might be an expression for total profits, which should be maximized, or total costs, which should be minimized.

months to obtain an estimate for the next month's rainfall. On the other hand, the model could be made extremely complex, taking into account such things as present conditions of upper layers of the earth's atmosphere, temperature data for the past several months, etc. Regardless of its simplicity or complexity, the model yields an estimate of an unknown variable.

In contrast, an optimizing model is employed to determine the "best" value for some variable which is under control. An example of an optimizing model is the economic lot size (or optimal order quantity) formula.[3] Here the objective is to determine the order quantity which minimizes the sum of order costs and inventory carrying costs. In this case the significant variable, order quantity, is completely under management's control and the model is used to optimize its value.

In both the predictive and optimizing models, once the model is specified, replication of that model with given conditions will always yield the same results. In the classical model relating force, mass, and acceleration, $F = ma$, application of the model for a given force and given mass always yields the same value for acceleration.

The important point here is that this property of "invariability" is not only common to both predictive and optimizing models, but also is essential in each case. Obviously, a model which predicted a different value for next month's rainfall (given the same conditions) each time it was used, or one which indicated a different economic order quantity each time it was calculated, given the same carrying costs, order costs, and demand rate, would be of little value.

It is noted, however, that "invariate" results are not necessarily "correct" results with respect to the actual situation since correct results depend on how well the model itself represents the real system. For example, the model $F = 2ma$ yields results which are as invariable as those produced by the model $F = ma$, but which do not describe experimental observations nearly as well.

This note considers next some of the current computer simulation activities and asks the question, "Do these simulations differ in kind (not just in complexity) from traditional applications of models?" In one very important respect they do differ in kind.

---

[3] One version of the economic lot size formula is $Q = \sqrt{2AS/i}$ where:

Q = size of an individual purchase (or production lot)
A = cost of placing an order
S = annual usage
i = cost of carrying inventory ($ per unit per year)
(see page 369 for the derivation of this formula).

Many real systems—the demand for items from inventory on any one day, for example—include fluctuations which cannot be predicted precisely. In other words, these systems contain a random element governed by laws of chance. The implication of this observation is that any model which expresses fixed relationships among variables of a system involving chance will be unrealistic, since the random fluctuations are ignored.

Some of the current work in simulation involves models which do provide for random fluctuations of significant variables within the model itself. These are often referred to as Monte Carlo simulation models—Monte Carlo because the element of chance is contained in the model in addition to specified relationships among the variables. These models in many cases behave much more like the real system they represent than do analytical models or nonstochastic models, which do not contain a random element.

Thus Monte Carlo simulation models differ from the more traditional models in that they do not yield invariable results. With given conditions, successive applications of a Monte Carlo simulation model yield results which vary because of the operation of the random element built into the model. In other words, Monte Carlo simulation models generate empirical data rather than exact solutions.

How are such models useful? If the results vary from one computation to the next, can the model be employed either to predict or to solve for the optimal value of some variable? Not in the usual sense. The Monte Carlo model yields numerous different results, each of which could (and eventually would) be produced by the real system being simulated (assuming that the model is a good representation of that system). Certainly, then, as a purely predictive device, the Monte Carlo model is unsatisfying. Similarly, the model does not lend itself to solving directly for optimal values. The Monte Carlo model can, however, be used to *test* suggested solutions, and more will be said about this later.

Although Monte Carlo simulation models always contain random elements within the model to simulate random fluctuations in the system being studied, it is possible to have a simulation model without a random element. Such models are usually referred to simply as "simulation models" or "nonstochastic simulation models." Indeed, many so-called "heuristic models" are in fact simulation models without a random element. An example of a nonstochastic simulation is a model of a job shop designed to test dispatching rules, or rules for deciding which job to run first on an available machine when

there is more than one job waiting to be run.   Given descriptions of a shop (i.e., the machines in the shop and their capacities) and a job file (a description of the routing and machine time requirements of all jobs waiting to be run in the shop), a simulation model can be used to compare, for example, the dispatch rule, "run the job with the earliest due date," with the rule, "run the job with the shortest processing time on the next operation."   Such a model needs no random element but simply schedules the machines according to the given dispatch rule, assuming that each job takes just as long on each machine as the expected time given on the routing in the job file.

Of course, no model is developed and run without an objective. The objective of the job-shop model just described might be to compare the average length of time that each job is in the shop in consequence of two alternative rules.   Another objective might be to compare the due-date performance or per cent on-time deliveries through use of the two rules.

As a final comment on this example of a nonstochastic simulation, it is interesting to note that this model could easily be transformed into a Monte Carlo simulation model by adding a random element to the machine time of each job as it is "run" in the simulated shop. For example, instead of using two hours of machine time for a job with an expected time of two hours in the job file, a random time could be drawn from a normal distribution with a mean of two hours and a standard deviation of 0.3 hours.   The time actually used in the model would then be anywhere between one and three hours and might simulate actual conditions in the shop better than using the two-hour expected value.

Simulation has been described as being "to the operations analyst what a pilot model or experiment is to a natural scientist."[4]   The analogy is a good one.   Often a production process is so complicated that pilot plants are constructed to try out various raw-material combinations and operating temperatures, pressures, and other critical factors.   The well-designed pilot plant is useful because it behaves like the real (larger) system being studied and is much less expensive. The pilot plant itself does not produce optimal solutions, but it does allow the builders to experiment and thereby find a solution which is at least close to the optimum.

Simulation similarly allows experimentation with a model which

---

[4] Robert Dorfman, "Operations Research," *American Economic Review,* September 1960.

behaves like, but is much less expensive than, the real system. In addition, simulation has the advantage of testing results much more rapidly than experimenting with either the real system or a pilot plant. Also, it may be possible to develop a simulation model in cases where a physical pilot plant is impossible. Simulation models do not generate the alternatives to be tested any more than a pilot plant generates values for temperature, pressure, etc., which should be tried. Possible solutions to be tested by the simulation model must be determined independently of the model itself.

Finally, we should note that simulation models should not be regarded as a substitute for more rigorous models if more rigorous models are feasible. One author has said, "It is certainly true that whenever an operations research problem can be reduced to a simple model and solved analytically, there is no need for simulation."[5]

Some characteristics of Monte Carlo simulation models (i.e., built-in random element; solutions that vary) are not immediately obvious. These characteristics can easily be seen by examining an actual model such as the one presented on the following pages. The chief virtue of the model presented here is its simplicity; the point in presenting this example is to show the characteristics of a Monte Carlo simulation model without an undue amount of detailed information.

Consider a trucking firm which has a fixed stock of trucks. The firm operates its own repair shop, which has a specific capacity in terms of the number of trucks that can be serviced at one time.

The firm receives "orders" for trucks on a daily basis and has no contracts to provide any trucks for any period longer than one day. The total number of trucks available to satisfy demand is limited to the trucks owned by the firm. A typical day includes the following activities:

1. The demand for trucks is determined by adding together the individual orders received.
2. The number of trucks available to satisfy demand is calculated by subtracting the number of trucks needing repairs from the total fleet.
3. As much of the demand as possible is met. If demand is greater than available trucks, the excess demand goes unfilled and is not carried forward to the next day. If the trucks available exceed demand, the extra trucks remain idle for the rest of the day.

---

[5] J. Harling, "Simulation Techniques in Operations Research," *Operations Research Quarterly,* Vol. 9, No. 1, March 1958. Reprinted in *Operations Research,* May-June 1958.

4. Some trucks in use during the day will malfunction. It is assumed that only one type of malfunction can occur and that any truck that malfunctions requires two days service time in the repair shop. When a truck malfunctions it is towed to an area near the repair shop. The job on which the truck was working is assumed to have been completed before the breakdown. Thus at the end of any day there is a queue of trucks outside the repair shop waiting for repairs. Trucks are not pulled into the repair shop at the time the malfunction occurs, even if there is space available in the shop.

5. The next morning, trucks on which repairs have been completed are removed from the repair shop and placed back in the pool of available trucks.

6. Trucks in the queue waiting for repairs are then moved into the repair shop until either the shop is filled to capacity or there are no more trucks in the queue.

7. The demand for trucks for the new day is then figured, demand met to the extent to which trucks are available, and the entire cycle of activities is repeated.

Figure 1 shows an operations diagram for this hypothetical system. It is assumed that the demand for trucks fluctuates greatly from

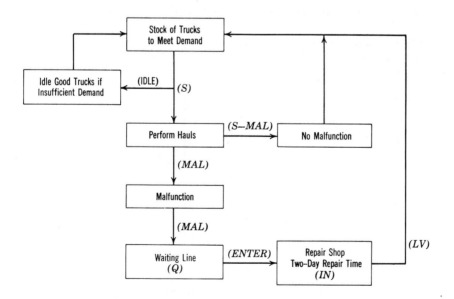

FIGURE 1. Operations diagram for trucking problem.

day to day due to conditions outside the control of the trucking firm. By analyzing historical records the firm can determine the frequency of various demand levels that have occurred in the past. From these frequencies, a probability function can be constructed which shows the probability of occurrence of possible demand levels. This example limits consideration to four possible demand levels as indicated in Figure 2.

It is further assumed that there are no regular fluctuations in demand such as seasonal cycles or regular "busy" days during the week. Thus, referring to Figure 2, it is just as likely that demand on any particular day will be 100 trucks as it is that demand will equal 25 trucks. The most likely demand is 75 trucks, which is six times as probable as a demand of 25 or 100.

The malfunction rate is similar to the demand for trucks in that it is never known exactly how many trucks will break down on any given day. Ignoring the complications of the age or condition of each truck, historical records will give an estimate of the probability that a truck will malfunction. In this model the assumption is made that the probability that a truck in use will malfunction on any given day is 0.2. Conversely, the probability that a truck will not malfunction is 0.8.

These probabilities for truck malfunction do not imply that each day 20 per cent of the trucks in use will malfunction—only that each truck in use has a 20 per cent chance of malfunctioning on any day.

At this juncture a question might be raised as to why a probability

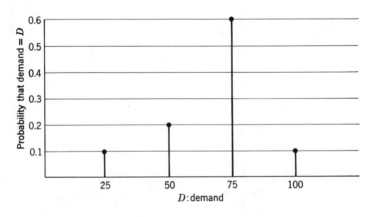

FIGURE 2. Probability function for demand.

function is used instead of actual data. Undoubtedly there are models where historical data can and should be used directly. Often, however, a probability function must be employed. Whenever the random element is affected by the solutions to be tested, historical data cannot be used directly. To use historical data to compute the number of malfunctions, it would be necessary to compute the percentage of trucks in operation which malfunctioned on each day and apply these percentages day by day to calculate malfunctions in the simulation model. This procedure might require considerable calculation and storage capacity in the computer and therefore be less convenient than using a probability function.

In other instances, the historical data readily available may not include some of the more extreme conditions the model builder believes may occur. That is, the record of the values actually taken on by a variable in the past represents only a sample from the total number of possible values it could assume. Hence a probability distribution which can be used to generate as much simulated data as is desired may provide a more complete and therefore more accurate test than historical data. Especially where the amount of actual data is limited, perhaps because the system is new or has been significantly changed recently, adequate testing of proposed solutions may require the use of a random element produced according to a probability distribution.

The management of the trucking firm would have two important variables under its control: the size of the fleet (i.e., the number of trucks owned) and the capacity of the repair shop. To help determine the best values for these two variables, management might want to try several combinations of fleet size and repair shop capacity and for each combination answer questions like the following:

1. How often would the firm be unable to meet demand and, when demand is not met, how many trucks are short?
2. How often will the firm have idle good trucks available and how many good trucks will be idle?
3. What per cent of the time will the shop be filled to capacity, or how much excess capacity exists in the shop?

A mathematical model of the trucking firm which would answer these questions is a Monte Carlo simulation model in which neither the demand for trucks nor the number of malfunctions for any particular day can be specified in advance.

Such a model can be constructed as follows:

Assume a fleet size of 100 trucks and a shop capacity of 25 trucks. Let:[6]

$$i = \text{day under consideration (an index)}$$
$$D = \text{demand for trucks}$$
$$S = \text{number of trucks supplied}$$
$$Q = \text{number of trucks in the queue outside the repair shop}$$
$$IN = \text{number of trucks in the repair shop}$$
$$LV = \text{number of (repaired) trucks taken out of the shop}$$
$$IDLE = \text{number of idle good trucks}$$
$$ENTER = \text{number of trucks put into the shop for repair}$$
$$MAL = \text{number of trucks that malfunction}$$

1. Determine demand for the day under consideration—D_i. A one-digit random number is generated and demand is determined by the value of this number.

If the random number is:	Set D_i equal to:
0	25 trucks
1,2	50 trucks
3,4,5,6,7,8	75 trucks
9	100 trucks

The probability of drawing any given one-digit number is 0.1. Thus the probability of setting demand equal to 25 trucks is 0.1, exactly the probability required. The probability of drawing the random number 1 or 2 is $0.1 + 0.1$ or 0.2, exactly the probability to attach to a demand of 50 trucks. (Clearly, one-digit random numbers can only be used to simulate probability distributions where all possible probabilities are multiples of 0.1. If, for example, the probability of a demand of 25 trucks was 0.15, two-digit random numbers from 00 to 99 would be used.)

2. Determine the number of trucks actually supplied—S_i. This value will equal either the number of trucks demanded (if there are enough good trucks to satisfy demand) or the number of good

---

[6] The notation used here is intended to aid the reader in identifying the variable in the model. Thus IN does not mean I multiplied by N, but rather a single variable. Similarly, $ENTER$ is also a single variable. This type of notation is often used in computer languages such as FORTRAN and COBOL.

trucks available (if demand cannot be met in full). Thus

$$\left.\begin{array}{l} S_i = D_i \\ \qquad \text{or} \\ S_i = 100 - [Q_{i-1} + (IN_{i-1} - LV_i)] \end{array}\right\} \quad \text{whichever is smaller}$$

where $Q_{i-1} + (IN_{i-1} - LV_i)$ represents the number of trucks that are broken down on the morning of day i.

3. Determine the number of idle good trucks—$IDLE_i$. This value is simply the number of good trucks available minus demand, when demand can be met—or zero when demand cannot be met.

$$\left.\begin{array}{l} IDLE = 0 \\ \qquad \text{or} \\ IDLE = 100 - Q_i - 1 - (IN_{i-1} - LV_i) - D_i \end{array}\right\} \quad \text{whichever is larger}$$

4. Determine the number of trucks in the shop—IN_i. This value can be found by subtracting the number of trucks discharged from the shop on the ith day from the number in the shop on the previous day and adding the trucks loaded into the shop on the ith day.

$$IN_i = IN_{i-1} - LV_i + ENTER_i$$

5. Determine the number of trucks in the queue—Q_i.

$$Q_i = Q_{i-1} - ENTER_i + MAL_i$$

The number of trucks in the queue on day i is the number in the queue on day $i - 1$ minus the trucks that left the queue on day i ($ENTER_i$) plus the trucks that entered the queue on day i (MAL_i). Note that this definition implies that the queue is measured at the end of the day after all malfunctioned trucks from that day are in the queue but before the shop is loaded the following morning.

These five steps yield the variables of interest to management. However, in order to calculate these variables it was assumed that values for the number of malfunctions, the number of trucks leaving the shop, and the number of trucks entering the shop (MAL_i, LV_i, and $ENTER_i$) were known.

6. The number of malfunctions on day i is generated in much the same way as was demand. First, a random number is generated for *each* truck in use on day i. If the number is 0 or 1 (0.2

probability), the truck is considered to have malfunctioned. If the random number is 2 through 9, no malfunction is assumed. Thus each truck is tested for malfunction individually, and MAL_i is simply the sum of the individual malfunctions. This procedure insures that a random element will exist in the malfunction rate and that the malfunctions on any given day will not be simply 20 per cent of the trucks in use on that day.

7. Since any truck which malfunctions requires two days to repair, the number leaving the shop on any day must equal the number of trucks which entered the shop two days previously, or

$$LV_i = ENTER_{i-2}$$

8. The number of trucks entering the shop on day i is limited by either the number in the queue or the available space in the repair shop. Since trucks are loaded into the shop early in the morning,

TABLE A   SIMULATION RESULTS

SHOP CAPACITY = 25

Day	Trucks Leaving Shop	Trucks into Shop	Trucks in Shop	Trucks Left in Queue after Shop Is Loaded in Morning	Trucks De-manded	Trucks Supplied	Idle Good Trucks	Trucks Malfunc-tioned	Trucks in Queue at End of Day
1	0	0	0	0	75	75	25	18	18
2	0	18	18	0	75	75	7	14	14
3	0	7	25	7	50	50	18	11	18
4	18	18	25	0	75	75	0	15	15
5	7	7	25	8	75	67	0	12	20
6	18	18	25	2	75	73	0	15	17
7	7	7	25	10	75	65	0	8	18
8	18	18	25	0	50	50	25	10	10
9	7	7	25	3	75	72	0	17	20
10	18	18	25	2	25	25	48	5	7
11	7	7	25	0	50	50	25	11	11
12	18	11	18	0	50	50	32	13	13
13	7	13	24	0	75	75	1	21	21
14	11	12	25	9	50	50	16	8	17
15	13	13	25	4	50	50	21	6	10
16	12	10	23	0	75	75	2	18	18
17	13	15	25	3	75	72	0	14	17
18	10	10	25	7	75	68	0	11	18
19	15	15	25	3	100	72	0	23	26
20	10	10	25	16	25	25	34	8	24
21	15	15	25	9	25	25	4	4	13
22	10	10	25	3	75	72	0	16	19
23	15	15	25	4	75	71	0	14	18
24	10	10	25	8	75	67	0	10	18
25	15	15	25	3	50	50	22	11	14

the size of the queue on the previous day is relevant.

$$ENTER_i = Q_{i-1}$$
or
$$ENTER_i = 25 - IN_{i-1} + LV_i$$
\} whichever is smaller

where 25 is the assumed shop capacity.

The foregoing equations and the demand and malfunction generators constitute the complete model for the simplified trucking firm. One can very quickly calculate the behavior of the system over time by setting initial values for the number of trucks in the queue and in the shop, and then generating data for as many days as desired.

This model was programmed for an IBM 1620 computer, using a fleet size of 100 trucks and two different shop capacities, 25 and 30 trucks. For each shop capacity 25 replications (days of experience) were run. Initial conditions for both cases included an empty shop and an empty queue. Results generated by the computer are shown in Tables A and B.

TABLE B   SIMULATION RESULTS

SHOP CAPACITY = 30

Day	Trucks Leaving Shop	Trucks into Shop	Trucks in Shop	Trucks Left in Queue after Shop Is Loaded in Morning	Trucks De-manded	Trucks Supplied	Idle Good Trucks	Trucks Malfunc-tioned	Trucks in Queue at End of Day
1	0	0	0	0	75	75	25	18	18
2	0	18	18	0	75	75	7	14	14
3	0	12	30	2	50	50	18	11	13
4	18	13	25	0	75	75	0	15	15
5	12	15	28	0	75	72	0	14	14
6	13	14	29	0	75	71	0	15	15
7	15	15	29	0	75	71	0	7	7
8	14	7	22	0	50	50	28	11	11
9	15	11	18	0	75	75	7	17	17
10	7	17	28	0	25	25	47	6	6
11	11	6	23	0	50	50	27	11	11
12	17	11	17	0	50	50	33	14	14
13	6	14	25	0	75	75	0	19	19
14	11	16	30	3	50	50	17	10	13
15	14	13	29	0	50	50	21	4	4
16	16	4	17	0	75	75	8	17	17
17	13	17	21	0	75	75	4	14	14
18	4	13	30	1	75	69	0	16	17
19	17	17	30	0	100	70	0	21	21
20	13	13	30	8	25	25	37	7	15
21	17	15	28	0	25	25	47	4	4
22	13	4	19	0	75	75	6	19	19
23	15	19	23	0	75	75	2	10	10
24	4	10	29	0	75	71	0	13	13
25	19	13	23	0	50	50	27	11	11

From these data it can be seen that demand was met 60 per cent of the time with a shop capacity of 25 trucks and 76 per cent of the time with a 30-truck shop capacity. The repair shop was full 80 per cent of the time with capacity = 25, 20 per cent of the time with capacity = 30. The average number of idle good trucks was 11.2 and 14.4.

It should now be clear that Monte Carlo simulation models generate emperical data rather than exact solutions. The fact that this kind of a model is used to test alternative solutions (e.g., test the solution 100 trucks and a 25-truck repair shop) rather than generate alternatives to be tested should also be clear.

In actual practice, the type of information presented in Tables A and B of the example problem would be of little value to the individual responsible for setting fleet size and shop capacity unless it was combined with several costs: the cost of buying and keeping a truck in the fleet, the cost of a unit of capacity in the repair shop, the cost of lost demand, etc. Also, several other combinations of fleet size and shop capacity should be tried in the search for a good solution to this problem.

Linear Programming

Linear programming is another important quantitative technique which has been widely used in production management. Like simulation, linear programming involves the use of a mathematical model. Unlike simulation, a linear programming model yields provably optimal results every time or, stated more cautiously, linear programming will always yield optimal results for the numbers used in the model.

Linear programming has found most fruitful application in problems involving the allocation of scarce resources. These are generally problems where there is a specific objective to be achieved, several alternatives for meeting the objectives, and some good reasons for not being able to use simply the best alternative to solve the entire problem (i.e., a limit on the supply of resources). Perhaps the most straightforward example of linear programming occurs in determining how much of what products to produce when production is limited (constrained) by capacity.

The method used in linear programming can be described as a step-by-step procedure for optimizing, actually maximizing or minimizing, a function where there are constraints on the values the function can assume because of scarce resources, technical or other considerations. The function to be optimized, called the objective function,

is usually a profit or cost function. The step-by-step procedure of linear programming is particularly useful where the alternatives for consideration are highly interrelated since the technique can keep track of all interrelationships within the problem. As will be shown later, linear programming also provides additional valuable information, including the costs of alternative answers to the problem.

The descriptive adjective "linear" is critical. The assumption of linearity applies to all relationships in the model—to the objective function to be maximized or minimized and to the relationships among variables within the model.

To clarify these notions and to demonstrate the power of linear programming, this note presents next a brief example of a product-mix problem, a problem handled by linear programming in many industries, notably, petroleum, chemicals, fertilizer, and animal feed.

Consider a manufacturer with a six-product line, each product made up of a common basic ingredient, a special additive, and a filler. Assume that supplies of the basic material and the additives are available in fixed quantities (limited resources) but that the filler is obtainable in any quantity. The recipes for the six products indicate the ounces of constituent materials required for each pound of finished product (Table C). These recipes are linear with volume. That is to say, to make 1 lb of product A requires 2 oz of basic material, 3 oz of additive 1 and 11 oz of filler. To make 1,000 lb of product A requires exactly 1,000 times as much of each ingredient. There are no economies of scale, no process changes when volume reaches a certain level, etc.

Table C also shows the per-pound profits for the six products which

TABLE C MATERIAL REQUIREMENTS

One Pound of Product	Profit per Pound	Basic Material	Additive 1	Additive 2	Additive 3	Filler
A	$0.90	2 oz	3 oz			11 oz
B	0.60	2 oz		3 oz		11 oz
C	0.75	2 oz			4 oz	10 oz
D	1.50	5 oz	8 oz			3 oz
E	1.40	5 oz		8 oz		3 oz
F	1.30	5 oz			10 oz	1 oz
Available supply		6,000 lb	3,500 lb	1,200 lb	5,000 lb	unlimited

will be the coefficients of the profit (objective) function to be maximized. The specific goal in this problem is to maximize the function.

$$\text{PROFIT} = 0.90X_A + 0.60X_B + 0.75X_C + 1.50X_D + 1.40X_E + 1.30X_F$$

where

$$X_A = \text{total pounds of product } A \text{ produced}$$
$$X_B = \text{total pounds of product } B \text{ produced}$$

etc.

This function is also linear, as it must be for linear programming.

In addition, Table C shows the amounts of the scarce resources which are available to be made into final products.

Putting all this information together expresses this linear programming problem as follows:

Product

A	B	C	D	E	F
Maximize $0.90X_A + 0.60X_B + 0.75X_C + 1.50X_D + 1.40X_E + 1.30X_F$					

Subject to the following constraints

	A	B	C	D	E	F	
Basic Mtl.	$2X_A +$	$2X_B +$	$2X_C +$	$5X_D +$	$5X_E +$	$5X_F$	$\leq 96{,}000\,\text{oz}$
Additive 1	$3X_A$			$+ \quad 8X_D$			$\leq 65{,}000\,\text{oz}$
Additive 2		$3X_B$			$+ \quad 8X_E$		$\leq 19{,}200\,\text{oz}$
Additive 3			$4X_C$			$+ \quad 10X_F$	$\leq 80{,}000\,\text{oz}$

Keeping in mind that $X_A = $ total pounds of product A produced, one can interpret these constraints as follows:

The first constraint says that the total basic material used must not exceed the available supply, which is 6,000 lb or (6,000 lb $\times$ 16 oz per pound) 96,000 oz. Basic material is used in all six products so the total amount used is 2 times the number of pounds of product A produced $(2X_A)$ plus 2 times the number of pounds of product B produced $(2X_B)$, etc. The second constraint is for additive 1. Since this additive is used in only two products, the total amount used is $3X_A + 8X_D$ and the constraint says that this amount must be less than or equal to the available supply of 3,500 lb $\times$ 16 = 56,000 oz. The other constraints have similar interpretations.

There are six other constraints which are implied but usually not stated explicitly. These are $X_A \geq 0$, $X_B \geq 0$, etc., and they reflect the fact that no negative production is allowed.

By looking at the column coefficients, note that the recipes for the six products are present in the constraints. In the first column the recipe for product A is 2 oz of basic material and 3 oz of additive 1. There is no entry for filler since this ingredient is available in unlimited quantity.

This problem can be solved manually in 15 or 20 minutes by a procedure called the simplex method of linear programming. The details of the simplex method are not included in this book,[7] but the problem's solution is presented in Table D. The results in Table D call for the production of only products A, B, and

TABLE D OPTIMAL SOLUTION TO
PRODUCT MIX PROBLEM

Produce Product

A	18,700 lb
B	6,400 lb
C	20,000 lb
D	0 lb
E	0 lb
F	0 lb
Excess basic material	5,800 lb
Total profit	$35,690 lb

C, even though products D, C, and F have much higher unit profits. This occurs because products A, B, and C use much less of the scarce resources per unit of final product and therefore are more profitable on the basis of profit per unit of scarce resource.

In linear programming the results generated do not end with an "answer" like that in Table D. The simplex method generates much additional useful information, as noted in the following paragraphs.

Suppose one wishes to answer the question, "How much would I lose if I were forced to make 1 lb of product F?" (The optimal solution says produce no product F, so the optimum is destroyed

[7] Introductory treatments of the simplex method of linear programming may be found in: E. S. Buffa, *Models for Production and Operations Management,* John Wiley and Sons, New York, 1963; R. H. Bock and W. K. Holstein, *Production Planning and Control,* Chas. E. Merrill Books, Columbus, Ohio, 1963. More complete information may be found in: S. I. Gass, *Linear Programming: Methods and Applications,* McGraw-Hill, New York, 1964; An-min Chung, *Linear Programming,* Chas. E. Merrill Books, Columbus, Ohio, 1963; W. R. Smythe and L. A. Johnson, *Introduction to Linear Programming, with Applications,* Prentice-Hall, Englewood Cliffs, N.J., 1966.

if we force ourselves to make some.)   Product F requires 5 oz of basic material, 10 oz of additive 3, 1 oz of filler and generates a profit of \$1.30.   There is excess basic material on hand (see Table D) and filler is available, but there is no excess supply of additive 3 available.   (Product C, which requires 4 oz of additive 3 per pound has used 5,000 lb $\times$ 4 oz per lb = 80,000 oz of additive 3, or the entire supply.)   Therefore making 1 lb of product F requires giving up some product C in order to get sufficient additive 3.   In fact, $2\frac{1}{2}$ lb of product C must be given up to get the needed 10 oz of additive 3. The result generates \$1.30 of profit for a pound of product F but loses $2.5 \times \$0.75 = \$1.875$ for a net loss of \$0.575.   This value is directly available in the simplex solution; it is not necessary to calculate the result indirectly as we have done here.

Another question easily answered by a simplex solution is "What is the value of an additional ounce of additive 1?"   The answer is \$0.30 since the extra ounce makes possible the production of $\frac{1}{3}$ of a pound of product A by combining the extra additive with excess basic material and filler.   This $\frac{1}{3}$ lb would generate a profit of $\frac{1}{3} \times \$0.90 = \$0.30$.   Furthermore, the simplex solution makes possible the calculation that 8,700 additional ounces of additive 1 can be used before exhausting the excess supply of basic material.

$$\frac{5,800 \text{ oz excess basic}}{2 \text{ oz basic}/3 \text{ oz additive 1}} = 8,700 \text{ oz}$$

The important point here is that linear programming not only provides answers concerning how much to make but also gives valuable information on the value of raw materials, the gains (losses) to be incurred by selling various products, and the costs of deviating from an optimal production plan.

Although the foregoing discussion has made it clear that linear programming is not universally applicable to production problems, it should be stressed that many problems which, on the surface, have not appeared amenable to this technique have been sucessfully solved with it.   Segmented (or piecewise) linear functions have been used to approximate nonlinear functions, very large problems have been broken up and solved in parts, and linear programming has been used to develop solutions for pieces of problems which can then be used in another model.   Thus, when applied with imagination and skill by knowledgable specialists, linear programming has proven to be an impressive aid in many production situations.   In addition, it is fair to say that production managers, even without a detailed knowledge of linear programming, will find the technique a useful way to set up and think about allocation problems.

Queueing Theory

Although supermarket checkout counters and highway or bridge toll booths are perhaps the most commonly known examples of waiting lines, many production problems involve situations which call for the analysis of a waiting line.   Examples include the furnishing of tools to machinists at a tool crib, the servicing of a bank of machines by a group of repairmen, and the unloading of trucks or railroad cars at a receiving dock.   The sample problem of trucks arriving at a repair shop presented a good example of a waiting-line problem.

In all of these examples the issue is essentially one of systems design—how many men should work in the tool crib, how many trucks should the repair shop be able to service at one time, etc.?   The answers to these questions must be developed through consideration of two important factors: the times of arrival of the men, trucks, parts, or machines, and the times to service these arrivals.

An interesting collection of quantitative techniques called *queueing theory* has been developed to deal with some specific classes of waiting-line problems, and a few of these techniques merit attention here.

Consider again the trucking firm, specifically, the queue of trucks outside the repair shop and the shop itself.   Looking at the column headed "Trucks Malfunctioned" in Table B, one can determine that an average of approximately 13 trucks per day malfunction when the repair shop capacity is 30 trucks.   Figure 3 shows a simple diagram of the system.

One might think that with an average of 13 trucks per day arriving, a 2-day service time, and a repair shop with capacity for 30 trucks, there would never be a waiting line of trucks outside the shop after the shop was loaded in the morning.   On the average, a 30-truck shop should be able to handle an arrival rate of 15 trucks per day. Nonetheless, Table B shows that on 4 simulated days, numbers 3, 14, 18, and 20, there was a waiting line of trucks left outside the shop after the shop was loaded in the morning.   This occurred because the truck arrivals at the repair shop did not equal 13 trucks every day.   Instead, 13 is the mean of a distribution of arrivals per day,

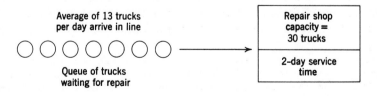

Figure 3.

Arrivals

Average λ per hour

Service rate
averages
μ per hour

FIGURE 4.

which, in the 25-day sample shown in Table B, ranges from 4 to 21 trucks per day.

The foregoing offers a good grasp of the central notion of queueing theory. It is basically a method of analyzing waiting-line problems which explicitly takes into account the fact that arrivals do not arrive at a uniform rate and that even though average servicing capacity exceeds the average arrival rate, there still will be a waiting line from time to time in many situations.

To deal somewhat more generally with the queueing theory, turn to another waiting line situation, shown in Figure 4. It is assumed that the service facility can service only one arrival at a time and that the arrival and service rates average λ and μ units per hour, respectively. Thus in contrast to the truck example, service rate as well as the arrival rate varies.

Readily available queueing formulas[8] make it possible to compute the expected value of several interesting variables, if *the distributions of the arrival and service rates are known and have a form for which formulas have been developed.* For example, if the arrival rates have a Poisson distribution, if the service times have an exponential distribution, and if there is a single service facility, the average waiting time of an arrival can be determined by the formula

$$W = \frac{\lambda}{(\mu - \lambda)}$$

Solving this formula for various values of λ and μ produces the data in Table E. Other formulas permit the calculation of the average time an arrival spends in the system (waiting and being serviced), the average number of units in the system, the average queue length, the average waiting time of only the arrivals who wait, etc.

Perhaps the most relevant question now is "How restrictive is the assumption of Poisson arrival rate and exponential service times?" Fortunately, it has been shown that the Poisson and exponential as-

---

[8] See, for example, M. Sasieni, A. Yaspan, and L. Friedman, *Operations Research: Methods and Problems,* John Wiley and Sons, New York, 1959; E. S. Buffa, *Modern Production Management,* John Wiley and Sons, New York, 1965.

TABLE E

Average Arrival Rate λ	Average Service Rate μ	Average Waiting Time for an Arrival
2 units/hour	3 units/hour	0.67 hours
2	4	0.25
4	5	0.80
4	6	0.33
6	7	0.86
6	8	0.37
8	9	0.89
8	10	0.40

sumptions are reasonable in a great many situations. Often the fit between an empirical distribution derived from historical data and the Poisson or exponential distribution is not perfect, but it is close enough to consider the Poisson and exponential distributions good approximations. This is not too surprising since the time between Poisson-distributed arrivals is assumed to be completely random, having no dependence on the time between previous arrivals or the state of the waiting line. Similarly, exponentially distributed service times are assumed to be random and independent of previous service times. Stated otherwise, a long service time would not necessarily cause one to expect a compensating short service time to follow if the exponential distribution holds.

Despite the fact that queueing formulas based on Poisson arrivals and exponential service times can be used in many situations, occasions often arise in which these formulas simply do not fit. Considerable work has been done to develop formulas for other problems[9] and several other arrival and service rate distributions can be handled. For problems where the distributions cannot be handled with known formulas, simulation has proven to be a valuable method for solving waiting-line problems. (As it did in the trucking problem in this note, where the arrival distribution was not known.)

Decision Trees and Probabilities

The final model introduced in this note is the "decision tree." Used with probabilities, this model can be a powerful tool for ordering

[9] Two excellent references are: D. R. Cox and W. L. Smith, *Queues,* Methuen and Co., London, 1961; P. M. Morse, *Queues, Inventories and Maintenance,* John Wiley and Sons, New York, 1958.

and analyzing many production problems. Consider the following example.

An owner-manager who contemplates buying a "five-axis," numerically controlled machine tool, which requires a total outlay of $465,000, is faced with two major uncertainties. He is not sure that the aerospace market which he serves will continue to place orders with him in the large and growing volume he now enjoys. He knows that efficient use of the numerically controlled machine depends heavily on the effectiveness with which machining operations are programmed, but since his programmers have experience only with much simpler machines, he is not sure what level of efficiency they can develop with this new machine. In contrast to these uncertainties, he feels confident from what the vendor has told him that 21 months will elapse between the time an order is placed and the machine is delivered, and that he can cancel at any time during the first 15 months. In cancelling, he would lose $100,000, which covers a deposit and the costs incurred in training workers.

The manager has decided to represent his choices and the uncertain events he faces with a decision tree, as shown in Figure 5. The following items may be observed in studying this decision tree. These items pertain not only to this example but also to decision trees generally.

1. The tree consists of branching points which represent either *acts* or *events*. The acts are points at which a decision is to be made between the alternatives shown on the branches; the events are points at which a number of outcomes are possible, as shown on the branches. The manager controls the act points; the environment will determine the outcome at event points.

2. In Figure 5 acts and events alternate, but it is possible in other drawings to have events follow events, acts follows acts, or both.

3. The decision tree is the creation of the manager, who is analyzing a situation. It must be responsive to the facts of the environment, but a tree, like other models, does not exist in and of itself. *It represents the relevant facts, the choices, and the probabilities as a manager sees them.* To illustrate this, consider event point B in Figure 5. The manager foresaw that if he placed an order for the numerically controlled machine now, he would review his decision in 15 months, the last date on which he could cancel, and at that time he would reevaluate the purchase of the machine in the light of existing backlog of orders. He considered that it would be critical whether or not the backlog was both growing and in excess of eight months' capacity of his other equipment. In his judgment, if this test were passed he could look forward

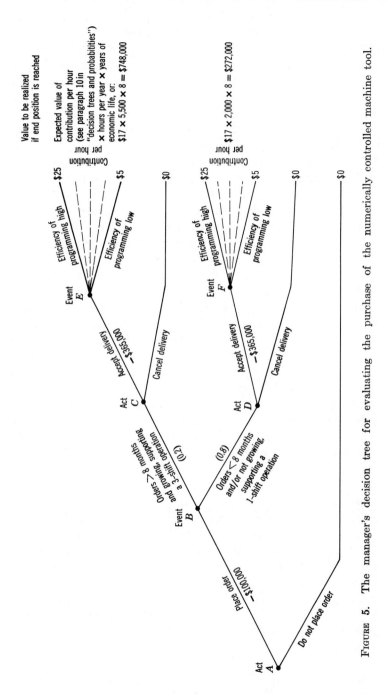

FIGURE 5.   The manager's decision tree for evaluating the purchase of the numerically controlled machine tool.

to three-shift operation of the new machine. Otherwise, he felt that one-shift operation would best represent the expected volume of work for the machine.

4. The scope of the decision tree represents those things that the manager deems advisable to consider together. If the manager felt he should consider other new equipment at the same time he considered the numerically controlled machine tool, this should be shown in the diagram. There is, however, a practical limit to the size and complexity of decision trees.

5. At each branch point the branches represent all the possibilities to be considered but they do not overlap. Stated rigorously, the branches are collectively exhaustive and mutually exclusive.

6. The diagram shows decisions and events in chronological order. More specifically, events whose outcomes will not be known to the manager making a decision until after his last date for making it follow such a decision on the tree diagram.

7. The manager who contemplates ordering the numerically controlled machine has assigned probabilities to the branches which follow events. Specifically, following event point B in Figure 5, the (0.2) represents his assigned probability that the backlog of orders will be in excess of eight months' capacity and will be growing. Likewise, (0.8) represents his assigned probability that the order backlog will not meet this test. Note that here and in all cases the sum of the probabilities assigned to the outcomes of an event is 1.0. In this example, the order backlog either will or will not meet the test, and hence the sum of the probabilities of the possible outcomes must add to certainty.

8. The manager has expressed his judgment of the level of skill his programmers will attain, and hence the productivity of the machine, through a statement of probabilities in a different form from that discussed in paragraph 7. Here a range of possible outcomes follows event points E and F in Figure 5. The highest efficiency the manager contemplates will yield a contribution to profit and recovery of the machine investment of \$25 per hour and the lowest efficiency \$5 per hour. To show his assigned probabilities within this range he prepared a supplementary, detailed statement, the cumulative probability distribution shown in Figure 6. This form is useful whenever a decision maker wishes to assign probabilities to an outcome which may turn out to be any one of many sequential numbers over a range.

9. Decision trees can show the cost incurred by electing to take a course of action. Thus in Figure 5 following act point A on the upper branch, the manager has shown as an outflow the deposit

and training costs of $100,000, the full amount for which he is committed as of that time if he places an order. Following act points C and D, he shows an additional commitment of $365,000, the balance of the cost of the machine, which is the amount he then irrevocably commits, if he elects not to cancel the order for the machine. These commitments will not take place at the same time and any subsequent recovery of cash will occur in the still more distant future. Arbitrarily, the time value of money will not be considered here in order to focus on basic characteristics of decision trees. Suffice it to say that the time of cash flows on branches can be identified and the time value of money calculated.

10. The value of being at the final event point E in Figure 5 is set equal to the product of contribution per hour multiplied by 5,500 (hours per year working three shifts) multiplied by 8 (expected economic life in years). In this equation the undetermined value is the contribution per hour, and this can be approximated by grouping the possible values for "contribution per hour" shown in Figure 6 into ten segments of unequal size, but each having equal likelihood of containing the unknown value, and letting the midpoint value of each represent that segment. This has

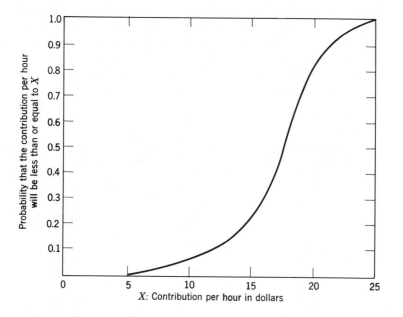

FIGURE 6. Cumulative distribution of probabilities of the value of contribution per hour.

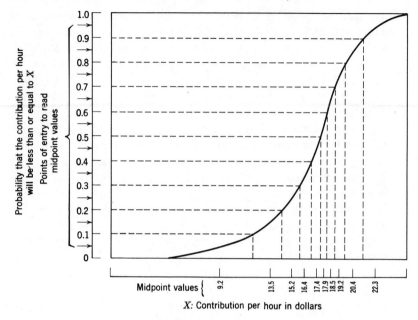

FIGURE 7. Cumulative distribution of probabilities divided into segments having equal probability of containing the unknown value.

been done in Figure 7. Since each segment has $\frac{1}{10}$ probability of containing the unknown value, each midpoint value may be multiplied by 0.1 and the products added in order to approximate the expected value. Ten midpoint values have been read from Figure 7 and the calculation has been carried out here:

I Midpoint Values of Segments Read from Figure 7	II Probability of Unknown Value Lying in this Segment	I × II
9.20	0.1	.92
13.50	0.1	1.35
15.20	0.1	1.52
16.40	0.1	1.64
17.40	0.1	1.74
17.90	0.1	1.79
18.50	0.1	1.85
19.20	0.1	1.92
20.40	0.1	2.04
22.30	0.1	2.23
	Expected value	17.00

The value of being at the final event point F is influenced strongly by the manager's assessment of available work if the order backlog fails to meet the test set. He considers that if the test is not met, he can count on only one shift of work, and this smaller number of hours is multiplied by the expected value of the contribution per hour.

In a somewhat similar manner, in all decision trees the expected value of all final branching points which represent events can be determined by multiplying the probability assigned to each event branch by the cash flow to be realized if that event occurs and then adding the products.

11. The next step is to select the path of decisions which will give the largest expected return. But before the manager can decide which branch to start down at the point of origin he must assign values to the subsequent branching points; he must start at the right and work backwards. This is called the "rollback": the calculation of expected values and the selection of choices working from right to left.

In Figure 5, at act point C, the manager sees a value for the upper branch of $+\$748,000 - \$365,000 = +\$383,000$ and for the lower branch a value of zero. Assuming he is influenced solely by expected values, he would choose the upper branch with its promise of a larger return. Hence the value of point C, if that point is reached, is logically $383,000. The value of being at point F is set at $17 per hour $\times 2,000$ hours per year (one shift) $\times 8$ years (economic life) $= \$272,000$. From point D the upper branch has a value of $+\$272,000 - \$365,000 = -\$93,000$. Since the lower branch has the higher absolute value of zero, this branch would be chosen if point D were reached, and hence zero becomes the value of being at point D. Next, rolling back to point B, there is a 0.2 probability of reaching point C (worth $383,000) and a 0.8 probability of reaching point D (worth zero). Weighting each of these values by its probability, as follows,

$$0.2 \times \$383,000 \ = \$76,600$$
$$0.8 \times \qquad 0 \ = \qquad 0$$
$$\text{Expected Value} = \$76,600$$

it can be seen that the worth of making the decision from point A in Figure 5 to start toward point B is

$$-\$100,000 + \$76,600 = -\$23,400$$

This is less attractive than the alternative choice shown, "do not place order," which leads to an end position value of zero. The choice of a course of action has come from the rollback.

12. The preceding paragraphs have been written with the assumption that the manager was willing to base his decisions on expected values. That is, as if he could weigh the loss of $100,000 against potential gains influenced solely by mathematical expectations and not by such things as the consequences in his over-all affairs of incurring a $100,000 loss. Stated another way, his "utility" for money is linear over the range considered. This is often not the case, calling for a different procedure—in particular, requiring special provisions to change the weights assigned to losses (and gains) to reflect the "risk aversion" of the manager making decisions.

Although usually used with numbers as presented here, decision trees can be used less rigorously, simply to show the relationships of alternative choices and possible events. In either usage, the decision tree is a formal way to order the logic of a problem under consideration. It can have the particular advantage of allowing a manager to think about the various parts of a complex decision individually and then pull together, in a rigorous manner, these separate considerations.

Channel 1 Television Corporation

On top of the broadcasting tower of the Channel 1 Television Corporation there is a flashing red beacon light to warn low-flying aircraft. The beacon light contains two high intensity incandescent bulbs. Historical data on bulb life give the following information:

Life	Probability
1 month	.05
2 months	.20
3 months	.25
4 months	.30
5 months	.15
6 months	.05

In other words, there is a 5 per cent chance (1 chance in 20) that a single bulb will last one month, a 20 per cent chance (1 chance in 5) that a bulb will last two months, etc.

It is estimated that the cost of assigning a workman to climb the tower to reach the fixture and remove and replace the weatherproof cover over the bulbs is $20. Bulb cost is $8 per bulb. Time involved in replacing a bulb is negligible once the fixture has been reached.

Assuming that the company wants both bulbs working all the time, develop a simulation model that will decide between the following bulb replacement policies:

1. Replace only the bulb that burns out.
2. Replace both bulbs when one burns out.

Is there any other policy which will result in lower cost?

Extracts from "The Computer as a Manufacturing 'Tool' "[1]

I. MODEST BEGINNING TO A REVOLUTION

The computer's subtle and pervasive presence today . . . is the center of a new technological storm moving over the American industrial landscape. Nothing less than the Second Industrial Revolution is approaching, and it becomes increasingly apparent that it will sweep away long-standing engineering methods, manufacturing practices, and traditional patterns of management thought and behavior.

* * *

The computer was largely a scientific prodigy when it was introduced to business and industry in 1952. Until then it had been totally committed to government-financed military and aerospace research and development projects. With its commercial availability, the computer became first the instrument of office automation and was used to mechanize payroll accounting methods. It then moved into the plant for the management of inventory and material control procedures. Here is where many people today think the computer's bearing on the functions of manufacturing ends. But since the mid-fifties, the computer has made rapid strides in engineering and production. Fast-growing sophistication in the use of computers, in better methods for their manufacture, and, very importantly, in developing techniques of programming—the methods of telling the computer what

[1] By Milton Alexander, formerly Associate Editor, *Production Magazine;* currently Editor, *Vectors,* published by The American Society of Tool & Manufacturing Engineers. Copyright © *Production Magazine,* reproduced by express permission.

to do—are responsible for the whirlwind picking up potency as it moves ahead.

Today, computer capability is ahead of application despite a growing list of assignments for it, particularly in manufacturing: Production forecasting and scheduling, assembly line balancing, job routing and even process engineering. The computer can distribute labor operations, and one day will make possible the numerically-controlled factory.

* * *

In many ways, the computer has arrived on the national scene in the nick of time—*deus ex machina*. Without the computer's ability to compress man-years of mathematical calculations into hours, the spacecraft taken for granted today would be non-existent. Without the computer's ability to collect, store and analyze masses of data, the ordering procedure for new autos would be bogged down in red tape created by the proliferation of models and options.

Its ability to perform lightning-fast calculations, to store and recall hundreds of thousands of facts, and to present these facts in thousands of inter-related ways is the reason for its ever-increasing role in business.

* * *

II. WHAT'S MANAGEMENT CONTROL WORTH?

It is very likely that much of management's constructive interest in the computer derives from a justifiable desire to offset mounting clerical and other labor costs. However, when actual dollar-and-cents justification is applied, "people" are not always prominent on the list. Surprisingly, the greatest of projected benefits can be visualized, if not immediately proven, through a new dimension called management control—the ability to systematize operations, pinpoint costs with accuracy and timeliness, and plan for the future with reasonable assurance that goals will be met.

* * *

III. THE PRODUCT IS INFORMATION

What are some of the operational advantages that provide management control, and make the computer an enticing prospect for managers and engineers? For one thing, the computer can tell where and how the company stands in day-to-day operations. "Before the

advent of the computer," says Ex-Cell-O [Corporation, producer of package machinery and machine tools], "there was no practical method or system we know of that could handle data fast enough to make the best use of it when needed." Now computer-aided control can reach into the furthest recesses of manufacturing details.

Ex-Cell-O makes a point from its company files. . . . An IBM 1410 computer at Detroit headquarters has established controls for slow-moving inventories and given the inventory control analyst the tools with which to study little-known but significant cost areas. Using the computer, the analyst literally conducts a bin-by-bin search for obsolete and excessive stores of parts, mainly through a breakdown of existing inventories by date. These reports provide a clear word picture of where the money goes in buying and stocking parts; it tells at a glance how much money may be tied up needlessly, and points to future alternatives. . . .

To manufacturing men, one of the most significant advances in computer technology is the new-found ability of the computer to integrate communications from various locations inside and away from the plant into a single network. In a sense, it allows production departments to "talk" with management. By means of remote data collection units—electronic message sending devices connected by wire—production data is sent directly from the shop floor to the computer. The computer accepts the information, supplied on a punched card based on data provided by the operator, makes necessary adjustments in its memory file and at the end of the shift, issues an up-to-date report of that department's activities, together with new production schedules. In most cases, the department supervisor knows within 12 hours how efficiently his group performed during the previous day. From the report he knows whether he is on, or behind, schedule and what steps he must take to correct an out-of-balance condition. At the same time, the system is programmed to provide identical information to plant management and to production control and payroll departments to keep their records timely.

Ex-Cell-O recently installed the first two of 52 IBM data collection units in a large machining department of one of its Detroit plants. With this system, the company expects to reduce the time spent to process labor and job statistics from days to just hours. And without the intervention of clerical help who normally collect, write and file the now-obsolete job and labor tickets, errors are expected to be held to an absolute minimum while management is provided in short order with a true picture of man-machine utilization.

A sophisticated version of the data collection unit provides a type-

writer for two-way communication with the computer. This is the basis for "real-time" data processing—a continual adjustment of shop loads and schedules based on incoming information to the plant. A foreman, for example, "asks" the computer to give him his schedule for the day by dialing an appropriate numerical code. An answer comes back immediately on the typewriter with all jobs listed in priority sequence based on delivery or customer demands. . . . Even a schedule planned a day ahead is inefficient compared to a real-time system that monitors and *reacts* to constantly changing order situations and priorities in the field.

In the forefront of users who see the computer as the hub of a giant communications network, Chrysler Corp. last year installed an electronic "switching" system, with a General Electric Data Net 30 computer serving as a communications center between Chrysler headquarters and plants, sales offices and parts warehouses around the world. The computer controls the teletype system, and can hold, or store, messages in its memory file until proper circuits are cleared. Messages that took as long as two hours to send formerly now are completed in four minutes. . . .

Ultimately, the development of management information systems will lead to the "total information system" with the computer at its center. This is what one company had in mind in 1962 when its first computer was installed. For Warner Electric Brake & Clutch Co., of Beloit, Wis., the purpose went beyond several real cost reductions—optimum inventories, faster order processing and delivery time—to the heart of the matter: A scientific management system designed for the optimization of men, materials and machinery. . . . The computer is employed in a program that ties together production forecasting, inventory management, machine loading, scheduling and utilization, and manpower planning and utilization.

* * *

Repetitive Thinking—Not Repetitive Production

The computer is designed to take over man's repetitive thinking processes, but it is seldom found near repetitive production operations. Paralleling the case of numerically controlled machine tools, the computer's headway has been greatest in job shop type of operations where multiple products with a large variety of manufacturing operations, varying lot sizes and variable costs are involved. . . .

At Caterpillar Tractor Co., the computer schedules some 300,000 different parts and balances assembly lines for bulldozers, earthmovers

and other road construction equipment. At J. I. Case Co., it's used for continuous-mix assembly of tractors with a range of 1,500 options. At Westinghouse's Homewood division, it's used for fast-in, fast-out service for spare electrical parts produced on n/c machine tools. At General Electric's jet engine department, it's used to process highly complex purchase orders in just 2.5 second each.

* * *

. . . Recently, the automakers have started steering computers in an abrupt turn into the plant, and they now are experimenting, for example, with the massive problem of balancing final car assembly lines. (Since 1962, Chrysler has used this technique on instrument panel assembly lines.) They are heavily committed to automation possibilities in styling and die making for body panels in an attempt to reduce lead time for new cars from three years or more to just months, and this effort involves not only n/c machine tools but a fairly new concept called computer graphics—picking off reference points from clay models, storing the data in a computer and projecting it on a 'scope in three dimensions. Through programming, the computer projects the body not only in different perspectives but can show shortened or lengthened views. Ford engineers have succeeded in reproducing these views on paper with some clarity. . . .

The big IBM 7090 at Chrysler headquarters operates around the clock nearly six out of seven days a week, performing about 70 tasks, including production control, corporate payroll functions, vendor releases, sales orders and warranty claims.

. . . When Chrysler expanded its iron foundry at Indianapolis, for example, [Gomer] Redmond [manager of corporate systems and procedures] and plant manager Paul Moore set operations researchers to work setting up a computer program containing all the known conditions under which the foundry would be operated, taking into account the materials, chemicals, furnace temperatures, production requirements and the range of prices for the materials. It took the OR staff people two years to write the program. But now it takes only two minutes of computer time to figure out optimum requirements and print out the instructions for a month's operation in advance. . . .

A similar approach was taken for Chrysler's new Detroit foundry. Even before the furnace was ordered, OR men were "pouring" iron on paper in a simulation of the operation under the conditions best expected to obtain an optimum grade of iron based on prevailing prices and demand. Further, mathematical models of various types and sizes of furnaces—both electric induction and cupola designs—

were "tried out" at various levels of material and mix and temperatures. The object was to arrive at not only desired quality levels but a furnace design best suited to Chrysler's needs.

On the assembly line, Chrysler has gone further . . . in applying computerized quality control techniques. Notable is its on-line Dynamic Quality Control system. . . . Planned by the Car and Truck Assembly Group, the system is unique in the fact that defects on a given car, reported by inspectors from as many as 20 check points on the line, are gathered immediately by a central computer, sorted, analyzed and printed—in time for correction while that car still is on the line. Normally, defects take a day or more for correction. In addition, the system's efficiency enables inspectors to examine many more items on the car, from the previous few hundred to theoretically all of the car's 6,400 component parts and 4,500 welds. More important, from a preventive standpoint, the computer will help spot sources of trouble by classifying defects by type, by department and by product. Quality Control will note at once that a welding gun, say, is causing poor welds. The computer also generates daily, weekly and monthly statistical analyses, trend patterns, comparisons—"evidence," Chrysler says, "upon which intelligent decisions can be made with measurable success."

Anticipating Defects Can Save Millions

The implications of computerized quality control are enormous for Chrysler in terms of advantages in production and design analysis, and reduced repair and warranty costs, not to speak of the effect of minimized field failures on owners. A 10¢ part replaced easily on the assembly line could balloon to $7.50 at the dealership. Potential savings of this kind can amount to millions of dollars—and an untold amount of customer good will.

One thing the computer can't do yet is accurately forecast auto sales. There's no way of in-putting whether the public whim next year will be for "fastbacks," chopped backs, razor-edged styling or willowy curves. This matter still is in the hands of the stylists and the market researchers and will likely remain there for quite some time. But the computer has done a remarkable service in enabling the auto-makers to build closer to market demands. The typical manufacturer utilizes the computer to maintain daily control of materials and sales orders, tally inventories every 10 days, and release parts orders to vendors and assembly plants about twice a month. With this relatively tight control—a vast improvement over that

of the not-too-distant past—the car manufacturer can move swiftly and adjust his releases and inventories close in the wake of changing orders. This allays one of the biggest bugaboos of the automakers— that long after buyers' tastes have changed, sheer momentum will keep obsolete models in production. . . .

Detroit knows it can't help making some wrong decisions. The trick is not always to be right, but to have the ability to react swiftly to the market.

*　*　*

SOME ADDITIONAL ILLUSTRATIVE PRODUCTION APPLICATIONS:

Computer Schedules Production . . .

J. I. Case Company, the Racine, Wis., manufacturer of farm and industrial tractors, found the computer a "natural" for the planning of a product mix that ranges over 1,500 tractor options, including combinations of front ends, transmissions and hydraulic power assists. Marketing forecasts for the year ahead set the stage for basic tractor configurations: Size and style of tractors, engines and clutch assemblies.

In use since 1962, an IBM 1410 random access computer is programmed to incorporate forecasting data, current orders and a 6–8 month history of usage into monthly requirements for parts and materials orders and production. From this data, the computer calculates and prints out a daily erection schedule for the tractor assembly line.

With this kind of flexibility, the company has been able to switch over from a previous 2- to 3-month batch assembly schedule (with the usual shortcomings where, if some customer somewhere isn't unhappy about waiting for the tractor he ordered, management is to some degree dissatisfied with the wasted effort in investment, sales and production of wrong types) to a continuous-mix schedule modified on a daily basis. . . .

What's more, daily inventory assessments by the computer are reflected in an eight-hour projection of materials, parts and fabricated job requirements—compared to a 5- to 6-week lag previously when done by the clercial force. With an IBM 357 data collection system, the status of the shop is brought into line with other types of reporting activity. These electronic reporting stations located in each department accept labor and job timekeeping data and transform it into

punched card information for the computer to digest at the end of every day's work.

. . . And Balances Assembly Lines

At Caterpillar Tractor Co., Peoria, Ill., an IBM 7074/1401 computer provides the action reports for controlling some 300,000 parts for engines, earthmovers, road scrapers, bulldozers and other road construction equipment, in an effort designed to better utilize manpower and machines. Following a three-year period of computer programming, the company is using the computer to set up an optimum distribution of operators on assembly lines.

The line balancing concept involves the breaking down of each job on the line into sequence, time required, tools required and other factors that distinguish one job from another. Then, after establishing a chart showing jobs by precedence relationship, punched cards are prepared with necessary data including product mix. The cards then are fed to the computer and it calculates the optimum combination of operations on the line.

The engineer can simulate many possible combinations on the line merely by changing the precedence relationships, and having new punched cards prepared. Thus, the effect of changes can be predetermined without actually disturbing the line.

Normally, the Caterpillar line is balanced once a month with the computer. In addition, similar techniques are used to schedule production on machine lines. The computer compares economic lot sizes, setup and manufacturing costs, and burden. Even machine layout is a factor which dictates the flow of in-process parts through the department.

Benefits Spill into the Shop

When high volume production and close tolerance manufacture are put together, a new generation of difficulties can be born. Pesco Products Division of Borg-Warner Corporation, a supplier of pumps, motors and systems for aerospace vehicles, avoids most of the expected problems by exercising tight control of work in process with the aid of a Univac 1004 Card Processor. This control is provided through reports produced twice-daily, weekly, monthly, annually and on demand by the compact, high-speed data processing system.

Products are not only manufactured to extremely narrow tolerances but are produced in critical quantities. . . . In addition, the urgency of space and national defense programs frequently imposes critical lead time for specific runs. Consequently, it is imperative for produc-

tion management to know, at all times, the exact status of the roughly 1,000-odd parts which may be in process at any one time.

With the Univac 1004, this information is updated twice daily via a printed Material Move Report. The report lists each part by number and name, work order number, quantity completed on that order, the day's date, departments the part is leaving and going to, and due dates for completion. The report covers about 150 parts moved during the half-day period, and is produced by keypunching information from expediters' move tickets and feeding it into the 1004. It replaces a similar, manual report which, like most manually-compiled production control data, was not timely enough to really do the job expected of it. In addition, parts periodically got "lost" temporarily in the plant, something that seldom occurs now.

Another data processing document vital to the production department is the Demand Report, a bill-of-materials explosion based on sales and production forecasts that are made up three times a month. The Univac explodes the forecast into a bill-of-materials for production control to initiate work orders or purchase requisitions. Set up in part number sequence, with designation as to purchased or manufactured parts, the Demand Report lists each part individually, in subassemblies, and in the finished product so it is not "lost" at any point.

* * *

Pesco uses data processing effectively in other areas, too:

- Operator and machine control are obtained through weekly, monthly and annual Production Efficiency Reports produced from labor job tickets. Listed in part number sequence and by operator, these reports compare actual hours necessary to produce a part with standard hours and are used to compare workers' efficiency.
- Tool inventory control is partially handled on the data processing equipment. . . . The Tool Inventory Report, produced weekly, lists items moving in and out, their recommended minimum and maximum quantities, when an item should be purchased, and in what quantity and price.
- Pesco is working closely with the Mobil Oil Co. on its MIDAC (Management Information Decision and Control) Program which utilizes the 1004 to determine specific lubrication needs of each piece of production machinery, based on its actual hours of usage. Also, maintenance repair orders are processed to produce a report set up by machine number and listing all maintenance and repair costs. This shows up chronic mechanical problems.

Instant Job Reporting

Mechanizing the job reporting function is one of the aims of Ex-Cell-O Corp.'s management information system that utilizes a computer to control everything manufactured on the floor of the company's three Detroit plants. Recent installation of two IBM 1030 data collection units in a large machining department of one plant—part of a 52-unit network eventually planned for—allows the machine operator to report his time and operations directly to the computer room; the delays normally attributed to manual timekeeping are eliminated and management has a complete report of the day's work in the department first thing the following morning.

Instead of punching in when reporting to work, the operator now inserts a plastic badge about the size of a credit card into a slot in the data collection unit. This actuates a remote key-punched (automatic punched-card typewriter) and produces a punched card that, in effect, "signs" the operator in. Then, as scheduled work is performed during the shift, each significant time factor used on the machine (e.g., setup time, run time, downtime) is logged by the operator together with other information, including pieces run, into the data input unit. The operator dials in the appropriate figures on a cartridge and puts the cartridge and job card into the slot. Each time this is done, the keypunch prepares a corresponding punched card. At the end of the shift, the stack of punched cards is fed into the computer. This fast, new means of collecting data is expected to be a factor in obtaining optimum control of the operations being performed on some 8,000 jobs on the floor at any given time.

Maximized Purchase Control

General Electric's large jet engine department at Evendale, Ohio, calls it Mechanized Material Management. Without automation, the purchase and control of 75,000 quantities of parts and materials would take a lot of paper shuffling. With a GE 225 computer the system put into effect since 1962 automatically handles the records for purchasing, expediting, receiving, inspection, traffic, in-process inventory, order status reporting and payment of the vendor's invoice. A substantial saving with the computer system is based on a net reduction of clerical and paperwork costs. When present plans are completed, GE says the computerized system will one day select suppliers automatically. Today, in addition to writing purchase documents at an average of 2.5 seconds per document, the computer produces 30 by-product reports. The purchase orders themselves are quite complex,

each containing as many as 99 items with up to 75 different schedule delivery dates and quantities per item.

Inventory Utilization

Sylvania Electronic Systems Division of Sylvania Electric Products Inc., Buffalo, buys time off an IBM 7070 computer at the parent company's data processing center for inventory control and procurement planning activities. The computer has produced these visible results: It increased the accuracy of records significantly, reduced procurement planning time cycles from an average six weeks to two weeks maximum for major systems procurement, and improved inventory utilization. While plant output was increased 25 per cent, material control personnel were reduced by one-third.

* * *

Work Scheduling Saves $300,000

Many companies don't need the full-time services of a computer. The market for part-time usage is sizable these days, and is being met by some 4,000 independent data processing centers which engineer and operate projects for a fee that usually can be measured against projected cost savings. These centers, or service bureaus, are staffed with people and computer systems that currently are providing a wide array of programs, from production scheduling to inventory control, work standards, PERT-ing and design automation.

One manufacturer with a problem in scheduling work loads recently contracted a program proposed by a service bureau that promises a payout of $300,000 a year, through reduced overtime losses, in return for a $15,000 annual program cost. "One of the biggest reasons for overtime is lack of timely information as to the status of the shop," says Wayne A. Rathwell, controller and overseas manager for the user company, Centri-Spray Corp., Livonia, Mich., producer of industrial washing machines and automation equipment. With a manpower loading schedule devised by The Service Bureau Corp., an IBM independent subsidiary, Rathwell says a daily shop status report will be on the plant manager's desk every morning. With up-to-the-minute information provided by the system, he also hopes to avoid unexplainable delays in letting work out to other shops, and to catch those often-overlooked but significant portions of the schedule.

Objective of the daily manpower loading schedule, prepared for the company's 200-man work force and 85-man engineering group, is to utilize manpower and machines over a range of an average of 45 jobs on the production floor at any given time, with an equal

number being engineered. Punched cards with timekeeping information on the day's work are dispatched to the service bureau, which arranges to have the information processed and returned in printed form the following morning. The report shows the manpower load by operation and by job, indicating the allowable hours for each job, the hours used and the remaining hours, or backlog. More important, it includes a column indicating the availability of hours for the job. . . . In effect, the reports monitor operations and show when manpower and jobs need to be shifted around to take care of contingencies or to meet new delivery dates. The system also provides a recap of costs on standard and previous projects which allows comparisons to be made with past work.

The company's management . . . eventually plans to have magnetic tapes flown in from plants in Mexico and Europe with timely reports on production and sales in those localities. At least three times each week top management will have in hand a consolidated report of the company's world-wide activities. . . .

"Total Systems" Engineering

The computer finds a home where a good portion of engineering content goes into the product. Since 1953, Reliance Electric and Engineering Co. of Cleveland has used computers for a-c and d-c motor design calculations.

"In one case," says C. G. Veinott, chief engineering analyst, "we estimated that the computer saved us a quarter of a million dollars by enabling us to get a line of motors on the market six months earlier than otherwise. This figure does not include other savings in engineering time. Nor does it include a saving in material in a better-designed product, estimated at five per cent of material costs."

The company's central engineering computer is part of a communications network connecting three remotely located engineering departments, one about 300 miles distant in Columbus, Indiana. Each remote department is connected to Central Engineering by a Friden Teledata communications system with a Flexowriter for input-output. A remotely located engineer needing a design calculation on a motor writes the design reference data on a computer input form. A teledata operator pulls a reference tape from her files and combines this and the engineer's new data on a new input tape and transmits the data by a leased-wire circuit directly into the Engineering Computer Center at Euclid, O. There, the input tape as received is fed to the computer which calculates the data and produces the answers on paper tape.

The tape is transmitted back to the remote center and converted to typed matter. In a matter of minutes, the engineer thus gets a copy of all input and output data for his new design.

This "total system" engineering network provides engineers with a common language and allows an engineer in one division to make full use of the experience and talents of those in other divisions. And by shortening the learning time for engineers, they have become more productive.

Teaming Up with N/C

Computer-aided n/c machines figure prominently in experimental die work at General Motors' Technical Center at Warren, Michigan. "N/c machining is found to be a valuable extension of our design processes," says H. J. Mainwaring, assistant staff engineer of the Center's Computer Design & Analysis Section. "With n/c we are producing certain parts faster, at less cost and with greater accuracy than by any other method known to us." Most of all, errors compounded in calculations and hand work on the previously hand-made masters with contoured surfaces are largely eliminated. Hand-made masters are almost impossible to inspect accurately, Mainwaring says, especially when the errors become hidden when blended in with a finishing file.

With a computer and n/c setup, calculating errors are caught before the tool is set in motion on the work. All data is printed out for verification and a plotted chart of tool center motions will reflect any bad data as surface irregularities.

With n/c, even countered surfaces not definable in APT or AUTO-PROMPT computer program languages are cut using coordinates of the part surface. Mainwaring explains . . . "We have reduced lead time by more than 75 per cent and now measure lead time in days rather than weeks."

* * *

Computer Writes Routine

What used to take a manufacturing engineer twelve hours to process transformer core cutting operations now takes a computer two minutes at Allis-Chalmers' West Allis (Wis.) Works. . . .

A transformer core consists of a number of .14-in. silicon steel sheets cut and notched to shape and stacked together. Since cores are seldom identical, the manufacturing operations for each core must be individually planned.

With the previous manual planning method . . . one hundred operations and up to twelve hours of the engineer's time were involved in planning one core.

* * *

The new method utilizes as computer input, the output from a computer design program. A FORTRAN program was written for an IBM 704 computer by converting the pick-off charts to formulas. For some of the charts, formulas were developed using multiple regression techniques. The use of formulas eliminates the steps inherently associated with the charts, and assures that processing time is accurately determined.

The output from the computer program can be put, optionally on reproducible master operation cards, or on labor tickets and operation cards. If he wishes, the engineer can enter a computer planning program with punched cards which are manually created after inspection of a drawing. And because the method is standardized, the input data can be prepared by clerical help rather than the manufacturing engineer.

After all operations have been printed, the computer summarizes the manhours for each department. These times plus the total manhours per core are used for scheduling purposes and for estimating costs of proposed designs.

For the company, computer planning provides unique manufacturing advantages over-all: While encouraging the standardization of design and manufacturing methods, it does allow considerable flexibility. Result: A large number of different sizes and configurations of the product fall within the new range of economical manufacture.

Mechanizing Tool Design

The computer is an integral part of cutting tool engineering at Barber-Colman Co., Rockford, Ill. . . . The computer, a Bendix G-15D, not only relieves tedious calculation but eliminates special development costs that tie up machines and manpower in the shop making sample tool forms. Now the designer fills out a format consisting mostly of customer information including a choice of how the tool is to be manufactured. In the case of a worm gear hob, inputs may be for a cutter cut worm, a hobbed worm or a plot from a sample worm. The engineer takes about ten minutes to fill out an input format and check the customer information. Running time to find the form of the tool and related tooling required for manufacture is 25 minutes. The output is in the form of horizontal and vertical

coordinates, and the designer may analyze the points by layout or send them back to the computer to be analyzed.

Besides saving time and money, the computer solution eliminates the errors which occur in the shop while attempting to duplicate the sample form. A better product is made at a lower cost and delivery promise dates are kept.

* * *

Computer Rushes Stock Orders

Computer-aided design is part of a rapid order processing system at Westinghouse Motor & Gearing Division at Buffalo. RONS (Rapid Order Negotiation Service) is designed to have a stock motor into the shipping department a half-hour after a sales office receives a customer's order. An IBM 305 RAMAC governs not only the filling of orders for 15,000 different motors available from stock, but is programmed to provide specifications for new motor designs based on customer requirements. After the new electrical specifications are translated into computer language, the data for the new design is printed out in a few minutes instead of a day or two, and is ready for turning over to manufacturing.

Key to the effectiveness of the RONS system is an expediting force at the plant made up of specialists: Salesmen, order interpreters, motor engineers, manufacturing information writers, product coordinators, stock controllers, order service correspondents, teletype operators and draftsmen. Each has a responsible part in the computer-controlled process that reduces the gap between order and shipment of stock items from a prior period of five days to 30 minutes.

* * *

A "Window" into the Future

Those engineers who fear the loss of their pencils and scratchpads to "the machine" can take heart; a sketchpad technique has been adapted to computer technology. A few years ago, a 26-year-old scientist, Ivan E. Sutherland of MIT, connected together a computer and an oscilloscope, and devised a unique "light pen"—a built-in electronic marker—as a data input device. Now available commercially, the light pen enables an operator to communicate with the computer. With the light pen, data flashed on the cathode tube screen is manipulated and "erased" at will. Instantaneous computational response of the computer shows the influence of changes in the new results on the screen. Alpha-numeric symbols and lines stored in

a buffer storage are displayed on the screen as a series of close-linked, tiny dots.

Called "a window into the computer," these visual display devices are used primarily as an engineering tool; however, they are applicable to production.   As IBM's Dr. Joseph Orlicky conjectures: "Suppose a production manager desires to learn the schedule for his machine floor for the following six weeks.   He presses certain coded buttons on the visual display console and is presented with that schedule on the TV-like screen.

"Looking closely, the manager notices a bottleneck in a particular section of the schedule.   With the light pen (or with buttons), he erases portions of the schedule, moves jobs around into different periods and writes in the new schedule.   He calls for a picture of the revised schedule to check the results and for other possible obstacles.   Thus, the manager is assured of an optimum schedule while saving precious time."

Gifford Valve Company

The Gifford Valve Company, one of eight major manufacturers of hydraulic control valves, pumps, and motors, was considering installing automatic data-processing equipment for controlling its production and consolidating its cost, billing, and payroll procedures into an integrated accounting system. The valve company had recently experienced a major growth in sales, which, according to the President, was due in large part to the recent elimination of late orders and a general reduction in delivery time. The Gifford management expected this growth in sales to continue at an annual rate of 12 per cent or better during the next two years. The growth in volume had caused the Production Manager to initiate a study of the requirements for automating the present production control system. He felt that Gifford's present production rate of 1,000 valves per week was the maximum the present production control group could handle. He thought by introducing data processing he could expand the capacity of the control system and obtain more detailed and timely information.

The Gifford company is considered by both government contractors and machine tool manufacturers to offer one of the most advanced engineered hydraulic products available. Their product line includes a wide range of control, relief, and special purpose valves in addition to a line of hydraulic pumps and motors (see Exhibit 1). Demand for hydraulic equipment has grown rapidly since 1952 as it is used extensively in missile launching sites, automatic handling equipment, and variable speed drives. However, up until 1958 Gifford had not enjoyed the general growth of industry but had tended to seek customers for specially engineered products. G. J. Woeffel, President of Gifford, commented that this sales policy was in large part due to the long lead time Gifford required to produce a product. In 1958 the

567

EXHIBIT 1   GIFFORD VALVE COMPANY

HYDRAULIC CONTROL VALVES

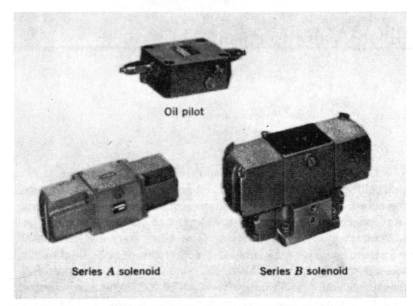

Oil pilot

Series *A* solenoid   Series *B* solenoid

INTERCHANGEABLE PILOT UNITS

A choice, from several pilot units is offered to satisfy the conditions of each individual system. Each of these units has its own characteristics with many extra advantages which cannot be combined into a smaller selection. Identical mounting surfaces allow field interchangeability, minimizing stocking requirements.

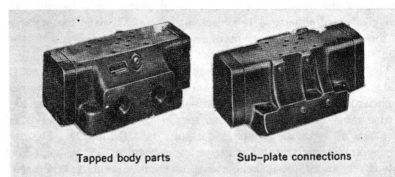

Tapped body parts   Sub–plate connections

INTERCHANGEABLE BODY ASSEMBLIES

A variety of connections are available on the main body sections of valves using the pilot units described above. These may have taper pipe or SAE straight threads in the body, taper pipe thread or welding type flanges, or gasketed connections for sub-plate mounting.

CIRCUITSTAK (SANDWICH) CONSTRUCTION

Certain pressure and flow rate controls can be furnished for mounting between the pilot unit and main body section, and others for mounting between the main body section and the sub-plate. These "sandwiches" reduce the amount of piping necessary and provide easy alteration of existing systems. They are usually space saving on new installations and allow greater latitude in design.

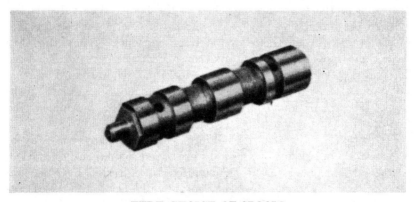

WIDE CHOICE OF SPOOLS

Fifteen different spools are cataloged for each of the above valves. These spools are interchangeable and satisfy a wide variety of circuit requirements. Each of these spools can be furnished spring centered, spring offset or with two-position detents. Ground angles on the spools minimize the shock in shifting. The speed of shifting can be regulated with optional throttling controls.

minimum lead time had been six weeks, and over 50 per cent of all orders were late. The emphasis on specialty products had increased the lead time due to engineering and tooling requirements. The trend toward longer lead times was reversed in late 1958. By 1962 Gifford's reputation among users as a reliable manufacturer had improved considerably as evidenced by a 200 per cent growth in standard valve sales over the three-year period. As of May 1962 all standard valves were consistently being delivered in two weeks, and specially engineered orders required only six to eight weeks.

This reduction in process time was a result of concentrating sales efforts on standard products, fabricating parts in larger lots, establishing finished valve and fabricated parts inventories, and improving the production process by new equipment, new layouts, and better work methods. Capacity had grown from fewer than 600 valves per week to over 1,000 valves and 300 hydraulic pumps per week. During this expansion the number of employees remained constant at about 300 men and women; about 180 of these were direct labor employees working on two shifts. Mr. Woeffel attributed a major portion of the productivity gain to manufacturing in lots of 160–200 rather than one or two units.

Production of hydraulic valves accounted for over 80 per cent of the output of Gifford's productive facilities. A hydraulic valve is composed of a valve body which contains one or more channels through which fluid can flow and a valve spool or plunger for controlling the flow. Devices which control the spool and thus the operation of the valve are attached to the body. The valve bodies start in the production process as purchased castings which are first rough ground to eliminate foundry attachments. They are then drilled and tapped for tubing and control connections and deburred. The valve spool is typically of bar stock and requires turning on a lathe and grinding on a centerless grinder to obtain correct dimensions. The spools and bodies are then heat-treated, assembled, and forwarded to inspection to be tested.

Production facilities of the Gifford Valve Company consisted of a large machine shop, an assembly area, and a final inspection and test area. The manufacturing operation was directed by a general foreman and organized into eight departments: (1) Lathe, (2) Drilling, (3) Grinding, (4) Heat-Treating, (5) Milling, (6) Deburring and Degreasing, (7) Assembly, and (8) Final Test and Inspection. A foreman was in charge of each department and reported to the general foreman.

PAST PRODUCTION CONTROL PROCEDURES

In 1958, Richard Stafford, a recent graduate of a well-known eastern business school, was hired by Gifford Valve Company as Controller and Production Manager. The Board of Directors instructed him to improve delivery times and to reduce operating costs as quickly as possible. In considering the production control practices at that time, Mr. Stafford said that he had found few systematic routines, and it seemed the shop had expanded beyond the capabilities of the intuitive approach used by the foreman. Raw material inventory control was maintained on cards by the stock control clerks with neither formal follow-up on actual status of stocks nor routine order procedures. The only control evident in the shop was identification tickets on parts by order number and expediters who worked for the general foreman to keep things moving. The manufacture of all valves was initiated and controlled by the customer order, whether it was for a standard product or a specially designed valve. Engineering dispatched all jobs to the shop when they had completed their designwork. Each foreman routed work from his department to the next appropriate department.

Mr. Stafford outlined the evolution of the present inventory classification system, routing, scheduling, and dispatching procedures to explain how the production process was controlled in the spring of 1962. His first goal had been to standardize procedures on the bulk of parts and encourage the Sales Department to concentrate their efforts on these standard parts.

The first step toward standardization of operating procedures had been to classify the valves according to market usage to provide a basis for control. Each of the 900 valve types in process or on order were classified into one of four categories, depending on their market potential. This classification formed the basis of the control system in May 1962. Class I consisted of all valves for which demand warranted the maintenance of an inventory of assembled valves. Class II consisted of those valves for which a smaller demand existed and which were subject to modifications; for Class II valves a supply of unassembled finished parts was maintained. Class III included those valves for which the demand was fairly predictable but which could not be fabricated beforehand because of the unknown design requirement of each customer; it also included those valves for which the demand was not adequate to warrant large runs. An inventory of

raw materials such as castings or special solenoids was maintained for Class III valves. Class IV consisted of all those valves built for a specific customer's desires and not normally manufactured at Gifford; no stock of these valves was maintained. As of May 1962 there were 405 Class I and II valves.

Mr. Stafford had next considered the production process itself with the intention of establishing better stock control of in-process and finished parts. In 1962 the Class I and II valves included 6,400 different parts, ranging from valve bodies to cap screws. Mr. Stafford noted that it took over four months to collect the basic data on the inventoried parts—their economic value, manufacturing time, purchase lead time, and the past year's demand for the part. Given the lead time and the cost information, all inventoried parts were put into one of three classes, A, B, or C, and a control procedure was established for each class. This classification was in full operation in May 1962; all inventory accounting was performed in the production control area on individual inventory record cards maintained in large file bins.

Class A parts were those for which a continual control was required because of usage or long lead time; a perpetual committed inventory record was maintained on all Class A parts. As an order was received for a Class II or III or out of stock Class I valve the number of parts to complete the order was subtracted from the stock balance and the order number recorded. When the uncommitted quantity of parts reached a preset minimum, an automatic manufacturing order was submitted by the stock control clerk for more parts. The order quantity was evaluated at least once each quarter to determine if the demand for the part had changed during the immediately preceding period.

Class B parts were those with a short lead time for which a fairly constant demand existed. They were often used in a number of different valves or pumps and included valve spools, end plates, and standard solenoids. A perpetual inventory was maintained in the production control center as the parts were utilized.

Class C parts were considered economically insignificant or were available from suppliers on a day's notice and no inventory record was maintained. As a Class C part was received, a label was attached to the last box in the bin directing the stock clerk to place an order for more parts when that box was opened. Typical Class C parts included bolts, screws, rivets, and plastic covers.

PRESENT PRODUCTION CONTROL PROCEDURES

Mr. Stafford had then established standard production control procedures to build up and maintain an inventory of Class I and II parts. In conjunction with Jim Swain, the production control expediter who had been at Gifford for six years, Mr. Stafford created a standard automatic manufacturing ordering procedure for Class I valves. Using a forecast prepared by the Sales Department in conjunction with production control, they established standard assembly quantities. These assembly requirements were exploded into projected parts requirements. On the basis of these requirements and estimated lead times, Mr. Swain set minimum stock levels for the parts.

When the system was first introduced, the shop worked overtime each Saturday to build up inventories and still meet outstanding obligations. It had been Mr. Stafford's goal to have all parts in inventory by the end of 1960. He commented that this had proved impossible since as soon as parts could be assembled from inventory, lead times were reduced and sales expanded, thereby reducing the inventory. As of May 1962 they were still working overtime and had achieved only 20 per cent of the finished goods inventory goal.

In the spring of 1959 Mr. Stafford hired Roland Watson, an experienced production controller, to supervise the production control section. Mr. Watson introduced an order-board follow-up procedure to enable Mr. Swain, the routers—Jack Pingry and Tom Nielander—and the foremen to keep track of what was happening, and to provide a more orderly planning procedure for parts. The order board listed every sales order for which delivery was promised during the next three weeks. Exhibit 2 is an example of how an order was posted on the board. The sales orders were grouped according to the Saturday of the week they were due to be shipped. Each order listed all valves and noted whether they were ready to go or not; if not, the parts responsible for delaying the assembly were identified or other necessary steps noted. Mr. Watson's goal was to have all Class I valves listed on the board followed by the date they were shipped from inventory.

By 1962 the order board had become the basic tool for the control and planning for the shop. Mr. Swain indicated that he didn't care how they automated the procedure as long as the board remained. Each Monday Mr. Watson, Mr. Swain, and the two routers, Mr. Pingry and Mr. Nielander, met with all the foremen to discuss all parts overdue, parts holding up assemblies, and possible machine bottle-

EXHIBIT 2 CONTROL BOARD SALES ORDER

SHIPMENT SCHEDULE — FOR WEEK ENDING 12-1

S.O. NO.	CUSTOMER	QTY. VALVES	VALVE AND PART NOS.	LOCATION OR PART NAMES	QTY. NEEDED	CLASS	LOCATION R.M.	H.M.	D.	H.G.	C.U.	ORIG. DEL'Y. DATE	NEW DEL'Y. DATE
6565	Butterfly	1	B+JF-10-14A 1	17-17									
			9671-8 body	1									
			9783-18 body	1									
			9809- plunger	1									
			9807- seat	1									
			9835-2 Cap	1									
			7587-8 spool	1									
			7588-5 sleeve	1									
			8843 spring	1									
			(1) F2-12wP										
		1	QBJ-06-16A1	16-17									
		1	QBJ-06-3M-15A1	16-4									
		1	QBJ-06-3M-17A1	18-17									
			9783-12 body	3									
			9661 spool	3									
			9835-2 Cap	2									
			7588-5 sleeve	3									
			7587-6 spool	1									
			7587-7 spool	1									
			7587-8 spool	1									

necks. Parts in fabrication that were necessary for orders to be shipped by Saturday were considered "hot" jobs; those holding up parts for the following week were considered top priority jobs; and those holding up parts for two weeks hence were noted and, if a Class I or II valve, considered priority. Mr. Pingry noted that they had been running on an average of 20 hot jobs a week during the spring of 1962; however, he considered this a low number since there were about 1,400 jobs in the shop at that time. Each Wednesday, the schedule was again reviewed and the status of all hot jobs discussed.

Mr. Swain mentioned that both Pingry and Nielander had over eight years' experience as machinists. This shop experience helped them to maintain a close working relationship with the foreman. The routers checked the tardy jobs at least once each day. Often a foreman called in to the routers when a hot job had been completed or came to the control board and drew a line through the completed part name and initialed the line.

Mr. Stafford hoped to achieve on-time delivery for at least 96 per cent of the orders. In commenting on this goal he considered it a prime part of Gifford's marketing strategy to insure prompt delivery

and felt 96 per cent was within the capacity of the production facilities. The goal was achieved in the winter of 1962 when less than 50 valves were late. However, the expansion of sales during the spring caused the backlog to build up, with a resultant increase in late orders. He felt this backlog would be further complicated by the annual plant-wide vacation the first two weeks in July.

PRESENT PRODUCTION SCHEDULING PROCEDURES

After the order board was functioning and it became apparent that inventories were not building up as anticipated, further planning procedures were introduced. The following procedure superseded Mr. Swain's preset parts minimums and was utilized in May 1962 for pre-planning production.

At the beginning of each month, Mr. Watson's clerk prepared a monthly ordering summary which listed for all Class I and II valves the number on hand, the past month's shipments, the number of valves in process, the back orders for these valves, and those available in inventory (see Exhibit 3). Mr. Stafford and Mr. Watson felt they would be able to meet the expanding demand if all Class I valves could have a seven-month backlog of valves in process, Class II a six-month supply of parts in process, and for Class III at least a five-month supply of critical raw material on hand. Each month Mr. Watson initiated assembly orders for all those valves which did not meet the minimum requirements by giving Mr. Swain a list of the number of assembled valves or valve parts required.

Mr. Swain issued assembly orders identifying the required parts for the valves to the stock controllers, Tom McConnell and Al Campbell. The stock controllers deducted the number of parts from the perpetual inventory record of Class A parts and forwarded the assembly order to the Assembly Department. Often these orders exceeded the supply on hand; this required a manufacturing order to fabricate the parts in a standard lot. In May 1962 no time data was available to determine an E.O.Q.; the lot size was set equal to three months' usage. This automatic dispatch of parts for inventory based on past demand was implemented to create a buffer of in-process parts. Such orders were low on priority of processing as they had no sales order. However, by 1962 they constituted 75 per cent of the fabrication volume in a typical lot size of 160 to 400 parts.

EXHIBIT 3 MONTHLY ORDERING SUMMARY

STANDARD AND SEMI-STANDARD VALVES (No special orders to be included)

MONTHLY ORDERING SUMMARY
STANDARD & SEMI-STANDARD VALVES
(NO SPECIAL ORDERS TO BE INCLUDED)

A CLASS	SYMBOL NUMBER 62-2	*B ON HAND FINISHED VALVES	C PREVIOUS 2 MONTHS SHIPMENTS	*D IN PROCESS	*E BACK ORDERS	F NOT SOLD (AVAILABLE)	*G LAST 3-MONTHS AVERAGE ORDERS	*G LAST 3-MONTHS LARGE SINGLE ORDERS	*H LAST 6-MONTHS AVERAGE ORDERS	*H LAST 6-MONTHS LARGE SINGLE ORDERS	*I ESTIMATED MONTHLY ORDERS	J PRESENT SUPPLY IN MONTHS	*K PROJECTED CASTING ORDER	L ORDER POINT (MNTHS)
	A. RELIEF VALVES													
1	BB-02	52	152	250	17	285	57	20,24,10,10,14	57	25,25,14	60	4.8	new ✓ 500	*7
1	BB2-155 FL	4	68	316	14	306	37	25,24,10,13,10	33	10	40	7.7		*7
1	CA5-160	37	156	438	6	469	91	180	70	38,10,10	60	7.8		*7
1	QB7-175 (165 & 170)	0	26	191	16	175	15	—	16	10	15	11.7		*7
3	*BTP-175 / BTP2-175	1	1	55	10	46	0	—	3	—	2	23.0		
1	QB6-185 (180 & 190)	49	27	119	39	129	8	—	15	30	10	12.9		
1	BT-03 & BT3-165		108		15		46	11,15	38	12,16				
1	BT-04 & BT3-170		23		23		11		12	15				
1	BT-06 & BT3-175				6 Can. 544		373	37,39,25 / 239,74,99,80,66	268	10,10,10,10 / 30,15,25,15,124	300	2.5	new ✓ 2000	*7
	TOTAL	28	691	1291	582	737	430		318		300			
1	BT4-180	0	13		8		6	—	6	—				
1	BT4-185	4	91		72		53	97,16	42	11,10				
1	BT4-190	0	16		17		8	—	7	—				
	TOTAL	4	120	446	97	353	67		55		65	5.9	old style ✓ 500	*7
3	BTF3-175 (165-170) / *BTF-06 (03 & 04)	3	15	99	5	97	6	—	6	—	7	13.9		
2	BTF5-185 (180 & 190)	1	14	129	29	101	9	—	14	16,10	11	9.2		
3	*BTF-195	0	5	91	35	56	2	—	7	30	5	11.2		
							769							
	B. SOLENOID RELIEF VALVES													
2	QBJ-06 / QBJ7-175 (165 & 170)	0	21	42	3	39	7	—	7	—	8	4.9	new ✓ 50	
2	QBJ6-185 / QBJ-10 (08 & 12)	1	41	163	102	62	40	50,50,15	33	50,15	25	3.5	new ✓ 200	
3	QBD3-175	0	0	0	0	0	0	—	0	—	0	0		
		1			955		769		634		0			

STANDARD DISPATCHING PROCEDURE

In May 1962 standard parts fabrication was initiated by one of the stock controllers who forwarded a manufacturing order to the Manufacturing Engineering Department for a process plan. The process plan consisted of a blueprint and master route card and was placed in a plastic envelope referred to as a shop packet. The packet was forwarded to Mr. Swain for data preparation and dispatching to the shop. When Mr. Swain received the packet, he assigned a job order and starting date and sent the master process list for each part to Dee Windecker, his assistant clerk. Miss Windecker typed out a list of the process steps and reproduced one master route card and two timecards for each operation. She added these cards and a blue-edged card, the manufacturing order on which she wrote the order and part numbers, to the shop packet.

The shop packet was then given to Mr. McConnell, the casting parts and raw material stock controller, who subtracted the necessary amount of raw material from his record, ordered material if necessary, and forwarded the order to Mr. Campbell, the bar stock manufactured parts inventory controller. Mr. Campbell performed the same routine for the bar stock requirements and placed the packets in a long box along the wall of the production control office. This box was divided into sections, one for each department; the job was placed in the section of the first operation—for example, the Lathe department—to be performed in accordance with its starting date.

For Class III and IV parts a different procedure was established providing an adequate dispatching procedure for introducing non-standard shop orders into the plant. All incoming Class III and IV orders went to Mr. Swain who considered how standard products might be modified and forwarded the order with such modifications to engineering. At this time Mr. Swain recorded all long leadtime raw materials and notified his purchase orderer, Helen Storm, of the desired purchase. Engineering, upon completion of its design specifications, forwarded the blueprints to the Manufacturing Engineering Department where a process plan listing the steps of manufacture for each part of the valve was compiled and the assembly procedures were defined. The plans were then placed in a plastic envelope and proceeded as a standard packet.

Once jobs were in the shop, the routers and foremen directed them from one department to the next as identified on the route card. There was no formal record of this progress, but both Pingry and

Nielander were able to keep track of most jobs. At times in 1962 there were as many as 1,400 different lots in the shop, each with an average of nine operations per lot. Mr. Stafford commented that it was amazing at times how quickly Pingry and Nielander could locate a job; they seemed to be able to sense future bottlenecks before they occurred. He attributed this to the regularity of the process and similarity of parts in addition to the routers' eight years of shop experience.

PRESENT PRODUCTION CONTROL PROBLEMS

In the fall of 1961 Mr. Stafford began to be concerned that the company was reaching the upper level of its present production control capacity. Planning procedures seemed to provide adequate control at an 800 to 900 valve-per-week rate; but as it grew to the 1,000 rate and a 1,200 valve-per-week output was attempted, Pingry and Nielander seemed to be unable to maintain control of all parts. The backlog of overdue orders had been building up and inventories of finished parts were being reduced. Mr. Stafford felt that with better information on the status of jobs in the shop better scheduling and routing might improve the output by 12 per cent. This could come from improved sequencing of similar lots through departments and detection of under-utilized departments in order to provide an even distribution of work in the shop. It was difficult for Mr. Stafford to estimate what utilization improvement was possible, since he had no data and there had been several equipment changes which made past experience unreliable for present evaluations. Mr. Stafford's projections of sales indicated they would have to climb to 1,200 or 1,800 valves-per-week by the summer of 1963 to maintain the same level of work force because of productivity increases, and to realize reasonable profits on the improved production facilities and expanded inventories. Although he had considered hiring a third router from the shop this would not necessarily have increased the capacity of the control system by 50 per cent. He felt further additions might increase confusion rather than capacity.

INVESTIGATION OF THE FEASIBILITY OF AUTOMATIC DATA PROCESSING

Mr. Stafford decided to investigate the feasibility of automating the present control procedures. This might allow his present staff

to expand their control capacity and in the long run provide the company with the best capacity for growth. With automatic data collection and processing he felt he might be able to obtain information concerning actual labor cost per part, actual machine-loading data which were not available at present, and additional data necessary to improve costs control. Although this information could be obtained manually, he felt it might be performed more economically with data-processing equipment.

In September Mr. Stafford contacted several large data-processing equipment manufacturers and presented his problem to them. Two of these firms produced some tangible evidence of interest and help. One sent a competent systems analyst to the plant who spent a week with Mr. Stafford, showing possible ways the present system might be automated. In fact, he provided most of the information required to continue the consideration of data-processing. During this investigation Mr. Stafford decided the best course of action for Gifford was to automate cost accounting, billing, and production control procedures.

In considering what to do next, Mr. Stafford and Mr. Woeffel decided that a consultant would not really be able to understand adequately Gifford's problems, nor would he be able to stay with the company to implement the decision. They decided, therefore, to hire a man as a permanent employee to carry out an investigation of how the present system should be automated and to implement the results of his analysis. After a six-month search, Mr. Stafford found and hired John S. Ivey, a man of 17 years' experience in the data-processing field. Mr. Ivey commenced work for Gifford Valve on March 1, 1962, to investigate the possibility of using automatic equipment to acquire improved and timely information for production control and to combine cost control and billing into one integrated accounting system.

At the same time a program was started to establish standard times with the use of MTM on all jobs. The plan was to have this data available for all Class A parts dispatched to the shop after September 1, 1962. Thus, in addition to the present standard process procedures the packet would include standard times for both processing and set-up. It was hoped that the systems being designed by Mr. Ivey could incorporate these standards and use them for standard cost procedures.

In discussing Mr. Ivey's assignment Mr. Stafford indicated that hiring a data-processing expert implied a commitment to involve Gifford Valve in some form of automated data processing. He was

not sure what form this should take and charged Mr. Ivey with making a complete analysis of Gifford's information and control systems to define what would be required to have an integrated exception reporting system. Mr. Stafford also recommended that at least one other system, less costly than the complete one, be designed. He believed that if he had a complete system he could better evaluate just how much Gifford could afford to use and how much it really could improve on the present system. Mr. Ivey was given until June 15 to provide a comparative analysis of cost of the other integrative systems and of improving the present manual production control system to include machine loading and more extensive labor hour accounting.

THE DESIGN OF OTHER INFORMATION SYSTEMS

Mr. Ivey said he felt a bit rushed since normally such a study would require at least six months. However, his 17 years of experience in data-processing systems enabled him to formulate working systems, ask the right questions, and expedite the normal investigation procedures. Furthermore, the management of the company had prepared the employees for the introduction of automatic equipment and guaranteed that no employee would lose his job. This created an environment that was receptive to questions and helpful in defining problems. Mr. Ivey did not have to spend time allaying fears and doubts but obtained complete cooperation from everyone he interviewed.

In discussing his assignment with Mr. Stafford, he had expressed the opinion that a data-processing system was no better than the people who used it and that its success depended on their acceptance and implementation of the procedures. Mr. Ivey felt a study should include and involve the individuals who would eventually use the information he could provide for them. With this in mind he spent about four weeks interviewing Mr. Watson and his crew, the accountants, and the billing clerks as to what they needed, examining past records of the company, and familiarizing himself with the valve business.

As a part of this analysis Mr. Ivey gathered data on the quantity and type of information that Gifford Valve managers required. In the production control area, he sampled the operation to obtain the information shown in Exhibit 4.

During the analysis of the system Mr. Ivey made a careful ap-

EXHIBIT 4   INFORMATION STATISTICS

281	Direct labor employees
	Average of 18 lots into shop per day-range is 3 to 56
163	Different operations completed per day
9.2	Operations per lot
395	Labor cards per day turned in at completion of job
262	Direct
133	Indirect
511	Labor cards if all report each day
351	Direct
160	Indirect
	With prepunched labor cards 4 per cent would still have to be hand written
7,355	Parts in inventory
3,500–4,000	Bills of material (assemblies)
405	Standard parts (Class 1 and 2)
42,095	Operation sheets
311	Different machines
1,000–1,500	Different jobs in shop at one time

praisal of available equipment. His own training and, in fact, Mr. Stafford's interest led him to the large data-processing equipment manufacturer who had assisted Gifford Valve in the early stages of the data-processing investigations. Considering the requirements, Mr. Ivey felt two courses besides the present manual system were open to Gifford: (1) an electromechanical system of punched cards utilizing card-sorting and tabulation equipment which was called a unit record system, and (2) a complete automated system which would involve storing all of the job information in a large disc file computer. The design of the system and evaluation of the equipment continued simultaneously and resulted in a set of specifications for the equipment required to implement the systems designed by Mr. Ivey.

From approximate data requirements and a notion of what equipment he would use Mr. Ivey formulated a complete model of what he felt the system should be. For example one part of the system was the labor cost control; Mr. Ivey designed the employee card and decided how it would be processed in the Accounting Department, who would get the information, and the form of the reports to the managers. He then went to each individual member associated with labor accounting and discussed it with them. He reformulated the design so that it was as close to their desires as possible and still com-

EXHIBIT 5   STRAIGHT TIME EARNINGS CARD PROCESSING ANALYSIS

---

1. Sort labor cards in clock number sequence, columns 49 through 52.
2. Merge employee hourly rate (master) cards in front of matching labor cards (clock number), columns 49 through 52. Select unequal secondary cards.
3. Intersperse gang punch employee hourly rate, columns 46 through 48. (Master cards contain x, column 20.)   Verify clock number and employee hourly rate, columns 46 through 52. Use punch x 4 and read x 4.
4. Separate master employee hourly rate cards from labor cards, zone column 20.   Lock out zero.   Rejects are labor cards x pocket cards are master employee hourly rate cards. File rate cards.
5. Calculate straight time earnings:
   actual hours, columns 68 through 70 (XX.X) times employee hourly rate, columns 46 through 48 (X.XX) equals straight time earnings. (XX.XX) Punch straight time earnings in columns 77 through 80.
6. List a straight time earnings report. Show:
   clock number, columns 49 through 52, minor control; employee hourly rate, columns 46 through 48; actual hours, columns 68 through 70, minor and final totals; straight time earnings, columns 77 through 80, minor and final totals.
7. File cards for use in cost analysis reports.

---

patible with the equipment, keeping in mind how it would fit into his over-all information system. (See Exhibit 5 for an example of one step in setting up the labor cost system.)   When two people wanted different things in one system he persuaded them to compromise to a single method by demonstrating how the proposed equipment could best handle the data.

DESCRIPTION OF PROPOSED
INFORMATION SYSTEMS

After completing the detailed system definitions based upon the information requirements, Mr. Ivey made a cost analysis of two different automated systems compared to an improved manual system. (See Exhibit 6.)   He expanded the current system to include information on machine-loading and labor cost-accounting in accordance with Mr. Stafford's desired controls.   He felt the fully integrated system would require a small random access computer and would have to be fully automated.   His alternative proposal was to put all present information on punched cards and process them on electromechanical accounting machines.   This unit record system would be

EXHIBIT 6 GIFFORD VALVE COMPANY

June 15, 1962
Butler, Maryland

To: Mr. R. L. Stafford
From: Mr. J. S. Ivey
Subject: Data-Processing Proposal

OBJECTIVE

A recommended management operating system through the use of accounting and statistical reporting. The system should be fully integrated, use exception type of reporting, and keep production information currently updated to provide fast reply to customer and management inquiry.

EQUIPMENT REQUIREMENTS

1. Large storage capacity
2. Moderate processing speed
3. Capable of being interrogated
4. Equipped to add, subtract, multiply, and divide
5. Process low-volume daily input
6. Moderate output (punched cards for detail reporting and auxiliary typewriter for exception reporting)
7. Peripheral equipment for key punching, sorting, reproducing, interpreting, and volume detail tabulating

RECOMMENDED EQUIPMENT FOR TOTAL OBJECTIVE

1. One random access computer without the standard printer
2. One accounting machine (tabulator)
3. One reproducer
4. One interpreter
5. One sorter
6. One printing key punch
      (Items 2 through 6, peripheral equipment)
Total monthly equipment rental $2,766.34 (including taxes)
Personnel—two machine operators and one key punch operator

RECOMMENDED EQUIPMENT FOR INTERIM PERIOD

1. One accounting machine ⎫
2. One reproducer   ⎪
3. One interpreter   ⎬ Equipment which will remain peripheral to the
4. One sorter   ⎪ computer system
5. One printing key punch ⎭
6. One verifier, alphanumeric—to be returned after master files are punched
7. One calculator—to be returned upon installation of the computer.

Total monthly equipment rental $820.52 to $876.72 (including taxes and the variance being the type 056 verifier rental)
Personnel—two machine operators and one key punch operator (one verifier operator on a temporary basis)
The purpose of the interim period is to prepare and verify data for storage in the computer and to produce detail reports for analysis of reporting values.

EXHIBIT 6 *(Continued)*   GIFFORD VALVE COMPANY

It should be noted that this equipment will produce timely reports in detail form showing activity on all items instead of reporting only exceptions. This detail form of reporting is necessary for a period of total analysis but is cumbersome and wasteful as compared to the daily "management by exception" control reporting.

INSTALLATION TIMING

September 1, 1962:	One printing key punch
	One verifier, alphanumeric
September 15, 1962:	One accounting machine
	One reproducer
	One interpreter
	One sorter
	One calculator
January 1, 1963:	Return one verifier, alphanumeric
April 1, 1963:	One random access computer without the standard printer
	Return one calculator

REPORTS *(For processing cost comparison see Chart #1)*

A fully integrated system of reporting should be a flexible one which allows for human decision and intervention. While being integrated, the reports are designed separately to be tools which aid management decision and are in no way designed with the intent to replace human decision.

The following reports are recommended:

1. *Productivity:* Prepared daily and shows the per cent of productivity based on actual and standard hours. Report requested and used by Manufacturing Engineering.
2. *Labor audit:* Prepared daily for report control and audit trail, and is used by Accounting and Tabulating Departments.
3. *Completed lot:* Prepared daily for the lots that are completed on the report date, and shows the cost and time consumed to produce the lot. The report will be used by Accounting and Production Control Departments.
4. *Production control:* Prepared daily showing the status of work in process by lot and operation. For use by foremen and Production Control Department.
5. *Orders and Billing:* Processed daily. By-product cards are used to prepare manpower, equipment and material requirements and for sales accounting and statistics.
6. *Stock status:* A detail report prepared weekly during interim period (after the computer is installed this report will be produced on request only. It will become a daily "management by exception" operation). The weekly detail will be used by Production Control Department for inventory control.
7. *Update inventory:* Processed several times daily after the computer system is installed. Each time data transactions are processed through the

EXHIBIT 6 (*Continued*)   GIFFORD VALVE COMPANY

CHART #1

Report Cost Comparison

	Prepared Now		Manual/Other		Unit Record		Computer Installation	
	Labor		Labor		Lab. Mat'l. and Rental		Lab. Mat'l. and Rental	
	Hours	$ Mo.	Hours	$ Mo.	% Ut.	$ Mo.	%	$ Per Mo.
Daily Report Processing:								
Productivity	—	—	193.5	483.75	7.0	170.31	4.0	175.12
Daily Labor Audit	150.5	376.25	—	—	7.0	170.31	1.0	43.78
Completed Lot Report	100.0	250.00	100.0	250.00	7.0	170.31	3.0	131.34
Production Control	172.0	430.00	—	—	15.0	364.95	4.0	175.12
Billing	508.0	1270.00	—	—	5.0	121.65	2.0	87.56
Update Inventory	80.0	200.00	—	—	—	—	10.0	437.80
Prepare Labor Cards	20.0	50.00	—	—	8.0	194.64	6.0	262.68
Weekly Report Processing:								
Stock Status	—	—	20.0	50.00	20.3	493.90	—	—
Factory Payroll Summary	—	—	—	—	6.0	145.98	.2	8.76
Factory Pay. Reg. and Cks.	24.0	60.00	—	—	1.5	36.50	.3	13.13
Monthly Report Processing:								
Labor Cost Analysis	—	—	190.0	475.00	.8	19.46	.6	26.27
Sales Statistical Analysis	—	—	196.0	490.00	.4	9.73	.2	8.76
Gross Sales—Accounting	—	—	—	—	.4	9.73	.2	8.76
Quarter and Annual Report Processing:								
SSlb (Qtr.)	1.3	3.25	—	—	.3	7.30	.1	4.38
Inventory (Semi-annual)	46.7	116.75	—	—	.4	9.73	.1	4.38
W-2 (Annual)	.4	1.00	—	—	.1	2.43	.1	4.38
Other:								
Accounts Payable*								
Budget and Expense Statements*	Not Available		Not Available		Not Available			
Simulation and Mg't. Requests							10.0	437.80
TOTAL	1102.9	$2757.25	699.5	$1748.75	79.2% Rental	$1926.93	41.8% Rental	$1830.02
	1802.4	$4506.00				1033}2433		2978}4378
						1400		1400
	$2.50 per hour				$14.40 per hour		$25.45 per hour	

* No estimate at this time.

EXHIBIT 6 (*Continued*) GIFFORD VALVE COMPANY

---

computer certain programmed controls are checked and exceptions (such as reorder point, out of stock, etc.) will be indicated by a typewritten message. Also the prepunched labor cards will be prepared in this operation.

8. *Prepare prepunched labor cards:* No report, but a daily operation to prepare time cards for each operation in each production lot. With the computer this operation is a by-product of updating the inventory.
9. *Factory payroll summary:* Prepared weekly. A report summarizing gross earnings by employee. Used by Accounting and Tabulating Departments.
10. *Factory payroll register and checks:* Prepared weekly.
11. *Labor cost analysis:* Prepared monthly. Showing cost by operations during the month, and a comparison of actual to standard (variance). Used by the Accounting Department.
12. *Sales statistical analysis:* Prepared monthly, showing shipments, orders and quota by distributor or customer, current month and year to date. For use by the Sales Department.
13. *Gross sales:* Prepared monthly, reporting sales and returns by product class. Used by the Accounting Department.
14. SSlb and federal withholding form W-2: Prepared quarterly and annually respectively. These forms are required by law and are a by-product of payroll.
15. *Physical inventory:* Prepared semiannually from the physical count of inventory. Used by Accounting and Production Control Departments.
16. *Other reports;* such as Accounts Payable and Receivable, Budget and Expense, Simulation Studies, etc., are a part of Management Operating Reports will be evaluated at a later date.

STATISTICS:

1. File arrangement in the computer (tentative):

a. Reserved for part number information—inventory, routing and labor cost (Bills of Material not maintained in memory file)	40,000
b. Sales statistical and accounting	5,000
c. Employee records	1,000
d. Expense statements	2,000
e. Open	2,000
TOTAL	50,000

2. Labor (Based on 14 days):

	Average per day
a. Current direct labor timecards	237
b. Current indirect labor timecards	120
c. Current total timecards	357
d. Direct labor timecards—if reported daily	295
e. Indirect labor timecards—if reported daily	135
f. Total timecards—if reported daily	430

g. Using a basis of one timecard for every three hours of standard hours scheduled, an average of 13 timecards would have to be completely punched each day.

EXHIBIT 6 (*Continued*)   GIFFORD VALVE COMPANY

3. Inventory:
   a. 3,747 pages of Bill of Material Data (20 lines per page)
   b. 7,355 part numbers listed on the inventory (approximate)
   c. 42,095 operations on active routings

4. Sales (Based on 13 days):   Average per day
   a. Total number of invoices   47
   b. Ship to different from Bill to   26
   c. Average items per invoice   2.3

EQUIPMENT UTILIZATION

   1. Unit record   79.2 per cent
   2. Computer   41.8 per cent

NOTE: 70 per cent utilization is full time one shift use of equipment. At 70 per cent overtime or more equipment would be required.

CONCLUSION

	Per Month Cost	
	Utilization	Total Cost
To process similar reports by manual methods, etc., with no additional capacity (labor only does not include purchase of additional posting machines)	$4,506	$4,506
To process similar reports using unit record equipment, with no additional capacity and no simulation or exception reporting (labor, material, and rental)	1,927	2,433
To process the integrated system using a computer system, with simulation and exception reporting and approximately 30 per cent additional utilization capacity (labor, material, and rental)	1,830	4,378

For desired management operating reports through data-processing and to maintain capacity for growth, the computer system is recommended to be placed on order for installation in the period between April 1, 1963, and July 1, 1963.

cheaper than the computer system but could not provide as rapid service or exception reporting.

To provide a consistent base for cost comparisons the manual system was analyzed in an expanded form which included a productivity report accounting for available machine hours and hours utilized, standard labor hours, and actual labor hour comparison. The Office Manager thought adding two clerks at an annual salary of $3,600 would give him enough clerical assistance to record manually the present machine-loading information on a daily basis and record actual and scheduled labor hours. In addition to what was being done currently, it would provide production control with daily in-

EXHIBIT 7   PRESENT

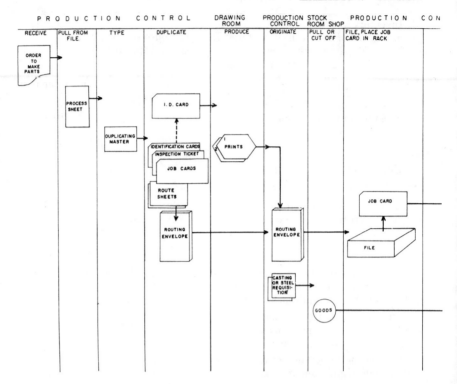

formation on job location. The new system was to supplement the present one by having a route card returned to production control system each time a job was moved. The billing and inventory control would be unchanged. It was expected that monthly labor cost analyses and improved statistical analyses of sales could be made in the manual system. All other reports would not be affected.

Under the unit record system the inventory control procedures would not change. However, productivity accounting would be more elaborate and include breakdowns such as set-up time, indirect labor, and direct labor expended on the production of standard or special stock items. Prepunched cards showing standard time per unit of production and a routing list would accompany each job in the packet. Upon completion of an operation one of the prepunched cards, known as a move ticket, would be forwarded to the data-processing center for tabulation to determine the location of each job as an operation was completed. Another prepunched card, known as a labor timecard, which identified the job a man worked on and recorded the actual

PRODUCTION CONTROL PROCEDURE

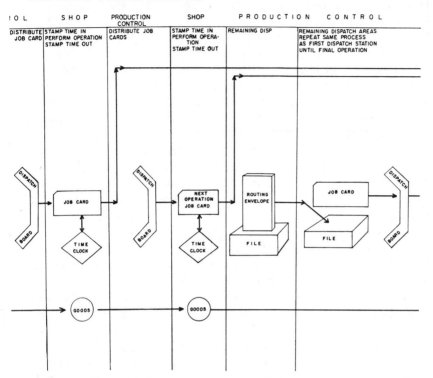

! O L	SHOP	PRODUCTION CONTROL	SHOP	PRODUCTION CONTROL
DISTRIBUTE JOB CARD	STAMP TIME IN PERFORM OPERATION STAMP TIME OUT	DISTRIBUTE JOB CARDS	STAMP TIME IN PERFORM OPERA-TION STAMP TIME OUT	REMAINING DISP	REMAINING DISPATCH AREAS REPEAT SAME PROCESS AS FIRST DISPATCH STATION UNTIL FINAL OPERATION

hours worked and the number of pieces produced would be returned daily to the processing room. Information from the labor timecards and the move ticket cards would give a "next day" accounting on the status of all the jobs in the shop. The system also would provide an analysis of labor and equipment utilization by comparing available machines and labor with that of actual utilization. This reporting system was based on the establishment of standard operation times.

The unit record system might also assist in the monthly review of finished parts to provide a tabulated report of the status of the inventories to aid the decisions of Mr. Watson and Mr. Swain in their production planning. This would allow them more time to deal with special parts and to smooth out the present exceptions and omissions that occurred on the standard items. However, under the unit system all information would have to be listed on the report and forwarded to the managers since the system could not print just those exceptions on which action was needed. Thus, jobs that were on time or ahead of schedule would be reported along with those which were

late. A significant change over the manual system would be that all data would be on punched cards which would facilitate further automation, if desirable, at a later date.

In the fully computerized system all jobs in the shop would be continuously accounted for in the memory of a computer. As the job was processed, prepunched cards would be returned from the shop which, as in the unit record system, would define location of job and what processing had been accomplished. This would be associated with information in the computer memory as to its due date, standard routing and times, and special instructions. All cost data would be gathered and compared to standards to provide a daily exception report of late, early, or high-cost jobs for the general foreman, Mr. Swain, and the routers for action the next day. It was hoped that eventually an automatic scheduling routine could be developed based on time standards, work in process, and due dates. This routine would provide the general foreman each day with a list for each of his foremen of jobs to do in the morning and jobs to do in the afternoon. The purpose of this would be to maintain a high utilization of machinery, keep jobs on time, and avoid bottlenecks before they occurred. It would review inventory status once each week and, on the basis of usage data, produce manufacturing fabrication requests for Mr. Watson's approval. Exhibits 7 and 8 are flow charts, in part, of the present and proposed production control procedures.

On June 15 Mr. Ivey submitted his recommendations as shown in Exhibit 6. These are based on the statistics of the data shown in Exhibit 4. A great advantage of the computer system, Mr. Ivey felt, was its ability to handle the potential growth of Gifford. He pointed out that the unit record system would almost be at one-shift capacity when installed.

In commenting on the report, Mr. Stafford said the growth potential of the automatic system was appealing to the employees as well as management. Profit growth was important to the employees' own income as the firm has an active profit-sharing plan and it seemed that the new production control system would allow an expansion of sales and hence more profits with the same number of people.

The Pillsbury Company[1]

Some Pillsbury managers gave particular emphasis to the rate of inventory turnover and the stock-out frequency as important control indicators. Other managers pointed out, however, that as important as these two indicators might be, they were only two factors in a complex situation. All agreed that high inventory turnovers and low stock-out frequencies were, by nature, antithetical.

Rapid inventory turnover accompanied by a high stock-out record[2] occurred, for example, in early 1963 during a large Pillsbury promotion of a new cake and frosting mix flavor combination, Swiss Chocolate cake and Coconut-Almond frosting. Consumer acceptance of this new product idea was so much greater than anticipated that Pillsbury was unable to satisfy the demand for six months, during which time the deletion rate ran as high as 40 per cent.

Production capacity was only a minor problem in supporting the promotion. The major reason for the inability to meet demand was a shortage of coconut, an ingredient which normally requires a procurement time of ten weeks. In July 1965, a Pillsbury manager, commenting on the Swiss Chocolate-Coconut-Almond episode remarked, "The trade still remembers our high deletion rate in 1963. In this business the trade is always sensitive to deletion rate."

Company Background

Historically a large flour miller, the Pillsbury Company was the second largest in the United States in 1965. During the 1940s Pills-

---

[1] This case was made possible through the generous cooperation of a number of managers at The Pillsbury Company. At their request, most figures in this case, including those in exhibits, have been disguised. Figures obtainable from the Pillsbury published annual report have not been disguised.

[2] Called the "deletion rate" at Pillsbury, since out-of-stock items were deleted from incoming orders.

bury started a program to decrease the company's dependence on flour sold to bakeries and to large industrial and export customers. As a part of this product diversification program Pillsbury introduced lines of cake, pie crust, frosting, pancake, hot roll and gravy mixes, instant potatoes, "Funny Face" drink mix, and Sweet-10, a noncaloric sweetener. Together with the other Pillsbury consumer products like family flour and refrigerated products, these new lines accounted for 58.6 per cent of the company's 1965 sales volume of $443 million compared with 28.5 per cent of 1949 sales. The number of grocery items marketed by Pillsbury increased from seven in 1946 to well over 100 in 1965, and more than half of the products in Pillsbury's 1965 consumer grocery line had been introduced since 1957. In 1965 sales were 41 per cent higher and profits 160 per cent higher than in 1957.

The change in corporate emphasis from one basic product (flour) requiring one manufacturing process (milling) to a broad line of convenience grocery products required Pillsbury to introduce many increasingly complex manufacturing processes. Typical of the new processes were the facilities used to make Swiss Chocolate and other cake mixes at the company's Springfield, Illinois plant. Swiss Chocolate Cake Mix is made by combining 15 different ingredients in 3,800 pound batches. The main ingredients are flour, sugar, shortening, and cocoa. Flour purchased from the Pillsbury flour mill adjacent to the grocery mix plant is blown through pipes from the mill to a large bulk storage bin on the top floor of the plant. Sugar is blown from rail cars to a storage tank on the roof of the plant. Flour and sugar, as needed, are blown from the storage bins into weighing bins until the proper amount for a batch has accumulated. The contents of the weighing bins are then blown into a mixer; this operation requires the setting of two dials and the throwing of four switches. Liquid shortening is piped from a tank to the mixer, and other ingredients such as cocoa, salt, baking soda, and flavoring are shoveled from bins or dumped from 100-pound sacks into large cans for weighing and then added to the batch.

Large paddles blend the contents of the mixer while the whole apparatus is vibrated at high speed. The cake mix is then emptied into a "surge bin" where it is held for a short time before being dumped, upon demand, into a storage bin feeding a packaging line. The packaging line storage bin and the surge bin each has capacity for one batch of cake mix.

The Springfield grocery mix plant has 16 packaging lines. The line used for Swiss Chocolate Cake Mix has a capacity of 1,800 cases

per shift. Operations are performed automatically along this line as follows:

At the beginning of the line, waxed paper from a large roll is cut and folded to form liners in the shape of a box.

At the next station, printed boxes (called shells) are fed in, flat. The machine folds and glues the sides and bottom of a shell to "assemble" it around the liner.

The lined box passes under a filling spout where a quantity of cake mix, measured by volume, drops into the box. The partially filled box is vibrated as it moves to a second filling spout where sufficient additional cake mix is added to fill the box. Pillsbury has found that this two-step filling process is much faster than a one-step process in which the box is vibrated while filling.

The filled box then passes onto an automatic scale where over- and underweight boxes are pushed off the line for rechecking by the machine operator.

Boxes that pass the weight test are sealed automatically.

At the last station in the line, 12 boxes are inserted into a case which then is sealed and labeled.

One man operates the entire Swiss Chocolate Cake Mix line. He spends most of his time near the weighing station adding or removing mix from boxes rejected at the scale, and visually checking the condition of filled boxes as they pass.

Automation does not stop at the packaging line. The filled cases drop down a chute and travel on a conveyor which collects the output of all the packaging lines. Cases of brownie mix, hot roll mix, pancake mix, frosting mix, etc., travel along the conveyor to the warehouse and shipping area.

Along the length of the conveyor are several branching spurs. Just before each spur a photoelectric device "reads" coded spots on the sides of the cases and opens or closes switches to the spurs. After passing through a series of these switches the cases are completely sorted. An automatic palletizer assembles the cases into pallet loads which are then stored temporarily in the warehouse or loaded directly into waiting rail cars for shipment.

The Shift to Centralized Scheduling

Prior to 1961 customer orders and factory scheduling were handled locally, at Springfield and at Pillsbury's nine other manufacturing plants, and at 80 small local warehouses controlled by sales personnel

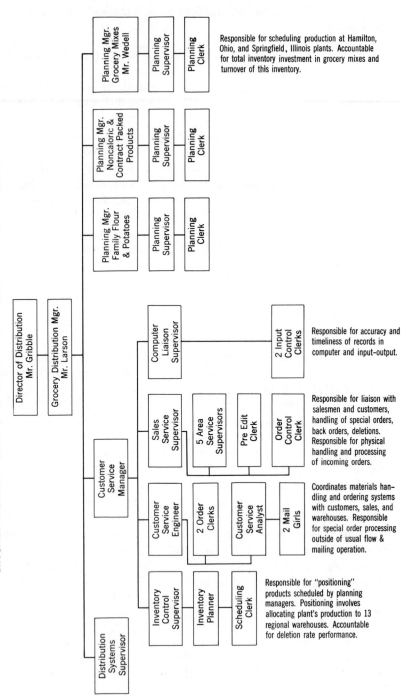

EXHIBIT 1   THE PILLSBURY COMPANY

GROCERY PRODUCTS PORTION OF DISTRIBUTION DEPARTMENT ORGANIZATION CHART

Responsible for scheduling production at Hamilton, Ohio, and Springfield, Illinois plants. Accountable for total inventory investment in grocery mixes and turnover of this inventory.

Responsible for accuracy and timeliness of records in computer and input-output.

Responsible for liaison with salesmen and customers, handling of special orders, back orders, deletions. Responsible for physical handling and processing of incoming orders.

Coordinates materials handling and ordering systems with customers, sales, and warehouses. Responsible for special order processing outside of usual flow & mailing operation.

Responsible for "positioning" products scheduled by planning managers. Positioning involves allocating plant's production to 13 regional warehouses. Accountable for deletion rate performance.

and used to fill emergency orders. As the number of items in the product line proliferated, interplant shipments to enable each plant to fill orders became increasingly difficult to control and customer service fell below the desired level. Accordingly, a change was made to 13 large warehouses located close to major markets and to centralized control of all scheduling and physical movement of material in the grocery products division.

Centralized control became the responsibility of the Distribution Department headed by Mr. Will Gribble, who said, "We surround all plans for the production and movement of products. There is no scheduling function at the grocery mix plants. We tell them what to make each week and how much of each day's production to ship to each of 13 Pillsbury regional distribution warehouses. These distribution warehouses, in turn, ship to customers as directed from our central office which processes all customer orders."

The partial organization chart in Exhibit 1 shows the people involved in scheduling grocery products in the centralized distribution organization. As shown on the chart, Richard Wedell, the planning manager for cake and other grocery mixes, held the responsibility for scheduling through the end of the manufacturing process. Next, the inventory control supervisor and his two assistants held responsibility for positioning the product in the 13 Pillsbury distribution warehouses, and a third group, the sales service supervisors, scheduled shipments from the warehouses to customers.

Production Planning and Scheduling

All production planning at Pillsbury begins with forecasts. Although the Marketing Department is primarily responsible for these forecasts, Mr. Gribble has said, "Marketing has, in recent years, become increasingly dependent on a forecasting model developed by the Mathematical Research Department."

A five-year forecast similar to the one shown in Exhibit 2 is used in developing capital expenditure plans for major items such as new plants, warehouses, and large pieces of equipment.

The one-year forecast shown in Exhibit 3 is prepared in February for the year June 1 to May 31. This forecast is used to develop budgetary plans, to determine manpower requirements, and to anticipate requirements for packaging materials and raw material ingredients such as flour, sugar, cocoa, and egg albumen. The one-year sales forecast serves also as a guide in the development of production plans for the year. A portion of the 1966 production plan for the

EXHIBIT 2 THE PILLSBURY COMPANY

GROCERY PRODUCTS—FIVE-YEAR PLAN—SPECIALTY VOLUMES

	F1963	F1964	F1965	F1966	F1967	F1968
Cake						
Layer	12,010*	13,200	13,200	13,400	13,500	13,750
Loaf	1,070	1,010	1,120	1,190	1,260	1,320
Share	35.0 %	36 %	37 %	37.5 %	38 %	38.5 %
Angelfood	1,105	1,030	930	990	990	990
Share	48 %	49 %	49 %	50 %	50 %	51 %
Pie crust	1,050	830	700	620	560	520
Share	35 %	32.5 %	31 %	29.5 %	27.5 %	26 %
Pancake						
Extra light	2,580	2,660	2,660	2,690	2,720	2,720
Hungry Jack buttermilk	870	1,030	1,220	1,330	1,360	1,430
Proliferation		149	476	580	640	640
		* * *				
Cornbread—regular	282	300	270	280	290	300
Cornbread—proliferation	—	—	95	200	175	175
Gravies	—	555	950	1,090	1,250	1,500
Potatoes						
Regular	2,400	2,000	1,720	1,800	1,880	2,200
Proliferation	—	—	—	70	125	175
Share—mashed	22 %	22.5 %	24.5 %	26 %	28 %	30 %
Share—total	29 %	25.6 %	25 %	26.8 %	28.8 %	31 %
Total volume	31,000	32,680	33,010	35,410	35,655	37,015
Advertising and sales						
promotion	$11,900	$12,560	$12,850	$13,720	$14,160	$14,755
Per unit factor	$.39	$.38	$.39	$.39	$.39	$.40

* Forecasts in thousands of cases.

EXHIBIT 3 THE PILLSBURY COMPANY

SALES ESTIMATE—ORIGINAL FORECAST NO. 1, FISCAL 1966

	June	July	Aug.	Sept.	Oct.	Nov.	Dec.	Jan.	Feb.	Mar.	Apr.	May	12 Month F-1966
Moist cake													
White	50*	67	63	183	134	142	67	159	159	100	150	159	1,433
Chocolate													
fudge	33	52	46	150	98	105	52	124	124	72	105	115	1,076
					* * *								
Swiss choco-													
late	62	76	65	150	128	120	61	157	150	97	155	140	1,361
Lord Balti-													
more	25	31	26	46	31	36	31	36	41	31	36	51	401

* Forecasts in thousands of cases.

Springfield grocery mix plant is shown in Exhibit 4. The need to coordinate marketing plans with plant capacity and raw material availability requires that the one-year production plan be developed through close coordination among executives in the Marketing, Distribution, Manufacturing, and Procurement Departments.

A shorter range production plan is based on a 120-day sales forecast which is developed monthly, showing expected sales by product and sales region. The 120-day forecast is developed by a computer program containing an exponential smoothing model which includes such factors as the effect of planned promotions and seasonal consumer habits. Working closely with the marketing manager for the particular product under consideration, the planning manager in the Distribution Department revises the forecast prepared by the computer when, for example, marketing has knowledge of a planned promotion which is not included in the model, or knowledge of a competitor's promotion or price move that would affect Pillsbury sales. In some instances, although the total forecast of a product's sales for the entire nation is not changed, forecasts for sales in some sales regions are shifted around slightly. Such adjustments are made when the marketing and distribution people feel a promotion would have more regional effect than the computer model has taken into account.

The figures as revised by the men in marketing and distribution become the inputs for further calculations in a second computer run. One of the calculations produces detailed 120-day sales forecasts by distribution warehouse, showing estimates of the sales for each item in the product line. Since warehouse territories do not correspond to sales regions, the breakdown of sales produced by the second computer run does not correspond with the breakdown in the first run.

EXHIBIT 4 THE PILLSBURY COMPANY

PRODUCTION PLAN NO. 1-F66—DISTRIBUTION

Stated in thousands

For Period June Thru May At Springfield Plant Date February 15, 1965

Product	Size	Code	J	J	A	S	O	N	D	J	F	M	A	M	Total
Extra-Lite	24-1#	PAN 6310	26	31	41	43	40	36	38	33	28	26	25	24	391
	12-2#	PAN 6315	10	73	97	101	93	85	89	79	64	61	58	57	867
	12-3#	PAN 6317	–	11	16	15	14	13	13	10	10	10	8	7	127
	12-4#	PAN 6319	8	10	13	18	8	11	12	10	8	8	8	7	121
	Total Pancake		44	125	167	177	155	145	152	132	110	105	99	95	1,506

Another calculation produces the "base stock," or minimum amount of inventory that should be on hand at all times for every product in each of the 13 distribution warehouses.   Base stock is considered a function of two variables: most likely lead time to replenish supply in a distribution warehouse, and average daily demand.   Given these two parameters, the computer determines the base stock by a look-up procedure in a table maintained in the computer memory.   The table was developed by combining the probability distributions of lead time and demand, and by determining through trial and error the level of inventory required to support a given level of customer service. Implicit assumptions underlying the use of the table for determining base stock are:

1. The discrete probability distribution for lead time has the following form for all most likely lead times K.

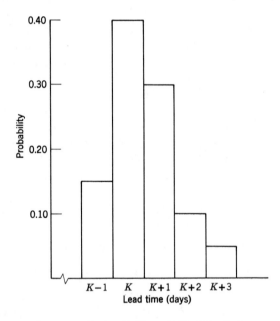

Shipments between Springfield and Ft. Worth have a most likely lead time of seven days, of which two are allowed for paperwork and five for transit.   The transit time is calculated by studying past performance to determine the most frequently experienced time from each plant to each warehouse.   From the probability distribution shown in the diagram, the probability of a six-day delivery of Swiss Chocolate Cake Mix from Springfield to Ft. Worth is assumed to be 0.15.   Similarly, on a shipment with a

most likely lead time of nine days, the probability of a delivery in eight days is also assumed to equal 0.15. Most likely lead times from grocery products plants to warehouses vary from 3 to 13 days.

2. The second assumption underlying the base stock calculation is that the distribution of demand can be described by the gamma distribution.[3]

The 120-day sales forecasts and the base stock figures from the second computer run provide the basic information for production planning charts prepared manually in the Distribution Department. One chart is prepared for each product in the grocery products line. When a product is packaged in more than one size, a chart is prepared for each size. Each chart, drawn by hand on large sheets of quadruled paper, has two lines; a line for cumulative forecasted sales and a line for the base stock required to support the fore-

EXHIBIT 5 THE PILLSBURY COMPANY

PRODUCTION PLANNING CHART FOR SWISS CHOCOLATE CAKE MIX
(April–August 1965)

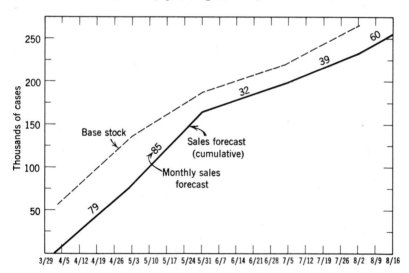

[3] The gamma distribution is a two-parameter distribution. The specific form of the distribution can be changed by changing the values of the two parameters. Thus the gamma distribution can be used to approximate several different kinds of observed demand distributions. For further reference see, for example, Robert Schlaifer, *Probability and Statistics for Business Decisions*, McGraw-Hill, New York, 1959.

casted sales. The calculated base stock is represented by the vertical distance between these two lines. The chart shown in Exhibit 5 was prepared in March 1965.

As actual sales figures become known, they are added to the chart as bars showing cumulative sales to date. Also, as production is scheduled, the cumulative production plan is entered on the chart as a series of x's. The partially completed chart for Swiss Chocolate Cake Mix as of August 5, 1965, is shown in Exhibit 6. As can be seen, the actual development of sales caused Mr. Wedell, the planning manager who prepared the chart, to change the forecasted sales line and, correspondingly, the base stock line shown on the original chart.

Mr. Wedell, with tongue in cheek, put the problem of production scheduling in simple terms: "All we have to do is to stay above the base stock line." He then enumerated some of the difficulties

EXHIBIT 6   THE PILLSBURY COMPANY

PRODUCTION PLANNING CHART FOR SWISS CHOCOLATE CAKE MIX
AS OF AUGUST 1965

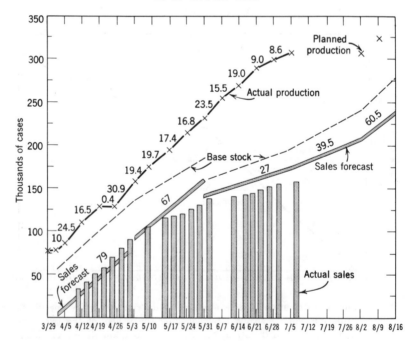

Note: On this and the following production planning charts the lines for sales forecast, base stock, actual production, and the bars for actual sales show cumulative values. The numbers over the lines show incremental quantities.

he encountered in scheduling cake mixes. "Although cake mix is packaged in only one size, through the year four or five different promotions might be run on a cake mix, some requiring special printing on the package. The bulk of our sales are in deal packages, and there is a constant problem of clearing out the previous deal packages before the new deal starts. In addition, for some products we carry a regular package along with the current deal pack since some customers will not accept a product with any cents-off, coupon offer, or other promotional markings on the package. Another difficulty arises because the chart does not show cake mix inventory positions at each of Pillsbury's 13 warehouses. We may be in fine shape in over-all inventory position but out of stock in a particular flavor at one or two warehouses and unable to get that flavor scheduled into production for two or three weeks. Faced with an out-of-stock situation, it is important that we carefully weigh the costs of shipping goods between warehouses versus the costs of breaking into our previously planned production schedule to get the goods out."

To aid in the monitoring of production schedules and to provide current information on sales, Mr. Wedell and his assistant receive a computer-prepared "Daily Stock Status Report." A portion of this report for August 13 appears in Exhibit 7. The information and data handling system behind this report is described in the following paragraphs.

Order Processing and Data Handling System

Eighty per cent of the grocery product orders received by Pillsbury come on Pillsbury-designed order forms in distinctive air mail envelopes. The remaining orders come by telephone or teletype and are transcribed in Minneapolis to the standard order form. The orders are sent by Pillsbury salesmen in the field; only on rare occasions does a customer order directly. Orders received by mail are checked for accuracy and completeness by an order clerk before being sent to the key punch room to be punched into cards. In situations when the Daily Stock Status Report indicates a stockout at the warehouse serving the customer whose order is being processed, an area service supervisor calls the salesman or the customer to work out a solution.

The orders on punched cards are fed into a computer which has the stock status of every item in each distribution warehouse on a magnetic disk. The computer decreases the amounts on hand at each warehouse by the amount ordered from that warehouse that day. This calculation produced the figures shown in the balance (units) column of the Stock Status Report (Exhibit 7). The computer also

EXHIBIT 7   THE PILLSBURY COMPANY

SPECIAL FORM 2545 (1-64).   DAILY STOCK STATUS

Consolidated YES

Date 08/13/65

Warehouse _____

Product Code	Stock Point Code	Current Orders	Planned Unload-ings	Position Today — Balance (Units)	Position Today — Balance (Days)	Orders versus Esti-mates	Future Orders	In Transit	On Requisition	Balance (Units)	Balance (Days)	Invoicing Mo. to Date	Inv. M.T.D. + Orders	Last Month	Month Before Last
7762 00	003	719	1,300	664	23	140				664	23	293	293	1,483	271
7762 00	005	1,479		707	4	162		2,600	650	3,307	19	2,935	3,654	3,003	2,297
7762 00	004	110		2,279	10	110				3,579	16	2,154	3,633	3,971	2,730
7762 00	002			2,291	27	60				2,291	27	365	475	1,458	953
7762 00	007	240	260	214	5	171		520		1,644	41	833	833	1,105	428
7762 00	015	346		2,653	11	158		1,300		3,953	17	3,421	3,661	5,179	1,890
7762 00	001	132		2,122	50	122		1,040		2,122	50	545	891	1,088	539
7762 00	008	50		466	8	130				1,506	28	374	506	1,267	615
7762 00	010			243	25	245			130	243	25	198	248	276	167
7762 00	016	5		648	29	93		130		908	41	147	152	360	222
EAST	TOT	3,081	1,560	12,287				5,590	780	20,217		11,265	14,346	19,190	10,112
7762 00	014	108		4,867	50	33				4,867	50	256	364	455	190
7762 00	013	196		6,226	50	22				6,226	50	250	446	509	679
7762 00	018	260		7,917	44	55				7,917	44	706	966	2,311	2,173
WEST	TOT	564		19,010						19,010		1,212	1,776	3,275	3,042
PROD	TOT	3,645	1,560	31,297				5,590	780	39,227		12,477	16,122	22,465	13,154

Column definitions (Position Today / Delivery Information):

- **Current Orders** — Orders received but not yet shipped by warehouse.
- **Planned Unloadings** — Inbound product from plant which warehouse plans to unload on day of report.
- **Balance, Units (Position Today)** — Amount on hand in warehouse after current orders have been filled.
- **Balance, Days (Position Today)** — Balance in days = balance in units ÷ estimated daily sales.
- **Orders versus Estimates** — [(Last 15 days actual sales) ÷ (daily sales estimate × 15)] × 100. 100 means actual sales equal estimates.
- **Future Orders** — Sales orders for delivery beyond the time for current orders.
- **In Transit** — Goods in transit between plant and warehouse.
- **On Requisition** — Ordered from plant but not yet shipped.
- **Balance, Units** — Current balance (Col. 5) + planned unloading + in transit + on requisition − future orders.
- **Balance, Days** — Balance (units) ÷ daily sales estimate.
- **Invoicing Mo. to Date** — Total number cases invoiced this month to date.
- **Inv. M.T.D. + Orders** — Total invoices month to date plus current orders.
- **Last Month** — Total shipments last month (whole month).
- **Month Before Last** — Total shipments month before last (whole month).

produces a loading order which is wired to the warehouses during the day. The loading order is a list of the products, arranged by product number, to be shipped by the warehouse.

When an order is shipped from a warehouse, a notice of shipment is wired to Minneapolis. This notice triggers the preparation of a customer invoice on the Minneapolis computer. The timetable of a representative sales order is shown below.

Sales Order Timetable

Day 1   Sale made
           Order air mailed
             ↓

Day 2   Order received and processed
           Loading order wired to warehouse
             ↓

Day 3   Order loaded and shipped
           Minneapolis notified
           Invoice prepared
             ↓

Day 4   Invoice mailed
           Shipment in transit
             ↓

Day 5   Invoice received by
            Customer
            Salesman
           Shipment in transit
             ↓

Day 6   Shipment received

Shipments from plants to warehouses are also scheduled by Minneapolis. The data concerning plant shipments on the Stock Status Report are derived from loading orders sent to plants and notices of shipment sent by the plants to Minneapolis.

Grocery Mix Plant Operations

James Shadler, manager of the Springfield grocery products plant, receives a production schedule from Mr. Wedell every Monday morning. An MBA graduate in his middle 30s, Mr. Shadler worked in the Distribution Department in Minneapolis prior to his move to Springfield. On the wall next to his desk is the motto, "Great leaders, like diamonds, are products of pressure." Speaking about production scheduling at Springfield, Mr. Shadler said, "The schedule we receive from Mr. Wedell is only a broad outline of what we should do, although in developing this outline Mr. Wedell has taken into account

such things as the production capacity of our lines, our cycling preferences, and manning requirements."

The production schedule received weekly by Mr. Shadler covers a six-week period and shows, by week, the number of cases of each product to be made during each week and the expected number of shifts required to produce each quantity scheduled. Mr. Shadler said, "From this six-week schedule we develop a detailed production schedule for the current week and a long-range plan for the five subsequent weeks. My detailed schedule shows which packaging line is to be used for each product, which shifts during the week will be used to run the product, and the number of men to be assigned to each line. In addition, my schedule shows assignments for auxiliary personnel like mechanics, oilers, sweepers, and relief men. My five-week long-range plan shows the products we plan to run each week, which lines will be used, the number of shifts planned for each product, and the number of men required.

"Sometimes it is necessary to change the schedule Minneapolis sends us. The most important consideration is our objective of leveling manpower requirements. Our union contract guarantees a full week's work to any man who is assigned a job on Monday morning. This forces us to smooth out our production during the week. We actually try to go beyond the weekly leveling of manpower because it makes good business sense. If a worker knows his job is secure and is always assigned to the same area, he takes much more interest in his job than he would if he were continually laid off and then rehired. Our operating efficiency has increased significantly since we started leveling our manpower requirements. Another reason for us to deviate from Mr. Wedell's schedule is difficulties with process. By process I mean equipment, quality of raw material, quality of finished product, etc.

"Basically, you might say that we negotiate production schedules with Minneapolis. I am in pretty close contact with Mr. Wedell and we do all we can to help him take care of problems and unusual situations, but sometimes we just can't do everything he calls for. The negotiations work pretty well though and we manage most problems quite smoothly."

Management Reaction to Centralized Scheduling

The shift in responsibility for scheduling to the centralized Distribution Department has been accepted after the fact by all, with varying degrees of enthusiasm. Everyone accepts the significance of the better information which the new system provides and of the great decrease

in the time required to get information on the current status of inventories and orders. Mr. Gribble, who initiated the idea of centralized control in the Grocery Products Division and implemented his ideas in that division, foresaw gains in extending centralized distribution control to other product divisions. In mid-1965 his Distribution Department was moved from the Grocery Products Division to the corporate level, but Mr. Gribble emphasized, "We will not extend centralized control of scheduling until the managers in other divisions are in sympathy with this move. Centralized control of groceries may, in retrospect, seem very logical, but we encountered opposition at times. You cannot have both centralized control and managers who build walls around their responsibilities."

On the same subject, Mr. Watson, vice president for personnel and organization planning, said, "Centralized control of the distribution of grocery products was a real achievement dependent on three things: First, improved communication between functional responsibilities. We do not favor cooperation simply for the sake of smoothing over differences. Opposition can serve a much needed role. But with varying degrees of conflict and accommodation our people are learning to work together effectively. Second, Mr. Gribble, himself, saw clearly the breadth of the problem as well as a possible solution and started a second career to spearhead the development of our present distribution system. Third, signals from higher management encouraged a change such as this. Our president played a significant role in our shift to consumer orientation; during the past few years he has strongly supported centralized distribution."

Mr. Holmes, manager of manufacturing for the Grocery Products Division, said, "We used to schedule manufacturing, but I have no doubt of the desirability of the Distribution Department doing the job. We tell them what the plant capacity is, what the optimal sequence of products is, and what costs are involved in stepping out of sequence. Without scheduling responsibility my manufacturing people have more time to improve process and quality reliability. We are called on to help with scheduling problems only when unusual scheduling situations require a detailed knowledge of process, and then we serve only as advisors.

"The schedules prepared by the Distribution Department go to a higher level plant man than formerly was the case. Greater skill of implementation is achieved now that the plant manager is given the schedule. In general, you might say that our old system was based on plant inventory and the new system is based on manufacturing capacity."

Scheduling Problems

This section describes four problems to which Mr. Wedell sought solutions during the summer of 1965.

1. During July the sale of Spice Cake Mix exceeded forecasts. As early as July 9, the month-to-date orders totaled 6,028 cases, as compared to planned sales of 5,000 cases for the whole month. One order alone, received on July 9, was for 2,400 cases. Mr. Wedell attributed this spurt in sales to the success of a "chain breaker" promotion. The term refers to a special deal designed to gain initial distribution in a particular grocery chain, and, if successful, to be made available to all customers. As early as June 21, marketing had revised the 5,000 case forecast as shown in the following table.

SPICE CAKE SALES ESTIMATES

| | For the Month of | | | |
	June	July	August	September
Computer forecasting model				
June 1	4.5	4.9	5.0	5.4
July 1	—	5.3	5.5	5.9
August 1	—	—	5.5	5.9
Marketing Department's forecast				
June 1	4.0	5.0	9.0	10.0
Revision 6/21	—	8.0	13.0	
July 1	—	8.0	14.0	10.0
August 1	—	—	24.0	12.0
Actual sales	6.3	13.4	—	—

The differences between the forecasts produced by the computer model and those produced by marketing can be explained by the computer model's failure to include a factor for the chain breaker promotion on spice cake. Mr. Wedell commented that this break-down in communications would have to be remedied to prevent similar occurrences in the future.

In early July when Spice Cake Mix sales had begun to run far ahead of forecasts, Mr. Wedell decided to wait until the next regularly scheduled run of spice cake rather than to break into the previously planned production schedule. As can be seen from the production planning chart in Exhibit 8, actual sales during July were still well below the base stock line. When marketing

EXHIBIT 8   THE PILLSBURY COMPANY

PRODUCTION PLANNING CHART FOR SPICE CAKE MIX
(August 1965)

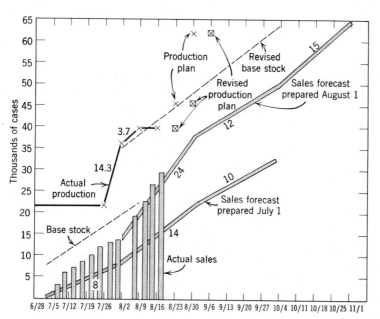

revised the August forecast upward from 14,000 to 24,000 cases, it became obvious that the regularly scheduled run in late July was not going to be sufficient to maintain supplies above the revised base stock line. During the week of July 26, while spice cake was being run at the Hamilton, Ohio plant, Mr. Wedell instructed Hamilton to extend the spice cake run as long as possible, or until the plant ran out of one of the ingredients. Although the regular run had been scheduled for 16,000 cases, Hamilton was able to run 2,000 extra for a total of 18,000 before running out of a flavoring extract used in the Spice Cake Mix. At the end of the spice cake run, during the week of August 2, Mr. Wedell could see that another run would be needed within a week if the over-all inventory position of spice cake were to be held above the base stock requirements. Upon finding out from procurement that additional shells could not be obtained until August 11, he scheduled another run of spice cake during the week of August 16. (See "original production plan" on chart.) On August 10, Mr. Wedell learned that the vendor who supplied the flavoring extract for spice cake was

shut down for a two-week vacation and could not ship any extract before August 23. Since there was no alternate source of supply for this extract, Mr. Wedell was forced to move the scheduled production back to the week of August 23. (See "revised production plan" on Exhibit 8.) As this delay would clearly cause deletions at some warehouses, Mr. Wedell was debating whether or not to suggest that Marketing limit the chain breaker deal to cut down on sales of Spice Cake Mix.

2. The forecast for hot roll mix sales had been 15,000 cases for July (typically a slack month for hot roll baking) and 27,000 cases for August (the beginning of the hot roll season). As of the second week of July, the rate of sales and information from salesmen indicated that July would be a 29,000 case month. Mr. Wedell and the Marketing manager for hot roll mix revised the August forecast to show a drop to 16,000 cases, in effect shifting the peak from August to July. But both men were uneasy for the following reasons: (a) Although the tremendous increases in July sales could not be completely explained, it was believed that the recent announcement of a price increase by a competitor was largely responsible. Thus it was difficult to predict how long the heavy sales would last. (b) A recent study by a market research organization reported that the market for hot roll mix would probably increase during the coming year. (c) The equipment for manufacturing hot roll mix was shut down for a major changeover until the third week of July; when the changeover was completed, the equipment would be set up to run a special double pack deal to be introduced in the fall. The changeover time to convert the equipment back to regular pack production would be three weeks, (d) The anticipated available stock of hot roll mix at all warehouses as of August 1 was 18,000 cases.

By July 26 the hot roll mix line was producing the special deal packs, but sales of the regular pack showed no signs of dropping off. On August 2, Marketing decided that the 16,000-case forecast was unrealistic and revised the forecast to 50,000 cases. Mr. Wedell was now in the difficult position of having to run regular pack to meet the August demand while the hot roll mix equipment was set up for the special double pack.

He decided to leave the machine set up as it was, but to run regular pack on the third shift during the week of August 2. Since the machine was set up to glue two packages together and insert the double packs into a large carton, the single packages had to be taken off the packaging line and inserted by hand into

regular side-opening 12-shell cartons. The third shift workers hired to hand pack and seal the cartons found that top-opening cartons could be packed much faster than side-opening cartons. As a result, Mr. Wedell ordered top-opening cartons, which were delivered to the Springfield plant within five days.

Hand packing continued on the third shift for a period of three weeks, during which the first two shifts ran the double packs. The double pack production fell behind original plans which had been based on full three-shift production. On August 16, Mr. Wedell informed Marketing that the double pack deal introduction date would have to be pushed back three weeks since he would not be able to have sufficient stocks of the double pack in the distribution warehouses by the originally planned introduction date.

3. Less pressing than the other two problems, in Mr. Wedell's opinion, but in the long run perhaps more important, was the oversupply of buckwheat pancakes and 30 other similar small-volume items. The forecast, protective stock position, and supply of buckwheat pancakes in one-pound packages are shown in Exhibit 9. Monthly sales of buckwheat pancakes averaged 3,000 cases for the one-pound package and 2,000 for the two-pound package, but it was considered uneconomical to manufacture in quantities of less than

EXHIBIT 9 THE PILLSBURY COMPANY

PRODUCTION PLANNING CHART FOR BUCKWHEAT PANCAKES

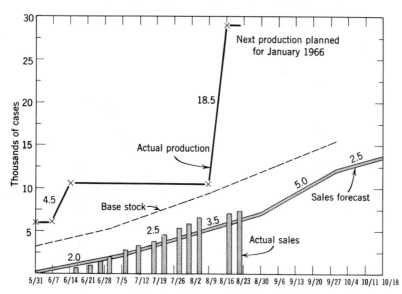

10,000 cases.   Furthermore, when the stock levels of the one-pound
package required replenishing, it was the practice to restock the
two-pound size, even though considerable stock remained; this was
done to avoid setting up for one-pound at one time and two-pound
at another.   Mr. Wedell said, "I simply keep stock in a strong
position on these slow-moving, small-selling items.   It would be
really grief to schedule our equipment closely on the many small-
selling items.   We'd be out-of-stock and breaking into schedules
on countless trivial things which individually have little influence
on our turnover.   We can make better use of our time and equipment by scheduling closely the heavy selling items which do influence turnover."   (See Swiss Chocolate Cake Mix planning chart,
for example.)

Since Mr. Wedell was held accountable for the total inventory of
the products which he scheduled, the very low turnover rate of slow
selling products like buckwheat pancake mix was of concern to him
and to the grocery distributionn manager, Mr. Larson.

In connection with the issue of tomorrow versus deletion rate, Mr.
Larson had prepared the graph shown in Exhibit 10 for a presentation to higher management.   Mr. Larson interpreted the steeper line
as a reflection of the substantial increase in the number of products
in 1964 and the resulting increase in difficulty of scheduling and
stocking the full line of products.   From this graph (Exhibit 10)

EXHIBIT 10   THE PILLSBURY COMPANY

SERVICE-INVENTORY RELATIONSHIP

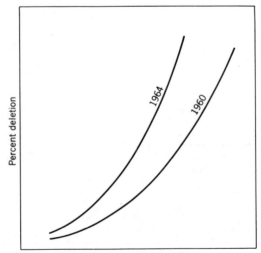

Turnover rate (annual)

and other information, Mr. Larson prepared a table showing annual distribution costs, which varied with turnover. A portion of the table is reproduced here. The investment column represents the cost of capital tied up in inventory. In the storage column, one month's storage costs are considered fixed for all turnover rates and the storage costs shown are only the incremental storage costs after the first month. Demurrage represents the higher costs incurred as

INVENTORY SYSTEM COSTS $000's

Annual Turnover	Investment	Storage	Demurrage	Deletions	Management	Raw Material	Production	Total
1	$3,100	$260	$40	$ 18	$ −50	$150	$ 25	$3,543
2	2,300	190	30	40	−30	125	30	2,735
3	1,500	130	25	50	−20	180	35	1,900
				* * *				
9	500	10	10	200	0	280	125	1,125
10	450	5	6	250	20	290	155	1,176
11	410	0	3	320	30	300	200	1,263

turnover decreases because of difficulty in getting freight cars unloaded. Deletion costs include the costs of reprocessing an order and the shipping penalty incurred by shipping small lots from plant to warehouse and from warehouse to customer.

Management costs are assumed to decrease as turnover decreases since very high inventories would allow loose control from the Distribution Department. Management costs are shown negative (i.e., savings) at very low turnovers since under these conditions the number of people in the organization can be reduced. The costs listed in the raw material column show that low turnovers would allow large manufacturing runs and consequent economies in volume purchasing. Production costs include overtime premiums, change-over costs, unemployment insurance costs, and hiring and lay-off costs.

Mr. Larson emphasized that other costs, particularly those of delayed service to a customer and of lost sales—which were not known and do not appear on the table—were of considerable significance; top management attempts to weigh the effect of these costs when making decisions.

4. Mr. Wedell knew that later in the week Mr. Larson wanted to discuss the current allocation of grocery products between the Ham-

ilton, Ohio and Springfield, Illinois plants. Both the Hamilton and Springfield plants have mixing and packaging facilities for cake mix and frosting mix. Until the early 1960s both had produced the full flavor line of these products. As the number of flavors in each line increased, the problems of short runs and frequent changeovers became increasingly bothersome and the Distribution Department began to allocate some low-volume flavors to only one plant. This practice of aggregating continued until July 1965, when all products were produced either at Hamilton or at Springfield. Recently, Mr. Larson had run rough figures on the extra transportation costs Pillsbury was incurring by not producing the full cake and frosting mix line at both plants and had mentioned to Mr. Wedell costs of some $150,000 per year.

Crest Corporation

In late 1958, Frank Johnson, Works Manager of the Crest Corporation, considered possible changes in the company's production control system. He was concerned particularly with the control of frame parts manufacturing. This was an important cost center for the company and an important source of parts for the company's assembly lines. During 1959, Crest intended to install a punched card data-processing system designed to increase the speed and accuracy of sales data analysis and other clerical procedures, including those for production control. Mr. Johnson thought that changes to increase the effectiveness of production control should be made in advance of the conversion to punched cards.

The Crest Corporation manufactures upholstered platform rockers, recliners, and similar chairs. Sales are nationwide to 10,000 dealers through company salesmen. Sales volume for 1958 was $12 million (estimated in late December, 1958) and a sales growth rate of 10 to 20 per cent annually had been projected by the company's general manager. All manufacturing takes place in Ashmount, a small community in North Carolina.

THE MANUFACTURING PROCESS

The Crest company is an integrated manufacturer, converting raw lumber, cotton, cloth fabric, and other materials into upholstered chairs. An upholstered chair is an assembly of three major elements: the frame (itself an assembly of a dozen or more wooden parts); upholstery materials (primarily springs and cotton, foam rubber, or foam plastic); and a cover fabric. In 1958, the company produced seven lines, or general types, of upholstered chairs on as many assembly lines; the other manufacturing activities of the company sup-

plied the required components to the assembly lines. The activity of particular concern to Mr. Johnson, frame parts manufacturing, was the process by which lumber was converted to finished parts to be assembled into chair frames.

Lumber Purchase and Storage

Crest frames were produced from solid southern hardwood lumber of varying species. Lumber was purchased by an independent commission broker who was familiar with sources in the southeast. The company management was satisfied that no appreciable saving could be realized through other methods of lumber purchasing. Lots of incoming lumber were differentiated according to grade and thickness. The company purchased three principal grades: first grade, number one common, and number two common. Five thicknesses were used: one inch, one and one-quarter inches, two inches, two and one-half inches, and three inches, designated in quarter-inches as 4/4, 5/4, 8/4, 10/4 and 12/4. About three-quarters of the lumber used was in the 4/4 and 5/4 thicknesses. Lumber cost about 10 cents per board foot.[1]

Lumber was stacked upon receipt to form loads of a single grade and thickness. A load was a stack of boards forming a cube roughly 12 feet in each dimension and containing about 10,000 board feet. As the boards were stacked, each layer was separated from the next by a slat which created a space through which air could circulate during the drying process. Undried lumber was stored out in the open in loads containing usually the equivalent of six months' requirements.

Lumber Drying

Lumber drying occupied a rectangular area roughly 350 feet long and 100 feet wide, with one end abutting the factory. The lumber loads were moved through this area on wheeled platforms over steel tracks. The area was divided across its length into three sections of about equal size, with the company's three dry kilns, each 100 feet long, occupying the center section. The section farthest from the factory was used as pre-dry storage. Here loads of undried lumber were lined up to await entry to the kiln. A full "charge" for each kiln was prepared before the kiln became available in order to minimize time spent in "recharging" an empty kiln. Drying time in the kilns varied with the lumber species and grade, its moisture content, and the season, so that exact drying time could not be pre-

---

[1] A "board foot" is the amount of lumber equal to 12" x 12" x 1".

dicted. Average drying time for a charge was about one week. The moisture content of the lumber was measured continuously during the drying cycle to determine when to discharge the kiln.

Subsequent to drying, the lumber moved into the third section—a covered, dry-storage area. Both the pre-dry and the dry-storage areas held an amount of lumber equal roughly to the total charge capacity in the three kilns. The dry-storage shed had a capacity of about 300,000 board feet; a few thousand additional board feet usually were to be found on the track leading into the rough mill. The size of the dry-storage area was limited by the location of the kilns, the factory wall, and by property lines. Mr. Johnson said that the cost of extra handling prohibited the use of other areas for storing dried lumber.

Maximum use of the kilns depended on availability of space in the dry-storage area to receive the dried lumber promptly upon completion of the drying cycle. In this regard Mr. Johnson said: "We don't want to use the kilns as warehouses." But a rapid and orderly use of dried lumber to free storage space depended on the degree to which the mix of sizes, species, and grades in dried lumber storage corresponded with the factory requirements at the moment.

Parts Manufacture

After being removed from storage the dried lumber was processed into frame parts in the frame shop. The frame shop had two departments: the Rough Mill Department which cut the incoming lumber into "core stock," and the Parts-Machining Department which processed the core stock into finished frame parts. These frame parts went into parts inventory.

In December 1958, the frame shop employed 54 men on the day shift and 32 men on the night shift. A full crew of 17 worked each shift in the rough mill while there was only a partial second shift in parts-machining. The frame shop foreman supervised a subforeman for each of the two departments on both first and second shifts. At the end of November both shifts had worked five ten-hour days a week. The workers in the frame shop were one-seventh of the total factory workforce.

Rough Mill Department

In the rough mill, lumber first was cut to length, planed, jointed, and sorted by conveyor along a production line operated by a nine-man team. Lumber was brought in from the dry-storage shed, a full load at a time, and placed on the "lowerator," a large variable-level platform, next to a pair of cut-off saws. Boards in a particular load

varied in quality, width, and length but were of uniform rough thickness. Stops on cut-off saws were usually set for three lengths, and the planer was set according to the thickness of the lumber at hand. The last operation in this sequence, called the "rough end," was performed by the jointer which smoothed the board edges. Then the boards, of uniform planed thickness but varying widths and lengths, were sorted on carts according to length. The rough mill produced boards in accordance with 70 standard length–thickness specifications.

Lumber from the rough end was cut to width on a rip saw to form core stock. Each piece of core stock was a finished oblong board of determined dimensions set by adding a standard allowance —for example, 3/8"—to each dimension of the finished part. The rip saw was operated by a four-man team. It was set to cut to a few selected widths. The cut pieces were sorted as follows: boards of desired width placed on handling carts according to size; oversize boards returned to the operator on the "feed" side of the saw for another pass; undersize pieces set aside to be moved to another department where they would be glued into larger boards; and scrap pieces placed on a special conveyor for removal. The rip saw operation called for special skills because of the rapid pace and the sorting decisions necessary. The rough mill dealt with approximately 250 core-stock dimensions.

Parts-Machining Department

In the Parts-Machining Department core stock was shaped to form finished parts ready for assembly into frames. Most of the 500 parts produced were of relatively simple shapes. For "straight-stock" parts, which were essentially rectangular and usually contained dowels or dowel holes, the machining operations were simple. Principal operations were double-end cut off to finished length, rip to finished width, and any necessary boring. Parts with more complex shapes were formed on band saws or shapers. The few parts which would be visible in the finished chair were sanded after machining.

The principal groups of machines in the Department were: cut-off saws, rip saws, miter saws, borers, band saws, shapers, and sanders.

Material moved through the parts-machining shop in lots; each lot traveled on one cart and contained pieces for one part specification. Each machine was tended by one operator who remained with his machine. In addition to the actual operation of the machine he was responsible for moving material to his workplace and performing any required set-up on his piece of equipment. When an operator com-

pleted work on a lot he informed the department foreman who assigned him another job.

Mr. Johnson felt that the control of set-up time was becoming more important as the company acquired multiple-purpose and high-speed equipment. For example, shaped parts could be produced at a much higher rate on an Onsrud automatic shaper than on the band saw or hand shaper. For the Onsrud machine, however, set-up required more than an hour, whereas the manually controlled machines required little set-up. The Crest company had recently installed a high-speed transfer machine combining the cut-off, boring, and dowel-insertion operations for straight stock. With one operator this new machine operated faster than the previous method which required three operators using three machines.

Parts Storage

After the last machining operation, four stock handlers moved the parts to bins in a 5,000-square-foot storeroom located between the parts manufacturing and assembly areas. In all, about 500 different parts were stored. These parts were required to build the 50 different "frame styles" which constituted the seven product lines. A few of the parts were peculiar to one frame style; many parts were common to several or all of the frame styles comprising one line; and some of the parts were used in more than one line.

Parts Withdrawal and Frame Assembly

Frames were assembled to meet the schedule of the final (upholstery) assembly line. A small buffer stock of assembled frames was used to "uncouple," or separate, the assembly of frames from the final line. Each assembler built complete chair frames, customarily in lots of 25 frames; lots often included two or more chair styles. Space limitations prevented locating more than the parts requirements for 25 chair frames near one assembler. The frame parts were wheeled on carts to the assembly operators by six "stockpickers." The pickers, working from lot tickets which listed the frame styles and the quantity of each style to make up a lot of 25, determined from memory what parts to remove from the stockroom shelves.

PRODUCTION CONTROL SYSTEM

The control of frame parts-manufacturing was dependent upon the company's over-all production scheduling and manufacturing control. The rate of production varied seasonally and was matched to customer

EXHIBIT 1   CREST CORPORATION

CHAIR ORDERS RECEIVED, PRODUCTION, AND SHIPMENTS BY MONTHS, 1955
THROUGH 1958, A GRAPHIC REPRESENTATION OF THE FIGURES GIVEN
IN EXHIBITS 3, 4, AND 5

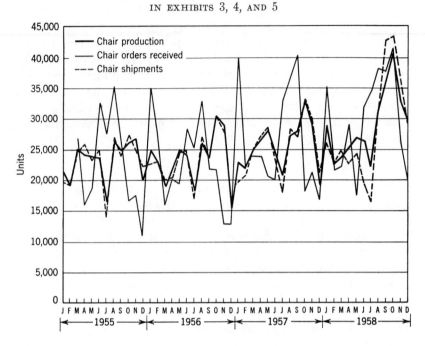

delivery needs (see Exhibits 1 through 6). In general, chairs were
shipped within two days after completion of final assembly. A long-
standing company policy against carrying finished goods inventories
had been modified only during the recession-induced slump in orders
in early 1958. At that time the Crest company built an inventory
totaling 10,000 chairs in a few popular items.[2] This entire inventory
had been sold by the end of 1958 at regular prices.

The production rate was set by the top management of the plant by
specifying the daily production goal, in units, for each of the seven
final (upholstery) assembly lines. Production rates for all contributing departments were then set to match this rate.

Customer orders specified delivery in a given month and upon re-

---

[2] To cover its 50 different styles of frames, Crest offered over 500 different
fabric pattern-color combinations and other choices such as springs or foam rubber
upholstery. As a result of these options, the variety in the final product numbered
several thousand.

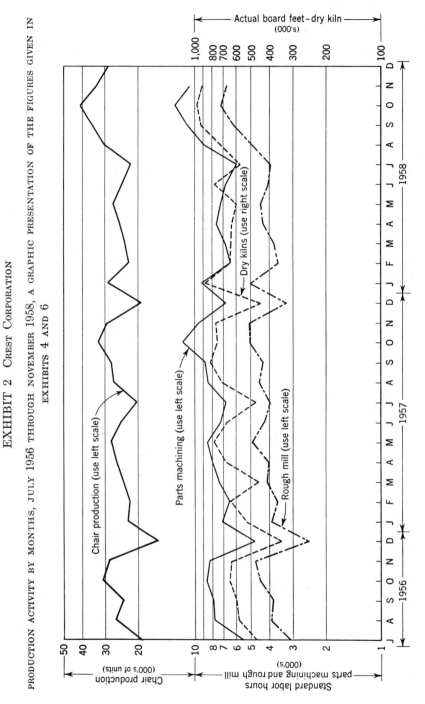

EXHIBIT 2 CREST CORPORATION

PRODUCTION ACTIVITY BY MONTHS, JULY 1956 THROUGH NOVEMBER 1958, A GRAPHIC PRESENTATION OF THE FIGURES GIVEN IN
EXHIBITS 4 AND 6

EXHIBIT 3   CREST CORPORATION

CHAIR ORDERS RECEIVED

(000 Units)

	1955	1956	1957	1958
January	n.a.	35.1	39.9	35.1
February	n.a.	27.4	21.9	21.7
March	26.8	15.9	23.9	22.3
April	16.0	20.2	23.8	29.4
May	18.3	19.4	20.6	17.4
June	32.7	28.6	19.9	32.2
July	27.7	25.3	33.2	34.4
August	35.4	33.2	36.9	38.3
September	26.8	21.9	40.3	37.9
October	16.6	21.8	18.1	41.8
November	17.7	12.8	21.5	26.6
December	10.5	12.9	16.9	20.0
		274.5	316.9	357.1

EXHIBIT 4   CREST CORPORATION

CHAIR PRODUCTION

(000 Units)

	1955	1956	1957	1958
January	21.9	24.8	22.9	29.2
February	18.8	23.0	22.0	22.6
March	25.0	18.8	24.1	23.7
April	24.2	21.4	26.6	25.4
May	23.8	25.1	28.4	27.1
June	23.7	24.1	24.8	24.1
July	16.3	18.3	20.7	21.9
August	26.8	26.3	27.6	30.6
September	24.6	24.0	28.2	35.7
October	26.2	30.6	33.1	41.1
November	26.8	28.8	29.3	32.9
December	19.8	15.7	19.3	29.0
	277.9	280.9	307.0	343.3

EXHIBIT 5 CREST CORPORATION

CHAIR SHIPMENTS
(000 Units)

	1955	1956	1957	1958
January	19.7	22.5	19.9	26.6
February	19.3	22.9	21.0	22.8
March	24.2	19.9	24.3	25.1
April	25.8	20.4	27.3	22.7
May	23.1	24.3	28.9	24.3
June	25.0	25.0	24.8	19.3
July	13.7	16.6	17.8	16.2
August	27.3	27.3	28.8	30.6
September	23.7	23.4	27.2	43.1
October	27.7	30.7	33.6	43.8
November	25.1	27.8	30.5	36.8
December	22.2	18.0	21.9	28.0
	276.8	278.8	306.0	339.3

ceipt were added by line to that month's backlog. When the backlog
for a particular month reached the available capacity of the planned
production rate for that month, the General Manager might decide
either to increase the production rate, a common event, or to stop
booking orders for that month. A report of orders received, backlog,
and available capacity for each of the next three months was issued
daily to top management. Orders to be shipped during a particular
month were substantially on hand by the 15th of the prior month,
and only exceptional orders were processed for shipment in less than
three weeks.

The over-all schedule for a month was broken down into daily production schedules dependent on shipping load plans, that is, lists identifying each chair to be shipped in a specified load on a specific date.
This conformance to shipping load plans reflected the magnitude of
freight costs. Customers paid freight costs on complete shipments of
their orders. To hold down freight costs customers expected that items
ordered together would be shipped together and that their shipments
would be pooled[3] with others destined for the same geographic area.
If some chairs on an order were not ready for shipment on the sched-

---

[3] Shipments occupying part of a truck or rail freight car cost considerably more
than would the same shipments "pooled" or combined with other shipments to
fill a "pool" car.

EXHIBIT 6   CREST CORPORATION

PRODUCTION ACTIVITY

	Dry Kilns	Rough Mill	Parts Machining
1956	(Actual Board Feet)	(Standard Labor Hours)	(Standard Labor Hours)
July	467,200	3,064	5,432
August	571,000	3,911	7,897
September	599,900	3,835	7,957
October	646,500	4,596	8,620
November	624,400	4,857	8,347
December	339,600	2,467	4,741
1957			
January	532,600	3,959	7,107
February	650,700	3,680	6,549
March	456,000	4,139	7,459
April	685,800	4,058	8,074
May	793,800	4,973	8,601
June	670,300	4,331	7,235
July	463,700	4,026	6,828
August	718,500	4,625	8,682
September	732,000	4,440	8,907
October	768,000	5,197	11,709
November	775,600	5,208	9,615
December	448,500	3,294	6,802
1958			
January	897,400	5,181	9,171
February	649,500	3,632	6,462
March	657,300	3,870	6,974
April	645,200	4,409	7,619
May	609,800	4,520	7,387
June	795,500	4,093	6,918
July	579,300	3,966	5,879
August	723,700	5,043	8,990
September	928,600	6,327	10,746
October	981,300	7,360	12,863
November	917,700	5,793	10,798

uled date, these were shipped separately at the Crest Company's expense. To satisfy customers' delivery expectations and to avoid freight charges to the company, the Crest company shipped completed orders by pool cars and trucks and emphasized planned production to meet such shipments.

The translation of customers' orders into shipping load plans was the responsibility of the traffic control clerk. He planned each day's shipping loads three weeks in advance, then, each Friday morning he turned over to the production control section the planned shipping loads for the five days ending on a Thursday three weeks hence.

The production control section, consisting of a manager and three clerks, used the shipping plans to determine the corresponding frame parts requirements. This was done with the help of the standard parts lists for the frames to be built. When parts requirements for a week were known, these figures were compared with the records of available parts.

Although shipping plans, by day, were established three weeks in advance, the "lead time" at which parts requirements were determined in advance of assembly was reduced considerably by these factors:

The shipping plans were accumulated each week until Friday. This achieved a "batching" of requirements but cut lead time.

Final (upholstery) assembly began two days before the planned shipping date and frame assembly two days[4] before that. This reduced lead time by nearly a week.

Production clerks were occupied from Friday until Tuesday in determining parts requirements and in comparing requirements with availabilities.

The net effect was that the actual requirements of parts to be assembled in any week were not known until Tuesday of the preceding week.

To compensate for the limited advance notice of known parts requirements, the Production Control Manager forecast parts requirements each week for one week beyond the requirements known. This one-week forecast was, in general, an extrapolation of a simple "visual" average of the actual requirements of recent weeks. Thus, on any Tuesday anticipated parts requirements for nearly three weeks were available. Requirements for the current week and for the following week were based on scheduled assemblies, and requirements for the third week were based on the Production Control Manager's forecast. In determining what parts to order from the frame shop, the Pro-

---

[4] The required time for a chair to move through frame assembly and through final assembly was considerably less than two days—a matter of hours. The extra time was used as a buffer and was represented physically by completed frames awaiting the final assembly line and completed chairs awaiting shipment.

duction Control Manager used the following formula: parts needed equals the requirements for three weeks (as established above), less the current book inventory, and less any quantity currently on order and not received into inventory. If this calculation showed a parts shortage, an order was placed with the shop equal to the standard order quantity (or a multiple of the standard quantity) established for each part. Each standard order quantity was based on the number of pieces of that part that would fit on one of the carts used to move work in the frame shop. It was set at 80 per cent of the cart capacity.

Every Tuesday the Production Control Department issued the week's frame parts orders to the frame shop foreman. These orders were represented by standard order tickets which specified the quantity ordered, the core stock to be used, and the standard routing through the Parts-Machining Department. For any part for which production requirements exceeded one standard order quantity, additional standard order tickets were issued. In all, several hundred order tickets were issued each week. Once the core stock had been cut for a particular part, the order ticket was placed on the cart and remained with the parts until they reached the stockroom. Then the order ticket was returned to the Production Control Department.

The frame shop foreman was given complete control in scheduling each order through his shop, subject to one restriction: all parts ordered were expected to be produced and in stock within two weeks of the date of issuance of the order. The foreman tried to schedule orders to balance the load on various machines and operators in the shop. His schedule was dependent also upon the availability of the proper species and quality of lumber in the rough mill. To keep a balance between the mix of lumber being dried and the requirements of the frame parts schedule, the frame shop foreman maintained an informal liaison with the dry-kiln foreman. Of the actual orders handled in the frame shop in October 1958, 70 per cent were completed within one week of issue, and 95 per cent were completed before the two-week deadline.

If all went well, on any Monday the parts inventory would assure the requirements for that week's frame assemblies. The Production Control Manager pointed out, however, that achieving this result depended upon:

1. The book inventory being correct.
2. No serious underrun on orders outstanding.
3. Accurate forecasting for one week beyond known requirements.
4. Completion of parts within the two-week time.

THE WORK MANAGER'S VIEW

Mr. Johnson felt that the company's production control system for frame parts presented several opportunities for improvements. His comments in this regard centered about three areas—parts-ordering, machine-loading, and control of the production rate.

Parts-Ordering

One of the characteristics of the company's operation was that excessive inventories frequently accumulated for some frame parts while other parts were unavailable when needed. This problem was ascribed to several factors: the foreman's considerable discretion in scheduling which parts to produce first; the lack of central control of overruns and underruns on parts orders; and clerical errors in reporting receipts and withdrawals from stock. The stockroom usually reported from one to three items out-of-stock daily. In such instances the production control records commonly indicated inventories of several hundred units. The discrepancy was usually attributed to failure to record some withdrawal. Often, however, it was simply unexplained.

The book inventory record was maintained by the Production Control Department. A new book balance was calculated weekly for each part by adding actual parts production and subtracting standard parts withdrawals. Standard withdrawal figures were determined by combining the count of frames actually assembled each week with the list of standard parts for each frame design. If assemblers used nonstandard parts, or if they used more than the standard quantity due to spoilage, the difference usually was not recorded. In some instances, assemblers, anxious to increase piece-rate earnings, had found that substituting one part for another speeded assembly. The stockpickers were supposed to report extra withdrawals and to choose only standard parts, but this was difficult to enforce.

Some of the difficulties in parts-ordering were related to the size of the job of handling production control information. The manufacturing of parts was dependent upon the processing of information. A standard two-day clerical delay existed between the time the shipping load plans for a particular week were accumulated and the time when the corresponding parts requirements could be compared with the record of inventory levels. Standard figures for withdrawals of parts for a week were used instead of detailed reports of actual withdrawals to conserve the time spent in clerical work by both stockpickers and production control personnel.

The Crest company seldom failed to meet a shipping load schedule because a frame part was out of stock. A load of the missing part could be rushed through the shop. This required special expediting attention by the foreman and subforemen. Frequently they spent time investigating why the stock records and actual stock condition disagreed. They also directed the "special handling" of needed parts through the shop and rescheduled loads that were displaced. In some instances extra set-ups were required when rush orders interrupted the machining of a load.

Machine Loading

The foreman and subforemen were given discretion as to what machine to use for each parts order. Mr. Johnson felt that this resulted sometimes in spending more machining time than necessary. He believed that the loading of at least some of the more important machines should be centralized in the hands of the production control group. Toward this end, steps had just been taken to plan loads for the automatic shaper. A production control clerk designated which jobs were to be done on the shaper following two rules. First, the clerk had been instructed to keep this automatic machine fully loaded; and, second, if the available work exceeded the capacity of the machine, the clerk was to select the long-run jobs in order to realize the best return from the higher set-up cost of this machine. The foreman had been pleased with the results of this and had asked to have all boring operations loaded in the same manner. In the absence of central loading, the mix of parts ordered in a given week frequently overtaxed the time available on one group of machines while leaving other machines and their operators idle.

The chief engineer felt, however, that more data were needed before effective machine load planning could be pursued on a centralized basis. Machine loads, he thought, should be scheduled by actual rather than standard times. Hence, it would be necessary to have data on set-up times by machine and performance ratios (actual to standard) prepared separately for set-ups and machining times. Present average output was 125 per cent of standard, but performance at individual work stations varied widely.

Production Rate

The seasonal character of sales and the Crest company's scheduling practice led to substantial fluctuations in employment and hours of work. Peak production in the fall of 1958 had strained the dry-kiln

capacity,[5] although both the Rough Mill and Parts-Machining Departments could have increased their volume of work appreciably without significant expenditures for additional equipment. Kilns were expensive, however; any one of the existing kilns had a replacement value of $27,000. Furthermore, no space existed for adding a kiln adjacent to the factory.

Mr. Johnson said that he preferred to operate the plant on a 45-hour week, but that this could be varied to adjust for small fluctuations. He set 36 hours as a minimum work week, but said that this could not be held for more than a month without a great loss in productive efficiency. Similarly, when the work week went above 45 hours, efficiency began to fall. It would be difficult, he believed, to get the men to work more than 50 hours weekly. The average hourly base rate in the frame shop was $1.25, with time and one-half paid above 40 hours per week. None of the attempts by an international union to organize the Crest workers had been successful.

In August 1958 a full second shift had been hired for the rough mill, and a partial shift had been added to break bottlenecks in parts machining. The personnel manager said that it was very difficult to get skilled operators to work the night shift. The cost of hiring was high, and the quality and tenure of second shift operators tended to be low. The Personnel Manager also indicated his belief that by January 1959 it would be necessary to cut back the workforce again to match sales demand.

Training costs in the frame shop were high, the Personnel Manager thought, although no exact figures could be obtained. It was known, however, that ten of the men hired for the rough mill at the beginning of August 1958 began work producing at 50 per cent of standard; their production reached 80 per cent by November 1, and 100 per cent by the first week of December. Similarly, boring machine operators hired in August started at 65 per cent of standard and reached 80 per cent by late September and 100 per cent in October. New employees were paid the full hourly rate until they reached 100 per cent productivity; they received bonuses above that level.

---

[5] Throughout 1958 and the immediately preceding years, the Crest company had the use of two 100-foot kilns and one 50-foot kiln. In December 1958 work was completed to lengthen the 50-foot kiln, giving Crest three 100-foot kilns; this expanded dry-kiln capacity by 20 per cent.

A STATISTICAL STUDY

A random sample of 50 of the 500 frame parts was chosen for a study of usage and production in 1958. Records covering a period of 22 weeks, from July through November 1958, were examined to calculate usage, inventory, and production data on the parts comprising the sample. The parts included in the sample accounted for 7.75 per cent of lumber consumed and 4.5 per cent of standard frame shop labor hours during the 22-week period. On the basis of usage, standard costs, and an assumed inventory carrying cost of 25 per cent an economic order quantity was computed for each part. This was compared with the company's existing standard order quantity, which was equivalent to 80 per cent of the number of pieces held on one cart. For the parts covered in this study, the average standard time allowance per lot for set-up was 0.46 hours, and the range of allowances was from 0.27 to 1.76 hours. The standard cost rate for direct labor and variable overhead in the frame shop was $1.71 per hour. The data of the study appear in Exhibit 7.

EXHIBIT 7 CREST CORPORATION

SAMPLE STUDY OF FRAME PART ACTIVITY

See page 233 for explanation of column headings

(1)	(2)	(3)	(4)	(5)	(6)	(7)
			Annual No. of Set-ups, based on		Parts Activity (22 weeks)	
Part No.	Economic Order Quantity	Actual Lot Size	Economic Quantities	Actual Quantities	Labor	Lumber
1 56	586	450	29	38	20.52	8.28
1 81	2,310	875	15	40	320.20	12.30
2 1	3,310	1,400	20	48	88.80	10.86
2 28	1,940	1,250	19	30	36.90	5.13
3 3	3,065	1,000	36	110	111.65	18.80
3 26	1,480	1,000	8	12	49.20	2.35
4 8	882	1,100	15	12	13.26	2.77
4 35	1,435	1,000	15	22	22.33	3.70
6 16	1,340	450*	1	4	3.59	—
6 72	820	215*	3	12	6.73	.17
7 53	310	110*	4	10	19.70	.59
7 74	1,071	300*	4	12	8.33	.24
21 1	1,461	500	13	38	86.83	8.81
21 37	2,110	500	13	54	153.63	13.74
22 4	770	350	20	44	37.84	10.01
22 45	2,285	1,100	11	22	55.55	3.57
22 58	650	300	12	26	17.16	4.35
23 17	316	167*	3	6	1.69	.16
24 16	3,015	1,000	13	38	45.98	2.14
41 3	1,130	600	13	24	76.68	4.77
41 123	622	275	19	44	216.92	10.22
41 147	2,140	800	14	38	132.24	6.55
41 158	878	200*	2	8	38.84	1.66
41 195	994	350	20	56	155.12	10.44
42 41	1,170	1,250	9	8	9.80	1.10
43 5	1,480	450	17	56	246.40	9.80
43 95	1,935	1,250	10	16	18.24	3.55
43 139	1,165	1,000	5	6	10.65	.94
43 146	1,360	2,500	3	2	28.10	.23
43 171	1,076	500*	4	8	8.44	.45
44 48	2,185	1,750	5	6	21.99	.70
44 50	377	100*	2	6	2.60	.17
45 9	838	1,000*	10	8	8.07	.83
46 30	427	500*	2	2	29.27	.15
48 46	2,440	625	34	134	229.81	33.61
48 51	806	450	16	28	16.24	4.17
49 87	986	400*	4	10	5.15	.53
49 98	1,525	600*	3	6	7.03	.09
51 35	614	625	6	6	9.24	1.28
62 2	786	1,100	9	6	9.75	1.14
62 9	721	1,100	6	4	6.50	.80
62 25	143	50*	1	2	.84	.08
65 1	861	175	61	302	638.73	96.68
66 3	1,950	1,000	13	26	65.00	4.68
81 11	610	1,800	2	—	—	.13
84 4	2,530	1,500	32	54	27.54	7.14
95 6	790	500	15	24	111.60	5.47
96 6	851	225*	2	8	3.12	.06
97 78	1,840	750*	2	4	3.93	.27
97 132	2,850	1,600	9	16	91.52	2.73
99 18	613	325*	4	8	53.76	.50
				Totals	3385.—	319.—

EXHIBIT 7 (*continued*)   CREST CORPORATION

SAMPLE STUDY OF FRAME PART ACTIVITY

The data in Exhibit 7 represent the results of a study of production and usage for a sample of 50 frame parts, randomly selected.

The data are based on a 22-week period from July 2 to November 28, 1958. These 22 weeks account characteristically for 50 per cent of annual production at Crest.

The data were analyzed to permit comparison between "economic" lot sizes and actual order quantities used by Crest. A corollary aim was to indicate the degree to which lumber usage and shop activity were concentrated on relatively few parts. These data are presented in seven columns of figures in Exhibit 7. The basis of the data in each column is as follows:

Column (1) Part Number: Identifies part.

Column (2) Economic Order Quantity: This is a theoretical economic order quantity calculated by the standard formula:

$$\text{Quantity} = \sqrt{\frac{2 \times \text{usage} \times \text{set-up cost}}{\text{inventory carrying cost} \times \text{variable unit cost}}}$$

Annual usage was estimated by taking twice the actual usage during the 22-week period of the study.

Set-up cost was calculated from standard set-up time allowances (on standard cost records) using a variable cost rate of $1.71 per hour and adding a $.10 allowance for the clerical cost of processing each order.

The unit cost is the total variable material, labor, and expense cost from standard cost records.

The inventory carrying cost was taken as an arbitrary 25 per cent.

Column (3)—Actual Lot Size: This column shows the quantities actually used for ordering. Figures followed by a star (*) are the average actual lot sizes for parts ordered in lots smaller than the established (80 per cent cart capacity) standard quantity.

A comparison of actual and standard order quantities for the 16 starred items is given in the following table:

Part No.	Average Actual Quantity	Standard Quantity	Part No.	Average Actual Quantity	Standard Quantity
6 16	450	2,000	45 9	1,000	1,400
6 72	215	2,500	46 30	500	1,250
7 53	110	600	49 87	400	2,500
7 74	300	2,500	49 98	600	1,250
23 17	167	1,000	62 25	50	500
41 158	200	250	96 6	225	2,000
43 171	500	1,750	97 78	750	1,500
44 50	100	1,500	99 18	325	1,750

Columns (4) and (5)—Annual Number of Set-ups: In Column (4) is the number of set-ups required annually to produce the required volume of each part if orders were based on "economic" quantities presented in Column (2).

EXHIBIT 7 (*continued*)   CREST CORPORATION

SAMPLE STUDY OF FRAME PART ACTIVITY

In Column (5) is the number of set-ups required annually using actual order quantities from Column (3). This figure is twice the actual number of set-ups during the 22-week period.

Columns (6) and (7)—Parts Activity: These two columns are intended to demonstrate the importance of each part. The "labor" column shows the standard frame shop labor hours required to produce the quantities of each part actually manufactured during the 22-week period.

The "lumber" column represents the standard quantity of lumber (in thousand board feet) required to produce the quantity actually produced in the 22-week period.

PART 6.   WAGES AND LABOR COSTS

Wages and Labor Costs

Labor cost is a significant factor in most production management decisions. The level of labor cost is influenced by the human element, the composition of a given job, the internal structure of the firm, and the external forces of the labor market. A discussion of the human element is beyond the scope of this book; we have, however, tried to provide a basis for understanding the composition of a given job or class of jobs. This introductory note and the subsequent cases are intended to create an awareness of how the internal policies and external economics of a situation can be considered in evaluating labor costs.

In today's industrial environment, most firms attempt to develop consistent policies and operating procedures to provide as equitable a basis as possible for worker remuneration. The methodology of these policies and operating procedures is common throughout most industry. This note is from Chapter 20 of *Modern Production Management* by E. S. Buffa.[1] It is a concise description of the influences upon and the common rationale for methods of wage payment. It is intended to provide the reader with a conceptual background for analysis of common wage administration or labor cost problems.

WAGE STRUCTURES

What is a wage structure? The simplest answer is, perhaps, the schedule of wages paid to people on the payroll. Basic economics tells us that we will find many potential employees who have basic skills, so that wages for low-skilled jobs will be relatively low. On

---

[1] E. S. Buffa, *Modern Production Management,* John Wiley and Sons, New York, 1961, second edition 1965 pp. 611–641.

the other hand, higher levels of skill are less plentiful and market forces will cause a bidding up of wages for jobs requiring these higher skills. The entire range of skills will have wages determined by economic forces in proportion to skill level. Theoretically, then, we have no problem of assigning wage rates to jobs, because market forces will do the assigning for us, and all will be done happily in proportion to over-all skill levels.

But before dismissing the problem, let us ask two questions: (1) How closely do market forces control wage levels for a given skill? (2) Are there realistic labor markets for all kinds of jobs? In answer to the first question, studies indicate that within the same labor market there are wide differences in wages paid for substantially the same jobs. Ranges of 50 per cent are common and ranges up to 300 per cent occur for comparable jobs in the same community (1). There are logical reasons why this might occur. Jobs in different organizations are never completely comparable, even though job titles may be identical. Also, workers on the jobs are not equally good; that is, they may vary according to various measures of performance, such as quality and quantity produced, personality characteristics, etc. Finally, imperfect knowledge of market values and individual skill levels by both employers and employees may lead to agreements for individual wages that are relatively high or relatively low. Regardless of the reasons, the fact is, although market forces may determine a range, that range is so broad that organizations are still left to determine where within the market range for a given job they will establish a base wage. Although market forces do control, they do not control so closely that the problem of wage structures vanishes for us.

Now to the second question: Are there realistic labor markets for all kinds of jobs? There are common jobs for which we can say that a formal or informal market exists. These are jobs for machinists, secretaries, clerks, janitors, etc. In some instances, union hiring halls provide a formal market place. But what about the thousands of uncommon jobs which specialization has created? In business and industry today we have cork shapers, pickle cutters, brick stickers, paper twisters, and others, in an interminable list of often ludicrous sounding job titles. There are no markets for jobs such as these, because they are so individual that often nothing really comparable exists, and yet people on these jobs must be paid, and good conscience dictates that we attempt to pay them in proper relation to their over-all skill levels.

The result of these factors is that business and industrial management has attempted to establish scales of job difficulty by which all jobs could be measured and placed in order of relative value. Then, by sampling local labor markets for common jobs, wage structures that make sense internally could be constructed, similar to that shown in Figure 1. Since market data yield a range of rates, management must determine where within or beyond the normal range it wishes to operate. As we know, unions are more than willing to help in this process of determining over-all wage level, and the scales are often the result of the balance of bargaining power rather than any conscious management selection of a level that meets its needs better than any other level. Finally, formal wage structures recognize individual differences in performance by variations in hourly base rates, by bonuses in addition to base pay, or by both of these.

JOB EVALUATION AS A MEASURE OF JOB DIFFICULTY

Informal valuation of the relative worth of jobs has existed as long as business organizations have existed. Formal job evaluation is fairly recent, however, becoming common during and after World War II. Formal job evaluations attempt to systematize judgments about the relative value of jobs so that a higher degree of consistency in valuation is possible. The methods of accomplishing these ratings

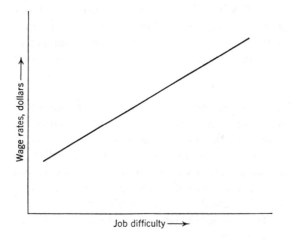

FIGURE 1. General relationship of wage rates and job difficulty.

of relative job worth are usually classified as: nonquantitative (ranking methods, classification systems); quantitative (point systems, factor comparison systems).

The main difference between the nonquantitative and the quantitative systems is that the nonquantitative systems rate the job as a whole and end up with simple relative values, such as, job A is of greater value to the organization than job B, and B greater than C; but no indication is implicit in the rating as to how much more valuable A is than B, or B than C. On the other hand, the quantitative systems consider job values to be made up of a series of compensable factors such as skill, degree of responsibility, physical and mental effort required, working conditions, etc. They establish scales for each of several compensable factors with numerical equivalents for different levels of each of the factors. The relative worth of a job is then indicated by the total of numerical scores for the several factors. Thus, the numerical score indicates not only that job A is of greater value than job B, and B greater than C, but the difference in numerical scores gives some indication of the differences in value.

There is disagreement over the use of nonquantitative versus quantitative systems based on the feeling of some psychologists that something is lost when we attempt to represent the total job value by the simple sum of factor ratings. They say that the whole is not necessarily the simple sum of its parts, but may be something greater or less because factors tend to interact and because factor definitions may leave out something that is important for certain jobs. Nevertheless, the quantitative plans are used a great deal more than the nonquantitative, and it seems likely that if errors in quantitative ratings from this source exist, they are somewhat smaller than the total error of rating due to human judgment and can be neglected.

Ranking and Classification

The ranking method involves the simple arrangement of jobs into their order of importance to the organization, based on a rating committee's knowledge of the jobs and brief job descriptions. The ranking method is not used to any great extent. Classification is in common use by federal and state civil service agencies and by some business concerns; it involves the definition of classes of jobs at different levels of over-all difficulty, often related to organizational levels. For example, the *Classification Act of 1949* provides for two basic classification schedules:

1. A General Schedule (GS), which covers professional and scientific service, clerical and administrative jobs.

2. A schedule for Crafts, Protective, and Custodial jobs (CPC). The GS schedule defines 18 different grades and the CPC schedule 10 grades. Figure 2 gives a sample of 5 of the GS grades. These grades are carefully defined in advance to cover classifications of

GRADE GS-1 includes all classes of positions the duties of which are to perform, under immediate supervision, with little or no latitude for the exercise of independent judgment, (1) the simplest routine work in office, business or fiscal operations, or (2) elementary work of a subordinate technical character in a professional, scientific, or technical field.

GRADE GS-7 includes all classes of positions the duties of which are (1) to perform, under general supervision, work of considerable difficulty and responsibility along special technical or supervisory lines in office, business, or fiscal administration, or comparable subordinate technical work in a professional, scientific, or technical field, requiring in either case (A) considerable specialized or supervisory training and experience, (B) comprehensive and thorough working knowledge of a specialized and complex subject matter, procedure, or practice, or of the principles of the profession, art, or science involved, or (2) to perform other work of equal importance, difficulty, and responsibility, and requiring comparable qualifications.

GRADE GS-10 includes all classes of positions the duties of which are (1) to perform, under general supervision, highly difficult and responsible work along special technical, supervisory, or administrative lines in office, business, or fiscal administration, requiring (A) somewhat extended specialized, supervisory, or administrative training and experience which has demonstrated capacity for sound independent work, (B) thorough and fundamental knowledge of a specialized and complex subject matter, or of the profession, art, or science involved, and (C) considerable latitude for the exercise of independent judgment; or (2) to perform other work of equal importance, difficulty, and responsibility, and requiring comparable qualifications.

GRADE GS-15 includes all classes of positions the duties of which are (1) to perform, under general administrative direction, with very wide latitude for the exercise of independent judgment, work of outstanding difficulty and responsibility along special technical, supervisory, or administrative lines which has demonstrated leadership and exceptional attainments; (2) to serve as head of a major organization within a bureau involving work of comparable level; (3) to plan and direct or to plan and execute specialized programs of marked difficulty, responsibility, and national significance, along professional, scientific, technical, administrative, fiscal, or other lines, requiring extended training and experience which has demonstrated leadership and unusual attainments in professional, scientific, or technical research, practice, or administration, or in administrative, fiscal, or other specialized activities; or (4) to perform consulting or other professional, scientific, technical, admin-

FIGURE 2. Five of the 18 grade descriptions for the General Service (GS) Schedule. Classification Act of 1949.

istrative, fiscal, or other specialized work of equal importance, difficulty, and responsibility, and requiring comparable qualifications.

GRADE GS–18 includes all classes of positions the duties of which are (1) to serve as the head of a bureau where the position, considering the kind and extent of the authorities and responsibilities vested in it, and the scope, complexity, and degree of difficulty of the activities carried on, is exceptional and outstanding among the whole group of positions of heads of bureaus; (2) to plan and direct or to plan and execute frontier or unprecedented professional, scientific, technical, administrative, fiscal, or other specialized programs of outstanding difficulty, responsibility, and national significance, requiring extended training and experience which has demonstrated outstanding leadership and attainments in professional, scientific, or technical research, practice, or administration, or in administrative, fiscal, or other specialized activities; or (3) to perform consulting or other professional, scientific, technical, administrative, fiscal, or other specialized work of equal importance, difficulty, and responsibility, and requiring comparable qualifications.

work judged to be of a similar level. The task of evaluation is then one of sorting jobs into the predetermined grades, based on descriptions of the jobs and the grade descriptions. The resulting lists of jobs placed into classifications represent the final relative values of the jobs. In both ranking and classification, job pricing is accomplished by a process of surveying wages and salaries paid for comparable jobs in the labor market, together with a consideration of the organization's wage level policies and collective bargaining agreements.

Point and Factor-Comparison Systems

In both the point and factor-comparison approaches to the determination of job difficulty, compensable factors are determined and either point or monetary scales set up for each, which reflect the expected range for the factor and a weighting of the relative importance of the factor. For example, skill factors are commonly weighted heavily compared to working conditions. For all practical purposes, we can consider all of these scales as being point scales (the monetary scales are point scales with a 1:1 conversion of points to monetary values). The main differences between point-systems and the factor-comparison system are the means by which the scales are developed originally. Factor comparison derives its scales by a somewhat complex procedure of intercomparison of a set of key jobs by factors.

This results in scales for each of the factors that reflect weightings and values of the actual jobs used as key jobs, based on the judgments of experienced people. Once the scale is developed, actual ratings of jobs on each factor are accomplished by comparing the job to be rated with the key jobs already placed in the scale.

Point systems are by far the most commonly used and the balance of the comments in this chapter assumes their use. Their scales are derived for each factor directly from the judgment of experienced people as to the weighting that the various factors should receive, the range, and assigned point values for each of the factors. Figure 3 shows the scales for the set of factors used by the National Metal Trades Association and the National Electrical Manufacturers Association. The factors fall under the four major headings of skill, effort, responsibility, and job conditions. Each factor is carefully defined so that overlapping in meaning between factors is minimized. Also, each degree of each factor is defined to cover the range of jobs that might be evaluated. Figure 4 shows typical definitions of factors and degrees for four of the factors. The actual rating of jobs then depends on the comparison of job characteristics with the degree

FACTORS	1st Degree	2nd Degree	3rd Degree	4th Degree	5th Degree
SKILL					
1. Education (14%)	14	28	42	56	70
2. Experience (22%)	22	44	66	88	110
3. Initiative—Ingenuity (14%)	14	28	42	56	70
EFFORT					
4. Physical demand (10%)	10	20	30	40	50
5. Mental—Visual demand (5%)	5	10	15	20	25
RESPONSIBILITY					
6. Equipment or process (5%)	5	10	15	20	25
7. Material or product (5%)	5	10	15	20	25
8. Safety of others (5%)	5	10	15	20	25
9. Work of others (5%)	5	10	15	20	25
JOB CONDITIONS					
10. Working conditions (10%)	10	20	30	40	50
11. Unavoidable hazards (5%)	5	10	15	20	25

FIGURE 3. Factors and scales of points used by the National Metal Trades Association and the National Electrical Manufacturers Association.

FACTOR 3.   Initiative and Ingenuity

Initiative and ingenuity appraise the independent action, exercise of judgment, making of decisions, or amount of planning which the job requires. This factor also appraises the degree of complexity of the work.

1st Degree

Requires the ability to understand and follow simple instructions and the use of simple equipment involving few decisions since the employee is told exactly what to do.

2nd Degree

Requires the ability to work from detailed instructions and the making of minor decisions involving the use of some judgment.

3rd Degree

Requires the ability to plan and perform a sequence of operations, where standard or recognized operation methods are available and the making of general decisions as to quality, tolerances, operation and set-up sequence.

4th Degree

Requires the ability to plan and perform unusual and difficult work where only general operation methods are available and the making of decisions involving the use of considerable ingenuity, initiative and judgment.

5th Degree

Requires outstanding ability to work independently toward general result, devise new methods, meet new conditions necessitating a high degree of ingenuity, initiative and judgment on very involved and complex jobs.

FACTOR 4.   Physical Demand

This factor appraises the amount and continuity of physical effort required. Consider the effort expended handling material (the weight and frequency of handling), operating a machine or handling tools, and the periods of unoccupied time.

1st Degree

Light work requiring little physical effort.

2nd Degree

Light physical effort working regularly with light weight material or occasionally with average weight material.   Operate machine tools where machine time exceeds the handling time.

3rd Degree

Sustained physical effort, requiring continuity of effort working with light or average weight material.   Usually short cycle work requiring continuous activity.   Or the operation of several machines where the handling time is equivalent to the total machine time.

4th Degree

Considerable physical effort working with average or heavy weight material.   Or continuous strain of a difficult work position.

5th Degree

Continuous physical exertion working with heavy weight material.   Hard work with constant physical strain or intermittent severe strain.

FIGURE 4.   Definitions of factors and degrees for four of the factors shown in Figure 3.

FACTOR 8. Responsibility for Safety of Others

This factor appraises the care which must be exercised to prevent injury to others, and the probable extent of such injury. Injury to the employee on the job being rated is to be considered under Unavoidable Hazards. Consider the possible accidents to others resulting from careless operation of machine or handling of materials or tools. Can other employees be injured by carelessness on the job? If so, how?

1st Degree
Little responsibility for safety of others. Job performed in an isolated location, or where there is no machine involved and the material is very light.

2nd Degree
Only reasonable care to own work necessary to prevent injury to others, and accidents, if they should occur, would be minor in nature.

3rd Degree
Compliance with standard safety precautions necessary to prevent lost-time accidents to others.

4th Degree
Constant care necessary to prevent serious injury to others, due to inherent hazards of the job, but where such other employees may act to prevent being injured.

5th Degree
Safety of others depends entirely on correct action of employee on job being rated and carelessness may result in fatal accidents to others.

FACTOR 10. Working Conditions

This factor appraises the surroundings or physical conditions under which the job must be done and the extent to which those conditions make the job disagreeable. Consider the presence, relative amount of, and continuity of exposure to dust, dirt, heat, fumes, cold, noise, vibration, wet, etc.

1st Degree
Ideal working conditions. Complete absence of any disagreeable elements.

2nd Degree
Good working conditions. May be slightly dirty or involve occasional exposure to some of the elements listed above. Typical machine shop working conditions.

3rd Degree
Somewhat disagreeable working conditions, due to exposure to one or more of the elements listed above, but where these elements are not continuous, if several are present.

4th Degree
Continuous exposure to several disagreeable elements or to one element which is particularly disagreeable.

5th Degree
Continuous and intensive exposure to several extremely disagreeable elements.

definitions for each factor. Data on job characteristics are usually summarized in the form of job descriptions and specifications, which indicate the tasks of the job and the minimum that the job requires of anyone assigned to it.

Job Analysis

Figure 5 is a fairly typical job description and specification used for job evaluation purposes. The job analysis phase (resulting in job descriptions and specifications) takes considerable time and effort and must be carefully done, since the resulting data is basic to the evaluation system. Experts agree that job analysis data for job evaluation need to be gathered by a process of interviews with job incumbents and consultation with supervisors and others who can shed light on the nature of the job and the minimum requirements imposed by the job on anyone coming to it.

Job descriptions are usually written in terse style that begins each sentence with a functional verb, as indicated in Figure 5, for example, "makes cams," "sets up machine," etc. Note that the attempt is to focus on the important evaluative aspects of the job rather than on any detail which tells how to execute the job. Thus, the description tells the kind of tasks involved, the kind of decisions to be made, etc.; and the description of how it is accomplished has the basic objective of indicating something of the skill levels of the activities. Therefore, two different jobs may require that measurements be made, but one may be accomplished with a foot ruler and the other require the use of precision gages. One job may require that complex blueprints be read in order to determine the detailed operations to be performed, whereas in the other job, detailed instructions are received from a supervisor. The first demands more practical education experience and initiative than the second. The result is that, although at first glance the descriptions may seem sketchy, when properly written they can pack in a great deal of evaluative information. In larger organizations where more than one analyst may be gathering job-analysis data, there needs to be considerable emphasis on uniformity, since those making the actual ratings often will have nothing beyond the descriptions and specifications on which to base their ratings. Differences in style, amount of detail, and the emphasis given the various aspects of the jobs can influence evaluations.

The Evaluation of Jobs

Jobs are usually evaluated by a committee. The composition of evaluation committees varies widely between organizations, but they

JOB ANALYSIS WORK SHEET

Machine and Manufacturing Co.

Job title BROWN & SHARPE MACH. OPERATOR, CAM LAYOUT   Code __12:104__
Other titles __AND CUTTING__

Suggested title _____

Dept. __CHUCKER_____ Dept. No. __12_____ Supr. __P. Wurtz____

No. on job_____ Lead Man _____

Persons interviewed __Joe Hall__

Analyst   __E.B.S._____ Date ___June 24, 1955___

Job Summary (key phrases that cover job):

    Makes cams for, sets up, and operates Brown & Sharpe machine.
    Procures materials, tends machine, sharpens tools.

Work Performed: What–How–Why (Use additional sheet if req'd.)

    1. Makes cams for Brown & Sharpe machine setups. Works from
    blueprints and M.O.T. to calculate travel lengths and rises on
    cams required to advance tools, set depth of cuts and timing
    of tools. Scribes pattern on cam and cuts out on doall saw,
    finishing by hand. Designs tooling for machine.

    2. Sets up machine. Works from blueprints and M.O.T. to set
    up cams and gears for required sequence of operations. Times
    machine; checks parts to be sure of proper set up.

    3. Operates machine. Checks parts periodically as machine
    automatically produces parts. Sharpens and replaces tools
    as they wear. Oils machine periodically (3 times/day).
    Gets stock and cams in preparation for next job.

Equipment, machines used:

    Brown & Sharpe #2   Doall Saw
    Precision tools for checking work   Hand tools.

FIGURE 5.   Typical job description and specification used for job evaluation.

Requirements of Job (Minimum)
(Think of the job—not the man)

SKILL

1. Education Requirements - Must be able to read blueprints, use precision gauges and know how to sharpen tools to required angles for materials used. Uses shop math. to calculate required travels and rises on cams.

2. Experience Requirements
Five years plus one year on cam making.

3. Initiative—Ingenuity   - Machine set up, cam making. Alert to new ideas and techniques.

EFFORT

4. Physical Demand - Runs last 1 - 3 days. Maximum lift of 35 lbs. only periodically to get and feed stock to machine (2 - 3 times/day).

5. Mental-Visual Demand   - Calculations and layout of cams. Read precision gauges, grind tools.

RESPONSIBILITY

6. Equipment or Process   - Bad collet may cause excessive wear or breakage up to $25. If machine out of time, possible damage up to $400.

7. Material or Product   - Proper cams essential to make good parts. Works from raw bar stock.

8. Safety of Others   - Whipping bar stock.

9. Work of Others   - None.

JOB CONDITIONS

10. Working Conditions   - Noise, dirt (oil).

11. Unavoidable Hazards   - Minor hand cuts from chips.

Employee   Joseph E. Hall (signed)   Supervisor   P. Wurtz (signed)

FIGURE 5 (Continued)

often include representatives of higher management, industrial engineers, personnel and industrial relations people, supervisors, union representatives, and sometimes workers. Whether or not union personnel are represented depends on both the company and union attitudes. The reasons for resorting to committee action are: (1) that a successful program needs the support of various elements of an organization because of the vital importance of the wage question; and (2) that greater faith is placed in pooled judgment than in the judgment of any individual, no matter how expert he is supposed to be. The usual procedure is for each committee member to make an independent rating and then results are pooled and differences are discussed. Often, one or more committeemen will be influenced by the arguments presented and wish to change their original ratings. Final committee judgments become the job ratings. Table I shows the point evaluations of 50 jobs from a small manufacturing plant after committee action. After all jobs have been rated, judgments are usually cross-checked to see if ratings have been consistent by factors and degrees. Usually some ratings are changed during this process.

Validity and Reliability of Ratings

The actual validity of ratings is very hard to determine, because an objective criterion of validity is not available. If it were, that is, if we had some measure of what the "right" relative values are, there would be no need for ratings in the first place. In the final analysis, the validity of the system depends on its acceptance by the various parties affected, and the scope of this acceptance is much more complex than that implied by the ratings themselves, depending on such factors as employee-employer relationships, union relationships, the way the program has been handled and presented, and, perhaps, a variety of other human factors.

Reliability of the ratings is quite another thing. It refers to consistency and the ability of the committee using the rating system to reproduce the results obtained. General studies of job-evaluation reliability have been made, which indicates 3 to 5 per cent errors and correlation ratios in the neighborhood of 0.97 between ratings made at different times.

Final Accuracy of the Job Difficulty Scale

Does Table I represent a realistic schedule of the relative values of the 50 jobs shown there? If it did, it would mean that we had point-to-point accuracy in making the ratings. But we have already noted that we have only a 3 to 5 per cent reliability, and our final scale

TABLE I. POINT EVALUATIONS OF 50 JOBS FROM A SMALL
MANUFACTURING COMPANY

No. of Points	Jobs	No. of Points	Jobs
320	Prototype machinist	226	Electrosubassembler
319	General grinder	225	Surface grinder B
306	Tool grinder	224	Floor inspector B
301	Electrical maintenance	221	Inspector, receiving and shipping
297	New Britain machine operator	221	Brown & Sharpe automatic B
297	Turret lathe A	220	Gear cutter B
297	Grinder A	220	Drill press B
292	Gear cutter A	220	Raw material stock clerk
292	Engine lathe	219	Mechanical maintenance
290	Inspector, layout and first article	218	Burring A
285	Inspector, gears	217	Tool crib attendant
275	Drill press A	190	Expediter's assistant
270	Chucker A	185	OSP shipping and receiving clerk
269	Electromechanical assembler	184	Turret lathe C
265	Floor inspector A	175	Stock clerk
265	Milling machinist A	171	Mechanical assembler
264	Production control clerk	169	Spray painter
261	Turret lathe B	160	Drill press C
261	Brown & Sharpe automatic A	160	Tumble burr operator
251	Expediter	160	Janitor
245	Material control clerk	155	Burring B
235	Inspector, finished machine parts B	130	Parts stamper
235	Inspector, finished assemblies	130	Parts stamper and filer
234	Hand screw machine	120	Parts wrapper
234	Chucker B	120	Electromechanical subassembler B
231	Mechanical assembler A		
229	Milling machinist B	120	Tool and gage crib attendant
228	Driver		

should reflect this. If we can make ratings consistently with a 5 per
cent error, we cannot justify a scale with such fine divisions on it.
Therefore, groupings, or classifications of jobs, are commonly made
with 10 to 12 classifications, fairly well representing the limit of accuracy of the final scale. All jobs falling into a given classification or
labor grade are regarded as being of equal relative value. The 50 jobs
of Table I were divided into 10 labor grades with point limits as
follows:

Labor grade I	120 to 140 points
Labor grade II	141 to 160 points
Labor grade III	161 to 180 points
Labor grade IV	181 to 200 points
Labor grade V	201 to 220 points
Labor grade VI	221 to 240 points
Labor grade VII	241 to 260 points
Labor grade VIII	261 to 280 points
Labor grade IX	281 to 300 points
Labor grade X	301 to 320 points

Thus, the first four jobs in Table I, the prototype machinist, the general grinder operator, the tool grinder, and the job of electrical maintenance, were placed in labor grade X and regarded as being of equal value, and so on through the table. This grouping of jobs into 10 labor grades was more realistic and also resulted in a schedule which was easier to administer than the schedule of raw point values in Table I.

AREA WAGE SURVEYS ESTABLISH RELATIONSHIPS OF KEY JOBS IN THE LABOR MARKET

Workers have never been willing to accept points in lieu of wages, so the point values determined by job evaluation must be converted to monetary values. Area wage surveys often play an important role in this procedure. As we noted earlier, some jobs are common enough that a market for them can be said to exist. The function of the area survey is to tie in the relative values of these jobs with the existing market values, to aid in the managerial decisions regarding wage levels and to aid in developing a workable wage structure.

In making wage surveys, the labor market area that services the organization is the one of interest. Wage data on comparable key jobs are obtained from a sample of organizations. The structure of this sample depends somewhat on the objectives of the company making the survey. Today, wage surveys are frequently made, and most organizations are cooperative about participating, particularly if they, too, receive the results of the survey. Many organizations have continuing wage-data exchange agreements with a group of select companies. Also, a number of national and local associations make periodic wage surveys and provide the results to member companies.

The major technical problem in making a wage survey is one of establishing job comparability. We cannot assume that similar job

titles have the same job content. For example, two turret-lathe operators' jobs might vary considerably in difficulty because one sets up his machine and runs the parts whereas the other has the machine set up for him. Two engine-lathe operators' jobs might differ in terms of the difficulty of the work accomplished. For example, one may be doing "run of the mill," loose-tolerance work, while the other works on close-tolerance prototype parts that require considerable skill, initiative, and ingenuity to read drawings, setting up the machine, and making the required cuts. Therefore, it is considered good practice to go to the companies being sampled with brief job descriptions and ask, "Do you have a job similar to this?" Figure 6 is a portion of a wage survey of seven companies which illustrates the point. The third job requires setting up and operating a turret lathe, and the fourth requires only the operation of the turret lathe. The average hourly wages was $2.29 versus $2.06. The job titles for these two jobs for the various companies were very confusing, however. Sometimes the two jobs were called Turret Lathe Operator A and Turret Lathe Operator B. Sometimes no distinction was made in job title, although pay differences existed for the two jobs, and one organization had no job that required only the operation of the turret lathe without the set-up requirement. If the careful distinction had not been made, these differences might have been masked. Figure 7 shows the results of a wage survey in graphical form with the approximate average line of relationship drawn in. This line can be compared with the existing average line of pay for the organization as a partial basis for determining if the over-all wage level is in line with company policies and needs.

Guides for Developing Wage Structures for Base Wages

When employees are paid hourly wages, questions such as the following need to be answered:

1. For a given labor grade, what range of wages should be paid, that is, what is the minimum wage for the grade and what is the maximum?
2. Should there be an overlap between pay ranges for adjacent pay grades, and, if so, how much overlap?
3. How many labor grades should be used?
4. On what basis will individual employees be advanced in wages through the established pay range for the grade?

In fact, the wage range, the overlap between grades, the width in points of labor grades, and the slope of the pay line are all

Job Summary:
Grinds tools to proper angles and dimensions.

Company	Min.	Max.	No. on Job	Weighed Avg.
1	1.94	2.24	10	2.19
2	2.15	2.44	21	2.41
3	2.17	2.61	5	2.55
4	2.16	2.43	12	2.32
5			4	2.24
6				2.40
7	2.36	2.70	1	2.70

Avg. Co. Max. $2.48   Avg. of Co. Means $2.40

Job Summary:
Drives light truck to transport light loads for relatively short distances.

Company	Min.	Max.	No. on Job	Weighed Avg.
1	1.59	1.86½	2	1.82
2	1.56	1.87		
3	1.80	2.17	10	2.17
4	1.78	2.00	5	2.00
5			3	1.32
6				2.03
7	1.50	1.80	2	1.58

Avg. Co. Max. $1.94   Avg. of Co. Means $1.82

Job Summary:
Sets up and operates turret lathe to fabricate parts from bar stock, castings or forgings.

Company	Min.	Max.	No. on Job	Weighed Avg.
1	1.94	2.24	40	2.13
2	2.03	2.33	43	2.33
3	2.11	2.49	47	2.46
4	2.00	2.21	16	2.15
5			13	2.06
6				
7	2.36	2.70	4	2.60

Avg. Co. Max. $2.39   Avg. of Co. Means $2.29

Job Summary:
Operates turret lathe to fabricate parts from bar stock, castings, or forgings.   Makes simple setups.

Company	Min.	Max.	No. on Job	Weighed Avg.
1	1.69	1.94	7	1.83
2	1.69	1.97		
3	1.92	2.30	33	2.11
4				
5				
6				2.03
7	1.98	2.40	6	2.28

Avg. Co. Max. $2.15   Avg. of Co. Means $2.06

Job Summary:
Sets up and operates grinding machines such as centerless, surface, internal, external and thread grinders.

Company	Min.	Max.	No. on Job	Weighed Avg.
1	1.94	2.24	18	2.15
2	2.03	2.33	34	2.33
3	2.11	2.49	11	2.49
4	2.27	2.53	5	2.52
5				
6				
7	2.40	2.70	13	2.46

Avg. Co. Max. $2.46   Avg. of Co. Means $2.39

FIGURE 6. Partial results of a wage survey.

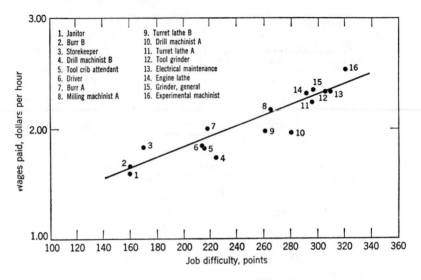

FIGURE 7. Results of a wage survey for 16 key jobs with approximate average line of relationship drawn in.

interrelated. A change in any one of these requires a change in at least one of the others. The slope of the pay line tends to be fixed by other considerations, as we have already discussed. However, we should not forget that it is a partial determinant of the wage range-overlap-width of grade combination.

Some changes in the width of grades to achieve the desired wage-overlap combination are quite feasible. Earlier in this chapter we said that the ±5 per cent reliability of job evaluation ratings indicated that we should not have more than about 10 to 12 grades. But what is the smallest number of grades that we can use? The number is indicated by the accuracy with which workmen (or anyone) can discriminate between the relative value of jobs without the aid of job evaluation. This is commonly taken as about ±10 per cent, which translates roughly into about 5 to 6 grades. The operating range of job evaluation is between these limits. We should not make the final classification of grades finer than about 12 grades, which represents the realistic limit of accuracy of job evaluation ratings, and we should not use fewer than 5 or 6 grades because the resulting scale is then so coarse that unaided judgment is just as good. Therefore, we can use this flexibility in the number of grades to good effect in developing the desired final wage structure.

Let us demonstrate the effect of these variables on a wage struc-

ture. We shall assume a given slope of the average pay line with 10 labor grades, and a range of wages for each grade as ±10 per cent from the average pay line. The resulting wage structure looks like Figure 8. Note that the overlap in wage ranges between grades is considerable. Suppose we wish to reduce this overlap. How can we do it? First, if we increase the slope of the pay line, maintaining 10 grades and wage ranges of ±10 per cent, overlap will be reduced. We have already noted, however, that the slope of the line will probably be dictated by other considerations. Overlap can also be reduced, either by reducing wage ranges or by reducing the number of grades. Figure 9 shows the result of reducing the number of labor grades from 10 to 7. A similar effect could be obtained if we reduced the limits of the wage range. There are, of course, other possibilities for manipulating the structure to obtain the desired effects. These involve the use of variable percentage wage ranges, variable slope of the average pay line, labor grades that increase in width as the difficulty increases, and simply "doctoring" the structure to obtain the result desired.

It is hard to answer the question of how much overlap between grades is desirable. Theoretically, there should be no overlap, since with overlap a worker near the top of the range in a lower labor grade

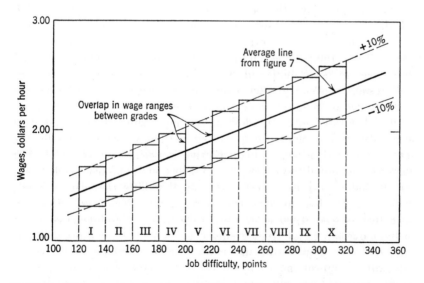

FIGURE 8. Wage structure based on average pay line from Figure 7, ±10 per cent rate ranges for each grade, ten labor grades, and resulting overlap in wage ranges between grades.

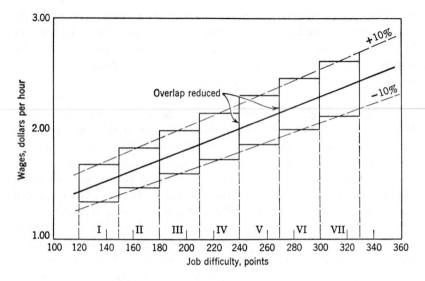

FIGURE 9. Overlap in wage ranges between grades reduced by reducing the number of labor grades from 10 to 7.

could have a higher wage rate than individuals on higher rated jobs. Even in the structure of Figure 9 the top of the range for labor grade IV is slightly above the bottom of the range for labor grade VII. Overlap to this extent poses human problems because of possible wage rate inequities. On the other hand, some overlap can be justified because, even though one job may have greater basic value, individual differences in performance of the employees on the jobs could very well result in a net greater value to the organization of excellent performance on a lower rated job as compared to poor performance on a higher rated job. In addition, overlap results in some operating flexibility for foremen and supervisors. Often, owing to absenteeism, scheduling bottlenecks, or high priority work, foremen need to shift workers temporarily to other jobs. When there is no overlap between grades, there are greater restrictions on the shifts that can be made under many labor management agreements. Therefore, from an operating viewpoint, some overlap is desirable. Good practice seems to limit overlap to adjacent grades or possibly within three adjacent grades. To accomplish this minimum overlap in practical wage structures often requires the use of relatively few labor grades, small wage ranges, steep slopes, or up-sweeping pay lines.

Given the overall structure, on what basis will individual employees move through the established wage range for the grade?

Possibilities are seniority and appraisal of performance and combinations of these. Organized labor has tended to demand seniority as the primary basis. Business management has preferred to emphasize appraisals of performance as the primary basis. Formal merit rating programs are often used to make these appraisals.

Nash Brick Plant

The basis for determining all wages at the Nash Brick Plant was changed in 1954. Seven years later a further change was made in order to adjust the earnings of one particular group of workers. The reasons which prompted these wage changes, the ways in which the changes were made, and the results constitute the central interest of this case. First, however, let us review plant operations, particularly the manufacturing process.

PRODUCTS AND PROCESS

The Nash Brick Plant, located in Nash, Arkansas, is one of seven plants operated by Simpson Brothers, within a three-state area. The company's products are brick, clay tile, concrete pipe, and concrete blocks. Three of these products—brick, tile, and pipe—are made at Nash, the greatest volume being brick.

Bricks are made from clay and shale. The common red brick contains 60% clay, dug from pits located on the Nash plant property, and 40% shale, trucked from four miles away. The only other raw material for red brick is barium carbonate, added in an amount less than $\frac{1}{2}$% of the total volume, to improve the color of the brick and to prevent discoloration of the brick surface. The shale is ground and screened to obtain fine consistency before being moved by conveyor to a storage bin. The clay, requiring no processing, is dumped from the pit trucks directly into a storage bin.

Machinery is used extensively as the materials progress through various stages to become finished brick (Exhibit 1). Endless belts convey the raw material from the storage bins to the first mixing chamber where mixing is done by heavy rolls revolving above perforated plates through which the material is forced. Next the material

EXHIBIT 1　NASH BRICK PLANT

SCHEMATIC DRAWING OF BRICK MANUFACTURING

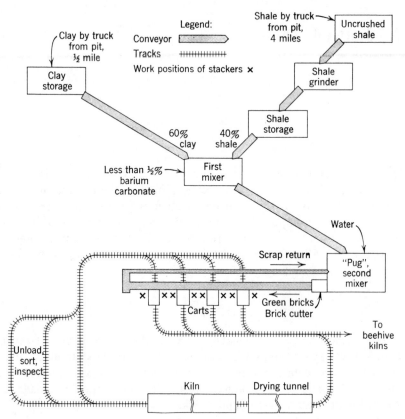

passes between heavy steel rollers set one-eighth of an inch apart, designed to crush any small lumps. The material then flows up a sharply inclined conveyor to enter the second mixing chamber, called the *pug*. Here, water, in small amounts, is added to bring the material to the proper consistency. The actual amount of water added depends on the moisture content of the materials and is determined by the judgment of the pug operator who reaches in and feels the shale and clay mixture.

Mixing within the pug is accomplished by 15 knife blades attached to each of two parallel shafts which rotate in the horizontal plane. These knife blades mix the brick material; because they are set at an angle, they act also as turning screws, forcing the material out through an opening. The rate at which the brick material is extruded can be

changed by adjusting the angle at which the knife blades are set, an adjustment which requires stopping the shafts. Most of the time, however, the flow of material is continuous from the storage bins and through the steps which follow.

The spout leaving the pug narrows and ends in a die which forms the brick material into a moving column equal in width to the long dimension of one brick. Immediately beyond the opening of the die is a reciprocating steel plate which carries the brick mass forward just long enough for 19 cutting wires, which move with the steel plate, to cut down through the material. In this way 18 bricks are formed. The column of material from behind pushes the cut bricks off the steel plate onto a moving, endless belt which carries the bricks forward at a slightly faster rate. The steel plate shoots back under the die and again supports and carries forward the column of material for the length of time necessary for wires to make the next cut of 18 bricks. The rate at which bricks are cut can be set as low as 10,000 bricks per hour or as high as 16,000 bricks per hour.

STACKING AND SUBSEQUENT OPERATIONS

The endless belt carries the bricks and the few inches of material pushed out of the die between successive cuts past the stackers. These men pick the bricks off the belt and stack them on the carts which carry them through the drying tunnel and the kiln. The stacking job is a hand operation, an interruption in the mechanized flow of material. Any bricks not picked by the stackers, as well as the few inches of material extruded between cuts, ride the belt to a point where this scrap falls onto another conveyor, which returns it to the pug.

The carts on which the bricks are stacked have low metal frames and wheels which run on tracks. Above this undercarriage, the load surface of a cart, 7 ft by 15 ft, made of firebrick gives heat protection to the metal parts below. Four tracks run at right angles under the belt so that four carts may be positioned partly or wholly beyond the belt for loading. On each cart the stackers build six stacks, called *cobs*, of the *green* (unfired) bricks to a height of 5 ft.

The cobs are constructed with care. Bricks in each layer are placed one-half inch apart to allow air circulation; a crisscross pattern provides stability; brick faces, the surfaces of the brick which have been smoothed by the die rather than cut by wire, are turned toward one another; holes are left near the bottom of the cobs to allow forklift trucks to remove the warm bricks from the carts after firing.

The normal complement of stackers is eight men, one on each side of the four carts; only six or seven stackers work, however, whenever the stacking of bricks runs ahead of kiln capacity. As many as 16 carts are loaded in the eight-hour work day.

The filled carts are tracked to the opening of the drying tunnel and forced in, one at a time, by hydraulic jacks. As one cart is pushed in, another is forced out at the end of the tunnel. Temperature in the drying tunnel, where a cart remains two days, is 200°F. Carts leaving the drying tunnel are again forced by hydraulic jacks into the kiln tunnel. There, temperatures up to 2,000°F are applied from oil blowers located along the sides. Bricks move through the kiln tunnel in three days. More than half the length of the kiln is used to reduce gradually the temperature of the brick, and heat taken from the cooling bricks is conducted to the drying tunnel.

Carts of bricks leaving the kiln are allowed to cool further and then the bricks are unloaded by fork-lift truck. After further cooling, the bricks go through their final operation, another hand operation. Bricks are inspected, graded, stacked in compact cobs, and secured with wire straps preparatory to shipping.

Sometimes beehive kilns are used to increase the plant's firing capacity. Lined with firebrick, these kilns have the shape of a half hemisphere with a diameter of 30 feet. For decades, all green bricks were stacked by hand within such chambers; the entrance was then closed, coal fires were laid in six fire boxes around the periphery and permitted to burn for days, and additional days were allowed for cooling, whereafter the bricks were removed by hand.

Other Products

Clay tile is made by the same process, except for a different die and cutter.

The concrete pipe, in diameters of 30 to 66 inches, is made in another part of the plant by pouring wet concrete between concentric steel cylinders. Reinforcing wire is imbedded; the moisture content of the concrete is controlled accurately; and the mold itself is vibrated during the pouring. These steps not only produce a strong, dense pipe, but also permit the mold cylinders to be removed within 10 minutes after the pouring, leaving a free-standing pipe section to dry. In another area, smaller sizes of concrete pipe, four to 24 inches are made in a mechanized process. The concrete is packed mechanically within the mold during the pouring operation, and an empty mold is rotated under the pouring spout as soon as the preceding mold is filled.

Jobs

The total employment at Nash is 108. Slightly more than half of the men are direct workers; the rest work on indirect production jobs. These include truck drivers, machinists for the maintenance shop, repairmen for the kiln trucks, electricians, and pipe fitters. Equipment, such as the mixing blades in the pug, is subject to considerable strain during normal operations, and equipment failures are not infrequent. For some types of failures, the production of bricks stops until the necessary repairs are made. At other times the repairmen are used in the actual construction and installation of new equipment, such as mixing and pouring devices for concrete pipe. Other workers maintain the beehive kilns.

HISTORY OF WAGES

Over the decades in which bricks were made by hand, and until 1954, Nash was basically a "one-rate" plant—one in which almost all employees were paid the same amount per hour, regardless of occupation. One manager commented, "The machinist and the wheelbarrow operator received the same amount."

In 1953 that amount was $1.20. The Plant Manager, Kenneth McKinnon, explained:

We were a one-rate plant for historical reasons. At one time all jobs were interchangeable. But years ago, before my time, the plant moved towards mechanization and specialization in work assignments. The skill required on the different jobs varied considerably, but at first no corresponding pay differentials were established.

We were not quite a one-rate shop. The men who handled bricks at the very end of the production cycle were paid by contract—an incentive scheme by which they were paid so much per thousand bricks for the final sorting and stacking. These men became the best paid workers in the plant, although their work required the least skill.

The skilled workers were dissatisfied. The fact that they made less than the unskilled workers seemed to bother them fully as much as the absolute amount of their pay. Despite the fact that the labor market is small in the Nash area, we lost a few of our best men, and the ones who stayed complained.

I, as plant manager, and the managers at the Little Rock head office discussed this thoroughly. The Simpson brothers, who are the owners, and Tom Johnson, who is Personnel Manager for the whole company, made the decision to establish a formal basis for pay differentials. Tom Johnson did most of the work in setting up the pay structure.

EXHIBIT 2

THE FIVE JOB EVALUATION FACTORS

1. Skill

Years to learn the job	¼	½	¾	1	1½	2
Points	30	60	90	120	150	180

2. Mental Requirements

Degree	1	2	3
Points	20	50	80

3. Physical Requirements

Degree	1	2	3
Points	10	20	30

4. Job Conditions

Degree	1	2	3
Points	10	30	50

5. Responsibility
   a. For Equipment

Degree	1	2	3
Dollar Value Risk	0–50	51–250	251–500
Points	5	15	25

   b. For Product

Degree	1	2	3
Points	5	15	25

JOB EVALUATION AND PAY DIFFERENTIALS

In response to a question, Johnson said:

You asked about my personal history. I'll be brief. This is the third company that I've worked for as personnel manager. Before that I was the president of a union. I got along well with both the union members and management, and both parties benefited. One day the company's general manager asked me if I would leave the union and take the job of personnel director for the company. It was a hard decision. I put it to a vote at a union meeting, and received a unanimous vote of support. Subsequently, I moved to an affiliated company in Little Rock and 10 years ago made the change to Simpson Brothers.

At both previous places of employment, pay differentials based on job evaluation systems were in effect when I took over. I felt that the same thing was needed at Nash, but it took me the better part of three months to decide on the pay structure for Nash. To establish pay differentials, there must be some justification for the differences. This sheet (Exhibit 2) reflects the criteria which I established. I was guided by three things: my own expe-

Nash Brick Plant

(CRITERIA) AND THE POINTS ASSIGNED TO EACH

						Maximum Points Possible
2½	3	4	5	6	7	
210	240	270	300	330	360	360
4		5		6		
110		140		170		170
4		5				
40		50				50
4		5				
70		90				90
4		5				
501–1,000		1,000–up				
35		45				45
4		5				
35		45				45
		Total				760

rience, two books[1] which helped my thinking, and my own detailed study of the actual work at Nash. I dealt not only with the problem of assigning criteria but also with the relative weighting of the criteria; with judging the degree of difficulty within each criterion; and with establishing pay levels corresponding to point values. (Exhibit 2 shows the assignment of points; Exhibit 3 gives guide lines for determining degree of difficulty as one of the factors; and Exhibit 4 shows pay levels corresponding to point values.)

While I was establishing point values, I did some tentative checking. I assigned points to a number of the jobs and compared the corresponding pay rates with my over-all assessment of the jobs. In addition, I asked Ken McKinnon to rank the jobs in order of worth as he saw them. Both of these checks confirmed my formal job evaluation work.

We had taken the union[2] into our confidence as we started job evaluation.

---

[1] Lanham, Elizabeth, *Job Evaluation,* McGraw-Hill Book Co., New York, 1955; and Otis, Jay Lester, and Richard H. Leukart, *Job Evaluation,* Prentice Hall, New York, second edition, 1954.

[2] On another occasion Mr. Johnson had said, "In the long run any management gets just about as good union relationships as that management deserves."

EXHIBIT 3 NASH BRICK PLANT

GUIDELINES FOR DETERMINING DEGREE OF DIFFICULTY FOR
FACTOR NO. 3—PHYSICAL REQUIREMENTS

Degree 1	Light work requiring little physical exertion; intermittent sitting, standing, or walking.
Degree 2	Physical effort required for continuous handling of lightweight materials or continuous sitting, standing or walking; lifting not over 25 pounds.
Degree 3	Repetitive or sustained physical effort; occasional pushing, pulling or lifting heavyweight materials or occasional difficult work positions; lifting usually not over 35 pounds.
Degree 4	Frequent pushing, pulling or lifting or frequent difficult work positions; considerable physical effort or frequent working with heavyweight material; may be called upon to lift up to 75 pounds.
Degree 5	Continuous physical exertion, working with heavyweight materials, or continuous difficult work positions; hard work with constant physical strain; lifting over 75 pounds and may be called upon to push or pull equivalent to the lift requirements.

They recognized that we had to do something for the skilled men. The union agreed to job evaluation and pay differentials with the provision that our assignment of points would be open to union inspection. We have had, and continue to have, very good union relations.

After union acceptance we completed the evaluation of all jobs at Nash and established corresponding pay rates. (Exhibit 5 shows point values assigned for all jobs at the Nash plant.) We raised the pay of men who received less than the evaluation indicated, but we did not cut the men who

EXHIBIT 4 NASH BRICK PLANT

PAY RATE SCALE—1961

		Seniority Rates			Merit Rates	
Point Range	Classification	Starting Rate	Six-Months Rate	Job Rate (One Year)	First Merit	Second Merit
425 and up	Tradesman I	$1.64	$1.68	$1.72	$1.76	$1.80
375–424	Tradesman II	1.54	1.58	1.62	1.66	1.70
325–374	Worker—Grade A	1.44	1.48	1.52	1.56	1.60
275–324	Worker—Grade B	1.34	1.38	1.42	1.46	1.50
225–274	Worker—Grade C	1.24	1.28	1.32	1.36	1.40
174–224	Worker—Grade D	1.14	1.18	1.22	1.26	1.30

EXHIBIT 5 Nash Brick Plant

POINTS ALLOTTED TO ALL JOBS AT NASH PLANT

Job Evaluation Factors

| Job Title | Skill | | Mental Require-ments | | Physical Require-ments | | Job Condi-tions | | Responsibility | | | | Total Points |
| | | | | | | | | | Equip-ment | | Product | | |
	Yrs.	Pts.	Deg.	Pts.	Deg.	Pts.	Deg.	Pts.	Deg.	Pts.	Deg.	Pts.	
Machinist	4	270	4	110	2	20	2	30	2	15	1	5	450
Main Mechanic	3½	255	3	80	3	30	3	50	3	25	0	0	440
Pipe Fitter	3½	255	3	80	3	30	3	50	2	15	0	0	430
Welder	2¼	195	3	80	2	20	4	70	3	25	1	5	395
Shovel Operator	2¼	195	2	50	3	30	3	50	5	45	2	15	385
Repairman	2	180	2	50	3	30	3	50	5	45	2	15	370
Tunnel Kiln Operator	1¼	135	3	80	2	20	3	50	5	45	5	45	360
Loader Operator	1½	150	2	50	3	30	3	50	5	45	2	15	330
Grinder Operator	1	120	2	50	3	30	4	70	4	35	2	15	320
Burner	1	120	2	50	3	30	4	70	4	25	3	25	320
Tradesman's Helper	1	120	3	80	3	30	3	50	2	15	1	15	310
Lift Truck Operator	1	120	2	50	2	20	3	50	4	25	3	25	300
Pipe Machine Operator	1	120	2	50	3	30	3	50	3	25	3	25	300
Kiln Repairman	1	120	2	50	3	30	4	70	1	5	2	15	290
Machine Operator	1	120	2	50	2	20	3	50	3	25	2	15	280
Brick Sorter	½	60	2	50	5	50	3	50	2	15	5	45	270
Pug Mill Operator	1	120	2	50	1	10	3	50	3	25	2	15	270
Branch Maker	½	60	2	50	3	30	5	90	1	5	3	25	260
Setters	1	120	1	20	3	30	3	50	1	5	4	35	260
Helper Mixer Operator	¾	90	2	50	2	20	3	50	2	15	3	25	250
Pipe Handler	½	60	1	20	5	50	4	70	2	15	4	35	250
Burner's Helper	½	60	1	20	4	40	4	70	3	25	3	25	240
Cutter Operator	¾	90	1	20	2	20	5	90	2	15	1	5	240
Fireman-Oiler	½	60	2	50	3	30	3	50	5	45	1	5	240
Tunnel Kiln Operator	½	60	3	80	2	20	3	50	2	15	2	15	240
Stacker	½	60	1	20	5	50	3	50	2	15	4	35	230
Clay Jitney Operator	¾	90	1	20	3	30	3	50	3	25	2	15	230
Truck Driver	¼	30	2	50	3	30	4	70	4	35	1	5	220
Fireman	¼	30	2	50	3	30	3	50	4	35	1	5	200
Jitney Operator	½	60	1	20	3	30	3	50	2	15	3	25	200
Laborer	¼	30	1	20	5	50	4	70	1	5	1	5	180
Transport Operator	¼	30	1	20	4	40	3	50	2	15	3	25	180

earned more than indicated. You can't take money away from a man. We froze the hourly pay rates of the men who were making more than indicated until such time as general increases brought them in line.

OPERATING EXPERIENCE

Ken McKinnon, Nash Plant Manager, commented:

I was pleased to see the job evaluation system and the pay differentials come into the plant. Some difficulties have arisen in the assignment of points, however. For instance, I may know very well that I can train a man for a job in 12 months. The union says 24 months. The upshot is that Tom Johnson compromises and assigns 18 months. On the other hand, I don't know that he has much choice. On the whole it has worked out well.

Tom Johnson explained further:

As the pay of the skilled workers moved above the pay of the less skilled men, the union got pressure from that group. The stackers particularly complained. They claimed that they had a backbreaking job, and indeed their work is hard. It's very hard physical work to be reaching and turning all day; and the bricks keep coming on the belt. The union suggested that the stacker's job was incorrectly evaluated and asked that it be reviewed. We checked the points as assigned, found that we were right, and made no change. If we had started to change points for this one job, just for expediency, we never could have held the line on other jobs. Just to be sure of our position we engaged an industrial engineering consultant from Fisk and Sanders.[3] He checked the points too, and confirmed our position

Next the union asked that since the stackers were under constant pressure to do hard physical work, they be given an incentive pay scheme for their job. We agreed to look into it. Again we asked Fisk and Sanders for their opinion, and their answer was, "Yes, pay incentives could be used there." We then agreed with the union to go ahead with incentives, and we engaged Fisk and Sanders to work with us. They recommended that our incentive system be preceded by very carefully set productivity standards, and to get the necessary accuracy, they recommended predetermined time values be used rather than stop-watch times. They recommended further that we train one of our own men in the setting of standards.

We selected one man from Nash, Ralph Jones, and another from our Jamesville plant. These men attended all-day study sessions here at Little Rock with the consultant from Fisk and Sanders to learn the MTM[4] system of predetermined time values.

---

[3] Fisk and Sanders is a well-known consulting organization.

[4] Methods-Time Measurement. For an explanation see Maynard, H. B., Editor-in-Chief, *Industrial Engineering Handbook,* McGraw-Hill Book Co., New York, First Edition 1956 or Second Edition 1963, or other industrial engineering handbooks.

SETTING STANDARDS BY MTM

Ralph Jones, the methods and time-study man at Nash, said:

It's been nearly two years since I first studied MTM. I now feel that I can set a good standard; but that first job could not have been done without the help of the consultant. We studied at Little Rock for three weeks. Then the consultant worked with us for two months in setting a standard for the stackers' job. We had to assign a time value for every motion and this required that we watch the stackers and analyze every motion. I won't go into the details of MTM other than to show you one sheet. This (Exhibit 6) develops the time value for one of the motion patterns. There are some

EXHIBIT 6 NASH BRICK PLANT

METHODS ANALYSIS CHART

Part: MAF2 Date: Mar. 31/61 Operation: Stacking Green Brick

Description Left Hand	LH	TMU*	RH	Description Right Hand
	Brick from Belt to Cob with Move and Flip			
		Solid Brick		
Same as Right Hand	R26B	22.9	R26B	Reach to Brick on Belt
	G1A	2.0	G1A	Grasp Brick
	M9Bm6	10.6	M9Bm6	Move Brick Clear of Belt
	~~mMBm6~~		~~mMBm6~~	
	T90M	8.5	T90M	
	~~mMBm6~~		~~mMBm6~~	
	M3B6	8.2	M3B6	Flip Brick
	~~mMBm6~~		~~mMBm6~~	
	RL1	2.0	RL1	
	R3B	5.3	R3B	
	G1A	2.0	G1A	
	M11C6	17.4	M11C6	Move Brick toward Cob
	P1SD	11.2	P1SD	Locate Ends Together
	M2C6	7.7	M2C6	Move Brick to Cob
	P1SD	11.2	P1SD	Locate Joined Brick to Cob
	RL1	2.0	RL1	Release Brick
		111.0		

$$\frac{111.0}{2} = 55.5 \text{ TMU*/Brick}$$

* In the Methods-Time Measurement procedure, involving predetermined elemental times, the basic unit is one TMU (time-measurement unit). One TMU equals 0.00001 hour, 0.0006 minutes, or 0.036 seconds.

twenty different motion patterns and time values for solid brick alone. Further, different distances and different time values are involved in laying brick at cart level, at middle levels, and at the top of the cob.

This particular time value (Exhibit 6) would not do for stackers working toward the end of the belt. There a man cannot always pick a brick immediately; he receives only bricks left by stackers further up the line. We studied in detail the number of "waits" an end-stacker experiences and the average length of these waits in order to set a standard for the end positions.

In addition to setting time values for the actual stacking, we determined the time for other duties. The stackers move carts, they must occasionally

EXHIBIT 7 NASH BRICK PLANT

CALCULATION OF HOURS EARNED

Date 11–16–61

	Stackers			Pug and Cutter Operator
Production: 15 cars × bricks per car		3,630		
Total brick =		54,450		
Std. Hours per thousand bricks: 1.03 × 54,450 =				
Hours Earned		56.08		
÷ by number of stackers =		7		
Hours earned by each stacker		8.01		

Hours on Incentive

Start	Stop	Elapsed Time		
7.00	12.00	5.00		
1.00	3.00	2.00		
——	——	——		
			7.00	7.00
Bonus Earned, in Hours			1.01	× 2/3 0.67

Down Time

Start	Stop	Elapsed Time		
3.00	4.00	1.00		
——	——	——		
——	——	——		
			1.00	1.00

Causes of Down Time

1. Wood in Clay
2. Cleaning Rollers
3.

| Total Hours | | 9.01 | | 8.67 |

replace a broken firebrick, they shake sand between layers of buff-colored bricks—I could mention thirty other duties.

I set few standards; most of my time is spent improving methods. For instance, at the stacking operation I relocated the sanding boxes. These were behind the stackers, and I had the boxes hung below the edge of the belt so that a man can reach for sand without turning. This cut a little time from the MTM standard for buff-colored bricks, but we did not change the rate. When the consultant was here he told the workers that when the sum of all such small improvements equalled 5 per cent, the standard would be tightened to reflect all such changes. They know that this will happen, although we have not reached 5 per cent yet. Similarly, if a job is made more difficult, the rate will be liberalized only when the added time values equal 5 per cent of the standard.

The consultant was surprised in one respect as he set up the system. He had expected that the company would gain as the stackers raised their productivity up to 100 per cent of standard, following which the men would be paid in proportion to any increase above 100 per cent. Things did not turn out that way. To his surprise, he found that the workers had been working at 100 per cent of the standard he derived by MTM. Thus, under the new system, we have paid the men in proportion to any increase in the number of bricks handled per hour.

Here is a sample of a sheet used to calculate the stackers' bonus (Exhibit 7). You will note that it is a "group incentive"; each stacker gets the same amount. In addition, we give the pug operator two-thirds as much extra as we give each stacker. The man who operates the pug controls the rate at which bricks come down the belt by the setting of the cutting device, by the speed with which he replaces broken wires, and by keeping the material in the pug up to proper level.

MANAGEMENT'S EVALUATION

McKinnon spoke further about the incentive system for the stackers:

When we went to incentives for this job, I was in favor of the change. Most workers today don't have the same outlook that workers had 10 or 20 years ago. Then they expected to come here to do a day's work. Now they come expecting long coffee breaks, several interruptions to go to the washroom, and frequent work interruption just to talk. I had hoped that an incentive payment would focus their attention on output and that we would benefit.

When the incentive first went in, the men worked at 130 per cent of standard. At that pace I felt we were getting something. With seven stackers, we could keep the tunnel kiln full and in addition take care of any special brick for the beehive kilns. We could do this in eight hours with no overtime and with no special lunch hour shift. After a month at this pace, the stackers settled back to an average of just about 115 per cent of standard. This sheet shows their performance for December (Exhibit 8). Some days they will earn a good premium. If there is no interruption in the machinery and if the bricks start flowing to them at a good rate early in the morning, they may go after the premium and work hard all day. But if they get off

EXHIBIT 8 NASH BRICK PLANT

STACKING OPERATION

Comparison of Performance with Standard, December 1961

Date	Actual Output as a Per Cent of Standard (see Notes)	Date	Actual Output as a Per Cent of Standard (see Notes)
1	Not available	15	Not available
4	111	18	120
5	113	19	122
6	98	20	118
7	102	21	130
8	112	22	130
11	108	26	100
12	128	27	108
13	138	28	110
14	Not available	29	103

Note 1: The belt did not run a full eight hours in any day. The actual output is shown as a per cent of standard outputs for the hours the belt did operate.

Note 2: The figures for December were similar to the figures for the five preceding months.

Note 3: The average is 114.8%.

to a slow start, that pace may last all day, and they end up close to 100 per cent for the day. They do not drop under 100 per cent; I think that 97 per cent has been our lowest day.

Production also drops on most days when an "outsider" is substituted on the crew. It's as if the regulars refuse to earn a bonus for the new man. I'm not saying that we have poor labor relations or anything like that. I know these men individually. Their relationship with the company is good. They won't produce under 100 per cent, but they do feel that there is a range of effort which is at their own discretion.

Six months ago we received a request to put the final operation—the inspection, sorting, and stacking by hand—on incentives. However, we plan to make methods changes in that operation. We explained this and said that any incentives would have to come after the methods changes. The union accepted this and is not pressing the matter further.

At the present rate of output I don't feel that I am getting much for the incentive payments to the stackers. We don't get all our bricks stacked by one crew; we need either a second partial crew or overtime. And you can imagine that we paid the consultants, Fisk and Sanders, very well.

On the other hand, I would like to see incentives paid for the making of wire cages—the reinforcing wire embedded in the concrete pipe. Each man who makes cages works alone; he is not dependent on anyone else. There's nothing for such a worker to do but to get mad at the job and produce.

Some of the managers at Nash and Little Rock commented that it might not be consistent to have only the stackers' job on incentives; they would like to form an opinion about the future of the whole wage structure at Nash before making further changes.

Tidwell Metal Products Corporation

For the past several months Mr. R. S. Vorhees, Production Manager of Tidwell Metal Products Corporation, had been attempting to develop a system of job evaluation and merit rating for company employees. He now was reviewing his ideas and conclusions before submitting his plan to the President, Mr. S. S. Tidwell, for approval.

Background

The Tidwell company, located in a community of approximately two million persons, specializes in the fabrication of items from heavy steel plate. Typical products include asphalt mixers, storage bins, tables, instrument panels, and frames for textile machinery. Such items usually are designed by Tidwell's engineers to satisfy functional requirements and dimensional specifications of a particular customer. A majority of orders involve only a single unit; orders calling for more than ten items of the same design are extremely rare.

Shop operations include the use of planers, shapers, shears, bending machines, radial drills, heavy-duty lathes, and welding equipment. The company also is often called upon to perform on-site installation of products it has manufactured. When this occurs, an erection crew of Tidwell employees, one of whom the shop superintendent informally designates as "in charge," often has to work several days at the customer's location.

The company was founded eight years ago. It now employs 185 production workers, roughly 40 per cent of whom have three or more years' service with the firm. All personnel are paid on an hourly basis.

The company workforce has more than doubled over the past four years, an interval characterized by heavy business activity in the surrounding area and by shortages in the local labor market.

To expand its operations during this period, as well as to counter the moderate personnel turnover usually experienced, Tidwell sometimes has found it necessary to hire inexperienced men or experienced men who, for any of a variety of reasons (inferior skill, poor performance record on prior jobs, etc.) would not normally be considered for employment. As a result, certain internal wage discrepancies have arisen, such as situations in which newly hired personnel were brought into the firm at the same or even higher rates of pay for a given type of work than those paid to more experienced or more able workers already in the company's employ. Such situations often have led to expressions of dissatisfaction among the more senior workers. It was Mr. Vorhees' impression, however, that in only a relatively few instances had long-service employees quit the company solely because of such discrepancies.

A union attempt was made to organize Tidwell's production force during the year, a period in which 15 per cent of the shop employees had been laid off because of declining sales volume. The union's organizing campaign had stressed what Mr. Vorhees termed "conventional arguments," contentions that wages in general should be increased, a formal seniority plan introduced, work conditions improved, etc. The campaign had culminated four months previously in an election conducted by the National Labor Relations Board which resulted in a 96 to 46 vote against union representation. Although he had no specific evidence, Mr. Vorhees suspected that the principal union support had come from employees in lower-paid jobs. Most of these were younger men with less than average periods of company service.

Shortly after the election, an unexpected upsurge in business permitted the company to recall all but a few of the recently laid-off employees who had not taken jobs elsewhere. Mr. Vorhees was aware, however, that differences in wages among men doing similar work still prevailed within the company. This, in his judgment, constituted a potential grievance around which further union efforts might center. Furthermore, sales prospects suggested that layoffs might again be necessary in another few months. Both factors strengthened Mr. Vorhees' interest in developing an effective system of job evaluation and merit rating, and his conviction that it would be desirable to launch such a plan in the near future.

Prior Attempts at Job Evaluation

Five years ago, just before Mr. Vorhees had joined the firm, the prior production manager had prepared brief written descriptions

of the 33 types of jobs required by the firm and had established three job classifications. Mr. Vorhees could find no indications, however, that either of these moves had been based on a careful evaluation of job content. Instead he suspected that they merely reflected his predecessor's efforts to persuade Mr. Tidwell to authorize wage increases designed to attract new employees. Furthermore, no effort had been made to review these descriptions and classifications, or keep them current. Mr. Vorhees concluded that he could safely assume that he "was starting from zero" in developing a new plan for the company.

Mr. Vorhees' Plan

After considering various approaches, Mr. Vorhees decided that simple job rankings and classifications without written job descriptions, formal grading criteria, point ratings, etc., would satisfy the company's needs. This decision reflected his conviction that since he spent much time on the floor of the plant, had a working knowledge of most of the jobs required, and even knew many of the workmen by name, he would be able—solely on the basis of personal knowledge—to make an accurate ranking of the various shop jobs in terms of the skill each demanded. After preparing this skill ranking, Mr. Vorhees next decided to identify several over-all "classifications" into which the 33 jobs in question might logically be grouped. To help determine the number of classifications to employ, and identify the jobs that should be placed in each, Mr. Vorhees had his secretary plot the various hourly wage rates Tidwell was paying to the employees in each of the jobs, the jobs themselves being listed in the "skill" order in which he had ranked them (Exhibit 1). From an inspection of the plotted points in Exhibit 1 and from his opinion or knowledge regarding the jobs that deserved or, by custom, received approximately equal rates of pay, Mr. Vorhees decided to employ five job classifications.

To set a maximum wage for each classification, Mr. Vorhees conducted an informal local-wage survey. As his first step, he had his secretary go to the local library and obtain the most recent wage information made available by the U.S. Bureau of Labor Statistics (Exhibit 2). Then, to obtain a more detailed impression of the practices of local firms comparable to Tidwell in size, type of workforce, etc., Mr. Vorhees talked with friends in the industry, examined "help-wanted ads" in the local press, and interviewed several of the recently recalled employees to learn of their experience while in "the job market." This latter source provided Mr. Vorhees with what he believed was a particularly valuable insight into the wage practices

EXHIBIT 1 TIDWELL METAL PRODUCTS CORPORATION

ACTUAL HOURLY WAGE RATES OF SHOP EMPLOYEES WITH THE FIVE PROPOSED
JOB CLASSIFICATIONS AND THE MAXIMUM AND MINIMUM RATES
FOR EACH CLASSIFICATION

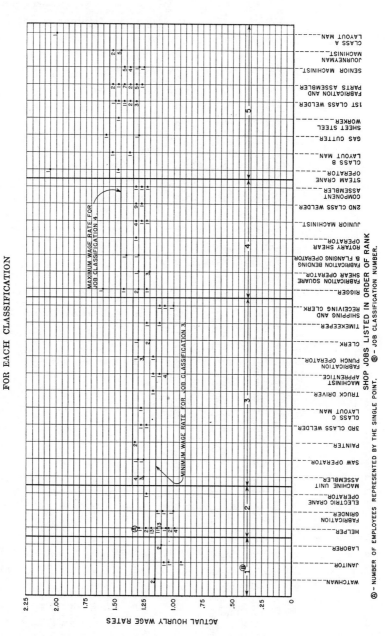

EXHIBIT 2   TIDWELL METAL PRODUCTS CORPORATION

Memorandum to: Mr. Vorhees

From: Dorothy Thrasher

Re: Data from U. S. Bureau of Labor Statistics

The most recent data I could locate at the library were about a year old. They reflected the results of a survey sample of a dozen local firms engaged in structural steel fabrication. The companies in question were of course not identified other than for the fact that none employed less than 8 workers. The total number of employees covered by the survey was 758. There was no breakdown by union or nonunion shops. I have included only those occupations which seemed to me to parallel the various jobs on the "skill-ranking" list you had me plot last week.

The BLS data were in a form that would permit me, in most cases, to give you a still further breakdown of the 20¢ ranges I have shown here. Please let me know if you want me to go back and get this added info.

Receiving Straight-Time Hourly Wage Rates ($) of:

	1.00 to 1.199	1.20 to 1.399	1.40 to 1.599	1.60 to 1.799	1.80 to 1.999	2.00 to 2.199	2.20 to 2.399	2.40 to 2.599	2.60 to 2.799	Average
Chippers and grinders			3	1						$1.57
Crane operators, electric bridge			3	6	5	4	5			$1.93
Fitters, structural steel, Class A				14	3	20	4			$2.09
Flame cutting machine op'rs.			3		18	4				$1.89
Janitors	6	4								$1.25
Layout men, Class A						17	11	6	1	$2.18
Painters, rough		5	3	3	3					$1.58
Power-shear operators, Class A			9	8						$1.78
Power-shear operators, Class B			5	8						$1.68
Punch-press operators, Class A			1	3	4					$1.76
Punch-press operators, Class B			1	2						$1.81
Stock clerks				12	2					$1.72
Truck drivers				1						$1.78
Welders, hand, Class A					20	30	1			$2.09
Welders, hand, Class B			1	14	16	56				$2.09

of most of the 14 local firms which were direct competitors of Tidwell.

The net conclusion which Mr. Vorhees reached after analyzing all the information thus obtained was that in most instances his company was in fact conforming to Mr. Tidwell's frequently stated policy of paying at, or above, the "going" community rate for firms of its type and size. To assure the continuation of this policy Mr. Vorhees then set the maximum rate for each of the job classifications at least equal to and, in several instances, higher than the maximum rates that his survey indicated were offered by similar local companies.

Mr. Vorhees then considered the minimum wage rate that should be established for each classification. Further study of Exhibit 1 revealed that the rates paid by Tidwell rarely fell more than 40 cents per hour below the maximum rate for any classification. Believing that such a "spread" would be sufficient to permit effective administration of a merit-rating plan, Mr. Vorhees determined the minimum hourly rate for each job classification by subtracting 40 cents from the maximum rate previously established.

Mr. Vorhees now turned to designing an "Employee Progress-Rating and General-Review Card" to be used for merit rating each employee. Drawing upon his 20 years' experience in metal fabricating, he identified eight "values" which he believed were particularly applicable to production jobs in this industry. He prepared written descriptions of them which he believed meaningfully characterized five different levels of employee performance in regard to each of these values. These descriptions, as well as space for certain general information regarding each employee, were included in the designed card (Exhibit 3).

Implementation Plans

Mr. Vorhees' thinking was that if his plan were approved, he would have each of the company's seven foremen immediately fill out a rating card for each employee under his supervision. From the five descriptive statements relating to the first value on the card, the foreman would choose the one which most nearly characterized the actual performance of the employee in question. In the space next to this value the foreman would place the letter of the vertical column containing the statement he had selected. After repeating this procedure for the other seven values, the foreman would transfer the eight-letter rating to the box at the bottom of the card, thus creating a "rating profile" of the employee. This process would be repeated every six months for each employee.

EXHIBIT 3 TIDWELL METAL PRODUCTS CORPORATION

EMPLOYEE PROGRESS-RATING AND GENERAL-REVIEW CARD (FRONT)

Name _____   Clock No. _____   Date Issued _____

Classification _____   Code No. _____

VALUES		A	B	C	D	E
1	Quality of work with reference to required standard.	C	Frequent errors or defects. Careless or wasteful.	Uncertain. Inclined to sacrifice quality for speed. Satisfactory on only a few jobs.	Satisfactory. Usually meets standard. Few rejections or mistakes.	Dependable for more complex quality or accurate jobs. Exceptionally neat and finished work.	Dependable to meet all requirements for highest quality jobs.
2	Quantity of Acceptable Work	C	Produces less than normal standard. Wastes time or slow.	Irregular. Does not consistently turn out sufficient work.	Dependable for accomplishing the normal output only.	Completes over the normal output. Tries to do his job more efficiently each time.	Exceeds the normal output. Uses time fully. Very fast workman.
3	Work Attendance	D	Frequent absences. Does not notify foreman. Weak or no excuse.	Irregular attendance. Questionable excuse. May or may not notify foreman.	Occasional absence. Has legitimate excuse. May or may not notify foreman.	Good attendance. Rarely absent and has reasonable excuse. Always notifies foreman.	Excellent attendance. Never out unless for good reason. Tries to arrange his absence so that work will not be delayed.
4	Supervision Needed	C	Close and frequent, even on routine duties.	Less and less because improving. Follows instruction.	Only occasional attention needed to obtain desired job done well and on time.	Needs little or no supervision.	Self-starter. Resourceful. Can or does do minor supervision of others.
5	Versatility or Adjustability to Change	D	Resists change or can't adjust. Good only on repetitive work.	Learns new ways slowly with instruction. Once learned, retains well.	Adjusts readily to ordinary change. Needs time and instruction when work changes radically.	Learns quickly and well whatever the extent of change. Needs little instruction on new work.	Capable at several new tasks. Quickly excels at skills. Resourceful. Creative. Meets emergencies well.
6	Job Knowledge	D	Little training or experience. Not learning even with instruction.	Confused, but learning through instruction and frequent checks.	Adequate training and experience for job needs. Rarely needs instruction.	Improving through experience, training or initiative. Well-informed and alert.	Master of job. An expert on his own or related jobs.
7	Disposition and Influence	C	Antagonistic. Inclined to cause trouble or disharmony of others. One-sided outlook.	Swayed by his own feelings. Enthusiastic or pleased if he likes assignment. Offensive or irritable if he dislikes assignment. Two-sided outlook.	Conscientious, willing, good-natured. Tries to cooperate. Good team worker. Well-rounded outlook.	Responsive and cooperative with associates and foreman. Takes personal interest in seeing the job well done.	Cheerful and considerate. Positive influence in any group. Sparks the team toward more output.
8	Safety	D	Unsafe on the job. Endangers himself and others. Lack of insight. Needs continual warning.	Somewhat hazardous due to carelessness. Improving through explanatory warning.	Unusually careful but inclined to take unnecessary chances. Occasional warning.	Always tries to be careful of his own safety and the safety of others.	Very careful workman. Sets a good example.

EMPLOYEE PROGRESS-RATING AND GENERAL-REVIEW CARD (BACK)

	Rarely	Frequently	Often	Always
1. Does he keep his machine and work place clean and orderly?	......	......	......	......
2. Does he return Company tools and equipment promptly?	......	......	......	......
3. Does he report for work on time?	......	......	......	......
4. Does he stop work before quitting time?	......	......	......	......

5. To your knowledge is he partially or fully limited in any way?

6. Do you recommend him for more difficult work?

7. Is he qualified for promotion to a better job in his present or related line of work when such an opening occurs?

8. Does his work performance indicate leadership ability which will qualify him for a supervisory position?

9. In your opinion is he classified in an occupation for which he is best suited by:

   A. Training   Yes   Needs more training

   B. Experience   Yes   Need more experience

   C. Aptitude   Yes   No

10. Additional comments or recommendations.

If employee is recommended for supervisory position, please check the appropriate answer.

Knows job but handicapped by language.

Difficult to understand.
Vague or impatient.

Can be understood well enough for job.

Reasonably clear on any matter.

Clear and concise and quickly to the point.

Can explain any phase of his work thoroughly.

Rated by:	(Ratee's Next Superior)
Reviewed by:	on _____, 19 __ (Next Superior Above)
Reviewed by:	on _____, 19 __ (Next Executive)
Received:	on _____, 19 __
Comments	_____, 19 __

PROFILE

	A	B	C	D	E
1	Quality				
2	Quantity				
3	Attendance				
4	Supervision				
5	Versatility				
6	Job knowledge				
7	Disposition				
8	Safety				

Mr. Vorhees planned personally to review each employee's card after each semiannual rating and to use the results in determining promotions and layoffs. Also, he intended to recommend to Mr. Tidwell that whenever company finances permitted, a 10-cent hourly increase be given every six months to each employee who obtained an over-all profile rating of "C" or better for the six months just completed. After an employee's pay rate reached the maximum for his job classification, however, further increases could be obtained only if he was promoted to a higher job classification. Mr. Vorhees did not feel that pay reductions should be given to an employee whose over-all profile rating during the prior six months was below "C." He did, however, see advantage in letting it be known that such employees would be the first to be considered for layoffs whenever business conditions necessitated.

Mr. Vorhees intended also to recommend to Mr. Tidwell that as soon as the new plan was introduced, any employee who was receiving less than the minimum rate established for his classification should be brought up to the minimum level in six equal, monthly increments. On the other hand, Mr. Vorhees was convinced that it was important that no worker receive a pay reduction as a result of the introduction of the plan. Wherever possible any employee receiving a rate above the maximum for his job classification would be transferred to a job in a higher classification. If this could not be done, the employee would be continued at his current rate and treated as a "pay-rate exception."

Before introducing his plan, Mr. Vorhees believed it would also be wise for him to acquaint the eight members of the "Employees Committee" with its features and obtain their endorsement of it. The committee, which had been instituted by management some two months previously, was authorized to hear employee grievances, present employee problems to management, and suggest improvements in working conditions. Its members, who were elected on a shopwide basis and were to stand for re-election every six months, currently included no one with less than five years' service with the company, nor any individual whose job fell below category 4 in the contemplated job-classification system.

Mr. Vorhees believed that once the new plan was in operation, the Employees Committee should be given access to the Employee Progress-Rating and General-Review Cards and should be encouraged to discuss the rating results with each individual employee. He believed that in this way the committee could help the workforce understand management's policies and decisions on wage increases, layoffs, and

promotions, and could also help individual employees improve their performance. Mr. Vorhees was firm in his conviction that the committee should not, however, participate in the actual evaluation of employees. Such decisions, in his judgment, were solely the prerogatives of management.

PART 7. SUMMARY AND REVIEW

Exemplar Bookbinding Company

Mr. Walter Dix, manager and sole owner of the Exemplar Book-binding Company, was evaluating the results of his firm's operations during the six and one-half months since he had purchased it, and, as a prelude to developing plans for the future, was assessing the strengths and weaknesses in Exemplar's current situation. Profit and loss statements for the period in question, and the most recent balance sheet, are shown in Exhibits 1 and 2.

COMPANY BACKGROUND

The Exemplar Bookbinding Company is a "library bindery," serving educational, business, professional, and private libraries by rebinding worn or damaged books and by binding magazines, newspapers, and other types of periodicals into volumes for permanent retention. Nearly all the company's manufacturing operations are performed on customer-owned articles, with Exemplar being fully liable for the care of these items while they are in its custody. Many of the books and periodicals processed by the company are difficult, in some instances impossible, to replace if lost or damaged.

The company is located in a large metropolitan area which also is served by three other library binderies. Approximately 15 additional firms of this type, many of them quite small, are located within a radius of 250 miles. Transportation considerations, however, usually restrict binderies to operations in their immediate locality. Selected statistics on the industry from the most recent U.S. Census are shown in Exhibit 3.[1] In contrast to the industry average, Exemplar's

---

[1] Figures in this paragraph and those in Exhibit 3 relate only to companies that perform binding operations on materials printed by firms other than them-

EXHIBIT 1 EXEMPLAR BOOKBINDING COMPANY

PROFIT AND LOSS STATEMENTS
(To Nearest Dollar)

	April 17–May 31	June	July	August	September	October
Sales	$21,106	$15,734	$17,448	$13,253	$ 9,908	$15,211
Cost of Goods Sold	16,275	11,531	12,567	12,733	8,913	12,459
Gross Income	4,831	4,203	4,881	520	995	2,751
Selling and Administrative Expenses						
Salary & Wages	522	617	608	576	826	799
Travel	29	11	1	—	1	—
Subscriptions	3	5	11	5	—	—
Donations	—	—	—	—	—	46
Telephone/ Telegraph	60	45	50	34	52	68
Professional Services	1,166	—	—	66	—	275
Sales Promotion	70	30	50	50	—	—
Depreciation-General	6	6	6	6	6	6
Entertainment	—	—	—	—	—	—
Miscellaneous	40	177	95	188	3,833	34
Freight Out	—	18	—	23	—	—
Postage	—	134	107	56	111	—
Taxes	—	2	—	9	1,164	584
Total	$ 1,896	$ 1,046	$ 928	$ 1,015	$ 5,993	$ 1,812
Net Income before Income Taxes	$ 2,935	$ 3,158	$ 3,952	$ (495)	$(4,998)	$ 940

Source: Company records.

product-mix usually includes very little "edition binding" or "mechanical binding." In regard to the latter operation, Exemplar's plant is equipped to perform only power-stapling operations.

Over the several years before Mr. Dix's acquisition of the firm, Exemplar's sales had averaged about $130,000 annually. Around 80 per cent of this volume was usually obtained from a large university located in the community. This institution's collection of books and

selves. They do not include binding operations performed by publishers, or by specialized bindery concerns, on newly published volumes.

EXHIBIT 2 EXEMPLAR BOOKBINDING COMPANY

BALANCE SHEET, JULY 31

ASSETS			LIABILITIES	
Current Assets			Current Liabilities	
Cash		$ 5,482.18	Notes Payable	$ 3,975.00
Accounts Receivable (less			Accounts Payable	2,608.49
reserve for bad debts)		13,724.28	Accrued Liabilities	
Inventory—Raw Materials		6,091.32	Payroll	1,549.39
Inventory—Work in Process		3,223.37	Payroll Taxes	1,486.94
Prepaid Expenses		1,698.06	Other	1,000.00
Total		$30,219.21	Total	$10,619.82
Fixed Assets	$14,017.00		Long-Term Note Payable	11,925.00
Less Depreciation	551.10			
		13,465.90	Net Worth	21,140.29
TOTAL		$43,685.11	TOTAL	$43,685.11

Source: Company records.

periodicals was among the largest in the world, currently numbering in excess of six million items. The university had relied upon Exemplar for all its binding requirements for many years. Over this period, Exemplar management personnel had developed cordial relationships with the university's business officers, the personnel in charge of the central library, and most of the librarians in the more than 50 specialized book collections maintained by various schools and departments of the university.

The balance of Exemplar's business was obtained from a variety of sources. These included a number of smaller universities and colleges in the area; local business concerns, particularly those engaged in research activities; professional people, especially doctors and lawyers; private libraries maintained by scientific or cultural societies; and private collectors of books. The local public library, however, had long operated a bindery department servicing its own needs. Local agencies of the state government similarly were served by a state-owned bindery.

The original owner of Exemplar had a number of other local business interests. He therefore had never devoted more than modest personal attention to the bindery, and eleven years earlier had retained Mr. Dix as bindery manager, giving him an almost entirely free hand in running the company. Mr. Dix, then in his late 20's, had just

EXHIBIT 3   EXEMPLAR BOOKBINDING COMPANY

THE BOOKBINDING INDUSTRY

General Statistics

	1939	1947	1951	1954	1955	1956
Value added $ × 10^6	33.4	90.2	67.3	84.7	94.5	104.4
Employees $ × 10^3	N.A.	22.2	16.3	17.2	18.1	19.7
Value of shipments $ × 10^6	44.6	116.0	85.0	119.9	N.A.	N.A.
Number of firms	620	686	N.A.	730	N.A.	N.A.
Payroll $ × 10^6	N.A.	57.5	51.1	59.0	N.A.	72.1
Cost of Materials $ × 10^6	11.2	25.2	17.7	27.2	N.A.	N.A.

					Number of Employees				
1954 Data	1–4	5–9	10–19	20–49	50–99	100–249	250–499	500–999	1,000
Number of establishments	274	124	137	127	38	21	6	2	1
Average Value Added $ × 000	13.2	38.8	71.0	150	350	710	1,600	4,813	N.A.

National Averages for the Industry in 1954

Average Value of Shipments per Company	$154,000
Average Number of Employees	23.5
Average Hourly Wages	1.65
Capital Expenditures	5,010 per year

Product Mix Based on Value of Shipments for Industry:

Edition binding—hard board*	40%
Pamphlet binding	28
Library binding	14
Mechanical binding†	7
Miscellaneous	11
	100%

---

i.e. The binding of specially printed volumes, published in small quantities, usually at the expense of the author.

† *i.e.* The use of brads, staples, plastic or metal spiral devices to bind the pages of a volume.

Source: *U.S. Census of Manufactures*, 1954 and 1956.

---

earned a Master's degree in business administration, and through his family was reasonably familiar with bookbinding operations. His starting salary with the bindery was roughly equal to the average earnings reported by other graduates of the program Mr. Dix had just completed.

Over the next four years, Mr. Dix increased Exemplar's annual sales from about $50,000 to $126,000. He also accomplished certain produc-

tion economies through methods and process improvements, and through increased mechanization of a few phases of the firm's operations. The average unit cost of a typical hardcover binding, for example, was reduced from $3.35 to $2.65 during this period.

After four years Mr. Dix negotiated an arrangement whereby the bindery's owner permitted him to accept an administrative position with another employer in the same city, while continuing to serve as bindery manager on a part-time basis. While this plan was in effect, Exemplar's sales volume and production efficiency continued to improve, although at a more modest rate than in the four years immediately preceding.

This arrangement was terminated three and a half years later by Mr. Dix's acceptance of a responsible position with a nationally known industrial-design consulting organization in another state. After Mr. Dix's resignation, the bindery owner was unsuccessful in obtaining the services of anyone whom he considered a satisfactory manager. The owner therefore assumed these functions himself, d voting to Exemplar whatever time he could spare from his other business commitments.

MR. DIX'S PURCHASE OF COMPANY

Three years later, while visiting the city, Mr. Dix was told by one of the bindery's employees that the owner was considering selling the company in order to devote more time to his other business interests. Mr. Dix therefore arranged an appointment with the owner who verified the employee's information. Mr. Dix stated that he would like to consider submitting an offer.

For the next five months, while conducting exploratory negotiations with the owner, Mr. Dix weighed the advisability of acquiring the company. Finally, in April of the current year, an agreement was reached under which Mr. Dix acquired full title to the firm, its equipment, raw materials, and work-in-process inventory for $25,900.

During the early negotiations Mr. Dix and the owner had substantial differences of opinion regarding the valuation of Exemplar's manufacturing equipment. A consultant retained by the owner had argued that Mr. Dix should purchase these items at their estimated replacement cost. Since much of the equipment was old, Mr. Dix maintained that replacement value was too intangible a concept to be utilized in reaching a purchase price, and contended that the attempt of the consultant to do so had yielded an unreasonably high figure. After much discussion, agreement was reached upon an equipment valuation of

$13,495. This was substantially lower than the figure originally proposed by the consultant, but closely approximated depreciated book value of the items in question. Little difficulty was experienced in agreeing upon a value of $7,818 for raw material, and $4,587 for work in process. No valuation was placed on the company name or on the goodwill attached to it.

Under the purchase agreement, Mr. Dix paid $5,000 in cash on April 15, and gave the original owner a mortgage note for $20,900 secured by the assets of the company. Mr. Dix was to pay an additional $5,000 the following July 15th, leaving a noninterest-bearing mortgage balance of $15,900 which was to be paid in twelve consecutive, quarterly installments of $1,325 starting the following October 15th.

Mr. Dix had entered into the negotiations with a cash position of $15,300, representing almost all of his personal savings. In the event of an extreme emergency, Mr. Dix believed that he could probably rely upon his family, or upon a small group of friends, for modest additional funds. It was his firm intention, however, to avoid such a necessity.

Mr. Dix's decision to purchase the company was based upon a variety of considerations. In his judgment, ownership of Exemplar offered an unusually attractive opportunity to satisfy his long-standing ambition to be in business for himself. It represented an industry, and a firm, with which he was already familiar. He was satisfied that the company was basically sound, its workforce thoroughly competent. While it did not represent "big business" in any glamorous sense, Mr. Dix was certain that Exemplar possessed significant profit potential. Although its past earnings had been only modest, Mr. Dix was confident that imaginative, full-time management could expand them appreciably. The likelihood of such expansion seemed reinforced by the numerous indications of a growing, nationwide emphasis upon education and research, and by the forecasts of rapid—even explosive—increases in college enrollments over the next decade. Mr. Dix reasoned that such developments clearly would intensify demand for bindery services. On the basis of these and related considerations, Mr. Dix had finally concluded that the long-term financial rewards he could achieve as owner of Exemplar would probably equal—and indeed might well surpass—those attainable as a salaried employee of a large corporation.

Before reaching a final decision, Mr. Dix also scheduled appointments with various officers and library personnel of the large local university to discuss future demands for bindery services. The general reaction he obtained appeared to be that although no firm commitment

could be made, there seemed no reason to believe that the university's long-standing association with Exemplar would be altered merely because of a change in the bindery's ownership. On the contrary, most of the university's personnel expressed the opinion that if Exemplar's services and prices remained satisfactory, their institution would probably continue to treat it as the major source of bindery services. A number of the persons with whom he discussed these matters had known Mr. Dix during his earlier service as bindery manager. Many of these individuals informally expressed pleasure at the possibility that Mr. Dix might be rejoining the firm as its owner.

Prior to the purchase Mr. Dix also held discussions with representatives of a number of companies supplying the bindery industry. Their views seemed to him to verify his conviction that future prospects for library binderies were bright. They also confirmed his impression that many firms in the industry were small, family-owned concerns. Mr. Dix believed that organizations of this type often went out of existence upon the death or retirement of the original owners. He concluded that the industry therefore might become less competitive in the years ahead.

OPERATING CHANGES INTRODUCED
SUBSEQUENT TO PURCHASE

Labor Relations

One of the first decisions confronting Mr. Dix after acquiring the bindery involved negotiation of a new labor contract.

At the time of purchase, Mr. Dix had made an informal commitment to the former owner to retain for at least 60 days all employees who wished to continue with the company. A notice to this effect was circulated among the workforce shortly before the purchase was completed. On the day following the change in ownership Mr. Dix was pleased to see that all personnel reported to work as usual. About half of these were persons whom he himself had hired during his former managership of the company. The 20 employees were equally divided between men and women. Their average age was about 40, and their average length of service with Exemplar was approximately eight years.

From his previous association with the firm Mr. Dix knew that in common with most of the industry, Exemplar often had experienced a high turnover among less skilled female employees. In recent years, however, the company had encountered almost no losses among the more experienced women employees, and none among its male per-

sonnel, all of whom were highly skilled. Mr. Dix believed that such labor stability was an asset of considerable significance, since it was virtually impossible to hire experienced bookbinders in the local market and since several years were normally required before an unskilled trainee became proficient in many phases of the work.

Under the former owner, Exemplar's hourly personnel had been organized as a local of a nation-wide craft union. The contract, however, was not phrased in such a way as to be binding upon a new owner. After consultation with his attorney, Mr. Dix elected to consider the former agreement invalid. Notice of this decision was included in his initial announcement offering continued employment, at prevailing pay rates, to the entire workforce.

On the second day after acquiring the firm, Mr. Dix was approached by a committee representing a substantial majority of the employees. They advised him of their desire to form an independent company union and to organize the bindery on a union-shop basis. Mr. Dix agreed to negotiate on these topics.

Within a week, with the assistance of attorneys representing both parties, a one-year contract was signed in which the company recognized the new bargaining unit. The working conditions, benefits, job classifications, and wage levels agreed upon were almost identical with those contained in the former contract. Mr. Dix believed that the wage rates specified in both the former and the new contracts were about 10 per cent below those paid locally by large union shops performing highly mechanized, mass-production binding of large lots of identical new volumes, but met or exceeded those paid by comparable small, library binderies in the area. The new contract did not provide retirement-pension benefits or group life insurance. Mr. Dix hoped, however, that it might some day prove possible for Exemplar to afford such benefits.

During the first several days of his ownership of the company, officials in the district office of the former union made repeated but unsuccessful efforts to see Mr. Dix. After the new contract was negotiated with the independent union, however, the representatives of the national union made no further efforts to approach him; nor did they challenge the jurisdiction of the new bargaining unit. One male employee who had been active in the former local, however, did voice strong objections to the formation of the independent union. Although becoming a dues-paying member of the new organization, he remained persistently outspoken in his criticism of its activities. After about a month, Mr. Dix discharged the employee for his lack of cooperation. This move had the energetic support of the officers of the new union,

several of whom had stated to Mr. Dix that "unless he [the 'trouble-maker'] goes, we go!"

Aside from this episode, it seemed to Mr. Dix that employee relations had proceeded satisfactorily. Beginning in late summer he had held informal monthly meetings with the union officers. These sessions were conducted at the plant after the end of the regular shift. In Mr. Dix's judgment the tone of these meetings had been exceptionally cordial, and he was particularly pleased that the union representatives had enthusiastically presented a number of suggestions for improving operations. It had been possible to implement most of these proposals promptly, and with apparently good results.

Discussions of more formal company-union matters also seemed to Mr. Dix to be carried out in a spirit of constructive cordiality. After Exemplar had moved to its new quarters, to be subsequently discussed, some employees had frequently expressed the view that the company had not yet regained the operative effectiveness it had enjoyed in the former location. Mr. Dix believed that the employees were correct in this conclusion, and saw no evidence that they offered this observation in a disgruntled or hostile manner. On the contrary, he believed that their remarks reflected their genuine concern for Exemplar's productivity and profitability.

Plant Relocation

Another major operating change occurring since Mr. Dix's acquisition of the firm was its transfer to a new location. Terms of the purchase contract had stipulated that Exemplar must be moved from its existing site no later than December 31 of the current year in order to free the building for other business activities of the former owner. Shortly after the purchase was executed, therefore, Mr. Dix had begun to look for a suitable new location.

After surveying a number of alternative sites, by midsummer Mr. Dix's interest had become centered upon an old but well-built, and currently unoccupied, four-story building several blocks distant from the present location. He was satisfied that with several thousand dollars' worth of improvements these quarters would be quite suitable for the bindery's operations. He also was convinced that the location was excellent in that it was within a few miles' radius of most of the company's regular customers, including the university. Mr. Dix was concerned, however, by the fact that it would be necessary to lease the building in its entirety, even though its 16,500 square feet of space represented almost four times the area available in the quarters now occupied. Although convinced that the present location did not pro-

vide enough space for maximum production efficiency, Mr. Dix still doubted that an ideal layout of equipment would require more than half the building under consideration.

After further study, Mr. Dix concluded that it would probably be possible to negotiate subleases for at least some of the excess space. After assuring himself that terms of the lease would permit subletting, he entered into a five-year commitment for the building. The lease terms called for payments of $950 per month, with a provision for subsequent adjustments to reflect any changes in the property taxes paid by the owner. The lease contained no formal renewal clause. The owner had assured Mr. Dix, however, that he would be allowed to extend it if he desired.

Exemplar's equipment, raw materials, and work-in-process inventory were moved to the new location over the Labor Day weekend. Most of the transfer was executed by the company's own personnel using a rented truck. Movement and installation of the heavier pieces of equipment, however, required the services of a commercial rigging firm. With the aid of the production superintendent and the advice of some of the employees, Mr. Dix developed a layout which employed only the second and third floors for bindery operations. Such an arrangement, in Mr. Dix's judgment, maximized the chances of negotiating a favorable sublease for the excess space available in the building.

The two weeks following the relocation were largely devoted to establishing the company in its new setting. Extensive cleaning and refurbishing of the building were required. It was also necessary to construct partitions to form offices. Accomplishment of these tasks created conditions which made it exceptionally difficult to carry out normal bindery operations. Mr. Dix, anticipating that this might be the case, had encouraged about half the workforce to take this period as vacation time. This allowed him to keep the remaining personnel busily engaged either in bindery work or, more frequently, in activities relating to improvements in the new quarters.

The cost of the move and the physical improvements to the building amounted to roughly $5,000. To help finance this, Mr. Dix successfully negotiated with a local bank for an unsecured loan of $4,500 at an interest rate of 6 per cent. Although the note was callable at any time, the bank officials had assured Mr. Dix that the balance outstanding could be repaid at his convenience. By the end of October, Mr. Dix had reduced the principal by $1,500 from Exemplar's sales income.

Shortly after the move, Mr. Dix sublet the first floor of the building to a nearby publishing firm for use as storage area. The agreement was to run for three months and called for monthly payments of $200.

The publishing house had indicated that it might wish to continue this arrangement, on a month-to-month basis, after the first of the year. Mr. Dix knew, however, that the firm was constructing new facilities on the outskirts of the city and was certain that its sublease arrangement with Exemplar was only temporary. Except for a small area used to store miscellaneous equipment not currently needed by the bindery, the fourth floor stood vacant.

OPERATING PRACTICES

Customer Requirements—Their Impact upon Manufacturing Operations

Customers' orders received by Exemplar vary in size from a single publication to many hundreds. Most orders, however, contain somewhere between 70 and 100 books, or several hundred periodicals,[2] or a roughly equivalent mixture of both. The individual items included in an order usually embrace a wide range of physical characteristics, with the publications differing as to page size, thickness, the type of paper on which they are printed, and their general state of repair. Exhibit 4 shows the width and length dimensions of the individual items included in the orders received in a fairly typical day.

These physical dissimilarities usually are compounded by differences in the covering materials, and in the variety of title stamping, which customers wish to have employed for the cover of each book. Some customers (including the university which is the company's largest account) have selected a single, standard grade and color of covering material, and a single form of title stamping, for all routine orders. Even in these cases, however, the variations in the size and condition of the diverse items included in any single order still pose significant production problems.

As a result of the lack of standardization in the physical characteristics of the items to be processed, Exemplar production personnel have always considered it virtually impossible to schedule long production runs. Instead, each order is scheduled into production as a self-contained unit, with every individual item receiving whatever treatment its size, its other physical characteristics, and the customer's

---

[2] A number of consecutive issues of a periodical, arranged in sequence, are usually combined into a single, bound volume. The number of issues per volume vary from periodical to periodical, depending on the thickness of a typical issue. The majority of the periodical binding performed by Exemplar is about equally divided between volumes containing six issues and volumes containing twelve.

EXHIBIT 4 EXEMPLAR BOOKBINDING COMPANY

WIDTH AND LENGTH DIMENSIONS OF ITEMS CONTAINED IN FOUR
REPRESENTATIVE ORDERS RECEIVED SEPTEMBER 5

Dimensions of Item	Number of Items in Order #			
	1	2	3	4
4½" x 7½"	—	—	—	1
4½" x 17½"	—	—	1	—
5" x 6½"	—	—	—	4
5" x 7"	—	—	—	7
5" x 7¾"	—	—	—	2
5¼" x 8"	—	—	1	—
5½" x 7½"	—	—	—	5
5½" x 8"	—	—	—	6
5½" x 8¾"	—	—	—	4
6" x 8½"	—	—	2	—
6" x 9"	—	125	—	—
6" x 9½"	—	75	—	—
6" x 10"	—	—	2	—
6½" x 9½"	—	25	—	—
6½" x 10"	—	—	3	—
7" x 10"	—	25	4	22
7½" x 10"	—	—	3	—
7½" x 10½"	24	—	—	—
7¾" x 10½"	24	—	—	—
8" x 10½"	—	—	—	78
8" x 11"	104	75	—	—
8½" x 11"	—	125	7	—
9½" x 13"	—	—	—	6
10" x 13¾"	—	—	—	1
Total	152	450	23	136

NOTE: Each of the orders included books, pamphlets, and periodicals. In the
case of the latter, a customer might request that as many as 12 consecutive issues of a single periodical be bound into a single volume.
Mr. Dix believed that the nature of the binding processes made variations in the width and length of the items being bound far more significant than variations in their thickness.

Source: Survey by Harvard Business School researcher.

instructions require. The company also makes relatively little use of the numerous types of mechanized equipment that are available in the industry. Mr. Dix believes that Exemplar's heavy reliance upon hand operations is typical of the practices of most library binderies. Highly mechanized operations are, he judges, generally confined to binderies that specialize in the manufacture of new books and are thus able to process large quantities of identical volumes.

Further complexities in Exemplar's production processes arise from the fact that customers often desire that the binding of a particular volume conform exactly to those of volumes that the company bound months, or even years, earlier. This is particularly true in the case of periodicals, since customers usually wish each successive volume to be identical with those previously bound, so that the complete series will be of uniform appearance. To achieve such conformity requires not only the use of the same grade and color of covering material, and variety of title stamping, but also steps to assure that titles are positioned on the cover in exactly the same way on each volume. To assure these desired characteristics in its finished products, Exemplar maintains files of production and design data on over 10,000 items that the company has previously bound for various customers and that seem likely, by their nature, to require duplication in the future.

The operating procedures of most libraries require that various clerical operations be performed before an item can be temporarily withdrawn from circulation and sent to a bindery for processing. In order to smooth out their own clerical work load, therefore, most libraries that regularly employ Exemplar's services send in orders of roughly equal size about once each month. Although this practice minimizes seasonal variations in Exemplar's volume, it accentuates the varied product mix in process at any time.

In the past, most of the company's customers have seemed satisfied with four to six weeks' delivery on routine orders. Mr. Dix believes that only one or two of his local competitors are able to render such service. By contrast, up until shortly before he took over the company, Exemplar had usually been able to make delivery in slightly less than four weeks.

On roughly 10 per cent of the items received for processing, Exemplar is asked to provide "rush-order" service, with delivery in a few days or "at the earliest possible date." Such requests usually arise in the case of publications for which demand is particularly heavy, making the library anxious not to have them out of circulation for any significant length of time. Rush orders can also arise when an unfore-

seen demand for an item occurs after it has been dispatched to the bindery for routine processing. In some such cases the library would request that the item be singled out for rush-order processing, or that it be withdrawn from the order and returned to the library unbound.

If necessary, an order of average size can be pushed through the plant in several working days; in an extreme emergency, a single item can be processed in one day. Any such rush order requires substantial disruption of previous shop plans, however, and entails a lowering of production efficiency. It has been Exemplar's long-standing policy, nonetheless, to make every effort to honor all such requests from regular customers, and to do so without additional charges.

Most orders arrive at the bindery accompanied by two copies of a customer packaging list describing the various items included and giving instructions regarding the binding and the delivery desired. The volumes usually are transported to the bindery in large wooden boxes that are retained by Exemplar and used subsequently in the delivery of finished products.

Sales Efforts, Sales Volume, and Production Backlog

In the past, Exemplar's sales efforts had received only modest emphasis except during the period of Mr. Dix's previous full-time managership. Many of the company's regular customers, such as university libraries, are organizations whose annual budgets include a definite allocation for binding services. Once this figure has been established for a given year it is rarely increased. By the same token, it is unusual for the personnel involved not to spend all of the funds that have been allocated to them.

These factors had led Exemplar's former owner to conclude that the demand for the company's services was relatively inelastic at any given moment, and probably would be largely unresponsive to any selling efforts. During his ownership of the company, therefore, its sales activities had usually been concentrated on maintaining close ties with established customers in the hope that they would call upon Exemplar for whatever bindery services they were in a position to afford. In recent years, with so much of his interest channeled along other lines, the former owner had usually not even responded to inquiries received from potential new accounts which approached the company.

Mr. Dix was confident that more intensive sales efforts would yield impressive results. He was certain, for example, that numerous manufacturing and engineering concerns were making increased use of technical journals. He believed that in many instances such organizations were not binding these publications for permanent retention

simply because no one had attempted to convince them of the advantages of such a practice.

In the face of the personal time pressures he had encountered since purchasing Exemplar, Mr. Dix had not yet been able to devote any major portion of his time to sales activities. Notwithstanding this fact, since April, orders from established customers had continued at least at their normal rates, and in some instances had even increased in volume. At the same time, even in the absence of any intensive sales efforts, a substantial number of orders had also been received from new customers. Many of these were companies or institutions whose business had been declined by the former owner of the bindery who, as previously noted, had not felt that he had time to devote to any expansion of Exemplar's operations.

As a result of these new orders, Exemplar's production backlog had risen noticeably since Mr. Dix's purchase of the firm. Since incoming orders were not checked until they were started into production, and were not priced until the production operations had been completed, it had not been possible to evaluate the exact dimensions of this increase. By visual inspection, however, Mr. Dix estimated that the backlog of items waiting to be processed was perhaps 50 per cent larger than that previously considered normal by the company. Exemplar's accountant also expressed the opinion that the amount of work in process had perhaps tripled since Mr. Dix's acquisition of the firm.

In view of the unexpectedly favorable sales picture, Mr. Dix was now frequently finding it necessary to quote delivery times of 12 weeks to both old and new customers. Thus far, there had been no indications of serious customer dissatisfaction with these conditions. Mr. Dix believed that this response was at least in part attributable to Exemplar's exceptionally high quality standards, a consideration to which he believed most customers attached major significance.

Production Processes and Controls

Exemplar's manufacturing operations were under the direct supervision of the Production Manager, Angelo Dichio. Mr. Dichio, who was in his mid-forties, had been with the company in a supervisory capacity for about ten years and was skilled in all phases of bindery work. In addition to serving as Production Manager he would, from time to time, actually engage in direct-labor operations to fill in for employees who were absent, or to help break production bottlenecks. Mr. Dix also took an active interest in all phases of the factory's activities and spent a considerable portion of his time on the floor

EXHIBIT 5   EXEMPLAR BOOKBINDING COMPANY

FLOOR PLANS (INCLUDING LOCATION OF MACHINERY AND EMPLOYEE WORK AREAS)

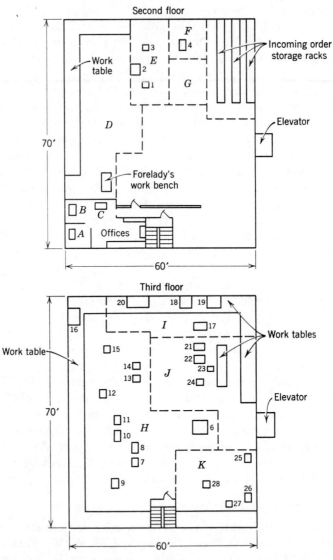

KEY

A, B, and *C,* Office area; *D,* Pulling area (including hand-sewing); *E,* Shear, saw, and press area; *F,* Machine sewing area; *G,* Inspection and write-up area; *1,* Power saw (used to cut slots in items requiring hand-sewing); *2,* National shear; *3,* Hand press; *4,* Over-sewing machine.   *H,* Forwarding area; *I,* Stamping area; *J,* Casing-in (cover-attaching) area; *K,* Pamphlet section; *6,* Seybold shear; *7, 8,* Backing benches; *9, 10, 11,* Hand shear (for cutting harboard covers); *12,* Skiver (used to bevel edges of leather); *13, 14,* Hand presses (floor type); *15,* Gluing machine; *16,* Turn-in machine; *17,* Ludlow typecasting machine; *18, 19,* Kensol stamping machine; *20,* Type storage cabinets; *21, 22,* Hydraulic presses (floor type); *23, 24,* Hand presses; *25, 26,* Wire stitching (stapling) machines; *27,* Gluing machine; *28,* Hand press.

of the plant in direct supervisory contact with the operating personnel.

Layouts of the manufacturing areas are shown in Exhibit 5.

PRODUCTION PROCESSES. Publications received for binding are stored on racks located in the second-floor work areas (Figure A) until the entire order in which they are included is scheduled into production. At that time, the forelady in charge of second-floor manufacturing activities removes the order from the rack and transports it to her workbench by hand truck. There she checks each item against the list that the customer included with the order. If any irregularities are discovered, or if the customer's specifications are not clear, the forelady confers with Mr. Dix or Mr. Dichio. If necessary, one of these men then consults the customer regarding the matter.

While executing this preliminary check of an order, the forelady also carefully examines each item to ascertain what production processes it will require. One of the most important objectives of this preliminary inspection is to determine whether a publication will need

FIGURE A. Incoming order storage area.

machine- or hand-sewing operations. The former process is quicker and more economical, and when used properly gives excellent results. If, however, the paper on which a publication is printed is particularly "soft" or "brittle," or if the printing extends too near the edges of the pages, a quality binding job can be achieved only by employing hand sewing. Differentiation between publications that can be satisfactorily sewn by machine and those that cannot is a matter of judgment requiring considerable skill and experience in binding operations. Mr. Dix believed that Mrs. McDuffy, the second-floor forelady, who had been with the company for almost 30 years, was the only member of the second-floor staff fully qualified to make this decision.

After completing this initial checking and inspecting of each volume, Mrs. McDuffy marks an identifying number lightly in pencil on its first page. This indicates the customer order in which this volume is included, and the "item number," in that order, that have been assigned to this particular publication. After thus marking each item, Mrs. McDuffy then moves the entire lot of publications on a hand truck to the workbench of one of the five "pulling operators." In making this work assignment, Mrs. McDuffy takes into account not only the goal of achieving an equal distribution of workload, but also the fact that the more complex orders require the services of the more experienced pullers.

Although considerable variations occur, depending on the physical condition of the items in an order, Mrs. McDuffy believes that she usually devotes about 60 per cent of each day to these initial inspection and routing functions. The remainder of her time is spent instructing and assisting the pullers, inspecting their work as well as that of the "oversewing operator," to be described subsequently, conferring with Mr. Dix and Mr. Dichio, and in related duties. If an order contains extremely difficult items, Mrs. McDuffy sometimes sets these aside and then personally performs the necessary pulling operations on them.

The responsibility of a pulling operator includes the removal of the old binding from each volume. This is accomplished by pulling off the cover, clipping the threads or, in the case of periodicals, removing the staples, and scraping off the paste that previously held the volume together (Figure B). These operations reduce the volume to a set of loose pages. The pulling operators are then responsible for seeing that these pages are arranged in the proper numerical order and, where appropriate, that they are mended and cleaned. In the case of periodicals, most customers also require that all full-page advertisements be removed from volumes being bound. In such in-

FIGURE B. Pulling operator at work. Production Manager is in background.

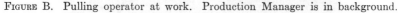

stances, the pulling operators are responsible for the page removal. This requires extreme care to assure that nonadvertising material is not unintentionally included in the pages being eliminated.

For planning and estimating, Mrs. McDuffy has employed a rule of thumb that, on the average, these initial pulling operations should require about 15 to 20 minutes of an operator's time per volume. The process is entirely manual. Over the years, Exemplar has tested numerous mechanical devices to assist in the pulling operations, but without achieving satisfactory results. The work is tedious and often involves coping with volumes that are soiled and covered with dust.

Mrs. McDuffy believes that it usually takes about a year before a new employee learns to perform routine pulling operations without considerable supervision. To acquire enough experience to handle independently all of the great variety of work that might be encountered requires perhaps another two years. Upon two different occasions after purchasing the company, Mr. Dix hired a new employee to be trained as a pulling operator. Each of the women quit within a few days, complaining that the work was hard, dirty, and boring.

After the pulling operations, all of the volumes in the order are routed to a large power shear located on the second floor. Opera-

tion of the shear trims the back (binding edge) of each volume, creating a smooth, even surface for the subsequent sewing operation. The shear operator then applies a light coat of glue to the freshly cut edge to hold the pages of the volume temporarily in place. According to Mr. Dichio, the trimming and gluing require an average of about one-half minute per volume. Responsibility for these steps is not assigned to any single individual. Instead, whichever of the forwarding operators—men regularly located on the third floor of the plant—can most conveniently be spared from his third-floor work is temporarily diverted to this job whenever the need arises.

After trimming and gluing, the entire order is next routed to the sewing operation. If Mrs. McDuffy has determined that hand sewing is required on any of the volumes, these are routed to one of the more experienced pullers. Hand sewing (Figure C) involves anywhere

FIGURE C. Hand-sewing operation.

FIGURE D. Oversewing machine operation.

from one-quarter to one and one-half hours per volume, depending on the thickness of the publication.

Volumes to be machine-sewn are moved by hand truck to the oversewing machine, which also is located on the second floor. The oversewing operation is progressive. The operator separates the pages of each volume into sections of about one-eighth inch thickness which are then clamped into the oversewing machine individually (Figure D). The machine punches holes along the left-hand edge of the section, and stitches the pages together with high-grade flax thread. By adding subsequent sections, the whole volume is assembled and sewn, including heavy paper "end pages" positioned at the front and back of the book. Mrs. McDuffy has estimated that the machine sewing typically requires two to three minutes per volume, depending on its thickness. Changes in the length of the pages being sewn require about a three-minute adjustment on the machine.

Thread breakage rarely occurs and seldom involves more than 20 minutes downtime, usually less.

After all second-floor operations have been completed on an order, each volume is inspected by Mrs. McDuffy. The entire order then remains on a hand truck or a workbench on the second floor until moved (usually by the third-floor foreman) via elevator to the third floor for the remainder of the binding operations.

The third-floor activities are supervised by a working foreman. Philip Wardell, who himself is a skilled "forwarder." His duties include the assignment of individual workers to specific jobs, and ringing the time-bell for breaks, lunches, and quitting time. He estimates that these functions account for approximately 25 per cent of his working day.

The remainder of Mr. Wardell's time is spent as the operator of a large Seybold shear to which all orders are routed as the initial third-floor operation. The Seybold, although larger in size, is similar in design and in operation to the shear employed on the second floor. To operate the shear (Figure E), Mr. Wardell inserts each sewn volume into the Seybold and successively trims the three unsewn edges, leaving each with a clean, even surface. Such trimming demands painstaking care to avoid cutting away any printed matter. On the average, Mr. Wardell believes that about a minute and a half is required to trim each volume, including the time taken to inspect the volume to ascertain the amount of paper that can safely be removed.

The assigning of all third-floor trimming operations to Mr. Wardell was an innovation introduced by Mr. Dix shortly after the company moved to its new location. Previously, each of the "forwarders," operators whose functions will be explained subsequently, had been responsible for trimming any order assigned to him. Under the new arrangements, after Mr. Wardell trims all of the volumes in an order, he piles them on any one of the numerous benches or hand trucks adjacent to the shear until one of the five "forwarders" in the department can be assigned to the order.

It is the responsibility of a forwarder to perform all of the remaining operations required to produce the components of a bound volume for each item in the customer order assigned to him. These operations include "rounding," "backing," and "cover-making."

"Rounding" is performed manually through the use of a broad-nosed hammer, and is a preliminary step to the "backing operation" described in the paragraph immediately following. To round a volume, the sewn and trimmed packet of pages is placed lengthwise on a table. By light taps of the hammer, the forwarder shapes the

FIGURE E.   Third-floor trimming operation.

bound edge of the volume into a convex curve along its entire length
(Figure F).   This forms a slightly concave cross section on the book's
opposite (outer) edge.   Approximately four volumes can be rounded
per minute.

The ensuing operation, "backing," is performed on either of the
company's two backing machines, each of which cost about $1,500
when new.   The purpose of backing is to "bend" the sewn pages at a
depth of roughly one-sixteenth of an inch along the entire length of
the sewn edge.   This "fans" outward the sewn edge of each page.
This fanning, together with the contour obtained through the rounding operation, permits the pages of a volume to turn easily after it
has been bound.

To accomplish this backing, the forwarder places a "rounded"
packet of pages lengthwise in the vise on a backing machine, with
the sewn edge up and roughly one inch above the vise jaws.   The
forwarder then pumps six to eight times on a hand-operated hydrualic

FIGURE F. Rounding operation. Packets in stack on the left have been rounded; those on the right are awaiting the rounding operation.

device to tighten the vise jaws securely. He next pounds the sewn edge with a hammer until the desired degree of fanning is obtained. By turning a hand wheel the forwarder then brings the machine's heavy metal roller into contact with the sewn edge, and manually guides the roller in an arc across the edge until its entire surface is smoothly curved (Figure G). Mr. Dichio has estimated that the entire sequence of backing operations, including workpiece setup, release, and machine adjustment, requires on the average about three minutes per volume.

The next step in the forwarding operation consists of making a cover for each volume in the order. This requires cutting to size two or three pieces of heavy cardboard, using a hand-operated shear, and cutting with scissors one piece of whatever covering material the customer has specified on the job sheet accompanying the order. In most cases, the covering material is special book cloth impregnated with a starch or plastic filler. The cut cloth is passed through the

rollers of a machine which coats a thin, even layer of glue across its entire inner surface. The cloth is then placed flat on a workbench, glue-laden side up. The pieces of cardboard are then carefully positioned on the cloth so as to leave a border of cloth around the outer edge of the boards, and to provide for the thickness of the packet of pages which, at a later point of the process, will be bound with this cover (Figure H). This positioning is done by sight and requires considerable skill, since the glue forms an almost instantaneous bond between the cardboard and cloth, preventing any major repositioning after the original contact has been made.

After any excess cloth has been cut away, the remaining edges of the cloth are turned in over the cardboard to form a tight cover. The cloth is then pressed down firmly to remove any air bubbles. The folding and pressing operations can be done by hand, using a small paddlelike instrument. Usually, however, these operations are performed by a "turn-in" machine which is operated by a girl who assists all five of the forwarders. Since this function normally occupies only about one-third of her time, this girl also works in Exemplar's pamphlet department. After completing each cover, the

FIGURE G. Backing operation. Roller is in contact with rounded, sewn edge of volume. Operator will now guide roller back and forth in arc across sewn edge until entire sewn surface is smoothly curved.

FIGURE H. Cover-making process (one stage only). Pieces of cardboard being positioned on glue-laden piece of cover fabric. Fold-in machine operation is visible in background.

forwarder writes the item and order number in pencil on the upper left-hand corner of the inner surface of cardboard.

A forwarder usually cuts cloth and boards for a number of volumes in an order at one time, processes these into covers, then cuts another pile of boards and cloth pieces, and so on. On the average, the cutting of the cover fabric requires about one-half minute per volume, and the cutting of the cardboard pieces one-eighth of a minute each. Mr. Dichio estimates that when assisted by the girl operating the turn-in machine, and using cloth and boards already cut to size, a forwarder can produce about 80 covers per hour. If the helper is not available, the forwarder's output drops to about 40 covers per hour.

From time to time Mr. Dichio and Mr. Wardell inspect items in process in the forwarding department. Mr. Dichio also usually spot-checks each order after all forwarding operations have been completed.

The sewn packets of pages of the items in the order then wait on one of the numerous benches or hand trucks located at random throughout the third-floor work areas, while all of the covers are sent to the stamping department to have titles affixed.

As the first phase of the stamping operation, one of the typesetters, working from both the job number on each cover and the information on the master job sheet, selects from one of the drawers in a storage cabinet the individual piece of metal type required for each letter in the title. These pieces of type are placed in proper sequence in a "chase" which holds them securely in position. The type and chase are given to one of the stampers, who heats them on a small burner until he judges them to be at the proper temperature for the material used for the cover. He then immediately places the chase and heated type in one of two Kensol stamping machines, the second of which had been added to the department about three months after Mr. Dix bought the company. The Kensol machines were designed to hold in proper alignment a book cover, a sheet of gold leaf, and a chase of type. Operation of the machine brings the heated type against the gold leaf and the cover, permanently transferring the gold onto the cover material in the form of the letters of the title (Figure I).

At the time of Mr. Dix's purchase, the stamping department consisted of two women, who functioned as typesetters, and two male stampers. In addition to setting up the type for each title and placing it in the chase, the two typesetters were responsible for dismantling the type and returning it to the proper drawer of the storage cabinet after the stamping had been completed. On the average these operations—assembly and disassembly—took about four minutes per volume.

The heating of the letters in the chases and the operation of the Kensol machines were performed by two stampers. Mr. Dichio estimated that when a stamper was not required to wait for either the chase or the cover, the total stamping operation required on the average about three minutes per volume. The stampers also did hand lettering on those few volumes requiring it, and performed touch-up lettering when necessary—as, for example, when a single letter in the title did not emerge clearly from the Kensol operation.

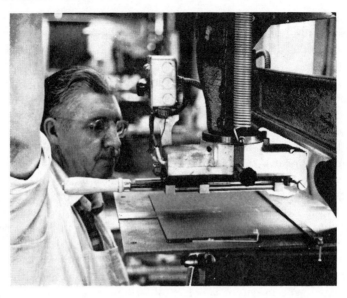

FIGURE I. Kensole stamping machine operation. Book cover is mounted on table of machine; chase filled with type (indicated by wooden handle) is also in position for stamping.

As one of his first sizeable investments in new equipment, Mr. Dix had purchased a $5,100 Ludlow type caster (Figure J) and accessories for use in the stamping department. The order had been placed in September, and called for a 15 per cent down payment with the balance payable to the vendor in monthly payments over the next three years, at interest of 4½ per cent.

With the Ludlow it became unnecessary to set type by hand, except in the case of a few special volumes requiring other than conventional lettering in their titles. Instead, the Ludlow operator would select type molds for each letter, insert all of the molds for one line of type into the machine, and automatically cast the entire line in the form of a single lead slug. All of the lines necessary for a title could then be passed to an assistant, who would lock them into a chase to be handed to the stamper for heating and use in the Kensol machine. After use, each slug could be remelted and the lead utilized in manufacturing subsequent slugs. Since each slug of type would be individually cast and used only once, Mr. Dix was confident that the Ludlow would assure the company excellent quality on all its stamp-

ings.   Recently some difficulty had been experienced in obtaining
good impressions with the old hand-set type which, through use, had
developed worn edges.

The Ludlow had been delivered to Exemplar only a few days
before and was just now being placed in operation.   Unable to locate
an experienced Ludlow operator, Mr. Dix had decided to train one
of his typesetters in its use, and to make the other typesetter her
assistant.   In both instances, the women would continue at their
former wage rates.   The local Ludlow sales representative had agreed
to assist in the training and had expressed confidence that no more
than four weeks would be required to bring the two women to reasonable levels of proficiency.

Mr. Dix hoped that the Ludlow would reduce operating costs,
and increase capacity.   He was confident, however, that the new
unit's contribution to quality improvement would in itself fully justify
its purchase.   With two Kensol machines in operation, he was also
convinced that the Ludlow could be kept reasonably loaded with work.

FIGURE J.   Ludlow type-casting machine.

For the time being, at least, Mr. Dix planned to retain Exemplar's entire supply of old hand-set type, saleable at perhaps a few hundred dollars, even though it was not required in the Ludlow operation.

The last remaining step of the binding operation consists of attaching the now stamped cover to the corresponding packet of sewn pages. This is known as "casing-in" and is performed by an "assistant finisher." The physical joining is accomplished by gluing the outside surfaces of the end papers, that is, the top and bottom pages of the sewn packet, and securing them to the cover of the volume (Figure K). Careful checking by the assistant finisher is necessary to assure that the identifying number on the sewn pages corresponds with the number on the cover itself, thus avoiding misbound volumes. After the cover has been attached, the book is placed under pressure in a large press for at least three hours to allow the glue to set firmly. Mr. Dichio believes that it usually is possible to perform these total casing-in operations at the average rate of about 20 volumes per hour, including loading and unloading of the presses.

Within both Exemplar and the bookbinding industry, forwarders and stampers are regarded as very highly skilled craftsmen. It is generally believed that to become competent in either operation requires a training period of at least four years. An even longer period is required to become skilled in the binding of leather volumes.

FIGURE K. Casing-in operation. Note large press behind worker, containing cased-in volumes.

Stamping in particular is considered an art. In order to assure a successful transfer of the gold leaf, the type has to be heated to "exactly the right temperature," and this differs for each of the numerous varieties of covering material. If the type is too hot, the cover will burn and have to be replaced. On the other hand, if it is not hot enough, there will be an imperfect bond between the cover and the gold, causing the gold to flake off after a short period of time.

PAMPHLET SECTION. Exemplar also operates a pamphlet section on the third floor. Here pamphlets, reprints, monographs, and other periodicals that normally see only limited use are bound in relatively inexpensive materials, usually cardboard covered with heavy paper. The cover is attached with heavy staples instead of sewing, and the entire manufacturing process is quite simple in comparison to hardcover binding. Exemplar normally employs two people in the pamphlet department. This staff from time to time is augmented by other third-floor personnel who are temporarily out of regular work. Customers usually do not expect prompt delivery on pamphlet binding and Mr. Dix believes that this work can, in large measure, be scheduled at company convenience.

During a recent summer, Mr. Dix hired four university students to work exclusively on pamphlets.[3] Mr. Dichio had shown the young men how to perform the required operations and then had allowed

---

[3] In view of the temporary nature of this assignment, the union waived membership requirements for the young men.

EXHIBIT 6   EXEMPLAR BOOKBINDING COMPANY

VOLUMES PROCESSED,* APRIL 17–JULY 31

	Periodicals†	Monographs and Rebinds†‡	Pamphlets	Theses†	Leather-Bound Volumes	Stamp Title Only	Mechanical Binding (Staple)
April§	668	700	2,943	86	0	32	0
May	2,201	704	608	396	69	154	928
June	1,949	1,362	4,060	76	139	36	0
July	2,459	808	6,259	29	21	217	0

---

* Excludes minor, miscellaneous work including repairs, orders for slip cases, and similar processes.

† Cloth-covered, hard-board bindings.

‡ Includes "Edition Binding."

§ Less than full month operation.

EXHIBIT 7 EXEMPLAR BOOKBINDING COMPANY

REPRESENTATIVE SAMPLE OF DIRECT LABOR TIMES ON ORDERS BY OPERATIONS*

Operation	BOOKS Number of Volumes in Order								PERIODICALS Number of Volumes in Order								Work Included in Operation
	67	77	78	79	77	112	91	135	120	95	84	85	88	84	89	105	
	Minutes Per Volume (Average)																
Pull	8.0	8.6	9.3	8.9	2.5	4.2	7.9	3.3	28.7	13.3	16.2	15.8	21.6	27.4	22.0	14.0	Remove old binding, clean binding edge, sort, collate
Trim	0.4	0.8	0.9	0.1	0.7	0.8	0.1	0.9	—	0.8	1.5	1.1	0.8	1.1	0.6	1.6	Trim, glue, separate sections
Saw	0.6	—	—	0.5	0.1	—	1.2	0.1	—	—	—	—	0.2	0.1	0.6	0.4	Saw slots for hand sewing
Machine Sew	3.5	3.5	3.5	2.5	3.3	3.2	2.6	3.1	5.5	5.1	5.0	5.5	4.4	2.1	4.2	5.9	Self-explanatory
Hand Sew	1.3	1.6	1.0	0.3	0.5	0.4	1.6	0.5	0.8	2.8	1.5	1.4	1.2	2.0	1.7	3.1	Self-explanatory
Check and Write Up	1.7	1.8	1.3	1.7	2.6	2.5	2.6	3.9	1.7	1.6	1.7	1.8	2.0	1.5	1.9	2.3	Check sewing and write on end paper information
Forward	12.7	14.3	11.7	12.0	11.7	11.2	10.3	10.0	12.0	11.6	12.0	13.2	14.0	11.5	14.2	14.3	Round, back, make covers
Set Type	2.3	5.9	6.4	6.5	7.8	2.7	5.7	2.4	1.0	3.7	2.9	3.4	2.2	3.6	3.0	5.7	Self-explanatory
Machine Stamp	6.4	6.7	—	5.9	6.2	4.2	5.5	5.5	4.5	0.7	5.9	5.5	6.5	3.9	4.0	1.6	Kensol machine operation
Hand Lettering	8.2	—	6.2	—	—	5.0	—	3.5	0.3	4.7	2.6	3.6	0.6	4.3	3.7	2.7	Self-explanatory
Assistant Finish	2.9	2.9	2.9	2.3	4.0	2.2	2.0	3.2	3.4	2.7	3.3	3.5	3.2	3.7	3.4	2.9	Casing-in
Inspect	0.5	0.4	1.5	0.8	0.8	0.5	0.7	0.5	0.3	0.5	0.4	0.4	0.4	0.4	0.4	0.4	Self-explanatory

* Derived by dividing total time shown on employee's time card on a specific order by the number of books in the order

NOTE: Times for third-floor trimming operations not available.

them considerable latitude in working out their own system of work scheduling. Both he and Mr. Dix were pleasantly surprised at the quantity of work the team succeeded in producing. Before leaving the company to return to school, the four men had reduced the average unit cost of a pamphlet binding from 35¢ to 27¢.

QUALITY CONTROL. In addition to the several formal inspections cited previously, various additional informal inspections are made by Mrs. McDuffy, Mr. Wardell, and Mr. Dichio during all stages of the production process. Mr. Dix also makes a final inspection of each item before it is delivered[4] to the customer, his normal practice being to examine each day's work before he leaves the plant that evening. Defects are only rarely encountered. Although formal records have not been kept, Mr. Dix judges that the reject rate rarely exceeds 1 per cent of the items processed. When errors are detected, however, Mr. Dix invariably has them repaired, even when this means repeating the entire binding process.

LABOR PRODUCTIVITY. Mr. Dix was convinced that in general worker productivity in Exemplar was good. Although most of the operators never appeared to be working at an intense pace, Mr. Dix believed that their speed was consistent with the highly skilled work they were doing, and the quality results demanded. The most recent available summary of company output, for the period April 17 through July 31, appears in Exhibit 6. Exhibit 7 shows what Mr. Dix believes is a reasonably representative example of average direct-labor performance on a variety of orders. Exhibit 8 shows a roster of wages and salary levels. Exhibit 9 shows a monthly breakdown of costs of goods sold and manufacturing expenses.

PRODUCTION CONTROL. While performing her initial check of an order being routed into production, Mrs. McDuffy assigns an identifying number to the entire order and to each volume in it, writing them lightly in pencil on the first page of each volume. Then she fills out, in duplicate, a job sheet covering the entire order, showing the identifying numbers assigned, and giving any necessary details regarding the cover materials and variety of title stamping required on each item. One copy of this job sheet, together with one copy of the list prepared by the customer, stays with the order throughout the entire production process. The duplicate copies of the job sheet and of the customer's list are sent to the office where they are logged and filed by the accountant. A separate slip of paper identifying the

---

[4] Delivery is generally by commercial trucks. Sometimes, however, Mr. Dix delivers small rush orders in his own car.

EXHIBIT 8 EXEMPLAR BOOKBINDING COMPANY

PERSONNEL ROSTER WITH WAGE AND SALARY LEVELS

Position	Usual Work Area (see Exhibit 5)	Hourly Wage or Monthly Salary
Owner-Manager (M)	A	Withdrawals
Accountant (F)	B	$410.00
Production Manager (M)	Entire Plant	$500.00
Secretary (F)*	C	$1.50
1 Forelady (F)	D	$2.00
5 Pullers (F)	D	$1.26–$1.53
1 Oversewing-Machine Operator (F)	F + K	$1.64
1 Apprentice Machine Operator (F)	F	$1.37
1 Inspector/Write-Up Clerk (F)	G	$1.53
1 Working Foreman (Seybold operator) (M)	H	$2.57
5 Forwarders (M)	H	$1.96–$2.43
1 Fold-In Machine Operator (also Pamphlet work) (F)	H + K	$1.31
2 Typesetters (F)	I	$1.26–$1.53
2 Stampers (M)	I	$2.43
1 Assistant Finisher (M)	J	$2.10
1 Pamphlet Worker (M)	K	$1.67
(M) Male	(F) Female	

* With company's concurrence, often works less than 40 hours per week.
† Page 554.

entire order is also kept with the order until it has passed through the sewing operation. After the volume is sewn, the second-floor inspector/write-up clerk adds the identifying number, together with the processing instructions, in pencil on the front end paper. The same identifying number, obtained from the job sheet, is also entered in pencil by the forwarder on the cardboard backing of each cover he makes.

Mr. Dix believes that this system has worked reasonably well. Individual items occasionally have been misplaced in the shop, however, and sometimes have remained lost for varying periods of time.

No other production-control techniques are now in use. For a short time Mr. Dix posted data to a large board to show the status of each job in the plant. This system was discarded after a brief

EXHIBIT 9 Exemplar Bookbinding Company

COST OF GOODS SOLD

(To Nearest Dollar)

	April 17–May 30	June	July	August	September	October
Sales	$21,106	$15,734	$17,448	$13,253	$ 9,908	$15,211
Cost of Goods Sold						
Raw Materials	3,002	2,117	1,009	1,818	1,144	1,668
(less) Sale of Gold Waste	141	—	—	83	—	28
(less) Discounts Taken	4	17	32	17	—	—
Net Raw Materials	2,857	2,100	977	1,716	1,144	1,640
Direct Labor	10,341	7,183	8,060	6,159	4,625	7,278
Manufacturing Expenses Unabsorbed						
Supervision	335	121	317	422	494	491
Apprentice Training	142	119	74	160	201	264
Vacation/Holiday/ Sick Pay	473	13	373	23	461	100
Supplies	47	317	230	248	293	472
Payroll Taxes	583	380	450	384	410	484
Depreciation	140	205	187	187	187	187
Insurance	282	114	132	132	132	132
Rental (net)	880	600	1,350	600	—	750
Utilities	—	—	—	—	32	130
Repair/Maintenance—Labor	7	4	38	5	31	2
Repair/Maintenance—Materials	—	2	—	1	—	—
Trucking	187	259	243	1,795	324	356
Freight	—	19	7	273	8	—
Miscellaneous	—	95	131	628	573	180
Total Actual Manufacturing Expense	3,077	2,247	3,531	4,857	3,144	3,542
TOTAL COST OF GOODS SOLD	$16,275	$11,531	$12,567	$12,733	$ 8,913	$12,459
GROSS INCOME	$ 4,831	$ 4,203	$ 4,881	$ 520	$ 995	$ 2,751

Source: Company records.

trial because of the considerable time required to keep the postings up to date.

The scheduling of an order into each of the various process stages is handled informally. Mr. Dix, Mr. Dichio, Mrs. McDuffy, and Mr. Wardell all check frequently on the orders ahead of each stage of the process, and on the delivery dates that have been requested by customers. On the basis of this knowledge, individual decisions are made regarding order sequence each time an operator is free to take on a new assignment.

COSTING AND PRICING. Most work performed by Exemplar is priced on a cost-plus basis. From previous dealings with the company, regular customers are able to judge the approximate charges involved in any work and thus can usually determine whether their budget will permit a particular order to be placed.

As the initial step in calculating the cost of an order, each operator turns in a daily time card showing the various orders on which he has worked, the operations performed, and the amount of time spent on each. The company's accountant uses this information to make daily postings in a "job book" showing the cumulative direct-labor hours spent on each individual order.[5]

When all of the operations on an order have been completed, the hours spent on each operation are multiplied by the hourly rate of the operators involved. An amount equal to 50 per cent of the total labor charges is then added to cover manufacturing overhead. Next are added the charges for raw materials and supplies. Usually these are based on a standard charge of 45¢ for each volume in the order. In the event that the materials used are sufficiently unusual to make the standard charge inappropriate, Mr. Dix uses his own judgment in determining the cost figures to employ. In the case of expensive leather bindings, the actual quantity of the leather employed is shown and costed on the job order. These various cost items are

---

[5] The foreman and forelady also fill out time cards to cover any portion of their time actually chargeable to a specific customer order. Whenever the Production Manager, Mr. Dichio, personally performs a manufacturing operation in the absence of a regular hourly employee, the time he spends is also charged to the job in question at the rate of either $2.43 per hour, or $1.53 per hour, depending on whether he does work normally assigned to a male employee or to a female employee. For internal control purposes, in the monthly cost summaries the total amount of time spent by supervisory personnel on direct production work is charged under the category of "Direct Labor." The difference between these charges and the total salary and wage payments actually made to the supervisors is included as a "Manufacturing Expense" item, under the category of "Unabsorbed Supervision."

then totaled, and an amount equal to 18 per cent of their sum is added to cover other expenses and profit. The customer is billed for the grand total.

If all of the operator time cards accumulated on an order calling for the rebinding of 74 books showed that total labor hours spent on this work represent $104.30 in wages, the customer would be billed $223.90, computed as follows:

Direct labor	$104.30
Manufacturing overhead (50% of direct labor)	52.15
Raw materials and supplies (at 45¢/volume)	33.30
Subtotal	$189.75
Expenses and profit (18% of subtotal)	34.15
Total billed to customer	$223.90

As a check on the system, Mr. Dix usually divides the total billing figure by the number of volumes in the order to establish an average unit price. In the case of the above order, for example, the unit price per book is $3.03. If this unit price is substantially higher, or lower, than the customer is accustomed to being charged for generally comparable work, Mr. Dix usually will adjust the total to bring it in line with the customary figure. He believes that such adjustments are appropriate, since substantial deviations from historic cost patterns are usually attributable to errors which operators make in recording data on their daily time cards. This can happen, for example, when an operator accidentally switches order cards, recording under one particular job the direct-labor hours actually spent on another order.

During the past several months, some of Exemplar's customers have begun to request price lists or to ask for quotations in advance of orders. The company also received an invitation to bid on a large order for a local U. S. Air Force installation which desired to have a collection of technical publications bound. Mr. Dix believed that requests of this type might increase in number, particularly if Exemplar were to make a concerted effort to expand by attracting new customers.

With these facts in mind, Mr. Dix was evaluating the strengths and weaknesses of the company's position to determine the action plan he should follow in the months ahead.

Blitz Company

In October 1961, Mr. Alfred Jodal, President of the Blitz Company, reviewed the company's position prior to planning 1962 operations.

The Market

The Blitz Company manufactures electrical circuit boards to the specifications of a variety of electronic manufacturers. Each board consists of a thin sheet of insulating material with thin metal strips (conductors) bonded to its surface. The insulating sheet acts as a structural member and supports electrical components and fragile conductors that connect the components into an electrical network. A typical example of the products produced by the company is a circuit board consisting of a 4 x 2 x $\frac{1}{16}$-inch plastic plate with 18 separate conductors bonded on its surface (Exhibit 1). In the customer's plant, assemblers position electronic components in the holes on the board, solder them in place, and install the assembly in final products such as two-way radios, electronic instruments, and radar equipment. Because circuit boards reduce the labor required in assembling and wiring electrical components, lessen the chances of human errors in assembly, and reduce the size of completed assemblies, the market for circuit boards has grown rapidly since World War II.

Competitive Advantages

Since the start of operations in 1959, the Blitz Company has specialized in making circuit boards for experimental devices and for pilot production runs. Earning statements and a balance sheet are shown in Exhibits 2 and 3. Most of the company's managers are engineers with substantial experience in the electronics industry. Mr. Jodal and the firm's design engineer, Mr. Alexander Krebs, have invented

720

EXHIBIT 1 BLITZ COMPANY

A TYPICAL CIRCUIT BOARD IN ITS STAGES OF FABRICATION

The raw material is a plastic sheet with a copper veneer.

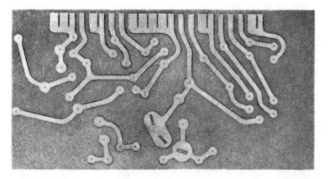

After etching and shearing, only plated conductors are left on the plastic sheet.

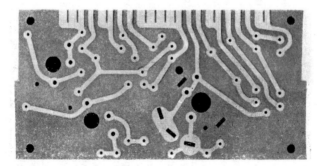

The finished circuit board has been shaped to final dimensions in a stamping operation and drilled.

EXHIBIT 2   BLITZ COMPANY

SUMMARY OF PROFIT AND LOSS STATEMENTS

	September 1961		August 1961		July 1961		Jan.–June 1961		1960	1959
	$	%	$	%	$	%	$	%	$	$
Net sales*	33,201	100.0	34,689	100.0	16,089	100.0	78,585	100.0	93,837	50,778
Direct material:										
Beginning in-process inventory	8,277	24.9	4,743	13.7	3,906	24.3	3,162	4.0	2,511	1,209
From stock and purchases	5,766	17.4	12,462	35.9	4,557	28.3	22,971	29.2	25,947	14,136
Chemicals, film, and supplies	2,325	7.0	3,627	10.5	2,418	15.0	10,044	12.8	6,603	3,999
Shop wages and foreman's salary	6,231	18.8	5,859	16.9	3,906	24.3	22,692	28.9	29,016	16,275
Overtime wages	279	0.8	1,023	2.9	0	0	1,023	1.3	n.a.	n.a.
Other expenses†	1,488	4.5	1,116	3.2	930	5.8	6,231	7.9	7,254	3,534
Total	24,366	73.4	28,830	83.1	15,717	97.7	66,123	84.1	71,331	39,153
Less closing in-process direct material	(6,603)	19.9	(8,277)	23.9	(4,743)	29.5	(3,906)	5.0	(3,162)	(2,511)
Cost of goods manufactured	17,763	53.5	20,553	59.2	10,974	68.2	62,217	79.2	68,169	36,642
Gross profit	15,438	46.5	14,136	40.8	5,115	31.8	16,368	20.8	25,668	14,136
Company overhead:										
Salaries (admin., engr. and office)	4,836	14.6	5,487	15.8	4,278	26.6	25,482	32.4	26,784	11,346
Other (rent, interest, telephone, utilities, etc.)	837	2.5	930	2.7	651	4.1	4,371	5.6	7,812	2,883
Profit (or loss) before taxes	9,765	29.4	7,719	22.3	186	1.2	(13,485)	(17.2)	(8,928)	(93)

* Recorded on day of shipment.
† Includes water, heat, power, payroll taxes, group insurance, and depreciation ($279 month in 1961).
n.a.—not available.
Source: Company records.

EXHIBIT 3 BLITZ COMPANY

BALANCE SHEET, SEPTEMBER 30, 1961

Assets				Liabilities			
Cash		$13,299		Accounts payable	$24,180		
Accounts receivable		53,196		Commissions	6,231		
				Taxes payable	3,069		
				Notes payable	14,229		
Inventory:							
Raw material	$ 2,976						
Supplies	2,232						
In-process	6,603	11,811					
Prepaid expenses		2,325					
Current assets			$ 80,631	Current liabilities			$ 47,709
	Cost	Depreciation					
Buildings	$14,880	$ 1,953		Long-term notes			2,604
Machinery	15,531	3,162					
Small tools	2,325	2,232					
Office equipment	3,627	651					
	$36,363	$ 7,998					
Fixed assets			$ 28,365				
				Net worth:			
				Capital stock	$63,519		
				Surplus 1-1-61	(9,021)		
				Profit for year	4,185	58,683	
Total			$108,996				$108,996

Source: Company records.

several of the company's processing methods and have patented applications, processes, and modifications of some commercial machinery. The president believes that the Blitz Company is more adept than its competitors in anticipating and resolving the problems inherent in new designs and production techniques.

MANUFACTURING PROCESS

The manufacturing process is divided into three stages: preparation, image transfer, and fabrication. In the first stage, patterns, jigs, and fixtures are produced and raw material is prepared for processing. The next step, image transfer, yields a sheet of plastic with appropriate conductors bonded on the surface. In the final stage, this material is transformed into shaped, drilled, and finished circuit

EXHIBIT 4 BLITZ COMPANY

Operation	Standard Production Times (in Min.)		September's Production		September's Total Standard Production (in Min.)			(in Hours)
	Setup	Run	Orders	Circuits	Setup	Run	Total	Total
Photograph	29	0	59	4,690	1,710	0	1,710	28.5
Inspect and shear	20	.5*	60	5,740	1,200	360	1,560	26.0
Drill (location holes)	10	.5*	60	5,740	600	360	960	16.0
KPR	1	10*	60	5,740	60	7,200	7,260	121.0
Touch up and inspect	10	3*	60	5,740	600	2,150	2,750	45.8
Plate	10	5*	52	5,616	520	3,510	4,030	67.2
Etch	10	4*	59	5,739	590	2,870	3,460	57.7
Shear (into circuit boards)	10	.5*	56	5,728	560	360	920	15.3
Drill (location holes)	10	.5†	53	5,709	530	2,855	3,385	56.4
Configuration:								
Rout	50‡	1‡	49	2,380	2,450	2,380	4,830	80.5
Punch press	150	.6†	4	3,329	600	2,000	2,600	43.3
Drill Holes:								
Green pantographic	50‡	0.05/hole	8	1,879#	400	9,400	9,800	163.3
Manual	15	0.10/hole	40	494	600	4,940	5,540	92.3
Epoxy painting	50‡	1†	8	1,000	400	1,000	1,400	23.7
Stake:								
Eyelet	20	0.07/eye	14	487	280	340	620	10.3
Terminals	20	0.15/term	3	257	60	40	100	1.7
Solder	30	1.5†	8	1,233	240	1,850	2,090	34.8
Inspect and pack	10	1.5†	60	5,740	600	8,610	9,210	153.5
Total			713	67,341	12,000	50,225	62,225	1,037.1

* Per panel.

† Per circuit board.

‡ Includes time for jigs and fixtures.

Only lots of more than 100 boards were drilled on this machine.

Assumptions: 8 circuit boards per panel; 100 holes per circuit board; 10 eyelets and 1 terminal per circuit board.

Source: Prepared by case writer from company production records and standard times estimated by Mr. Jodal.

boards. The most common sequence of operations is listed in Exhibit 4.

Preparation Stage

The pattern used in the image-transfer stage is made by photographing the customer's blueprint and producing a "panel" negative showing a number of the circuits in actual size, side by side, on a 12 x 18-inch film. This negative is then used in conjunction with a light-sensitive chemical (KPR) to be described later. In other preparatory steps, simple drilling jigs and fixtures and routing fixtures for the fabrication operations are made using bench drills, a

circular saw, a band saw, and hand tools. Stamping dies, when required, are obtained from subcontractors.

The principal raw material used by the company consists of plastic panels with a thin sheet of copper facing bonded to one surface. This material usually is purchased in sheets of desired thickness measuring approximately 48 x 36 inches. In the preparation stage, these sheets are inspected visually for flaws and are then cut on a shear into smaller panels measuring approximately 12 x 18 inches. The panel's exact dimensions are chosen by the operator so that the maximum number of circuit boards can be obtained from the sheets. Location holes, used to facilitate positioning in later processes, are then drilled in each panel.

Image Transfer

In the image-transferring process, the panels are washed, dipped into a solution of a light-sensitive chemical (KPR), and baked. A panel negative is then laid over the KPR-coated copper surface and the assembly is exposed to ultraviolet light for two minutes. A finishing dip in a solvent removes that portion of the KPR coating which has been covered by the dark portions of the negative and has not been exposed to the ultraviolet light. After this step the areas of the panel's copper surface corresponding to the desired conductors remain bare.

Next the bare surfaces (conductors) are protected with a metal plating. The plater inspects each panel, touching up voids in the remaining KPR coating and removing any excess before inserting it into a 50-gallon plating tank, where a 0.001-inch thick coating of lead-tin alloy or other metal is deposited on the panel's bare surfaces. In the following etching operation, the plated panels are placed in rubber-coated racks and successively submerged in a coating solvent, a rinse solution, an acid bath, and another rinse. The acid eats away the unprotected copper, producing a sheet of plastic with a pattern of plated conductors on its surface.

Judgment and experience are important in the photographing, plating, and etching processes, since the operators have to compensate for such factors as changes in the shop's temperature and the slow deterioration of the chemical action in various solutions.

Fabrication

Subsequently, the etched panels are cut into individual circuit boards on the same shear used previously to cut the plastic sheet

into panels. Two location holes are drilled in each circuit board on a bench press.

Each individual board is then reduced to the desired final size and shape either by die-stamping in a 20-ton punch press or by shaping on a routing machine. The operator of the routing machine, which is similar to a vertical milling machine, places each circuit board on a fixture which controls the way it is fed into the cutting tool.

On the average, 100 holes are drilled in each circuit board, using either ordinary bench-drill presses or the company's modified Green pantographic drill press.[1] An operator using the pantographic press can drill as many as three circuit boards simultaneously by stacking them on top of each other in a fixture positioned on the machine's worktable. The location of all the drilled holes is controlled by a master pattern, that is, a plastic plate with the proper hole pattern drilled in it, mounted alongside the worktable. To position the tool and drill the circuit boards, the operator simply inserts the machine's follower stylus successively into each of the pattern's holes.

After drilling, some circuit boards are coated with an epoxy resin in a painting process to inhibit damage caused by corrosion, scratching, and rough handling. Care is required to position both tools and workpieces accurately and to prevent scratching or marring of the circuit boards. To reduce the chance of damage in transport, panels and circuit boards are moved and stored between operations in racks holding as many as 15 pieces. Some typical operations are shown in Exhibit 5.

To assemble eyelets and terminals in the holes of the circuit boards, an operator sits before a simple staking machine and places the hole to receive an eyelet or terminal on the machine's anvil. Eyelets are fed and positioned automatically; terminals are positioned manually.

In the soldering operation, each circuit is dipped into a vat of molten solder for a few seconds.

In final inspection, any production employee who has run out of ordinary work visually checks each finished board for omitted operations, scratches, and poor workmanship. Items passing inspection are wrapped in kraft paper and deposited in a shipping container.

Although the work normally progresses through the sequence of operations described, some orders by-pass two or three operations. For example, some initial operations are omitted when the customer

---

[1] Occasionally these holes are punched out in the preceding stamping operation.

EXHIBIT 5 BLITZ COMPANY

TYPICAL SHOP OPERATIONS

The photographer inspecting and retouching a panel negative before sending it
on to the image-transferring operations.

The plater examining a panel during the plating operations. Panels in process
appear behind him.

EXHIBIT 5 *(Continued)* BLITZ COMPANY

TYPICAL SHOP OPERATIONS

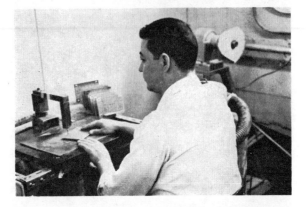

An operator shaping circuit boards to their final configuration and dimensions on the routing machine.

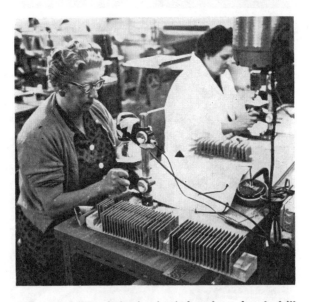

Two employees drilling holes in circuit boards on bench drill presses.

supplies precut boards or negatives; others are omitted when the customer prefers to do them in his own shop. Occasionally an order is sent ahead and then returned to continue through the normal sequence of processes.

Supervision

Supervisory responsibility for various phases of production is shared by three men: Joseph Hadler, the expediter; Alexander Krebs, the design engineer; and Michael Beck, the shop foreman. Messrs. Hadler and Krebs report to the president; Mr. Beck reports to Mr. Krebs.

Mr. Hadler was hired in August 1961. He keeps track of orders in process and initiates action if an order fails to progress through manufacturing satisfactorily. When the foreman's daily progress report, showing the last operation performed on each order, indicates a delay, Mr. Hadler investigates and usually obtains the missing supplies or instructions, tells the foreman to start the job moving again, or calls the customer and advises him of possible late delivery. On the average, Mr. Hadler investigates two to three slow orders each day. In addition, he confers with the sales manager and president to determine how many small, special orders, usually having a four-day delivery date, should be sent into processing.

Mr. Krebs' primary duties are to inspect the customer's blueprints and requirements in order to locate design errors, to determine the best means of processing, and to identify unusual production problems. He commonly spends ten hours a week talking with shop employees about these problems and others that crop up in processing.

Mr. Beck, the foreman, is in charge of all other aspects of manufacturing from the time he receives a shop order and blueprints until he ships the order. In total, Mr. Beck supervises the activities of 20 production employees. Four of these are lead men who spend about 10 per cent of their time instructing people in their areas or advising the foreman on various problems.

The Shop Employees

In 1961, the shop was nonunion, and employees were paid an hourly wage averaging $1.72 per hour. They used simple, manually controlled apparatus to perform light, short-cycle, repetitive tasks and commonly performed two to three different operations every week. Only the photographing, plating, and etching operations were not

traded among a number of workers. The photographer alone used the company's camera and darkroom to produce and develop negatives used in image application. The plater and etcher exchanged jobs between themselves but not with other employees. The usual pattern of work was such that most workers interrupted their tasks seven to nine times a day to obtain more work from another room, to seek advice on a problem, or to deliver completed work to the foreman's desk or other storage area.

Order Processing

As the first step in the preparation of a factory order, Mr. Jodal and Mr. Krebs estimate material and costs. These estimates are used in preparing a bid for the customer. If the customer subsequently accepts the bid, the Blitz Company promises delivery in three weeks for orders of less than 1,000 boards and five weeks for larger orders. The estimate sheet and blueprint are then pulled from the files by a secretary and delivered to Mr. Krebs who writes detailed material specifications (30 types of copper-plated plastic panels were in use in 1961) and a factory order showing the delivery date, the number of circuits, the material specifications, and the sequence of operations. The order is sent to the treasurer, who requires one or two days to locate the needed raw material at a low price and to order it. (The materials used in September 1961 are shown in Exhibit 8.) A secretary then enters the order in a log and sends the blueprint and factory order to the foreman. Most orders reach the foreman about four days after the bid has been accepted.

When the foreman receives a factory order he uses his own judgment in scheduling preparatory work. Usually he delays his scheduling decision for several days until the raw material arrives from the vendor. He then estimates the labor required in each step, examines the work in process at critical points, figures the difficulties in meeting the new order's shipping date, weighs the sales manager's priority on orders already in process, guesses at the possibilities of these orders being held up, and then decides when to schedule the order. The foreman spends much of his time determining when to move jobs ahead of others in process and when to shift workers from one operation to another. Until a job is shipped, the factory order and blueprints are kept by the foreman, who gives them to any worker requiring information. A ticket denoting the factory order number is kept with the first rack of material as it moves through processing.

Facilities and Layout

When the company moved to its present location in January 1960, Mr. Jodal had chosen a production layout which he felt minimized installation costs, preserved the life of expensive machines, and isolated the operations' diverse environments (Exhibit 6).[2] Cost had been an important consideration because the company had committed most of its funds for equipment and had not been able to attract outside capital. The plating apparatus had cost about $5,000. The photographic equipment, the Green pantographic drill press, and the punch press were purchased for approximately $1,500 each. The company had paid an average of $300 apiece for the shear, eight bench drill presses, the routing machine, band saw, and circular saw; and less than $3,000 for all the other equipment.

Mr. Jodal had spent $1,000 to install the partitions for isolating the production processes. Removing these and putting up six others would cost about $3,000. The plating and etching processes, which released acid vapors, had been located far from the machining operations to prevent excessive corrosion of the machine tools. Similarly, the machining operations, which created dust, had been separated from the photography, KPR, plating, and etching processes, which were sensitive to dust and dirt. After a year and a half, neither the machine tools nor the photographic equipment showed signs of corrosion. Similarly, dust from the machining areas had not contaminated other processes, although no doors had been installed to seal the passages between the process areas. In October 1961, the company was fully utilizing the space in its existing plant. An 1,800-square-foot addition was due to be completed in November.

CURRENT OPERATING PROBLEMS

In assessing the company's operating position in October 1961, Mr. Jodal was most concerned about the difficulties that he described as bottleneck, performance, quality, and delivery problems.

Production Bottleneck

The bottleneck was perplexing because it shifted almost daily from one operation to another, without pattern. Anticipating where work would pile up in the shop on a given day had proven difficult because

[2] This plan shows the location of the addition to the plant due for completion in 1961 as well as a possible second addition projected for 1963.

EXHIBIT 6   BLITZ COMPANY

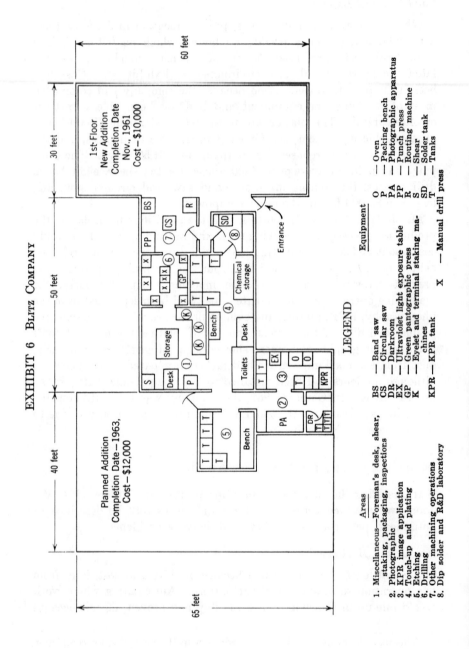

LEGEND

Areas

1. Miscellaneous—Foreman's desk, shear, staking, packaging, inspections
2. Photographic
3. KPR image application
4. Touch-up and plating
5. Etching
6. Drilling
7. Other machining operations
8. Dip solder and R&D laboratory

BS — Band saw
CS — Circular saw
DR — Darkroom
EX — Ultraviolet light exposure table
GP — Green pantographic press
K   — Eyelet and terminal staking machines
KPR — KPR tank

Equipment

O   — Oven
P   — Packing bench
PA — Photographic apparatus
PP — Punch press
R   — Routing machine
S   — Shear
SD — Solder tank
T   — Tanks

X   — Manual drill press

individual orders imposed varying work loads on each operation. These variations stemmed from differences in order size, from orders by-passing some operations, and from differences in circuit designs. Also contributing to fluctuations were the four-day rush orders received about three times a week, orders requiring rework at one or two operations, and work delayed in process pending a customer's delivery of special eyelets and terminals or a design change, of which there were one to nine a week. Approximately a fourth of the jobs delayed in process were held as a result of telephone calls from the customers' engineers who had encountered a problem. Then, any time from one day to two weeks later, the customer would grant permission to complete the order as originally specified or give new specifications. About an equal number of jobs were stopped as a result of processing problems or mistakes made in operations which could be overcome by a specification change. These orders were held until Mr. Krebs could obtain permission to deviate from the customer's original specifications.

During the past several months the foreman had found it increasingly difficult to compensate for these variations because he had no accurate way of predicting where work would pile up or run out, or of assessing the future effects of any corrective action. A recent day's events were typical. Early in the morning, three men engaged in manual drilling had run out of work. The foreman, therefore, shifted them to other tasks until other boards could be readied for the drilling operation. In this case, the foreman decided to meet the situation by expediting two orders that required work in only one or two operations preceding drilling. By midmorning one of the men transferred away from drilling had completed his new assignment and had to be given a different job. In the afternoon, by the time the expedited orders had reached the drilling operation, the foreman found that two employees assigned to certain of the steps by-passed by the expedited orders had run out of work.

Only the small orders of ten circuit boards or less seemed to pose no scheduling problems. Such orders always were assigned to a senior employee, Arthur Dief, who carried each one from step to step, doing the work himself or having someone else perform it. Dief consistently met delivery deadlines, even on four-day rush orders, and his reject rate was usually zero.

Performance and Methods

Mr. Jodal realized that it was impossible to evaluate shop productivity precisely. During his daily trips through the shop, however, he

had noticed that several of the machines were idle more often than he would have expected. In commenting on the summary of productive labor shown in Exhibit 4, the president noted that total standard man-hours did not include time spent reworking or replacing circuits that failed inspection or were returned by customers. In addition, he believed that the time required to move boards from one operation to another and between elements of an operation was not adequately reflected in the standards. The time standards used in Exhibit 4 were based in part on a synthesis of what the company knew to be the standards applied in competing firms from which they had hired various workers and supervisors, and in part on judgments of Mr. Jodal and Mr. Krebs after long experience in performing and observing those jobs in the Blitz Company. In preparing time estimates for bid preparation, Mr. Jodal actually used figures substantially above those standards.

The president felt, however, that the job methods in use were far from ideal and that the standards did not reflect improvements which could probably be made in almost any job in the shop. As a specific example, he cited the plating operation. The plater worked at a desk inspecting (touching up) panels and then carried the panels to plating tanks 18 feet away, inserted them, and returned to inspect more panels. He interrupted his work at the desk every three or four minutes to inspect the panels in one of the tanks. Mr. Krebs thought that the plater sometimes spent 15 per cent of his time simply walking between the desk and the tanks.

Mr. Jodal suspected that methods improvements were not being introduced because of the pressure for output, the constant shifting of men from job to job, and other immediate problems which inhibited experimentation with new ideas. Furthermore, job improvements often seemed, in retrospect, to have created more problems than they solved. For example, those infrequent cases in which improvements had increased production substantially at one station often resulted in work piling up at the following operations. The foreman was then forced to reschedule orders and reassign workers, thus adding to the general confusion and occasionally creating personal friction.

Quality and Delivery Problems

Mr. Henry Sacks, who joined the company as the sales manager in April 1961, was concerned about recent failures in maintaining quality standards and in meeting promised delivery dates. Since August, customer returns had increased from 4 to about 8 per cent and shipments on the average were nine days late. Mr. Sacks felt that a con-

EXHIBIT 7 BLITZ COMPANY

PRO FORMA PROFIT AND LOSS STATEMENT

Prepared by Rothchilde and Rommel, Inc., Management Consultants, on November 21, 1960

(in thousands of dollars)

	1961		1962		1963		1964	
Net sales	$199	100%	$336	100%	$521	100%	$823	100%
Direct material	45	22.4	75	22.4	116	22.3	181	22.0
Chemicals, film and supplies	17	8.4	32	9.4	56	10.7	74	9.0
Wages and foreman's salary	50	25.2	88	26.3	135	25.9	214	26.0
Other expenses*	11	5.6	18	5.3	28	5.4	47	5.6
Cost of goods sold	123	61.7	213	63.4	335	64.3	516	62.6
Gross profit	76	38.3	123	36.6	186	35.7	307	37.3
Company overhead:								
Salaries (adm., engr. and office)	42	21.0	56	16.6	79	15.2	130	15.8
Other overhead (rent, interest, utilities, etc.)	13	6.5	20	5.8	28	5.4	42	5.1
Profit before taxes	21	10.8	47	14.1	79	15.2	135	16.4

* Water, heat, power, depreciation, etc.

Source: Company records.

tinuation of these conditions would impede his hope of increasing the present sales volume and achieving the company's sales goals. The sales goals (Exhibit 7) had been developed by a local consulting firm in November 1960, after a month's study of the potential market. The sales manager predicted that volume would reach only $600,000 in 1964 if he began promising the four-week deliveries on small orders that four competitors were quoting. If, on the other hand, the company were able to regain its pre-August delivery performance, Mr. Sacks felt sales should exceed $1.5 million in 1964. Both Mr. Sacks and Mr. Jodal believed that the company should continue to bid only for low-volume, special circuit-board business. Their sales estimates, therefore, were based on an order-size profile similar to that actually produced in September 1961 (Exhibit 8).

Quality

Mr. Jodal was concerned also about the present inspection system, in which formal inspections of raw material and finished boards were

EXHIBIT 8   BLITZ COMPANY

THE ORDER SIZE AND NUMBER OF ORDERS PROCESSED DURING SEPTEMBER 1961

Order Size (Number of Circuit Boards in Each Order)	Raw Material Code Letters	Number of Orders	Total Number of Circuit Boards
1	A, B, D, E	7	7
2	A, B, F, H	8	16
3	B, D	2	6
4	A, B, C, F, H	10	40
5	A, D	2	10
6	B, C	2	12
10	B, D, E	3	30
11	D, F	2	22
12	A, J, K	3	36
14	A, E, G	3	42
20	D	1	20
40	B, K	2	80
50	C, E	2	100
60	C	1	60
84	J	1	84
100	C	1	100
113	E	1	113
136	C	1	136
140	F	1	140
154	A	1	154
200	D	1	200
229	E	1	229
252	A	1	252
800	G	1	800
1,000	D, M	2	2,000
1,050	A	1	1,050
		60	5,739

Source: Company records.

supplemented by each worker's informal examination of the units as they moved through processing. The president felt that any effort to specify quality standards more exactly and to enforce them more rigorously might not be feasible because the standards varied from customer to customer and even from order to order. For example, in one episode a customer's engineers had praised the quality of the Blitz Company's work on one order even though the boards were scratched

and marred and had one or two holes located out of tolerance. A week later, other engineers at the same company had rejected 25 apparently perfect boards because one conductor on each had a single 0.005 x 0.010-inch nick in it.

A tenth of the boards returned were damaged or out of tolerance. The remainder were sent back because the Blitz Company had failed to perform one or two required operations. These boards were reprocessed and shipped within one or two days. The company's preshipment reject rate in September amounted to 7 per cent, of which 4 per cent consisted of total losses and 3 per cent of missing operations.

EXHIBIT 9   BLITZ COMPANY

VALUE OF ACTUAL SHIPMENTS IN SEPTEMBER 1961
(In Dollars)

Date	Daily	Cumulative
1	$ 2,957	$ 2,957
4	(316)*	2,641
5	1,079	3,720
6	451	4,171
7	592	4,763
8	2,242	7,005
11	637	7,642
12	(182)	7,460
13	681	8,141
14	1,576	9,717
15	(39)	9,678
18	1,051	10,729
19	3,515	14,244
20	2,678	16,922
21	1,479	18,401
22	605	19,006
25	47	19,053
26	(353)	18,700
27	(2,121)	16,579
28	4,771	21,350
29	11,851	33,201

* Negative shipments, shown by parentheses, indicate that receipts returned for rework or refabrication exceeded shipments.

Source: Company records.

Deliveries

Mr. Jodal always had emphasized a shipping policy aimed at clearing all the work possible out of the shop prior to the end of each month. As a result, substantially fewer shipments were made in the first half of each month than in the second half (Exhibit 9). Actual deliveries in August, September, and the first part of October had averaged ten, eight, and nine days late, respectively. During the period, the company had continued its historical practice of quoting three weeks' delivery on orders of less than 1,000 circuit boards and five weeks' on larger orders. In August, when deliveries climbed to a volume of $34,700, eight new people had been added to the production force. Mr. Jodal observed that these eight workers had developed some skill by the second week in August, but believed that they would require three months to become as skilled as the company's more senior employees.